Ewan MacLeod

Bought at the
National Portrait Gallery
1st December 1990

The Raj

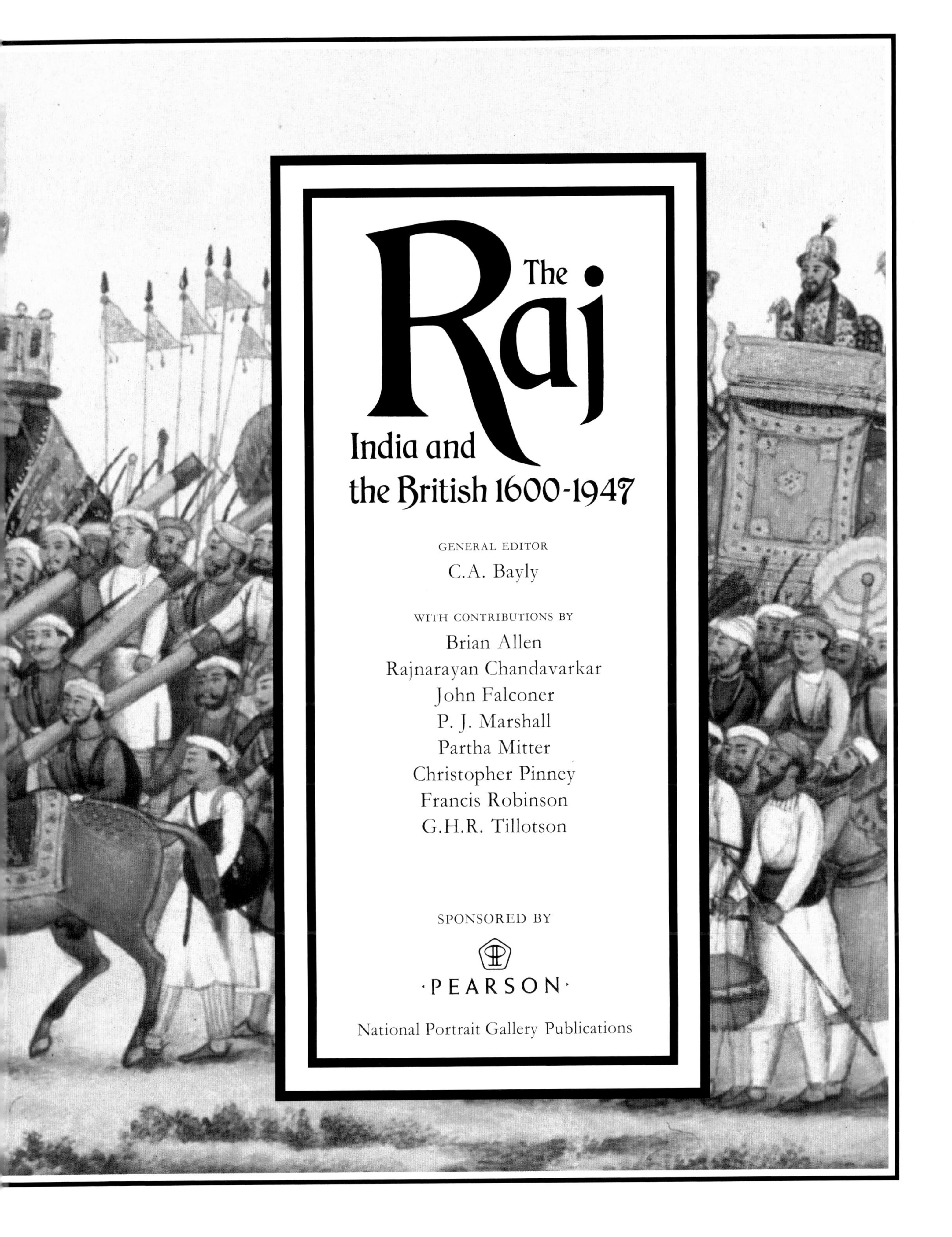

The Raj

India and the British 1600-1947

GENERAL EDITOR

C.A. Bayly

WITH CONTRIBUTIONS BY

Brian Allen
Rajnarayan Chandavarkar
John Falconer
P. J. Marshall
Partha Mitter
Christopher Pinney
Francis Robinson
G.H.R. Tillotson

SPONSORED BY

·PEARSON·

National Portrait Gallery Publications

Published for the exhibition at the National Portrait Gallery, London from 19 October 1990 to 17 March 1991

Published by National Portrait Gallery Publications, National Portrait Gallery, 2 St Martin's Place, London WC2H 0HE, England, 1990

British Library Cataloguing in Publication Data
The Raj: India and the British, 1600–1947.
1. India, history
I. Bayly, C.A. (Christopher Alan) *1945–*
954

ISBN 1-85514-026-8
ISBN 1-855141-027-6 pbk

Catalogue edited by Gillian Forrester and Denny Hemming

Designed by Harry Green
Maps by T.A.S. Ltd

Phototypeset, printed and bound in England by Butler & Tanner Ltd

Front cover: *Maharaja Dalip Singh* by Franz Xaver Winterhalter (detail; no. 208). Reproduced by Gracious Permission of Her Majesty The Queen ©.

Back cover: *Captain John Foote* by Sir Joshua Reynolds (no. 124). Reproduced by kind permission of York City Art Gallery ©.

Title page: *Panorama of a Durbar Procession of Akbar II* by unknown artist, Delhi school (detail; no. 201). Reproduced by kind permission of the India Office Library ©.

Contents

Pearson is delighted to be sponsoring *The Raj: India and the British 1600–1947*, the largest exhibition ever to be staged by the National Portrait Gallery. From the great Mughal Empire and the formation of the East India Company to the withdrawal of the British in 1947, the exhibition brings to life vividly the wealth of India, the rise and expansion of British power and the struggle which ended in Independence.

Together with this magnificent catalogue, which illustrates over five hundred of the exhibits displayed, it is a unique and timely contribution to our understanding of the complex and multi-faceted relationship which developed between India and Britain over three hundred and fifty years.

Michael Blakenham
CHAIRMAN, PEARSON PLC

Foreword

'East is east and west is west'. Although ruling classes over the ages have made valiant and sometimes successful attempts to comprehend alien cultures, this familiar adage has a distinct measure of truth to it. *India and the British*, the largest historical exhibition the Gallery has ever mounted, examines a noble theme: the long relationship between the peoples of one of the great ancient civilizations of the East, largely Hindu but part Muslim, and the representatives of a vigorous Western trading nation which, faced with the dissolution of the Mughal Empire, developed in the course of time one of the most remarkable administrations – efficient and evangelizing – since the heyday of the Roman Empire. In recent years the British treatment of this subject has been dominated, understandably enough, by a nostalgia for the imperial past and for the public school system which sustained the high-minded bureaucracy that ruled India for the last hundred years or so of the Raj. We have tried to look beyond this partial approach and, in particular, to see the British from the Indian point of view. In selecting the exhibits we have endeavoured to be as comprehensive as we possibly can, but inevitably, even with a larger area than usual at our disposal, the limitations of space have imposed constraints upon the material we were able to include. We believe, however, that we have achieved a just balance.

The exhibition could never have been assembled without the energy, enthusiasm and balanced scholarship of Dr Christopher Bayly, Reader in Indian History in the University of Cambridge, who, in spite of increasing administrative as well as academic responsibilities, willingly agreed to give up his spare time to act as our Principal Consultant. Dr Bayly has not only shaped the exhibition, but done the lion's share of the work, writing the bulk of the catalogue entries himself. Peter Marshall, Rhodes Professor of Imperial History at King's College, London, and Dr Christopher Pinney have been a tower of supportive strength to him. These scholars, architects of the exhibition, have been ably assisted by Dr Rajnarayan Chandarvarkar, John Falconer, Dr Partha Mitter and Dr Francis Robinson. Dr Brian Allen, Deputy Director of the Paul Mellon Centre for Studies in British Art, kindly responded to my call, and helped in selecting and cataloguing the pictures. In addition, Dr Giles Tillotson has chosen and compiled the entries for the section dealing with the Picturesque. Katherine Prior, assisted by Patrick McGinn and Emma Shackleton, has been responsible for most of the research.

We are greatly indebted to Barry Mazur, ever practical and imperturbable, for the sensitive design and ingenious layout of the exhibition. Harry Green, working with his customary energy, has designed an elegant catalogue for us. On the Gallery staff, Carole Patey and John Adamson have been, as always, the most skilful of negotiators. The prodigious tasks of administering and coordinating the loans and of editing the catalogue have been in the capable hands of Kathleen Soriano and Gillian Forrester respectively. Gillian Forrester has been diligently assisted in her work by Denny Hemming. John Cooper, Sarah Kemp and David Saywell have all helped enthusiastically and beyond the call of duty.

To the innumerable institutions and individuals who have so generously agreed to lend to the exhibition the Trustees and I are profoundly grateful. Her Majesty The Queen has graciously lent from Osborne House the magnificent Winterhalter of the Maharajah Duleep Singh which is reproduced on the cover of the catalogue. Lord Plymouth, with characteristic public spirit, most generously permitted scaffolding into his home so that his huge and important West of Clive receiving the grant of the Diwani of Bengal from the Mughal Emperor could be taken down from its position in the staircase hall; this picture, not seen in public since its original exhibition at the Royal Academy in 1795, has been specially cleaned and restored by Alan Bush. Howard Hodgkin has been especially accommodating about the use of his painting in connection with our publicity material. The many museums and libraries that have contributed to the exhibition have been unfailingly helpful in the planning and research stages as well as with loans; at the risk of being invidious I would single out J. P. Losty, Curator of Prints and Drawings at the India Office Library, and Patricia Katterhorn and Rod Hamilton at the same institution, which has lent a high proportion of the exhibits, and the staffs of the British Library and the National Army Museum. For facilitating loans from India and Pakistan we are much indebted to Salman Haidar, the Indian Deputy High Commissioner, Bhaskar Ghose, Secretary of the Department of Culture in New Delhi, Khalid M. Shafi, the Pakistan Acting High Commissioner, Khawaja Shahid Hosain, Federal Secretary of the Ministry of Culture, Sports and Tourism in Pakistan, and Mrs Yasmin Hosain.

Few exhibitions can be mounted these days without substantial financial support. The Trustees and I are deeply grateful to Pearson's for their exceptionally generous sponsorship which has made the exhibition possible.

John Hayes
DIRECTOR, NATIONAL PORTRAIT GALLERY

The National Portrait Gallery would also like to thank the following who contributed in many different ways to the organization of the exhibition and preparation of the catalogue:

Air India
Seema Alavi
Johanna Awdry
Bruce Barker-Benfield
Barnes & Webster
T. A. Barringer
Bernard Battley
Battley Brothers
Dorothy Benson
Glen Benson
V. P. Beri
British Association for Graveyards in South Asia
Iain Brown
Charles J. Burnett
Jane Carmichael
Lionel Carter
Stuart Cary Welch
Mrs Mary Clapinson
Sara Colegrave
Luci Collings
Rosemary Crill
Joan Duff
Brian Durrans
Mardie Esterkin
Giles Eyre
Charles Greig
Anthony Griffiths
Ralph Hancock
Frances Hazlehurst
Hazlitt, Gooden & Fox, London
Inchcape UK Ltd
Indian Army Association
International Fine Art Conservation Studios Ltd
James Ivory
Brian Jenkins
Gordon Johnson
James Joll
Norman Kent
Ann De Lara
Rosie Llewellyn-Smith
Alan MacFarlane
James Masselos
Barry Mazur
Claire Messenger
Mark Nicholls
Foy Nissen
Oberoi Hotel Group
Rosalind O'Hanlon
Dottie Owens
Pakistan International Airways
Paton Walker Associates
Clare Peddell
Ralph H. Pinder-Wilson
Michael Pollock
Venetia Porter
Caroline Potter
A. J. Prescott
Process Colour
Thom Richardson
Catherine Rickman
Angela Roche
Katrina Rolley
Paul Sant-Cassia
David Scrase
Graham Sheffield
Maurice Shellim
Jayne Shrimpton
Robert Skelton
Susan Stronge
Deborah Swallow
Annabel Teh Gallop
Peter Thornton
Frank Thurston
Townsend Hook Ltd
Travelling Light
John Tustin
Major Neville Williams
Ronald Wilson Esq.

General Editor's Preface

Though it is nearly half a century since the last British soldier marched away through the Gateway of India, the passions stirred by the memory of the British Raj have not died away. British, Indian, Pakistani and Bangladeshi assessments of the merits of that empire, and of the consequence of its demise differ radically, and in this exhibition and catalogue we have attempted to present rather than minimize these differences of opinion. What no one now disputes is the extent to which the nature of British dominion was shaped by Indian as much as by British people, and as much by their cooperation as by their resistance. For this reason the exhibition and catalogue begin, as they end, with a significant representation of items which reflect the lives and culture of the Indian people.

The aims of the catalogue are several: first it sets out, simply, to tell a story. This is the remarkable story of how an English company, trading in the produce and manufactures of the East, became ruler of nearly a quarter of the world's population. The East India Company suppressed open warfare, unified the subcontinent and introduced a new legal system. The narrative goes on to show how the British Crown took over the government of that company's empire after the suppression of a mutiny and rebellion in 1857, and how in due course, the Raj foundered as British economic weakness combined with the insistent demands of Indian nationalists for freedom. Out of the violent endgame of the Raj emerged three great nations of today: India, Pakistan and Bangladesh.

Secondly, the catalogue charts the creation and projection of British images of Indians and their lives, and of Indian images of the British. In the first section of the exhibition, we progress from the delicate miniature paintings of the Mughal period through to the great British history paintings and portraits of the eighteenth century. During this period Indian princes wished to proclaim their power and glory to East India Company officials and to a wider European and Indian public, so they employed some of the finest portraitists of the day. During the Seven Years War with the French which ended in 1763, the British for their part began to conceive their national character and destiny in terms of imperial conquest and war, and also used visual representations to portray their evolving self-image: this tradition of British history painting of Indian subjects reached its apogee when the British defeated or achieved the submission of their most feared enemies, the Sultan of Mysore and the Marathas.

In the nineteenth century British artists and their Indian employees elaborated new, and less dramatic, images of a peaceful India subject to benevolent British rule. India was still mysterious, and the British sought to rationalize the landscape by portraying it in terms of European aesthetic categories, the Picturesque and Sublime. In the so-called Company School of painting, Indians themselves were shown as representatives of types, of tribes, of castes and of religious sects. The invention of photography together with the arrival of academic anthropology, and the idea of the museum, resulted in a proliferation of publications which sought to classify the people of the subcontinent.

Until the mid-nineteenth century, Indian artists often tried to diminish the importance of the presence of the foreign rulers, except when they were directly commissioned to work for them. They continued to portray British officials as no more than equals, sometimes even inferiors, of the rajas and princes who held the centre of their compositions. After the Rebellion of 1857–8 and the defeat of the old order, this fiction could no longer be maintained. As Indian aspirations to nationhood took shape, however, Indian artists, photographers and political cartoonists began to create images to challenge the Raj's depiction of a land irrevocably fragmented by caste and religion, showing instead Indian unity in diversity. They brought into service those symbols of Indian tradition and Indian religion used by earlier artists, but with a different purpose – to challenge the legitimacy of British rule. So the third level at which we can approach the exhibition is to look for the refashioning and use of symbols within these broader images. For instance, the gods and goddesses of the Hindu pantheon, appear again and again, but with subtly different meanings. The Elephant-headed Hindu God Ganesh appears as the family deity of an Indian ruling family in a picture by the artist James Wales. In his guise as patron god of Learning he is introduced by Arthur William Devis into a portrait of the great Oriental scholar, Sir William Jones. Then, in the later nineteenth century, Ganesh was recruited into the political battles of the period: he became a symbol of the anti-British struggle for the western Indian leader Bal Gangadhar Tilak, who instituted a public festival in his honour; one such festival was photographed for British political files. In a gentler mood, Ganesh was again invoked by an Indian cartoonist to caricature the powerful Viceroy, Lord Curzon.

The divine beings of the Hindu pantheon, the symbols of the Islamic faith, and representatives of individual Indian occupations (such as the 'water-carrier') appear repeatedly in different forms and mediums. So also does the theme of the durbar, the Indian royal assemblage. Two great durbar scenes and a suit of mailed elephant armour hold the centre of the exhibition. They reflect its central themes: the transaction, and the conflict, between Indians and the British over nearly three hundred and fifty years.

Many people and institutions have played a part in the organization of the exhibition and writing of the catalogue. But two debts must be acknowledged with particular sincerity. The first is to the late W. G. Archer and Mrs Mildred Archer. Mrs Archer bears no responsibility at all for any part of the enterprise, but nothing could have been done without the inspiration of her scholarship and her pioneering effort in locating and cataloguing so many of the items which appear here. Secondly, Dr J.P. Losty and the staff of the India Office Library in London have far exceeded the call of duty in helping to locate and prepare the many superb items from their collection for the exhibition. My colleagues Dr Brian Allen, Dr Christopher Pinney, Dr Giles Tillotson and Professor Peter Marshall have provided desperately-needed aid and expertise; Kathy Prior has helped with characteristic thoroughness and efficiency. Finally, I would like to thank Dr John Hayes, the Director of the National Portrait Gallery, for cheerfully allowing a simple historian to trespass into the groves of art history, and staff of the National Portrait Gallery for their help. The energy, patience and commitment of Kathleen Soriano and Gillian Forrester have been a constant support.

C. A. Bayly

Notes and Abbreviations

Both exhibition and catalogue are arranged chronologically in four sections, *Mughal India and the Rise of the East India Company 1600–1800*, *Company Supremacy and Indian Resistance 1800–58*, *The Victorian Raj and the Rise of Nationalism 1858–1914* and *The Road to Partition and Independence 1914–47*. Though the term 'British Raj' is often technically applied only to the period when India was ruled by the British Crown (1858–1947), the term 'Company's Raj' was widely used, both before and after the Rebellion. Exhibits are arranged in broad chronological order; some modern representations of historical figures and events are included to draw attention to contemporary interpretations.

Sizes of exhibits are given (height before width) in centimetres with the size in inches shown in parentheses. Dates of exhibits in parentheses denote the original date of copyprints, facsimiles and other reproductions. Exhibits not available for the exhibition are indicated by †.

The original titles of exhibits are given wherever possible, and their eccentricities of spelling replicated.

Bibliographical references in the catalogue entries cite the author's surname and date of publication. Full references are given in the Bibliography. Exceptions are made in the case of works without known authors where the full titles are cited. Titles of more than one book by the same author are listed chronologically by the dates of publication.

The contributions to the catalogue entries are identified by the following initials:

SA	Seema Alavi
BA	Brian Allen
CAB	C. A. Bayly
RSC	Rajnarayan Chandavarkar
GJ	Gordon Johnson
PJM	Peter Marshall
JM	James Masselos
FN	Foy Nissen
R O'H	Rosalind O'Hanlon
CP	Christopher Pinney
VP	Venetia Porter
KP	Katherine Prior
FCCR	Francis Robinson
JS	Jayne Shrimpton
RS	Radhika Singha
GHRT	Giles Tillotson

SECTION I

MUGHAL INDIA AND THE RISE OF THE EAST INDIA COMPANY

1600–1800

The Seventeenth and Eighteenth Centuries

P. J. MARSHALL

Fig. 1 Imperial armies besieging a Rajput fortress; illustration from the *Akbarnama,* opaque watercolour and gold

Direct contact between Britain and India dates back to the beginning of the seventeenth century. English merchants went to India, as they went to other parts of the world, to obtain exotic and expensive commodities for which there was an increasing demand throughout western Europe. In 1600 Elizabeth I granted a charter (no.46) to a group which became 'The Governor and Company of Merchants of London Trading into the East Indies', known throughout its long history as the East India Company. In its early years the primary concern of the Company was to ensure that English merchants had a direct role in the supply of Asian spices and pepper to Europe, especially in the face of formidable Dutch competition. Indonesia was the major source of spice and pepper exports, and therefore the Archipelago rather than India was at first the main focus for the Company's operations. It was, however, attracted to Indian ports by the huge quantities of textiles – silk and cotton goods – that were sold there. These textiles were needed to barter for Indonesian spices and pepper, but some of them could be sold in Europe. To obtain Indian goods the Company sent ships on its third voyage in 1608 to the great port of Surat on the western coast of India. Surat became the site of the first English 'factory' or permanent trading post in India (no.57).[1]

Surat was under the authority of the Mughal emperors, the rulers of a vast domain already extending right across northern India, to which additions were being made that were taking Mughal rule deep into the Indian peninsula (Figs. 1 and 2). Until late in the eighteenth century the English had few direct dealings with the great centres of Mughal civilization in northern India: cities such as Agra, Delhi or Lahore. The affairs of foreign merchants on the periphery of their dominions were of very little interest to the rulers of what was one of the most powerful territorial empires in the world. In attempts to gain concessions from the imperial government, occasional English embassies were, however, sent to the Mughal cities. Sir Thomas Roe (no.4), who arrived at the court in January 1616, spent nearly three years there. From the accounts of such travellers and from shipments of luxury items made in the Mughal workshops – miniatures, jewellery, weapons and textiles, English connoisseurs could gain some idea of the richness and sophistication of Mughal culture.

Seventeenth-century Indian ports were outlets for regional economies with their own specialities in textile production aimed at markets in different parts of Asia. In addition to their post at Surat, the English sought access to the ports of the Coromandel coast, which carried on a huge trade with Indonesia.

Fig. 2 Emperor Akbar's new city at Fatehpur Sikri, built 1590s; modern photograph by C. A. Bayly

Their first Coromandel factory was established at Masulipatnam, on the northern sector of the coast. In 1639 they obtained a grant to create a fortified trading post in the village that was to become the settlement of Madras (no.64). By the middle of the seventeenth century the English were beginning to establish a foothold in Bengal, another major trading region. In 1690 they were allowed to set up their principal Bengal factory in the village on the Hughly river that was to be called Calcutta (no.41). Local factories were opened at other trading centres throughout the province. On the west coast the Company gained another foothold in 1668 (no.62), when Charles II handed over to it what had been the Portuguese settlement of Bombay. Factories to purchase pepper were opened on the south-western or Malabar coast.

English factories, wherever they were established in India, at first had certain obvious similarities. They conformed to a pattern recognized throughout Asia, whereby foreign merchants were permitted to live in their own quarters of port cities according to their own customs and religion. Such concessions were licensed either by Mughal officials within the empire or by local rulers where the Mughal writ did not run. The East India Company's factories were staffed by its 'servants', appointed by their masters, the Company's Directors at Leadenhall Street in London (nos.42–54), to serve long terms in the East, supposing that they survived a very high rate of mortality. Their work began with disposing of the cargoes which they received on the

Fig. 3 The East India Company Coat of Arms, *c.* 1730, carved wood, painted and gilded (India Office Library and Records; no. 54)

ships coming out from England (nos. 51–52). Because of the difficulty of selling English goods in Asia before great reductions in cost were achieved in the nineteenth century, most of what they received was in fact silver bullion. They obtained Indian goods through contracts with Indian merchants. These goods they either shipped back to England or dispatched to another part of Asia. By the middle of the seventeenth century the Company's trade with India had settled into a regular pattern (Fig. 3). Silver from England was being exchanged for textiles, above all cotton goods, calicoes and muslins for the London market. From the 1660s especially, sales of Indian cotton cloth, for which there was as yet no effective European competition, were expanding very rapidly. Millions of 'pieces' of cloth were being sold in London and Amsterdam by the English and Dutch East India Companies. The dominance of textiles in British-Indian trade meant that by the end of the seventeenth century Bengal, as the cheapest and most abundant source of cotton goods, had a crucial role in the East India Company's operations.

As the Company's trade grew throughout the seventeenth century, some of its factories expanded into what can be regarded as British enclaves in India. Wherever possible the Company's servants tried to extract additional concessions of territory and immunities, and in some cases they succeeded. From the outset the English enjoyed sovereignty over the whole island of Bombay (no. 62), where a very varied community, including Parsis displaced from other ports, lived under the rule of the Company's servants. During the seventeenth century the British settlement of Madras grew spectacularly. A very large Indian 'black town' was added to the small 'white town' of the English. Similar developments took place in the first half of the eighteenth century at Calcutta. By 1750 the population of the city was estimated at well over 100,000. Bombay, Madras and Calcutta became separate 'Presidencies', or local centres of the Company's operations, with their own governors and councils who ruled over the towns. In the white towns lived the Company's servants, the small garrisons of soldiers and a limited number of other British subjects, who earned a living as licensed merchants trading from port to port in Asia. The rapidly growing Indian population of the English settlements consisted of merchants doing business with the Company and with other merchants, artisans, servants and labourers.

By the early eighteenth century the commercial success of the English in India was impressive. The East India Company shipped more Indian goods to Europe than did any of its rivals, while the English communities in the ports of Bombay, Madras and Calcutta had won a considerable stake for themselves in India's seaborne trade with other parts of Asia. The strong position which the Portuguese had built up in Indian trade in the sixteenth century had been undermined in the seventeenth, when their lead passed to the Dutch. By 1740, if not earlier, the Dutch were being eclipsed by the British. A French challenge appeared in the 1720s, causing the British real concern and producing political consequences of very great importance; but in commercial terms the French enterprise was failing by the 1740s.[2]

Britain's undoubted success in India by the middle of the eighteenth century needs to be kept in perspective. From the British point of view Indian trade was still a small proportion of overseas trade as a whole. In terms of the whole of India, overseas trade was of limited significance and the British involvement in it was of no great consequence. On the other hand, from the perspective of coastal regions such as Bengal, where exports by sea were an important element in the economy, the growth in the British presence had serious implications. Nevertheless, even on a regional scale, by the middle of the eighteenth century the British had played virtually no political role outside their enclaves. The use of force had rarely been attempted, beyond some early seventeenth-century naval scuffles with the Portuguese and a disastrously unsuccessful attempt to coerce the Mughal empire in the 1680s.

Changes were to come thick and fast from the middle of the eighteenth century. The British quickly developed a spectacular political role. Their troops were to fight wars in southern India, in Bengal and even in the heartlands of the old Mughal empire. Out of war was to come a British empire. In 1765 the East India Company were awarded the *diwani* of Bengal by the Mughal emperor. This meant that they were recognised as the effective rulers of a province that probably contained something like 20 million inhabitants. By 1765 the British were also dominant along the Coromandel coast. The major Indian power on the coast ruled as their puppet, subject to their control. Through a garrison of their troops, the Company were also able to assert a decisive influence over the great north Indian state of Awadh.

Events in this great transformation such as the siege of Arcot or the battle of Plassey, or such personalities as Clive, Dupleix and Warren Hastings have, over the years, attracted a vast body of writing. Explaining why the transformation came about, however, now seems to be a complex and intractable business. Earlier generations were less troubled. If their sympathies lay with the empire that had emerged out of these events in the nineteenth century and which remained essentially intact until 1947, they tended to argue that a peaceful trading company had been compelled to take up arms because of the breakdown of ordered conditions and a slide to anarchy over much of India following the collapse of the Mughal empire. To make matters worse, the French had tried to exploit the Mughal failure by attacking the British first. Albeit reluctantly, the British found that they had no alternative but to resort to arms to protect their trade, chastise their enemies and eventually to restore India to what was usually taken as a much higher state of order than any that had existed under the Mughals. Those who were less well disposed towards the British Raj tended to argue that India in the mid-eighteenth century had been the first victim in a wave of systematic imperial aggression which Europe, and Britain in particular, was to unleash on the world in the nineteenth century.

These old certainties now seem flawed to most present-day historians. While there can be no denying that the Mughal empire had disintegrated, the eighteenth century is no longer seen as a period of disorder and anarchy affecting most of the subcontinent. In some cases Mughal rule was broken by persistent rebellion, as in the Punjab, but more commonly it withered away with relatively little disruption. It was succeeded by the regimes of great noblemen who had ruled provinces as governors in the name of the empire, as was the case in Bengal, Awadh or the Deccan; or by the rebels of the past who had reached accommodations with the empire, such as the Marathas. These regimes exercised authority over populations often comparable to those of an eighteenth-century European state. Within their domains some of the new rulers of the eighteenth century showed a capacity to develop new techniques of administration in order to enhance the revenue of their states and to maintain effective armed forces. If their courts lacked some of the splendour of those of the seventeenth-century Mughals, cities such as Hyderabad, Murshidabad and Lucknow became major centres of learning and artistic patronage, often reflecting the cultural traditions of the regions of which they were becoming the capitals. Some degree of economic growth, especially in the first half of the eighteenth century, seems to have underpinned this process of regional devolution. Cities like Delhi declined disastrously and some trade routes were disrupted by war, but other regions flourished and new commercial centres emerged. In short, it now seems difficult to portray eighteenth-century India in general as a land plagued by disorders so serious that they brought about a marked deterioration in economic conditions and thus compelled Europeans to intervene in order to maintain their trade.[3]

On the other hand, it seems equally difficult to sustain an argument that India was the victim of calculated British aggression. Events were to show that, although there was as yet little qualitative difference between European and Indian military technology in the age of the cannon and the musket, armies of European soldiers and sepoys trained and organized by Europeans could be devastatingly effective in the eighteenth century. There is, however, very little evidence that would suggest that the British were aware in advance of their potential military advantages or that the Company, let alone the British Government, planned to exploit them. Both were very conscious indeed of the cost of war and of the absence of any obvious commercial benefits to be derived from it. Official policy was nearly always to avoid war and to concentrate on peaceful trade. Nevertheless, to deduce from this that the British were simply the victims of other people's bellicosity and only retaliated in self-defence would be a serious oversimplification. At a sailing distance of six months, official policy from home could be defied with relative ease by men in India who, by the middle of the eighteenth century, had developed reasons of their own for resorting to force.

In seeking to explain why a British empire came so suddenly into being in the middle of the eighteenth century, historians are now inclined to look less for global explanations, such as the collapse of the Islamic empires or the unleashing of a new industrial imperialism from Europe, and more at local situations and the interaction between new regional states and such burgeoning colonial enclaves as Madras or Calcutta. The courts of seventeenth-century Mughal emperors and the factories of the East India Company had lived in entirely separate worlds which never met. The port cities of the mid-eighteenth century and the capitals of coastal regional states were part of the same world.[4]

For Indian states a European settlement offered a mixture of advantages and threats, but it could hardly be ignored. As European trade grew it became an important element in the revenue of coastal states. The Europeans and their Indian partners took an ever larger proportion of the produce of artisans and peasant cultivators on which the state's taxation depended. The eighteenth-century Indian states, like contemporary states in Europe, required rich merchants to advance them money. The prosperity of such merchants was often based on their dealings with the Europeans. At the European ports Indian rulers could obtain arms for their new armies and could even hire the Company's troops. On the other hand, huge accumulations of wealth in towns like Madras or Calcutta, which were outside the jurisdiction of the local ruler, could not but cause resentment and apprehension. As European trade spread inland, immunities and privileges were claimed for it. Put crudely, eighteenth-century Indian rulers were facing a dilemma that was to become familiar to future generations in what has come to be called 'the Third World': how to balance the potential generation of new wealth through a foreign presence in their territories with the loss of autonomy which that foreign presence undoubtedly entailed.

Even though the English might resolve to live in a self-contained manner within their settlements, by the mid-eighteenth century they could no longer do so. With the increase of their trade, both corporate and private, they felt it necessary not only to protect the immunities of the settlements, but also to claim privileged access to markets and sources of commodities far inland. The ruler's needs could be their opportunities: they too could advance money to Indian rulers. The ultimate temptation was to intervene in the politics of the state to extract concessions or to support one faction against another in return for favours.

A world of new states and growing settlements, in which Europeans and Indians could be both partners and rivals, now seems to be the context in which to place the famous events that brought empire to the British in the eighteenth century. The first portents of what was to happen appeared on the Coromandel coast in the years after 1744. Here the English and French settlements of Madras and Pondicherry were locked in rivalry, which spread

Fig. 4 The Walajah Mosque, Madras, built by the Nawabs of Arcot, late 18th century; modern photograph by C.A. Bayly

to draw in Indians on both sides. The French under the enterprising Dupleix (no.92) may have been the first to see the possibility of winning greatly enlarged concessions from supporting Indian claimants to power, but the English were quick to match them by adopting the cause of other claimants. Along the Coromandel coast small armies of English and French regular and Company soldiers, regiments of sepoys and the forces of their Indian allies fought one another for strategic points, like the great fort at Trichinopoly (no.96). After many fluctuations of fortune, in 1761 the English under Sir Eyre Coote (no.108) won a decisive victory at Wandiwash and besieged and captured Pondicherry. The outcome was that the British claimant to control of the Carnatic state on the Coromandel coast was confirmed in power. This was Muhammed Ali Walajah, the famous 'Nabob of Arcot' (no.142). For many years he maintained a nominally independent court which became a magnet for British clients, including those anxious to paint him. The reality behind his independence was that the territory of the Carnatic was protected by British troops and that the Company claimed the right to seize and make use of his resources whenever emergencies arose (Fig. 4).

The French played a much less conspicuous role in the events that brought the British to power in Bengal. From early in the eighteenth century the British involvement in Bengal's trade had become very large indeed and the potential for conflict with the ruler, the Nawab, was accordingly very high. Tension had built up under the powerful Nawab Alivardi Khan, who reigned from 1740 to 1756. It boiled over under his successor, the young Siraj-ud-Daulah. The new Nawab seems to have been determined to curb Calcutta's autonomy and to extract what he regarded as proper financial contributions from the British. When the Company's servants refused to negotiate seriously with him, he attacked Calcutta in 1756 and took it with surprising ease. The death of part of the garrison in the Black Hole, an episode around which much later emotion was to be generated (no.99), was an unintended consequence of the Nawab's victory. Calcutta was, however, quickly recovered by an expedition of troops from the southern battle front on the Coromandel coast, dispatched from Madras under one of the officers who had most distinguished himself against the French, Colonel Robert Clive (no.100). Within a few months Clive became aware that his army could be used to support a conspiracy against Siraj-ud-Daulah, which promised to yield major gains for the Company and huge rewards for the individuals concerned. Clive came to terms with the conspirators, who ensured that the main part of Siraj-ud-Daulah's army would desert him. This they duly did at the battle of Plassey in 1757, leaving the British victorious. Siraj-ud-Daulah was deposed and killed and his successor, Mir Jafar (no.107) conferred the promised benefits on the Company and its servants.[5]

Clive's intention when he intervened in Bengal's politics was probably limited to obtaining a new Indian regime that would in future be a pliant ally of the Company. Within a very few years, however, the Company had destroyed even the semblance of an independent regime and had itself become the ruler of Bengal. Between 1757 and 1765 nothing could be done to protect a succession of Nawabs from ruthless demands for concessions, both public and private. The Company insisted on receiving ever larger allocations of taxation to pay for its troops, while individuals levied 'presents' for themselves and claimed the right to trade on their own terms in any commodity in any part of Bengal. Mir Kasim, one of the Company's appointed Nawabs, resisted these demands to the point of a new war in 1763. The war took the Company's troops out of Bengal and involved them in a fresh round of fighting with the Wazir of Awadh, who had joined in a coalition against the British. In 1764 the Company's army won the battle of Buxar in northern India. This left them in a position to dictate terms not only for the future of Bengal but for the territories adjoining it. The settlement was made in the following year by Clive on his return to India. At the Treaty of Allahabad of 1765 (no.112) Clive accepted the *diwani* of Bengal, a recognition that the Company had made it impossible for any Nawab to retain even nominal authority. He also established a British diplomatic and military presence for the Company at Lucknow. There a number of Englishmen, including painters, seem to have made themselves at home at the Wazir's court.

The 1765 settlement was to last in essentials until late in the eighteenth century. Clive's successors had, however, to work out the practical implications of what would be involved in British rule of Bengal. Clive's original intention had probably been to leave all the layers of Indian authority intact. In the event, British Company servants were placed in some of the senior positions of what was still essentially an Indian state apparatus. Calcutta, the residence of Warren Hastings, the first Governor-General (nos.132–5), and of his Council, became the seat of government for the whole province. In

Fig. 5 The Mausoleum of the Sultans of Mysore, Seringapatam; modern photograph by C.A. Bayly

what came to be known as 'districts' junior Company servants began to concern themselves with levying taxation, the central preoccupation of the new regime as of the old, and even with supervising the administration of justice.

On these foundations a bureaucratic colonial administration was eventually to be established, but for most of the eighteenth century it would be more realistic to describe what the Company was doing in Bengal as the management of the state apparatus that had emerged under the Nawabs through Indian intermediaries and collaborators – such as Warren Hastings's famous *banian* (steward and business manager) Cantu Babu – under the somewhat remote supervision of the East India Company's servants. Some of these men, like Hastings himself, were assiduous administrators and developed an interest in the country they governed that added greatly to Western knowledge of it. Most, not surprisingly, also showed a keen concern for the personal advantages that the conquest of Bengal offered them. With what they acquired some of them were able to live in considerable style in Calcutta or other centres of British power. Stories of their wealth induced a number of the most accomplished contemporary British painters, such as John Zoffany, Tilly Kettle, Ozias Humphry, or Arthur William Devis, to take ship to India in search of patrons.[6] For the most part they painted rich and powerful sitters, both British and Indian, but some of them were also intrigued by ordinary people and by Indian landscapes, which they tried to represent, usually within the conventions of the 'picturesque' (nos.245–65).

By the end of the eighteenth century the British began to strike out of the bridgeheads which they had consolidated in Bengal and at Madras. Expansion from Madras brought the Company into bitterly contested wars with the powerful regional state of Mysore under the rule of Haidar Ali and his son Tipu Sultan. Until the Company could organize massive forces, they were by no means certain of victory over Mysore. In 1792 Tipu was worsted, and in 1799 his capital was taken and he was killed (Fig. 5). By then he had acquired the reputation of being the Indian Hannibal, the dauntless enemy of the new Rome, and he and his wars were depicted in highly dramatic terms, often by painters who never left Britain. From Bengal the British tightened their grip on Awadh and in the first decade of the nineteenth century, under the direction of the Marquess Wellesley (no.153), their armies extended British rule beyond Delhi and imposed British hegemony over the Marathas. Their power over the subcontinent was now unassailable.

NOTES

1. For the origins and early history of the East India Company, see Chaudhuri 1965.
2. British commercial dominance by the early eighteenth century is analysed in Holden Furber 1976.
3. For reappraisals of eighteenth-century India, see Alam 1986; Barnett 1980; Bayly 1983.
4. For this world, see Bayly 1988, ch. i, ii; Washbrook 1988, XXII, pp. 57–96.
5. For the 'revolution' in Bengal, see Khan 1969; Marshall 1988.
6. Archer 1979.

From Plassey to Seringapatam: India and British History Painting *c.*1760–*c.*1800

BRIAN ALLEN

By the middle years of the eighteenth century the few history painters active in England were beginning to explore the possibility of employing scenes from *British* history as subject-matter for their pictures. This phenomenon is closely related to the rise of antiquarian studies in eighteenth-century England. Important publications like Paul de Rapin-Thoyras's *The History of England ... Done into English, with additional notes ... by N. Tindal*, first published in an English translation in 1725, and David Hume's *History of England* of 1754 had begun to furnish the history painter with the literary basis so vital for success. Rapin's history enjoyed enormous popular acclaim due, as a reviewer in the *London Magazine* in 1732 put it, to its ability to 'furnish the people of England with the best materials against the two worst evils under the sun i.e. superstition and tyranny; and therefore this book should be in the hands of every Englishman, and engraven on his heart.'[1]

In 1749 the London publishers John and Paul Knapton and Robert Dodsley attempted to exploit this growing fashion for the representation of Britain's historical past by issuing a subscription for an elaborate series of fifty prints, representing as they put it 'the most memorable Actions and Events, from the landing of Julius Caesar to the Revolution'. The bankruptcy of the Knaptons led to the demise of the project after the publication of only six of the prints, all after designs by Francis Hayman and Nicholas Blakey; but even the conception of such a scheme is significant in this context.[2] Although Hayman managed to use some of his designs in a related context – as illustrations for Tobias Smollett's *A Complete History of England from the descent of Julius Caesar to the Treaty of Aix la Chapelle, 1748* – he was only too aware of the difficulty in finding patronage for *paintings* of English history. As Hayman's and Hogarth's friend André Rouquet, the Swiss miniaturist, put it in his fascinating little book *The Present State of the Arts in England* (1755):

> History painters have so seldom an opportunity of displaying their abilities in England, that it is surprising there are any of them at all who apply themselves to this branch: Whosoever happens to fall into this business, very rarely meets with a rival. Those who are acquainted with the force of emulation, will therefore readily conclude that it is impossible there should be such able history painters in that country, as might be, if they had more emulation.[3]

At the time Rouquet was writing, the painting of scenes from contemporary history had yet to begin, and unless we include Hogarth's modern comic history paintings, like *Calais Gate or the Roast Beef of Old England* of 1748 (Tate Gallery) or *The March of the Guards to Finchley* of 1750 (Thomas Coram Foundation), there is nothing to suggest the emergence of the genre. At least by the end of the 1750s there was some form of official encouragement with the establishment of the 100 guineas annual premium offered by the Society for the Encouragement of Art, Manufactures and Commerce for the best history painting from 'English History only'. However, the subject-matter of the early premium pictures was deeply rooted in the medieval past or beyond. In 1760 Robert Edge Pine won the first of these awards with his *Surrender of Calais to Edward III*, the second prize going to Andrea Casali for *The Assassination of Edward the Martyr*.[4]

It was not until the 1750s and Lord Clive's victories at Calcutta, Chandernagore and Plassey that India became sufficiently part of British political consciousness to warrant any serious representation in art. The East India Company – the one organization with a vested interest in promoting a British view of India – was too commercially orientated to be an enlightened patron of the arts.[5] Had the Company been more adventurous as patrons its Leadenhall Street premises (see nos. 42–43) could have been decorated in the manner of the Foundling Hospital by artists of the avant-garde St Martin's Lane Academy.[6] Although some landscapes of Company settlements were commissioned from George Lambert and Samuel Scott for the Directors' Courtroom (see no. 62), the only decorative element comparable to the Foundling Hospital's Courtroom was the elaborate marble chimneypiece commissioned from John Michael Rysbrack in 1728. This contained a bas-relief overmantel depicting *Britannia receiving the riches of the East* (Fig. 6).[7] Here Britannia, shown seated beneath a rocky outcrop, looks towards the East from whence India approaches proffering a casket of jewels. Behind stand Asia and Africa, leading a camel and lion respectively. Beneath Britannia two *putti* pour out the contents of a cornucopia while to the right a river god, symbolizing the Thames, leans on the rudder of a ship. Commerce and labour are symbolized by the fleet of ships and the figure cording a bale.

Fig. 6 Britannia receiving the riches of the East, John Michael Rysbrack, 1728; marble bas-relief overmantel (Commonwealth Relations Office)

Fifty years later another room in the Company's headquarters – the Revenue Committee Room – was embellished with an oval ceiling by the little-known Spiridione Roma (d.1787). Roma came to England from his native Corfu soon after 1770 and built up a practice in London, working mostly for City companies as a picture restorer and portrait painter. He was a curious choice as a decorative painter since his only other known work of this type, produced for Horace Walpole's friend John Chute, consisted of *trompe l'oeil* fan tracery in Perpendicular style for the chapel at The Vyne in Hampshire.[8] Roma's ceiling at Leadenhall Street (Fig. 7) also depicts *Britannia receiving the riches of the East*. In this work Britannia is seated firmly on a rock which symbolizes the stability of the Company. A river god, representing the Ganges, pours his stream at Britannia's feet while to the right Mercury presents the Eastern lands to her. Other countries represented include Persia with silks and drugs, China with tea and porcelain, and India with pearls and jewels. In the background is an East Indiaman under sail, symbolizing the commerce from which Britannia and the Company derived its prosperity.

The Company, of course, wanted to celebrate its successes of the later 1750s and commissioned the sculptor Peter Scheemakers to make statues of

Fig. 7 The East offering its riches to Britannia, Spiridone Roma, 1778; ceiling painting from East India House

Lord Clive, General Stringer Lawrence and Admiral Pocock with the general court resolving on 24 September 1760 'that their Eminent and Signal Services to the Company may be ever had in remembrance.'[9] Clive had recently returned from India and, as a result of his triumph at Plassey, the revenue pouring into the Company's coffers had been considerably increased. Admiral Pocock's successes at sea before and during the Seven Years War, and General Stringer Lawrence's victories on land, had virtually ended French power in India. These commissions, however, were hardly bold acts of patronage and it was left to another commercial entrepreneur to exploit the potential of the Seven Years War as subject-matter for art.

Jonathan Tyers, the proprietor of Vauxhall Gardens on the south bank of the Thames, had long since realized the potential of employing large-scale works of art in a public setting. The introduction of Louis-François Roubiliac's freestanding statue of *Handel* to Vauxhall in the spring of 1738, and the elaborate series of paintings adorning the supper boxes flanking the Grove that followed in the early 1740s, had helped to transform the physical appearance of the gardens. They also did much to reverse Tyers's flagging fortunes, changing Vauxhall from a 'rural Brothel', as one commentator described it, into one of London's most fashionable nightspots.[10]

Most of Hayman's pictures at Vauxhall[11] were lighthearted and even frivolous in their subject-matter, but several others, notably those by the marine painter Peter Monamy (no. 51), depicted episodes from the current conflict with Spain, the so-called War of Jenkins' Ear (1739–48) which was caused by the British attempt to break the Spanish monopoly of trade with South America. Two of Monamy's large canvases (both now lost) depicted *The taking of Porto Bello in 1740 by Admiral Vernon* and *The taking of the St. Joseph, a Spanish register ship, in 1742 by Captain Tucker in the fowey man of war.*[12]

Jingoistic pictures of this type had a tradition of sorts in marine painting but they hardly qualified as history painting in the accepted academic sense of the term, or at least not in the same way as the large-scale works of Louis Laguerre, produced at the beginning of the century. These included elaborate mural decorations for the Saloon, walls and staircases at Marlborough House, which commemorated the victories of the 1st Duke of Marlborough in the War of the Spanish Succession.[13] Monamy's works were in many ways on a par with the battle pictures of John Wootton done in the 1740s, which were considered little more than topography although in some cases they also served as a vehicle for Royal portraiture.[14] Battle painting was not taken very seriously as a genre, essentially because it rarely required the exertion of the imagination and the intellect which was considered the attribute of great history painting. As the influential theorist Jonathan Richardson put it earlier in the century, the history painter 'must possess all the good Qualities requisite to an Historian ... he must moreover know ... the Habits, Customs, Buildings, &c. of the Age, and Countrey, in which the thing was transacted ... he must yet go higher, and have the Talents requisite to a good Poet; the rules for the Conduct of a Picture being much the same with those to be observed in writing a Poem ... requiring an elevation of Genius beyond what pure historical Narration does; the Painter must imagine his Figures to Think, Speak and Act, as a Poet should do in a Tragedy, or Epick Poem.'[15]

The paintings that were added to Vauxhall Gardens in the early 1760s owed far more to Richardson's high-minded ideals than to Wootton's or Monamy's efforts. Jonathan Tyers was constantly seeking ways of keeping Vauxhall Gardens in the public eye, but it is not known if the impetus for the production of the four enormous history paintings on the theme of the current Seven Years War came from Tyers or the artist, Francis Hayman. The latter must have relished a return to the theatrical environs of Vauxhall with its enormous fashionable captive audience.

Although the first regular public exhibitions of works by living painters had begun in 1760 at the premises of the Society of Arts, Manufactures and Commerce just off the Strand, it was at that stage by no means clear that it would become an annual event. For Hayman, the opportunity to paint the sort of large historical pictures so rarely commissioned from a living British artist was not only a great confidence booster but it also gave him the ideal excuse to avoid the potentially undignified competition for one of the Society's premiums. Hayman's imminent decline as a history painter was in part the result of a serious challenge from a number of Italian decorators in England after the mid-1750s, but as late as 1808 the painter Edward Edwards could still refer to Hayman as 'unquestionably the best historical painter in the kingdom before the arrival of Cipriani'.[16]

Hayman's four giant canvases (12 feet high by 15 feet long) were placed in large frames in the Saloon, the annexe to the Rotunda which Tyers had built at Vauxhall around 1750. This was part of a major re-decoration of the Gardens, undertaken in the late 1740s to try and counteract the growing attractions of nearby rival Ranelagh Gardens. The four frames in which the pictures were placed were originally designed to take portraits of Frederick,

Fig. 8 The inside of the Elegant Music Room in Vaux Hall Gardens, H. Roberts after Samuel Wale, 1751; line engraving, detail (The Trustees of the British Museum)

Prince of Wales, and his family (the Prince was the ground landlord of Vauxhall and its most important patron), but his untimely death in 1751 made this proposal highly inappropriate.[17] As a result the frames remained uncomfortably empty (see Fig. 8) until Tyers commissioned Hayman to fill them, which he did between 1761 and 1764. Although none of the four original pictures survives, with the aid of an engraving after one of them, *modelli* for two of the others and a lengthy printed description of the fourth picture, it is possible to reconstruct a fairly accurate idea of their appearance.

The first to be completed was *The Surrender of Montreal to General Amherst*, unveiled in 1761. Hayman must have worked in haste on the large canvas since Montreal had only been captured on 8 September 1760, but the event was of the greatest significance since, combined with Wolfe's victory at Quebec, Canada had effectively become British. Instead of depicting a battle scene, Hayman chose to paint the moment of Amherst's magnanimous gesture of feeding his captives, who had endured weeks of siege. The viewer was clearly meant to draw an analogy with the actions of the great generals of antiquity – Scipio and Alexander – episodes from Greek and Roman history that were widely familiar to an eighteenth-century audience. As related by Livy, the continence of Scipio Africanus, arguably the greatest of Roman generals, had as its basic tenet the notion of righteousness triumphing over needless sacrifice and, by association, the British public were to be left in no doubt about the validity and wisdom of British rule in the North American continent. According to contemporary descriptions, on a stone in one corner of the picture was the inscription:

POWER EXERTED
CONQUEST OBTAINED
MERCY SHOWN
MDCCLX[18]

The second picture to be completed – *The Triumph of Britannia* – was ready by June 1762 (the composition is now known only through Ravenet's engraving; Fig. 9).[19] This was an elaborate allegory designed to celebrate the great naval victories of the British over the French, particularly the decisive action at Quiberon Bay, off the coast of Brittany, on 20 November 1759. Portrait medallions of the victorious admirals, Pocock, Boscawen, Hawke, Anson, Saunders, Keppel and Howe, were borne by Nereids in the wake of Britannia, whose chariot was drawn by Neptune.

Later in 1762 the third picture, *Lord Clive meeting with Mir Jaffir after the Battle of Plassey,* was completed. This is probably the first picture to deal with an event from Anglo-Indian history and it transported the viewer at Vauxhall Gardens to the other extreme of the expanding British Empire. It survived until about 1840 when it disappeared after the sale of the contents of Vauxhall Gardens. A close idea of its appearance, although not its scale, can be deduced from a reduced version, possibly a *modello* for the large picture, which was acquired by the National Portrait Gallery in 1979 (no. 107). This small version had long been mis-attributed to Mather Brown, but it is undoubtedly by Hayman. It corresponds almost exactly to a lengthy description of the Vauxhall picture which appeared in the press in 1762 and 1763.[20] Hayman, who

Fig. 9 The Triumph of Britannia, Simon F. Ravenet after Francis Hayman, 1763; etching and engraving (Yale Center for British Art, Paul Mellon Collection)

Fig. 10 Sketch for Lord Clive meeting with Mir Jafar after the Battle of Plassey, Francis Hayman, *c.* 1762; oil on canvas (Private Collection)

never went to India, must have based the few Indian details in his composition on written descriptions or verbal accounts supplied by those who had greater familiarity with the country. The costumes of Mir Jafar and his entourage were probably based on Indian miniatures but Hayman was clearly not at ease with other details. It is difficult to take very seriously a published account of the picture which described the elephant as 'according to the greatest judges from the East Indies ... the best they ever saw in painting'. Despite its inadequacies the finished product must have been a considerable improvement on an earlier design for the composition. In a very small, crude sketch (Fig. 10) Hayman had introduced a number of Indian servants carrying gold vessels filled with bullion on their heads. These absurdly inaccurate figures, which looked more like Egyptians, were removed in favour of Mir Jafar's son, and a particularly inept rendition of an elephant was much improved. It is also worth noting that Mir Jafar's obsequiousness in the first sketch has given way to a more equal exchange of bows in the finished work.

Nothing is known about how this decorative scheme at Vauxhall was to be displayed, but Hayman may originally have intended to include another Indian subject for, at about the same time, he painted *The Surrender of Pondicherry to Sir Eyre Coote* (no.93). It is possible that this was rejected because a second Indian subject would have created an imbalance in the iconography of the scheme as a whole. As it transpired, Coote was honoured in the last of the four pictures, a military allegory entitled *Britannia distributing Laurels to the victorious Generals*; the only one of the four of which no visual record survives, although a long descriptive account of it was published in the press in June 1764.[21] Here the generals were portrayed as full-length figures in 'Roman habits', reflecting the change towards a more neo-classical taste.

Nothing comparable to these pictures had ever been undertaken in England, and they are particularly significant not only because they dealt with contemporary events but also because three of the four were seen by a large audience well before that dramatically successful war was over. Jonathan Tyers would no doubt have endorsed Edmund Burke's words that during these years of conflict commerce had been 'united with, and made to flourish with war'.[22] They were the first genuinely popular history paintings and the public was eager to welcome pictures glorifying their contemporary history in the same way that theatre audiences welcomed a similarly jingoistic repertoire. Two of David Mallet's plays, *Britannia* and *Elvira* for instance, were inspired by contemporary political events. *Britannia,* a masque set to music by Thomas Arne, was first performed at Drury Lane on 9 May 1755. With Britain on the brink of war it was specifically written to rouse the national spirit. *Elvira,* first performed at Drury Lane on 26 November 1762, contained an attack on Lord Bute who had just negotiated a peace treaty with France that was considered by many to be disadvantageous to British interests. There are numerous other examples of authors and playwrights using episodes from England's legendary past to dramatic purpose in the mid-century.

Under Pitt's leadership the heroes of the classical past were replaced in the minds of the common people by men like Wolfe, Clive and Hawke, and Hayman's pictures captured the public imagination at precisely the right moment. It should also be remembered that these works were on public view almost a decade before Benjamin West completed his *Death of General Wolfe,* so often cited as the exemplar of the modern history picture.

While Hayman was content to undertake large-scale commissions of this type for Tyers at Vauxhall, he and his fellow members of the newly formed Society of Artists were rather more conservative in their choice of subject-matter for pictures sent to the by now annual exhibitions. Acutely aware of the difficulty of finding buyers for modern subject pictures, those artists who professed to be history painters mostly exhibited scenes from Greek and Roman history, classical mythology, the Bible and, increasingly, Shakespeare. There was certainly no representation of the Black Hole of Calcutta comparable to the scenes depicted by artists a century later, which charted the more bloodcurdling episodes of the Indian Rebellion. Although George Romney exhibited *Death of General Wolfe* at The Free Society in 1763 and Edward Penny a canvas of the same subject a year later at the Society of Artists, the one image that perhaps owes something to Hayman's promotion of the ideals of humanitarian military leadership was Penny's enormously popular *The Marquis of Granby giving alms to a soldier*, a version of which was exhibited in 1765, although this is as much a conversation piece as a history painting.[23]

The popularity of Penny's *Granby* must surely account for his being commissioned by the East India Company to paint *Clive receiving from the Nawab of Bengal the grant of the sum of money for helping disabled soldiers as well as the widows of those dying in the Company's Service* (no.111). With the Parliamentary enquiry into Clive's amassment of his fortune proceeding at the same time as this picture's exhibition at the Royal Academy in 1772, the Company must have hoped the picture would bolster his reputation and help make him as popular a figure as Lord Granby had been in the mid-1760s.

All things considered, the Vauxhall pictures did not inspire a rash of paintings depicting episodes from the Seven Years War in Canada or India. In about 1763 William Watts, a loyal East India Company servant for many years, did commission from Benjamin Wilson a large picture showing him negotiating the treaty with Mir Jafar after the capture of Calcutta, and Wilson apparently painted a second picture commissioned by Watts entitled *Lord Clive's placing Mir Jaffir upon the Throne of Musnad* (now lost), but these are isolated examples at this early date.

Lord Clive himself apparently intended to commission a series of large paintings by Benjamin West depicting the most important events of his Indian career to decorate the Eating Room at Claremont, the house he acquired in Surrey in 1769. Although one of the pictures was eventually completed – *Lord Clive receiving from the Mogul the Grant of the Duanney* (no.112) – Clive's death in 1774 caused the abandonment of the scheme.

The American War of Independence dominated foreign policy in the later 1770s and early 1780s, and it was not until the end of the century that the last of the various Anglo-Mysore Wars focused British attention once again on the Indian subcontinent. The ultimate defeat and death of Tipu Sultan – the 'Tiger of Mysore' – in 1799 did far more to inspire British history painters than the exploits of Clive had done a few decades earlier. The British obsession with Tipu Sultan continued long after his demise both in literature and the visual arts, and episodes connected with the Anglo-Mysore Wars provided the painter with more subject-matter than any other topic in Anglo-Indian history.

The harsh treaty forced on Tipu by the British after his defeat in 1791, which resulted in Lord Cornwallis taking two of the ruler's sons hostage, inspired numerous pictures, perhaps because it allowed for another self-conscious display of British magnanimity in victory. Tipu's personality seemed to fascinate the English so much that shortly after the conclusion of the treaty *The Pantomime Story of Tippoo Saib* was performed at Sadler's Wells. The *Public Advertiser* of 3 May 1792 remarked that the story would make a very suitable libretto for an opera.[24]

Of the numerous 'hostage' pictures that ensued perhaps the most historically accurate are those by Robert Home and A. W. Devis (see no.157). Home was the only artist to have actually witnessed the handing over of the two young princes to Cornwallis, but it was Devis's arrival in Madras late in the summer of 1793, with plans for a painting of the subject (Fig. 11), that prompted the former to make his own record of the event. However, following in the tradition of large-scale history painting established by John Singleton Copley in the previous decade, neither of these images offered any radical new departure in either style or composition.

Meanwhile, in London the American painter Mather Brown (1761–1831), who had been a pupil of both West and Copley, approached the East India Company in August 1792 with a view to dedicating to them a forthcoming picture of 'the late important events in India'.[25] Brown exhibited his work at Orme's Morland Gallery in Bond Street in November 1792 with a view to publicizing the engravings after two small paintings – *The Departure of the Sons of Tippoo from the Zenana* and *The Delivery of the Definitive Treaty by the Hostage Princes to Lord Cornwallis* – before embarking on a third and much

Fig. 11 Lord Cornwallis receiving the Sons of Tippoo, Arthur William Devis, 1793–1805; oil on canvas (Private Collection)

larger picture of *Lord Cornwallis receiving the Sons of Tippoo,* now in the Oriental Club.[26] The crowded composition of the latter relies on the sentimental aspect of the narrative far more than the pictures of either Home or Devis. In this it is consistent with the strain of Romantic history painting encouraged by Boydell for his Shakespeare Gallery, opened in 1789, or the pictures commissioned by Robert Bowyer for his 'Historic Gallery'.

Other 'hostage pictures', notably by Henry Singleton, were exhibited at the Royal Academy in 1793 and 1794, and many other artists translated the event into more ephemeral designs for tin tea trays or even Chinese glass paintings. Almost all these images are consistent in their portrayal of the vulnerability of the young princes in the company of the corpulently avuncular figure of Cornwallis.

Apart from Robert Home's pendant to his portrayal of the hostage princes – *The Death of Colonel Moorhouse at Bangalore* of 1793–4 (Fig. 12), a deliberate essay in the manner of West's *Death of Wolfe*[27] – the legend of Tipu continued to fuel the imagination of artists. It was a legend that culminated with his death after the storming of Seringapatam on 4 May 1799. In England painters and engravers worked frenziedly to produce the first rousing depictions of those dramatic events, and the first of these were two very inaccurate scenes by Thomas Stothard,[28] which were quickly engraved.

Easily the most impressive and ambitious must have been *The Storming of*

Seringapatam by the young Robert Ker Porter, a gigantic canvas approximately 21 feet high by 120 feet long and covering 2,550 square feet. It was said to have been painted in eight weeks and was exhibited on a curved screen at the Lyceum Theatre in the Strand from 17 April 1800 to 10 January 1801.[29] This was yet another manifestation of the mania for panoramas which captured the public imagination from the 1790s to the 1820s. It was apparently offered to the East India Company which refused to purchase it, and was later destroyed by fire. John Vendramini's engraving in three sections, published between January 1802 and January 1803, gives some idea of its appearance. This was the English equivalent of the sort of battle painting that flourished in Napoleon's France but which was usually eschewed by British painters. Its public display during a period of war therefore gives it a role analogous to Hayman's Vauxhall pictures of forty years earlier.

Fig. 12 The Death of Colonel Moorhouse at Bangalore, Robert Home, 1793–4; oil on canvas (National Army Museum, London)

The discovery of the body of Tipu Sultan after the storming of Seringapatam was a subject also tackled by Ker Porter. On a considerably more modest scale than his previous work, it was nonetheless one of the least fanciful renderings of the event.[30] A comparison with Henry Singleton's picture, *The Body of Tippoo Sultaun recognised by his family*, a belated adaptation of Gavin Hamilton's overtly neo-classical *Achilles bewailing the Death of Patroclus* of the early 1760s, shows that Ker Porter's picture had more in common with West's *Death of Wolfe*. The appearance of S. W. Reynolds's mezzotint after Ker Porter's picture may have prompted A. W. Devis to paint his two versions of the subject. With its Rembrandtesque lighting, the version in this catalogue (no. 169) captures the dramatic tragedy of the solemn moment when a British officer announces the discovery of Tipu's limp body by General Baird. Devis's first-hand knowledge of India undoubtedly helped him convey the scene in a far more convincing way than artists such as Ker Porter and Singleton, who never visited India.

Yet Tipu was to remain a source of fascination for years to come. One of Sir David Wilkie's last exhibits at the Royal Academy in 1839 was *Sir David Baird discovering the body of Sultaun Tippoo Saib* (Fig. 13). This huge picture, Wilkie's largest single work, is a hybrid mixture of conventional portraiture and history painting. It was commissioned by Baird's widow, who was determined to re-instate her deceased husband's reputation which had suffered in competition with Lord Wellington (at the time of the sack of Seringapatam Wellington had been a junior officer under Baird's command). To this end Lady Baird employed a biographer to eulogize her husband's life and commissioned Wilkie to paint Baird at the moment of his triumph.[31] Forty years after the event the picture had a mixed reception, and two more decades were to pass before the public was again stirred by pictorial accounts of the Indian Rebellion.

Fig. 13 Sir David Baird discovering the body of Sultaun Tippoo Saib, Sir David Wilkie, 1839; oil on canvas (National Galleries of Scotland)

NOTES

1. *The London Magazine*, I, 1732, p. 360.
2. Allen 1987, pp. 146–8.
3. Rouquet 1755, pp. 21–2.
4. For further details of the early premium pictures see Sunderland 1974, pp. 317–25.
5. See Archer 1965, pp. 401–9.
6. The East India Company and the Foundling Hospital both shared the same architect, Theodore Jacobsen. The Company's Leadenhall Street premises were rebuilt by Jacobsen in the late 1720s.
7. See Archer 1986, p. 102, no.147, pl.XXXI and Baker 1982, pp. 35–6.
8. For Spiridione Roma see Croft-Murray 1970, II, p. 270. Roma's canvases at The Vyne were taken down from the chapel in the nineteenth century and were put up, in a mutilated fashion, in the Chapel Gallery, where they can still be seen (see National Trust 1988, pp. 18–19).
9. Minutes of the General Court, quoted Archer 1965 (see note 5), p. 406. For the Scheemakers statues see Archer 1986, pp. 103–4, nos.148–50, pls. 30–32.
10. See Lockman n.d. (1752), p. 28.
11. For the most recent discussion of Hayman's supper box paintings see Allen 1987, pp. 113–33.
12. The titles are taken from a list of the pictures published for the first time in the anonymous Vauxhall guidebook *A Description of Vaux Hall Gardens*, 1762.
13. See Croft-Murray 1962, I, pp. 61 ff. and Walker 1976, pp. 11 ff.
14. See Meyer 1984, pp. 18–19.
15. Richardson 1725, 2nd edn., pp. 18–19.
16. Edwards 1808, p. 51.
17. For further details see Allen 1987, pp. 64–6.
18. See (Anon.), *Description of Vaux Hall Gardens*, 1762, p. 26.
19. Allen 1987, p. 65, fig. 35.
20. See the *Public Advertiser*, no. 8905, 20 May 1763 and the *London Magazine*, XXXII, May 1763, pp. 233–4.
21. Unidentified cutting, dated 12 June 1764, in 'Wroth Collection of Cuttings related to Vauxhall Gardens', Museum of London Library (L.75, 85), III, p.7.
22. These words are taken from the inscription composed by Burke for John Bacon's monument to William Pitt the Elder in the Guildhall in the City of London.
23. For a stimulating discussion of Penny's picture see Solkin 1986, pp. 1–23.
24. See Evans 1982, p. 111.
25. Ibid., p. 111.
26. Ibid., p. 116. The two smaller pictures are reproduced as figs. 94, 95.
27. See Carman 1971, pp. 161–5.
28. One of these, showing the attack on Seringapatam by night, is in the collection of the Duke of Wellington at Stratfield Saye; the second (Private Collection; see Archer 1979, pl. 337) shows the hostage princes leaving the *zenana* and suggests that Stothard, in haste and without reliable information, is confusing the surrender of the hostages in 1792 with their surrender to Baird in 1799.
29. See Hyde 1988, p. 65.
30. See Archer 1979, pl. 340. The original painting is in the Victoria Memorial Hall in Calcutta.
31. For full details of the Wilkie picture see Miles and Brown 1987, pp. 42–3, no. 42.

The Embassy of Sir Thomas Roe to India, 1615–19

Towards the end of 1614, 'His Majesty [James I], at the request of the East India Company sent Sir Thomas Roe, Knight, ambassadour to the Great Maghoore, whome some corruptly called Mogall ... unto whome this ambassadour had commission to make and contract a league between his Majesty and his subjects for commerce and traffique in his dominions, and to procure and establish a factory for our nation in sundry parts of his dominions, as well seaports as inland towns ... Hee is the first that ever was imployed in this hie nature to any of these farre remote eastern princes' (Stow's Annals, 1615, cited in Foster 1926, p. xiii).

Sir Thomas Roe's embassy put on a formal footing the diplomatic contact between the British Crown and the Mughal empire, which was not ruptured until the last vestiges of Mughal authority were swept away in the aftermath of the Indian Rebellion of 1857. British relations with some of the descendants of the subordinate magnates of the erstwhile Mughal empire even survived until 1947 when, at Independence, the British Crown abrogated its right to paramountcy in the Indian subcontinent. This was not simply a matter of diplomatic niceties. The English East India Company was to build up much of its trade and political influence within the ambit of the Mughal empire. Later, as territorial ruler, the Company derived its notions of power and authority, of rights and ritual, from the Mughals. The British were to adopt their methods of taxing the land, of counting their people, and even their administrative language.

C.A.B.

1

1 James I of England and VI of Scotland (1566–1625)

After John de Critz the Elder
Oil on panel, 57.2 × 41.9 ($22\frac{1}{2}$ × $16\frac{1}{2}$)
National Portrait Gallery, London (548)

The reign of James I was an age of commercial expansion when the Crown, the rapidly growing City of London and the gentry cooperated in raising capital for overseas voyages of plunder and settlement. With the plantations in Ireland and Virginia, and the foundation of the English East India Company in 1600, the English began to challenge the Dutch as Europe's most efficient seaborne mercantile power. Once little more than licensed pirates on the fringes of the great Spanish world empire, the English made inroads into the monopolies both of the Dutch and the Portuguese (now dependants of the Spanish) in the Eastern seas where they had voyaged in search of spices and textiles. King James, pictured here in middle age, was particularly concerned to swell the nation's tax returns from trade and excise. C.A.B.

PROVENANCE: Transferred from the British Museum 1879.

LITERATURE: Chaudhuri 1965.

EXHIBITION: Burnley, Towneley Hall, *The Pendle Witches*, 19 May–30 September 1972 (71).

2 Map of the world from Richard Hakluyt's *Principal Navigations, Voyages, Traffiques and Discoveries of the English Nation, 1599*, 3 vols.

Edward Wright
Engraving, 46.1 × 65.6 (18⅛ × 25⅝)
The British Library Board (638. h. 5)

The success of Dutch ships in making voyages directly to Asia for spices in the 1590s stimulated an English response. These plans took definite shape on the last day of 1600 when Queen Elizabeth I granted a charter, with rights to exclusive trade with the Orient, to 'The Governor and Company of merchants trading into the East Indies'. An important prerequisite for the worldwide expansion of English trade was the development of the science of map-making. London map-makers adapted and refined information culled from Spanish, Portuguese, Dutch and French maps.

Richard Hakluyt (*c.* 1553–1616) was a confidant of many of the leading explorers and seamen of the age. He gathered much cartographical information while he was in Paris acting as Chaplain to the English ambassador. The first edition of his chief work, *The Principal Navigations, Voiages* [*sic*] ... *of the English Nation*, was published in 1589, followed by a much fuller edition, with significant additions to the geography of the East Indies culled from Dutch sources, in 1599–1600. This map, the first made in England on the Mercator projection according to the principles laid down by Edward Wright, was prefixed to the second volume of *Principal Navigations*.

In 1600, Hakluyt was listed as an advisor to the East India Company, supplying it with maps and providing information about markets. C.A.B.

LITERATURE: Hind 1955, ii, pp.178–81: Quinn 1974, pp. 64–73.

3 *Purchas his pilgrimes in five bookes*, London, 1625

Samuel Purchas
Printed book, 35.3 × 50.5 (13⅞ × 19⅞)
The British Library Board (984.h.5)

One feature of Roe's embassy to the Mughals was the exchange of images of the respective rulers and of other notables between the two sides. Roe wrote that 'In the art of limninge [painting], his [the Great Mughal's] painters worke miracles' (Foster 1926, p.xxxix). This engraving, which appeared some years later (1625) in *Hakluytus Posthumus or Purchas his pilgrimes*, the illustrated travels of Samuel Purchas, shows the Emperor Jahangir (on the left) and his son Prince Khurram (later Shahjahan). It is possible that the engraver used one of the miniatures that Roe had brought back from the imperial workshop. For the Mughals the possession of physical likenesses of other contemporary rulers, of their own nobles and even of their enemies, seems to have been particularly important. The emperors gave copies of their own portraits, along with a ring, to their particularly favoured personal dependants. This desire to docket the images of the great men of the age, and so perhaps to 'capture' their virtue, helps explain the high quality of miniature portraits produced by their court. C.A.B.

LITERATURE: Foster 1926, p. xxxiv; Hind 1955, ii, p. 388, pl. 244.

4

4 Sir Thomas Roe (1581–1644)

G. Vertue after Michiel Jansz van Miereveld, 1741
Print, 31 × 19 (8¼ × 7½)
The Trustees of the British Museum, Department of Prints and Drawings (P I–173, Cracherode Collection)

Born at Leyton into a prominent City of London family, Roe was typical of the new breed of trained Crown servants who served the growing English state. He attended the Inns of Court and accompanied a voyage to Guiana on the *Spanish Main* in 1610. He went to India, it appears, for a reason which dozens of his successors would have understood: 'to repair his fortune'. The embassy was designed to give royal support to the struggling East India Company which was trying to establish itself in mainland India in the face of strenuous opposition from the Portuguese, who declared the English 'all theeves'. After many delays occasioned by the Portuguese and the Mughal Governor of Surat, Roe finally caught up with Jahangir (reigned 1605–27) as he moved through the cities of central and western India during the winter of 1615–16. Roe declared that he was 'treated with more favour and outward grace ... than ever was sheowed to any ambassadour, eyther of the Turke or Persian , or other whatsoever.' Jahangir rejected the claim of King James I to be treated as an equal; after all he was simply a tribute-bearing 'Frank'. But Roe did receive a royal charter (*farman*) which gave promises of protection for resident English merchants, and on his return journey he was able to consolidate English commercial relations in the Persian Gulf. Roe's distinguished diplomatic career continued with an embassy to the Ottoman Turks in 1621 and the negotiation of a major treaty between Sweden and Poland in 1629. He became a Privy Councillor in 1640. The Dutch painter Miereveld (1567–1641) graduated from altar-pieces to portraits of the Princes of Nassau. The large number of his English paintings suggests that Miereveld visited England. C.A.B.

LITERATURE: Foster 1926.

Mughal India at its Height : a Rule of Pen and Sword

The Mughal or Timurid empire in India had been consolidated by Jahangir's brilliant father, Akbar, who ruled between 1556 and 1605. Akbar perfected the art of Turkish warfare based on cavalry and artillery. He defeated or cowed into quiescence the great Hindu Rajput princes of north India and incorporated some of the most important of them into his military system. His huge realm, which probably contained at least a hundred million people, stretched from Afghanistan in the north into central India and from Sind in the west to the borders of Burma in the east. Tranquillity over this vast area was maintained, ultimately, by bodies of mailed cavalry established in major towns, along the trade routes and at fords, passes and other strong-points. The nobles of the empire, Hindu and Muslim, were responsible for the recruitment and equipment of certain numbers of these elite cavalrymen. The nobles were ranked within the imperial hierarchy according to the numbers of men they raised, and they were rewarded with cash salaries from the imperial treasury or with the rights to collect the land revenue in certain provinces (*jagirs*). By reassigning *jagirs* and moving their officers around, Akbar and his successors hoped to prevent the concentration of overmuch power in the hands of local magnates.

The Mughal empire was a construct of the pen as much as of the sword. A skilled Persian-writing bureaucracy comprising Hindus as well as Muslims dispensed imperial justice, kept records of rights and, above all, collected the land revenues. These revenues, systematized and reassessed during Akbar's reign, were paid in silver rupees. They formed the basic fund of resources upon which the nobility and the military subsisted. High productivity in agriculture and a flourishing internal and external trade in manufactures were necessary to keep money flowing around India and into the imperial coffers.

After 1765, when they became revenue managers of Bengal, the British adapted the Mughal system of land revenues to their own purposes. Mughal grants and the level of Mughal taxation provided important precedents for the emerging European power. C.A.B.

5 Abul-Fazl presenting the first book (*daftar*) of the *Akbarnama* to Akbar

Govardhan, *c.*1605
Gouache, 24 × 13.5 ($9\frac{1}{2} \times 5\frac{1}{4}$)
Inscribed on the margin: *Govardhan*
The Trustees of the Chester Beatty Library, Dublin (MS 3 no.117 f. 176b)

The Emperor Akbar is shown accepting the celebrated chronicle of his reign, the *Akbarnama*. He is depicted in the classic

5

pose of Indo-Islamic royal painting, receiving his courtiers from his cushioned throne (*gadi*). The *Akbarnama* is a vital visual record of the high Mughal period. Its vivid miniature illustrations depict in great detail the military and administrative life of the late sixteenth century and emphasize Akbar's central role in the establishment of the flexible diplomatic and economic system which was to sustain the empire for the next century. The court chronicle and also the great 'Domesday Book' of the empire, the *Ain-i-Akbari* (nos.6, 7), was produced under the direction of Abul-Fazl (here shown presenting the document to his ruler), the master administrator and a leading intellectual of Akbar's court. The relationship between Akbar, a soldier of Turkish descent, and Abul-Fazl, an Indian Muslim brought up in the Persian school of science and administration, epitomizes the strengths of the Mughal empire itself.

This illustration to Abul-Fazl's postscript (*khatima*) appears at the end of his account of the first thirty years of Akbar's life (up to AD 1572). The actual presentation, however, must have taken place after April 1596 when this *daftar* was finished. No.5 is from the royal copy of the *Akbarnama*. C.A.B.

LITERATURE: Abul-Fazl 1902, pp.544–76; Blochet 1929, ill.pl. CLXXXII; Arnold and Wilkinson 1936; Schulberg 1968, p.177; Hambly 1968, ill. fig. 9.

EXHIBITION: London, Victoria and Albert Museum, *The Indian Heritage* 1982 (35).

6 *Ain-i-Akbari* (An account of the court and empire of Akbar by Abul-Fazl)

Early 17th century
Manuscript, 391ff., 35 × 23 (13⅘ × 9)
The British Library Board, Department of Oriental Manuscripts (Add.Or.2169)

The single most famous document of Mughal India, the *Ain* was compiled in the 1590s as a kind of 'Domesday Book' for the Mughal empire. Abul-Fazl (no.5) was in overall charge of the project. It was intended to provide an administrative manual of the whole empire, listing local notables and the numbers of their armed forces, the size of territories, prevailing prices and other statistics. The Emperor's interest in his Hindu subjects (and of course in the possibilities of taxing them) is reflected in the attention paid to places of pilgrimage. Other sections of the work deal with the organization of the royal household and the duties of the major officers of state. The *Ain* was one of a number of types of administrative manual which were still in common use in the eighteenth century. C.A.B.

LITERATURE: Blochmann 1873–96; Rieu 1883, vol.III, p.1070.

EXHIBITION: London, Victoria and Albert Museum, *The Indian Heritage* 1982 (45).

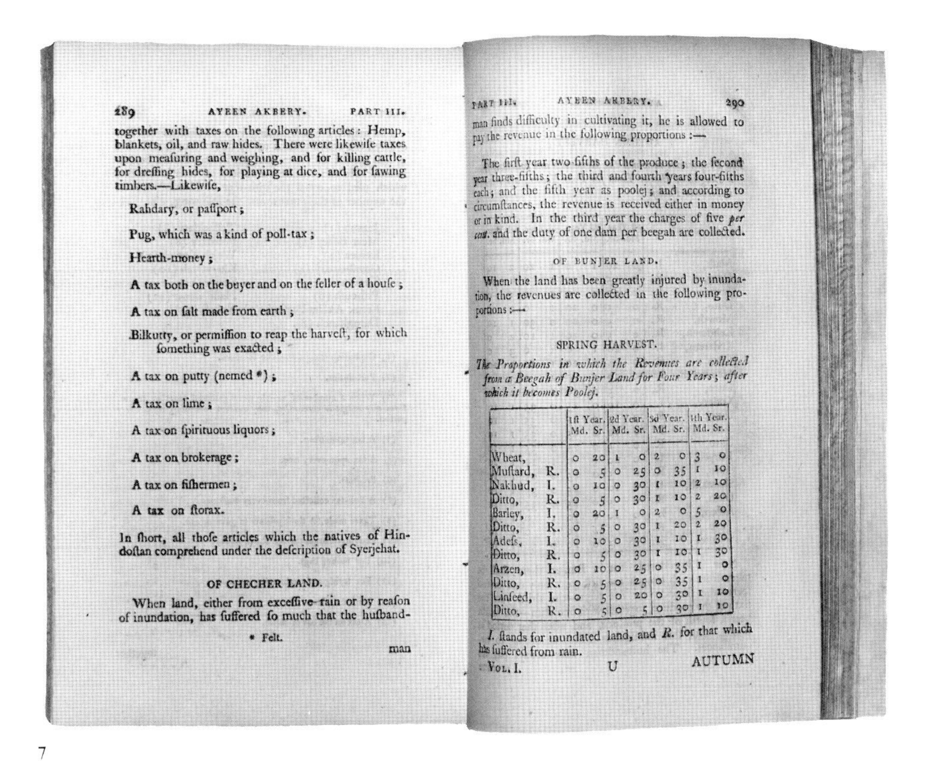

189 AYEEN AKBERY. PART III.

together with taxes on the following articles: Hemp, blankets, oil, and raw hides. There were likewiſe taxes upon meaſuring and weighing, and for killing cattle, for dreſſing hides, for playing at dice, and for ſawing timbers.—Likewiſe,

Rahdary, or paſſport;

Pug, which was a kind of poll-tax;

Hearth-money;

A tax both on the buyer and on the ſeller of a houſe;

A tax on ſalt made from earth;

Bilkutty, or permiſſion to reap the harveſt, for which ſomething was exacted;

A tax on putty (nemed *);

A tax on lime;

A tax on ſpirituous liquors;

A tax on brokerage;

A tax on fiſhermen;

A tax on ſtorax.

In ſhort, all thoſe articles which the natives of Hindoſtan comprehend under the deſcription of Syerjehat.

OF CHECHER LAND.

When land, either from exceſſive rain or by reaſon of inundation, has ſuffered ſo much that the huſband-

* Felt.

man

PART III. AYEEN AKBERY. 290

man finds difficulty in cultivating it, he is allowed to pay the revenue in the following proportions:—

The firſt year two-fifths of the produce; the ſecond year three-fifths; the third and fourth years four-fifths each; and the fifth year as poolej; and according to circumſtances, the revenue is received either in money or in kind. In the third year the charges of five *per cent.* and the duty of one dam per beegah are collected.

OF BUNJER LAND.

When the land has been greatly injured by inundation, the revenues are collected in the following proportions:—

SPRING HARVEST.

The Proportions in which the Revenues are collected from a Beegah of Bunjer Land for Four Years; after which it becomes Poolej.

		1ſt Year. Md.	Sr.	2d Year. Md.	Sr.	3d Year. Md.	Sr.	4th Year. Md.	Sr.
Wheat,		0	20	1	0	2	0	3	0
Muſtard,	R.	0	5	0	25	0	35	1	10
Nakhud,	I.	0	10	0	30	1	10	2	10
Ditto,	R.	0	5	0	30	1	10	2	20
Barley,	I.	0	20	1	0	2	0	5	0
Ditto,	R.	0	5	0	30	1	20	2	20
Adeſs,	I.	0	10	0	30	1	10	1	30
Ditto,	R.	0	5	0	30	1	10	1	30
Arzen,	I.	0	10	0	25	0	35	1	0
Ditto,	R.	0	5	0	25	0	35	1	0
Linſeed,	I.	0	5	0	20	0	30	1	10
Ditto,	R.	0	5	0	5	0	30	1	10

I. ſtands for inundated land, and *R.* for that which has ſuffered from rain.

VOL. I. U AUTUMN

7

7 Francis Gladwin's translation of the *Ain-i-Akbari*

1800
Printed book, 22 × 15 (8⅝ × 5⅞)
Private Collection

As soon as they became administrators of parts of Bengal and began to collect taxes as *diwans* of the Mughal emperor, officials of the English East India Company began to mine the information in the *Ain* for social and revenue statistics. This translation, entitled *Ayeen Akbery; or the Institutes of Akber, translated from the original Persian by Francis Gladwin, in two volumes*, (J. Swan, London, 1800) was made during Warren Hastings's period as Governor-General. He wrote that the work would prove 'of the utmost utility to the Company', and would also aid in 'the Promotion of the knowledge of Indian literature' (vol.2, iii). In the nineteenth century British imperial District Gazetteers and the all-important reports on the revenue settlements referred to the *Ain* as the beginning of the 'official history' of various territories of north India. Civil servants were brought up on it; this copy belonged to the library of Lord Meston, a civil servant in the United Provinces who later became its Lieutenant-Governor. C.A.B.

PROVENANCE: Presented by the present Lord Meston to present owner.

LITERATURE: Moosvi 1987.

8 *Farman* issued by the Emperor Aurangzeb appointing a man to the office of *kazi* 1677

Ink on paper, 88 × 48 ($34\frac{1}{10} \times 10\frac{7}{10}$)
Signed and dated in Persian: *ta'liq 4 zu'l-qa 'da 1088* (19 December 1677)
India Office Library and Records (IO 4370)

The Mughal state had a relatively small body of office-holders, both at the centre and in the provinces. These were selected from learned and administrative families of either Indian or foreign descent. Most of the officials were Muslim but often there were appointments from the Hindu clerical and business castes (Khattris and Kayasths, for instance). Appointments were made by imperial charter like this one, and officials were quite often moved to avoid the emergence of local 'family circles' that might impede the imperial will. *Kazis*, however, tended to remain in their offices longer and many had connections with local landholding families or themselves received revenue-free grants of land for service. They were one of the three most important officials of the towns and subdivisional units (*parganas*). The *kazi* was a registrar of rights and the local upholder of Muslim Sharia law, but he often became a local leader in his own right and represented the local community in negotiations with higher officials such as the provincial governor (*subahdar*). Other important local officials were the *kotwal*, a chief executive or police officer, and the *muhtasib* or controller of the markets and moral censor. Men were still being appointed to these positions in the nineteenth century, but the East India Company tended to sever their formal connections with Muslim law. Under Company regulations the *kazi* became little more than a land registrar while the *kotwal* became a kind of chief of police.

The charter specifies that the *kazi* should among other things attend to 'the propagation of Islamic law' and 'the arbitration and adjudication of cases and causes of suit'. C.A.B.

PROVENANCE: Presented to present owner by a Mr Price and accessioned on 15 June 1815.

LITERATURE: Shakeb 1982, pp.5–7.

EXHIBITION: London, Victoria and Albert Museum, *The Indian Heritage* 1982 (81).

9

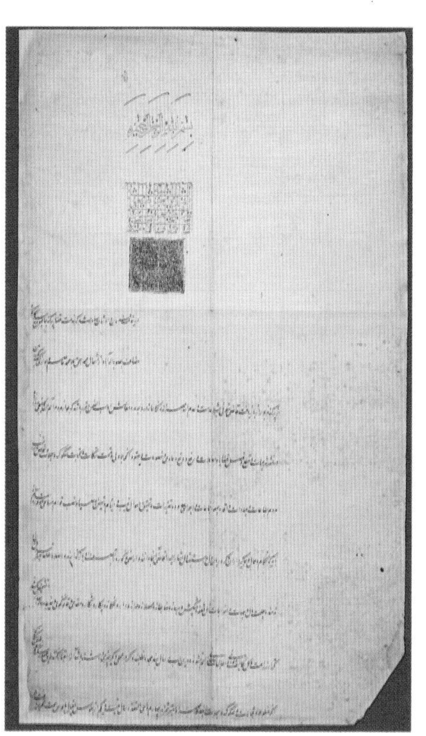

8

9 *Farman* issued by Shah 'Alam II conferring a title on Sophia Elizabeth Plowden, 1788

Gold paint and ink on paper, mounted on 18th-century printed cloth, 69.5 × 114 ($27\frac{3}{10} \times 43\frac{9}{10}$)
Sealed, dated and inscribed in *ta'liq*
India Office Library and Records (IO 4439)

Most British rights and privileges in India were derived – directly or indirectly – from Mughal grants and were dependent on Mughal authority. This was as true of the Company itself as it was of private individuals who received titles and properties from the Mughal state. The fiction of Mughal authority, and the grants associated with it, were continued until the Rebellion of 1857. This charter confers a Mughal title on Sophia Elizabeth, wife of Richard Chicheley Plowden, an officer in the Bengal infantry who served for a time in Lucknow. She is referred to as 'Begum' (Princess) and 'Queen of Sheba'. See no.136. C.A.B.

PROVENANCE: Purchased through Messrs Luzac and Co.; accessioned on 17 July 1934.

LITERATURE: Chicheley Plowden 1914, pp.35, 151–75; Archer 1979, p.412; Shakeb 1982, pp.5–7.

10 Shah Jahan in his durbar

Unknown Mughal artist, *c.* 1650
Gouache with gold, 30.5 × 22 ($12 \times 8\frac{1}{2}$)
Inscribed on reverse in Persian: *tasvir-i shah jahan* (a picture of Shah Jahan)
India Office Library and Records (Add. Or. 3853)

During the reign of Shahjahan (1628–58), formerly Prince Khurram (no.3), the Mughal empire reached the height of its prosperity, having successfully absorbed the rich commercial provinces of Gujarat and Bengal. Shahjahan restored relations with the Muslim jurists which had been strained by the somewhat unorthodox beliefs of Akbar and Jahangir, but he also vigorously projected imperial power through magnificent building programmes and the glorious ceremonial of the imperial assemblage or durbar (*darbar*). The imperial durbar was to be 'reinvented' by the British rulers of India in the later nineteenth century.

Here Shahjahan, seated in the hall of public audience, is flanked by bearers of ceremonial fly-whisks (*chauris*). He holds a ruby and an attendant holds a tray of jewels. For the Mughals, precious stones marked wealth, but they also symbolized the entrapment of light in matter. Mughal dynastic theory asserted that the emperors embodied the radiance of special enlightenment, signified by the 'halo' surrounding their heads in miniatures. This light had been passed down from Timur (Tamerlane), the founder of the dynasty. In the foreground, Shahjahan's son Prince Alamgir (later the Emperor Aurangzeb, 1658–1707) performs respectful salutation (*taslim*), faced by a group of Muslim and Rajput officers. The miniature perhaps records an event in 1649, some eleven years

10

before Aurangzeb deposed his father, who was imprisoned in Agra. It was said that Shahjahan's only consolation in his captivity was to gaze out on his greatest monument, the Taj Mahal, the mausoleum of his beloved wife Mumtaz. The architectural feature in this miniature is decorated with the characteristic tulip design in *pietra dura*, the distinctive emblem of much of Shahjahan's architectural legacy. C.A.B.

PROVENANCE: Unrecorded.

LITERATURE: Foster 1906, no. 66; Foster 1924, no.71; Archer and Falk 1981, p.84, no. 80, ill.pl.5.

EXHIBITION: London, Victoria and Albert Museum, *The Indian Heritage* 1982 (68).

11 Mughal ceremonial axe (*tabar*)

Pretentiously 1589–90
Iron with gold and silver damascening, 42 × 12 ($16\frac{1}{2} \times 4\frac{7}{10}$)
The Trustees of the British Museum, Department of Oriental Antiquities (1954.2–16.2)

This early eighteenth-century example was modelled on Mughal prototypes and, along with ceremonial maces (*dandas*), represented the judicial power of the monarch. Travellers such as the Frenchman François Bernier commented on the respect and fear with which the *chobdars* or *mihrdars*, bearers of the ceremonial maces and symbols of power, were regarded in the Mughal court and camp. A visit from the mace-bearers was a summons to appear immediately before the Emperor, for better or for worse. This example is engraved with the names of the Prophet and his companions, a reminder of the fact that the power of the Emperor was seen as a direct reflection of his inheritance of the temporal power of the Messenger of God. Under the British, of course, the Islamic legitimacy of royal and imperial office was gradually eroded. C.A.B.

PROVENANCE: Presented by P.T. Brooke-Sewell Esq.

LITERATURE: Richards 1986, p.73.

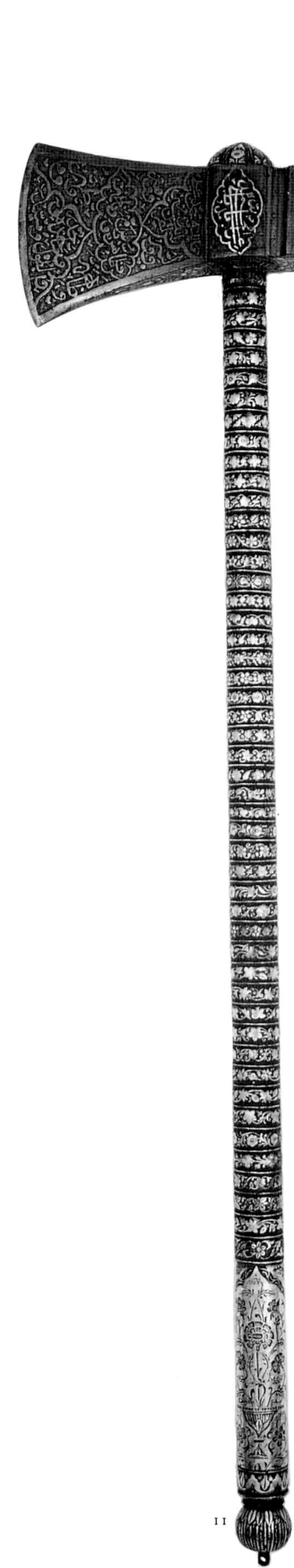

11

The Mughal War Machine

12(i) Armour of mail and plate (*zirah bagtar*)

Mughal, early 17th century
Royal Armouries, HM Tower of London (XXVI.148A)

Mailed cavalry were the shock troops of the Mughal empire. They were the ultimate guarantee of the 'Mughal peace': peasant and landholder (*zamindar*) rebels might ravage the countryside and attack travellers and Mughal officials, but during the heyday of the empire they were not well enough equipped or disciplined to withstand a charge of the Mughal heavy cavalry. Cavalrymen, who provided their own horses, were recruited from military families throughout the empire in Iran, Afghanistan and Central Asia. They were often urban Muslims and 'gentlemen' (*sharif*) by culture. But as Mughal rule put down deep roots in India, men of the Hindu warrior castes, especially from the Rajputs of Rajasthan, were recruited into the Mughal army under their own rajas and chiefs. Great office-holding notables (*mansabdars*), Muslims and Hindus, did the recruiting for the Mughals' grand army. They were assigned rank and rewards appropriate to the number of cavalrymen they raised and their political experience. This 'aristocracy of office holders' subsisted on cash salaries disbursed from the central treasury in Agra and Delhi, or on grants of land revenue (*jagirs*) assigned to them in different localities. Though the emperors tried to prevent these men from developing local bases of power by moving them around and reassigning their *jagirs*, by the early eighteenth century some of the most powerful of them had established local strongholds and direct landholding in the provinces. Some men from the former Mughal military families entered the cavalry wing of the East India Company's army in the later eighteenth and early nineteenth centuries, but the British, along with

Indian regimes of the eighteenth century, broke decisively with Mughal military culture by establishing infantry and artillery forces based on peasant recruits. Body armour made of a combination of mail and plate became common in the fifteenth century amongst the Mongol successor states, and continued to be used by the Mughals until the middle of the seventeenth century. It is seldom visible in the miniatures of the period since a coat (*angirkhah*) was worn over it.

The cavalry wearing armour of this type were armed with a composite bow and arrow, sword, mace or saddle axe, and sometimes a light lance. They were protected additionally by a helmet, forearm defences, thigh and knee defences and a cane shield. C.A.B./T.R.

PROVENANCE: From Gwalior; presented to the Board of Ordnance by the East India Company, 1853.

LITERATURE: Hewitt 1859, class XV, no. 10, p. 93; Dillon 1910, class XV, no. 204, p.14; Robinson 1968, pl.XIV, pp. 94–5.

12(ii) Helmet of mail and plate (*tōp*)

Mughal, early 17th century
Royal Armouries, HM Tower of London (XXIV.57A)

Although this helmet is of typical Mughal manufacture of the early seventeenth century, it was still in use among the Mughal bodyguard of Tipu Sultan, who seems to have worn *zirah bagtar* of the same period. T.R./C.A.B.

PROVENANCE: From Seringapatam, 1799; Major-General Codrington collection; sold 1863.

LITERATURE: Hewitt 1865, ad. no. 364, p.12; Egerton 1880, no. 591T, p.125, fig.30; Dillon 1910, class XV, no. 511, p.35, pl.30.

13 Horse armour of mail and plate

Mughal, early 17th century
Royal Armouries, HM Tower of London (XXVI.18H)

Horses were an immensely valuable commodity in Mughal India and were one of its most prized imports. The country bred its own varieties in Cutch (Gujarat) and along the river valleys of the upland Deccan. But many of the finest animals were brought over the Hindu Kush and by sea from Iran where Arab breeds had long been established. Horse merchants sometimes reached high positions in the commercial and political world of the empire and its competitors. The Mughal rulers, however, also patronized local horse fairs and instituted special breeding programmes within the court and army to ensure the quality of the horse stock. Animals were branded with an imperial mark to distinguish them from inferior stock. In the eighteenth century the Marathas of western India were able to build up their own horse-borne guerilla armies by breeding the tough Deccan horses for speed and endurance. These were crucial to the Marathas' success against the imperial forces. Later the English East India Company built up its own stock by importing Arabs from Europe, the Middle East and South Africa.

The primary purpose of horse armour was to protect the horse against archery. Its use was thus widespread throughout Asia, where warfare was based for centuries on the mounted archer. Heavy cavalry in Mughal India are depicted with barded horses from the sixteenth century into the seventeenth. The bards were frequently covered wholly or in part with fabric. C.A.B./T.R.

PROVENANCE: Purchased by William Bullock for his London Museum and Pantherion, 1809; sold in 1816 to Mr Gwennap for the Oplotheca, 20 Lower Brook Street, London; purchased by the Board of Ordnance at auction, George Robins, Laing's Shooting Gallery, Haymarket, London, 10 June 1833 (or purchased by a Mr Bentley at Gwennap's sale and sold on to the Board).

LITERATURE: Bullock 1812, p.23; Oplotheca 1816, no.173, p.22; Gothic Hall 1818, no. 31, p.14; Royal Armoury n.d. (*c.*1820), no.2; *A New and Improved History and Description of the Tower of London* 1834, pp.26–7; Hewitt 1841, p.50 and fp.; Hewitt 1845, pp.74–5, Hewitt 1854, pp.63–4; Hewitt 1859, class XV, no. 389, p.110; Dillon 1910, class XV no.15, pl.29; Robinson 1967, pl. XIX c; Borg 1974; Richardson 1987, pp.98–9.

14 Sword (*talwar*)

Persian blade, Mughal hilt, 17th century
Royal Armouries, HM Tower of London (XXVI. 97S)

From as early as the twelfth century Indian metallurgy enjoyed a worldwide reputation in the fashioning of swords and one prominent source thought Indian damascened swords were the best in the world. Other types were made with soft iron alloyed with copper and silver, and some, from Kurij in Cutch (Gujarat), were made of steel. The Mughals and their successors continued to patronize this tradition through royal workshops or *karkhanas* (*CEHI*, i, p.81), and some of the most exquisite items still in existence came from this source. But the tradition was also widespread across the countryside and certain villages and small towns boasted concentrations of men of the Lohar (iron smith) castes who worked as confederations of producers and sold their weapons in local or regional markets. In the mid-nineteenth century India was still a heavily armed society where landholders and chiefs could quickly put together levies of peasant soldiers. In some areas, such as Rohilkhand in the north, the frontier areas and Rajasthan, the skills of sword-making and swordsmanship were preserved almost up to the present day.

The curved sword originated in Central Asia, and was probably introduced into India by the Mughals in the sixteenth century. The finest blades were imported from Iran. They were made of crucible steel whose crystalline structure gives the characteristic watered appearance. The 'Indo-Muslim' hilt, with its typical dish-shaped pommel, seems to have been introduced by the Mughals, and spread throughout India together with the curved-blade, or *talwar*.

C.A.B./T.R.

PROVENANCE: Transferred from the Royal Collection, Windsor Castle, no.54, 1954.

LITERATURE: Kalus 1980, pp. 45–6.

15 Sword (*khanda*)

Mughal, dated 1072 H (1623)
Length 89 ($34\frac{7}{10}$)
Royal Armouries, HM Tower of London (XXVI.25S)

This type of sword was one of the typical accoutrements of the Indian nobility. In later centuries it became a prominent feature of the court dress of the Hindu Rajput warriors who grafted many Mughal traditions onto the indigenous customs of Rajasthan. The sword is one of the Indian weapons seized at the time of the Rebellion. Many of the weapons used during the Rebellion were quite old, but still serviceable. This is an example of a sword made in the Hindu tradition, with a straight blade. The inscription along the back of the blade reads *Na<ja>bat Khan jalla jalal*, possibly referring to one of a number of Central Asian (Turani) *mansabdars* in Mughal service in the mid-seventeenth century. The hilt, however, is of the Indo-Muslim type introduced to India by the Mughals. C.A.B./T.R.

PROVENANCE: From the disarmament of 1859 following the Indian Rebellion; presented by the Indian Government, 1861.

LITERATURE: Hewitt 1865, ad. no. 203, p.7; Egerton 1886; no. 560 T, p.117, fig. 24; Dillon 1910, class XV, no. 660, p.13.

16 Tiger claw (*bagh nakh*)

Mahratta, 18th century
Royal Armouries, HM Tower of London (XXVI.11M)

Used in savage hand-to-hand fighting, this vicious weapon for disembowelling an enemy was occasionally turned to use in political assassination. One famous incident in 1659 concerned the rebellion against the Muslims of the Hindu Marathas of western India under their famous leader Shivaji (see no.87) during the reign of the Emperor Aurangzeb. Muslim chroniclers accuse Shivaji of having set up a parley with the Muslim commander Afzal Khan of Bijapur, and then treacherously murdering him with a claw weapon hidden under the long sleeves of his robe. The Marathas argued that Shivaji only did so to forestall an assassination attempt against himself. The incident was not forgotten, and towards the end of the nineteenth century, when nationalists in western India began to take up Shivaji as an embodiment of anti-imperial patriotism, Muslim leaders and publicists reminded their co-religionists of the murder and warned them to distance themselves from the anti-British struggle. C.A.B.

PROVENANCE: From Lushkur (Lashkar, near Gwalior?); presented by the East India Company, 1853.

LITERATURE: Hewitt 1859, class XV, no. 27, p.94; Dillon 1910, class XV, no. 221, p.29.

17 The victory of Ali Quli Khan over the Afghans on the banks of the Gumti in 1561 (illustration to the *Akbarnama*)

Kanha and Banwali Khurd, *c.*1590
Opaque watercolour and gold, 35.5 × 20.25 (14 × 8)
The Trustees of the Victoria and Albert Museum (IS 2–1896 f.13)

Akbar's armies perfected the heavy cavalry charge and the use of cannon against attacking enemies which were to sustain imperial power for more than a century and a half. Here the young Akbar's lieutenants, Bairam Khan and Ali Quli Khan, make the Mughal empire safe for him, crushing a dangerous rebellion of the Afghans who had previously held dominion in north India. Both men later revolted against the Emperor themselves. In this miniature, the impact of the heavy cavalry on the fleeing enemy is clearly shown, while the mortars mounted on the boat indicate the importance of artillery in Mughal warfare. The bridge over which the cavalry ride is reminiscent of the fine Mughal bridge which still survives at Jaunpur in the province of Awadh, near the scene of this action. C.A.B.

17

18 Akbar's entry into Surat (illustration to the *Akbarnama*)

Farrukh Beg, *c.*1590
Opaque watercolour and gold, 20.25 × 33 (8 × 13)
The Trustees of the Victoria and Albert Museum (IS 2–1896 f.117)

Once Akbar had crushed the Hindu Rajputs and incorporated several of their most important kings into his nobility he proceeded to attack the rebellious princes of Gujarat and absorb them into his realm. Surat was the richest trading city in India, and the part to which European merchants and trading companies were increasingly resorting; it was also the embarkation point for the holy cities

18

of Mecca and Medina. Akbar entered the city on 26 February 1573. Here he met a band of Portuguese, who were dismissed by the chronicler Abul-Fazl as a 'crew of savages', an indication of a cultural arrogance which was to contribute to the long-term failure of the empire. Here Akbar, preceded by a musician and an attendant carrying royal insignia followed by the royal standard, is welcomed by the citizens of Surat. Behind him on the road are troopers of his fast camel corps, whose dash from Agra helped to save the Mughal cause in Gujarat. Throughout, the *Akbarnama* propagates the message in pictures and words that Akbar is a superhuman figure, recipient of that special enlightenment which has been handed down from his ancestor Tamerlane. This was the theory of royal legitimacy expounded by Abul-Fazl. The architectural embellishment of the city signifies its riches. The blue decorated tilework, Koranic inscription and lattice work designs are more typical of Persian architecture than of the Mughal and Afghan styles as they survive today in north India, or are depicted in the *Akbarnama*. Surat traded with the Persian Gulf and the artist perhaps wished to impart a sense of the local culture of the city. C.A.B.

LITERATURE: *CEHI*, IV, 1937, P. 105.

Beyond the Imperial Writ

Not all of what became 'British India' felt Mughal power directly. For most peasants it was the local landholder (*zamindar*) or the nearby warrior chieftain who was the great power on the horizon. In the localities remote from the imperial capitals of Delhi and Agra and in the realms of the great Rajput princes, the emperor was a distant suzerain only. In central India independent Muslim sultanates ruled until the 1680s when they were conquered by the Emperor Aurangzeb. In the far south, Hindu warrior chieftains ruled their fiefdoms and patronized the great temples and trade marts of a society which was – and was to remain – quite different from the north in culture and language. C.A.B.

19

19 A prince in a garden

Rahim Deccani, 1670–80

Gouache, 12.6 × 23.4 ($5 \times 9\frac{2}{10}$)

Signed: *raqam-i-banda rahim Dakani* (the work of the slave Rahim Deccani)

The Trustees of the Chester Beatty Library, Dublin (MS 66 no.1)

Until the 1680s, when it was conquered by the Emperor Aurangzeb, the Deccan or central plateau was ruled by a number of Muslim sultanates from the cities of Bijapur, Ahmednagar and latterly Golconda, the old fortress site near the eighteenth-century city of Hyderabad. These Deccan kingdoms had been subject to different cultural and political influences than those which had created Mughal north India. At times, Persian culture and the Shia branch of Islam were in the ascendancy in the south. As Muslims were only a small percentage of the population, Brahmin administrators and warriors from the Telugu-speaking Hindu castes were very influential. Portuguese Goa was on the other side of the Western Ghats, and Portuguese soldiers and savants frequented the Deccan courts. Rather than advertising their power and grandeur, princes of the Deccan preferred to style themselves as 'musicians, poets ... or munificent patrons' (Zebrowski 1983). This cultural preference is reflected in Deccani painting which reached its height in the late sixteenth century, but revived, partly under Mughal influence, in the seventeenth. Here a prince is entertained by three girls. One plays a stringed instrument (the *vina*); another offers betelnut for chewing (*pan*); a third, dressed in a European costume of about 1660, offers wine; a fourth, embracing a flowering tree, is teasing a fawn. C.A.B.

LITERATURE: Barrett n.d., pp.2–5, 24; Zebrowski 1983, pp.201–4.

20 The Great Bull at Tanjore

Thomas and William Daniell, 1793
Folio aquatint, 55 × 75 ($21\frac{3}{4} \times 29\frac{1}{2}$)
The Syndics of Cambridge University Library

South India presented a contrasting cultural and political world to the north. Its languages were different, and in the river valleys great ancient temples such as the Brihadeshwara Temple at Tanjore (Thanjavur) survived in a glory unknown to the Muslim north. This temple, sacred to the god Shiva, was founded by the Chola dynasty in the eleventh century. Nandi the sacred bull, a favourite deity, is the vehicle or companion of Shiva. In the fourteenth and fifteenth centuries the traditions of Hindu imperial power were maintained by the Vijayanagar rulers of the south. They were defeated by the Muslim powers of the Deccan in 1565, and their empire fragmented into smaller kingdoms ruled by regional dynasts (*nayaks*) and by local warrior chiefs, the 'poligars' (*palayakkarars*). But worship at, and endowment of, the great temples remained part of the code of even these little kings. When a Maratha dynasty took control of the rich principality of Tanjore in the late seventeenth century these Hindu conquerors also revered and embellished the great temple. In the 1760s the British, from their base in Madras, along with Muhammed Ali of Arcot (no. 144), began to penetrate this land of small Hindu principalities with their rich rice-growing river valleys and dry turbulent hinterlands. The original drawing for no. 20 was made during the Daniells' 1792–3 tour of south India, an area opened up by Lord Cornwallis's wars with Tipu Sultan. C.A.B.

LITERATURE: *Oriental Scenery* 1797, folio II, no.22; Appadurai 1977; Archer 1980, p.124; Meister 1983, I, i, pp. 234–9.

21

21 Two bronze piers from a model of Tirumala Nayak's *mandapa* at Madurai

Bronze, height 24.3 ($9\frac{3}{5}$)
The Visitors of the Ashmolean Museum, Oxford (1956. 673–4)

The regional feudatories and lieutenants of the erstwhile Vijayanagar empire flourished as *nayaks*, warrior chieftains who ruled over both the dry uplands and the rice-growing valleys of southern India from small fortress towns. These kings constructed some of the great irrigation works of the south and were also responsible for the embellishment and expansion of some of the magnificent temples whose towers still rise above the south Indian countryside. One such famous king was Tirumala Nayak (1623–59) who built the famous pillared hall (*mandapa*) at Madurai in 1645; it was used as a hall for pilgrims and dedicated to the deity Sundeswara. Several examples of models of this sort, which were apparently made for votive purposes, have survived from the seventeenth century.

At one end of the left pier stands a four – armed Shiva tending a deer, making a teaching gesture and holding a bird (a reference to local legend). Shaivite saints (*Nainmars*) are depicted at the bottom. On the right pier there is an image of the wrathful goddess Kali (*ugra* Kali). Musicians and dancers also appear. C.A.B.

PROVENANCE: Bequeathed by Rev. W. Bentinck Hawkins, 1894.

LITERATURE: Fergusson 1910, pp. 386–90; Ludden 1985; Harle and Topsfield 1987, pp.56–8; Stein 1989.

22

22 Figure of Patanjali, the south Indian sage

South Indian, 16th-17th century
Bronze, height 28.5 (11⅕)
Lent anonymously

South Indian Hindu worship revolved around the deities of the great temples, and also the veneration of sages and seers, particularly the Shaivite and Vaishnavite saints of the first millenium AD (the *Alvars* and *Nainmars*). These were represented by votive bronze images placed in the temples, which became the recipients of offerings of food and clothes. Patanjali derived from an earlier historical period. He was a commentator on the famous ancient grammarian Panini, who wrote at some time before 150 BC. But Patanjali also appears in south Indian legend as a divine manifestation of Adisesa (Ananta), Lord of the Serpents, who became a devotee of Lord Shiva at the temple town of Chidambaram, and taught the ascetic science of yoga. Several mythical and historical figures appear to have been linked in this cult, which illustrates the tendency of south Indian popular Hinduism to deify human figures associated with temples and other places of sacred power. C.A.B.

LITERATURE: Mani 1964, p. 583.

A Complex Culture

The Mughals and many of their greatest courtiers were Muslims of the Sunni branch of Islam; some great nobles from Persia (including the family that was later to rule the province of Awadh) were of the minority Shia branch. But Muslims together could only have accounted for 20 per cent of the population of the empire at its greatest extent. Over the rest of India the various sects and schools which went to make up what is now called Hinduism were dominant; these ranged from the most cerebral philosophies to cults of propitiation and blood sacrifice. In ancient times the Jain religion had decisively separated itself from Hinduism, and many of India's most important tradespeople were members of this small community. In modern times, and mainly in the Punjab, the new faith of Sikhism, which was articulated in the sayings of the gurus or founding masters and the sacred book, the *Granth Sahib*, spread among farmers and merchants. Around Goa on the west coast and in the far south Roman Catholics had also made converts. In Kerala there were ancient communities of St Thomas Christians and Jews.

Before British rule members of the different religions occasionally engaged in bloody conflicts over the locations of temples and mosques or over precedence at holy places, for instance. Under the pious Muslim Emperor Aurangzeb (reigned 1658–1707) discrimination against Hindus provoked resistance. In general, however, the Mughal emperors and other Indian rulers offered even-handed protection to all faiths. Akbar himself was interested in other religions and fascinated by the Hindu tradition of asceticism. Most of India's people lived in peace, if not always in harmony. Hindus and Muslims attended each others' religious festivals and weddings in towns and villages; the imperatives of life in town and country alike meant that sharp religious boundaries could never be maintained.

Under the Mughals Indian culture was also eclectic and responsive to outside influence. In music and architecture as in miniature painting it is difficult to separate specifically Hindu and Muslim traditions. Indian artisans and craftsmen also assimilated European influences, borrowing from European styles of painting, ornamentation and clothing. C.A.B.

23 Brahmin and Muslim learned man (dervish) in dispute

Mughal School, early 17th century
Gouache, 25.5 × 14 (10 × 5½)
The Keir Collection, Ham (V56)

Early Muslim rulers in India had taxed Hindus as idolaters. Akbar thought otherwise. He understood that Mughal rule could not survive in the face of the hostility of the majority of its Hindu subjects, so he abolished the tax on Hindus (the *jizya*), made special arrangement for the protection of Hindu worship and himself adopted Hindu styles of dress and vegetarian food. The evidence suggests that this was not simply a question of political prudence, for Akbar and others at his court had a deep interest in Hindu rituals and philosophy. Against the complaints of the horrified doctors of Muslim law (*ulama*) he urged the need to understand and debate with other religions. He patronized those Sufis ('dervishes') or mystical adepts amongst Muslims whose beliefs came nearest to those of the Hindu polytheists and he visited Hindu holy men and ascetics such as those pictured here. He even experimented with a personal blend of all the major religions which he called the *Din Illahi*, or simply 'belief in God.' Aurangzeb, the last of the great emperors, reversed many of these policies, and though the point can be exaggerated, the disenchantment of many leading Hindus with his more rigid and Islamic court was one reason why the empire foundered.

No.23 is an illustration from a manuscript, possibly a copy of the works of Sa'di, the celebrated Persian poet (*c.*1208–92). It depicts a dervish and a Brahmin (identified by his sacred thread) holding an animated discussion on the terrace of a small domed pavilion in a garden, possibly the hospice of a Sufi saint. Among the onlookers are other holy men and a man washing his feet. A herdsman and his boy milk a goat and there are two gardeners, of whom one tends a Persian wheel, a form of irrigation which was becoming popular in Mughal India. At Aurangabad in central India, a Sufi hospice and shrine (the *Panchaki*) remarkably similar to the building in this miniature has survived. Here a channel irrigation system, including a water-wheel, was used to irrigate the garden land, to provide water for ablutions before prayer, and to grind corn for the pilgrims. A later inscription at the top of the picture reads *bisṭāmi raḥmatu'l-lāh 'alai-hī'* ('Bistami, the mercy of God be upon him'). This refers to the Muslim saint Bayazia of Bistam who lived in the ninth century AD.

C.A.B.

LITERATURE: Rizvi 1975; Skelton 1976, p. 255, pl.123.

23

24 The Holy Family and the Infant St John in a landscape

Indian copy of a Persian imitation of a European drawing, *c.* 1660
Pen and ink and body colour, 11.9 × 21.6 (4½ × 8½)
The Syndics of the Fitzwilliam Museum, Cambridge (M.40, f.39)

The influential community of St Thomas Christians had existed in India from the early Christian era, but the Portuguese Padroado ('Royal Patronage') and the Society of Jesus began active proselytization in the mid-sixteenth century. Small bodies of Portuguese and Indo-Portuguese Christians were already established at all the main centres of the Portuguese Viceroyalty of the Indies (Estado da India), which stretched from East Africa and Persia to the Indonesian Islands. In the next century Christian

24

25

influences, which often took a decidedly Hindu appearance, spread inland, particularly in south India. By the early nineteenth century perhaps 6 per cent of the population of the Madras Presidency were Christian. These were overwhelmingly Catholic, since the English East India Company did not encourage proselytization, but Protestantism was represented by an active Danish mission at Tranquebar (no.59). Indo-Portuguese Christians from Goa and Madras later played an important part in education and government service in British India. Mughal north India, however, was poor soil for Christian activity. Akbar and Jahangir consulted Catholic priests on occasions, but with the swing back to Islamic orthodoxy under Shahjahan and Aurangzeb, church-building and evangelism were officially discountenanced. Several Indian miniatures of Christian religious scenes, usually taken from Flemish originals, exist, but the intermediate Persian stage of this one is revealed by the distinctive 'moon faces' of its subjects. C.A.B.

PROVENANCE: Marlay Bequest, 1912.

EXHIBITION: London, Victoria and Albert Museum, *Persian Miniature Painting* 1967 (90).

25 A Group of Servants at the Outskirts of the Camp of some Great Personage

Govardhan, *c.*1620–5
Gouache, 23 × 16.7 (9 × $6\frac{3}{5}$)
Inscribed: *amal-i-Govardhan*
The Trustees of the Chester Beatty Library, Dublin (MS 7, no. 11)

A singer accompanied by a player on the stringed instrument (*rabab*) performs outside a tent on the fringes of the imperial camp. A Hindu holy man, possibly a devotee of the Gorakhpanthi tradition, and a man with a parrot look on. A wheeled vehicle somewhat like the nineteenth-century *tikka garhi* stands in the background. The Mughal military camp, like the hospices of the Sufi saints, was a great cultural melting pot. Muslim Mughal commanders tolerated, and sometimes even venerated, Hindu holy men attached to the army, while the great Rajput Hindu nobles paid respect to Muslim learned and holy men. The musical traditions of the Middle East, Central Asia and India also reinvigorated each other, and important schools of performance developed in Delhi, Farrukhabad and elsewhere under the patronage of Mughal and eighteenth-century rulers. Govardhan, the artist,

26

was one of the many Hindus who worked for the imperial painting school; he painted several of the finest of the illustrations to the *Akbarnama*. C.A.B.

PROVENANCE: The Earl of Minto; sold Sotheby's, 1925?

LITERATURE: Arnold and Wilkinson, i, p. 30; iii, frontispiece; Welch 1978, pl. 28; Kolff 1990.

EXHIBITION: London, Victoria and Albert Museum, *The Indian Heritage* 1982 (47).

26 A Marriage Procession passing through a Bazaar, Rajput, Punjab Hills

Bilaspur or Mandi, *c*.1680
Gouache, 32 × 49 ($12\frac{3}{5}$ × $19\frac{1}{4}$)
Howard Hodgkin, London

Rural and small-town bazaars such as this were essential to the functioning of the economy of Mughal India. Here lived the moneylenders and bankers who circulated the silver coins in which the state's land-revenue was paid. Here also were the artisans who produced fine wares for the aristocracy and military leaders who lived in the towns and vaunted their prestige in opulent weddings or the support of religious festivals. Mughal towns were once thought to have been 'parasitic' on the countryside; but more recently it has become clear that they provided protection and services and also channelled essential goods such as salt, iron and brassware into the hinterlands.

This picture shows the youthful bridegroom on the right, mounted on a horse and escorted by foot-soldiers, an elephant, noblemen, mounted and walking musicians, and two drummers bringing up the rear. The populace watches this *tamasha* or spectacle from the rooftops. Seven bazaar shops are also shown in unusual detail: from left to right, they are selling *lotas* and other vessels, *pan* (betel nut preparations for chewing), sweetmeats, ceramic and glass vessels, knives, daggers and sword-hilts, textiles, grains and pulses. C.A.B.

PROVENANCE: Acquired by present owner, *c*.1970.

LITERATURE: Digby 1973, fig.13; Glynn 1983, p.53, fig.13.

EXHIBITION: London, Victoria and Albert Museum, *The Indian Heritage* 1982 (160).

India: A Great Centre of Trade and Production

Under the Mughals, India was far from being a 'subsistence economy'. It was probably the world's greatest textile exporter until the beginning of the nineteenth century, despatching fine luxury cloth and humbler fabrics to southeast Asia and the Middle East as well as to Europe on Portuguese, Dutch, French and English ships. Caravan routes dealing in shawls, fruits and horses linked north India with west and central Asia. River transport connected Delhi and Bengal.

To support the demands of the imperial nobility and war-machine, large quantities of silver rupees had to be raised from land taxes and taxes on trade. There is disagreement among historians about how much of the gross produce of the land was actually absorbed by imperial taxation and landlords' dues, but clearly an intricate and efficient network of markets must have existed in order to ensure that the peasantry had the resources with which to pay their revenues and rents. C.A.B.

27

27 Village life in Kashmir

Mir Kalan Khan, Lucknow, *c.*1760

Gouache with a little gold, on an album page with yellow and apricot borders, the outer border sprinkled with gold, 28.8 × 33.5 ($11\frac{3}{10}$ × $13\frac{2}{10}$), page 38.7 × 54.3 ($15\frac{1}{5}$ × $21\frac{3}{10}$)

Inscribed on border in Persian: *Majlis-i Kashmir, 'amal-imir Kalan* (A Kashmiri assembly, the work of Mir Kalan)

Square seal on reverse; second seal erased

India Office Library and Records (Add.Or.3)

In no.27 villagers in Kashmir, one of the Mughals' favourite provinces, are shown on their daily round. In addition to gathering wood and cooking, people are shown picking grapes and weaving. These last two activities illustrate the way in which the Mughal empire had begun to create a subcontinental economy in India. Grapes were dispatched as a delicacy to Agra, Lahore and Delhi, the great court centres of north India. In addition to cotton, Kashmir weavers also wove the famous *pashmina* fabric (nos. 34, 35) which was used for making shawls. *Pashmina* was a woollen cloth made from belly fleece of long-horned sheep. The presence in the painting of such a sheep suggests that the artist intended to represent the weaving of shawl wool. Kashmir shawls were sent to north India both as trade goods and as tribute to the emperors. Mir Kalan Khan, the artist, may have been a Delhi painter who moved to Lucknow with the decline of the imperial city. His style is evidently influenced by Flemish and Dutch models and itself became a prototype for the nineteenth-century Lucknow school of Company painting. C.A.B.

PROVENANCE: Purchased by present owner, 13 April 1954.

LITERATURE: Habib 1963; Archer and Falk 1981, p.137, no.238, ill. p.435.

Mughal Coinage

Unlike much of southeast Asia and Africa, the Indian subcontinent had become a money economy very early. Under the Mughals, revenue, official salaries and a significant proportion of rents and dues to overlords were paid in cash. The silver rupee was the basis of the system, though gold mohurs formed a unit of account and a currency for hoarding, while copper pais and even cowry shells were used in many ordinary transactions. But India's reserves of silver were small. Large quantities had to be imported to augment the money supply in line with the growth of population and productivity. One historian has calculated that the amount of money in circulation more than trebled during the seventeenth century. It was this which gave Europeans, now flush with the silver supplies of the New World, their entrée into Indian trade. The Emperors and their Governors realized that for all their violence and importunity, the Europeans gathered near ports such as Surat and Hughly were important as suppliers of bullion. Indians needed little else that Europeans could produce at this time. To secure their supplies of fine textiles and spices, the Dutch, Portuguese and English brought in large quantities of silver bullion for goods. The Dutch Company imported copper from Japan. The imports were coined in Mughal state mints at all the major centres. This brought the Europeans into contact with the (largely Hindu) commercial classes of India who were also the purchasing agents for the manufactures of local artisans. India's growing dependency upon the European bullion importers made her vulnerable to exploitation by the Europeans.

Coining rupees and pagodas (the currency of the south) was not simply an economic act: it was also a mark of political legitimacy. To coin meant to assert independent power. It is interesting that the English East India Company continued to coin in the name of the Mughal emperor until the Indian Rebellion of 1857. The Company was not sovereign; it was merely the revenue manager (*diwan*) of Bengal. C.A.B.

28(i) Rupee of Emperor Akbar

Minted at Ahmadebad, 1576
Silver, weight 11.31
Dated: *984*AH (AD 1576)
The Trustees of the British Museum, Department of Coins and Medals (1922 4–24 1857)

28(ii) Rupee of Emperor Akbar

1584
Silver, square, weight 11.44
Dated: *992*AH (AD 1584)
The Trustees of the British Museum, Department of Coins and Medals (BMC 141)

28(iii) Mohur of Emperor Jahangir

Gold, weight 10.86
Obv: portrait of Emperor Jahangir
Rev: a lion surmounted by the setting sun
The Trustees of the British Museum, Department of Coins and Medals (BMC 313.X)

28(iv) Mohur of Emperor Jahangir

Gold, weight 10.86
Obv: portrait of Emperor Jahangir
Rev: a lion surmounted by the setting sun
The Trustees of the British Museum, Department of Coins and Medals (BMC314.IX)

28(v) Twelve mohurs of Emperor Jahangir illustrating the signs of the zodiac

Minted at Agra, 1618–20
Gold, each illustrated with a sign of the zodiac:
a) Capricorn, weight 10.94
b) Aquarius, weight 10.91
c) Pisces, weight 10.90
d) Aries, weight 10.90
e) Taurus, weight 10.88
f) Gemini, weight 10.90
g) Cancer, weight 10.57
h) Leo, weight 10.92
i) Virgo, weight 10.89
j) Libra, weight 10.84
k) Scorpio, weight 10.92
l) Sagittarius, weight 10.89
The Trustees of the British Museum, Department of Coins and Medals (a) BMC 351; (b) BMC 383; (c) BMC 358; (d) BMC 322; (e) BMC 324; (f) BMC 330; (g) BMC 333C; (h) BMC 334; (i) BMC 339; (j) BMC 342; (k) BMC 346; (l) 1929 5–1 51

28(vi) Rupee of Emperor Aurangzeb

Minted at Lahore, 1703
Silver, weight 11.42
Dated: *1114:47*AH (AD 1703)
The Trustees of the British Museum, Department of Coins and Medals (BMC 830)

28(vii) Rupee of Emperor Aurangzeb

Minted at Lahore, 1704
Silver, weight 11.32
Dated: *1115:48*AH (AD 1703)
The Trustees of the British Museum, Department of Coins and Medals (1911 7–9 1094)

28(viii) Mohur of Emperor Aurangzeb

Minted at Burhanpur, 1703
Gold, weight 10.96
Dated: *1115:47*AH (AD 1703)
The Trustees of the British Museum,
Department of Coins and Medals (BMC 723)

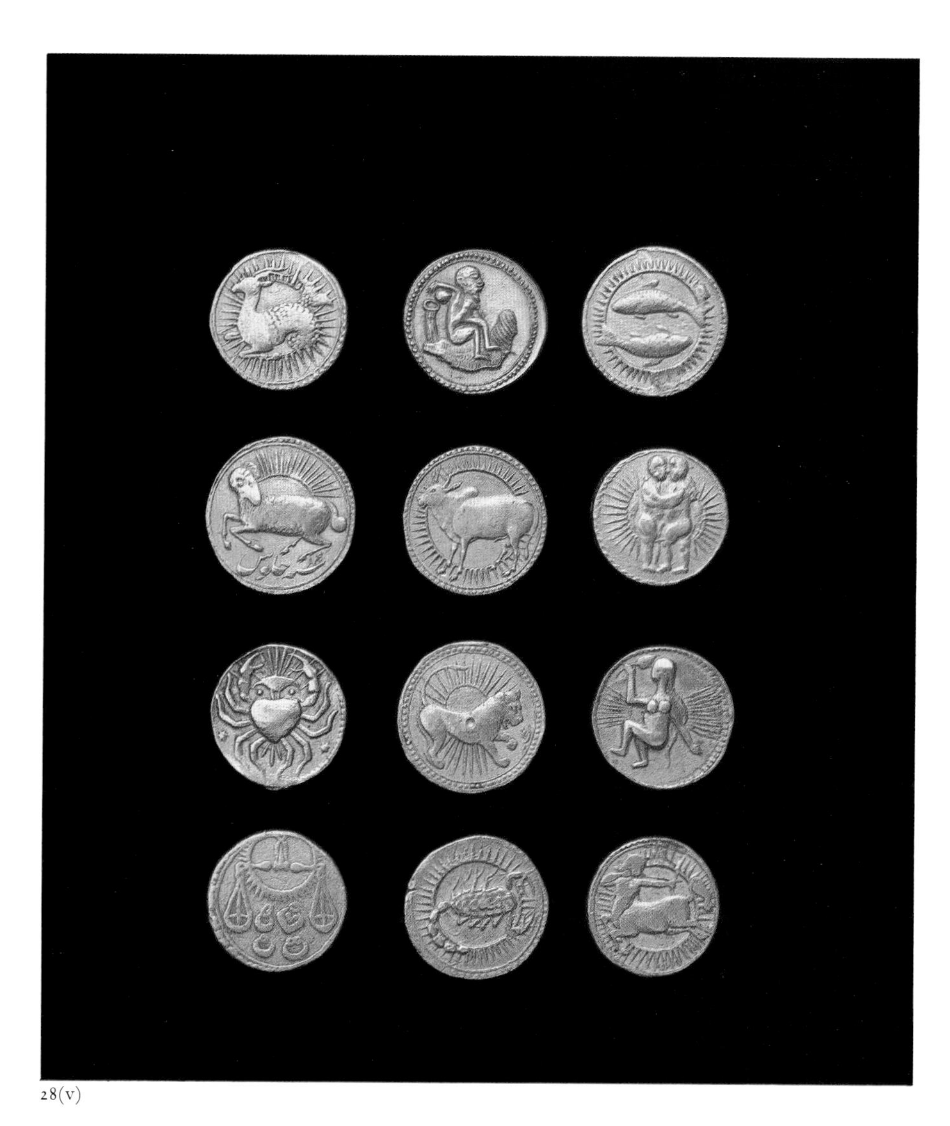

28(v)

28(ix) Rupee of Emperor Aurangzeb

Minted at Etawah, 1703
Silver, weight 11.42
Dated: *1115:47*AH (AD 1703)
The Trustees of the British Museum,
Department of Coins and Medals (BMC 831)

LITERATURE: Lane Poole 1892; Richards 1983; *CEHI*, i, 360–82.

Money was not simply a medium of commercial exchange. These coins functioned as presentation pieces. Strict Islamic laws forbid representation of the human form, and until the middle of Akbar's reign coins did not feature any representation other than the Emperor's name and the date of coinage. Akbar and Jahangir moved away from rigidly orthodox Islamic ideas, emphasizing the charisma of the Timurid imperial family and making subtle concessions to the Hindu subjects' notions of divine kingship. In Jahangir's reign coins and tokens with the Emperor's head and other representatives, even zodiacal signs such as these, were struck. Under Aurangzeb, coins generally abandoned representation again. C.A.B.

29

29 Caravan at rest

Mughal School, early 18th century
Gouache on paper, 16.6 × 24.7 ($6\frac{1}{2} \times 9\frac{7}{10}$)
The Trustees of the British Museum, Department of Oriental Antiquities
(BM 1921–7–12–04)

While waterborne transport dominated commerce from Delhi to the east, the capital was linked to Gujarat in the west, and to the Punjab, Central Asia and Iran by regular caravan trades. Merchants' agents and individual operators would gather themselves under the protection of a chief or *rais* who provided security and made arrangements for passports and customs payments. While on imperial territory the caravans could avail themselves of the well-appointed and well-protected *caravan serais* which it was the duty of imperial officials to assist. The travails of the eighteenth century added to the hazards on the road, but the traveller George Forster commented on the vigour of the caravan trade into Central Asia as late as the 1780s and 1790s. In no.29 two travellers sleep protecting their box of merchandise, a graphic illustration of the insecurity of unprotected trade routes. C.A.B.

PROVENANCE: Purchased from Maggs Brothers; donated to present owner by G. Eumorfopoulos, Esq., through the National Art-Collections Fund.

LITERATURE: Forster 1798, I, pp.219 ff.

30

30 Small vase

Probably Bidar, pre-Mughal period
Brass, cast, rounded base, squat body
Height 10 (4), mouth diameter 7.7 (3)
Inscribed on body
The Keir Collection, Ham (170)

Indian metallurgy was highly developed before the Muslim invasions, and all major centres had quarters for iron-smiths, silversmiths and brass-smiths where commodities were produced both for the local aristocracy and for ritual use in Hindu temples or on pilgrimages. Most of these products were the handiwork of occupational castes of Hindus or Muslims who were settled in separate quarters of towns and *qasbas*. They seem to have been bound to the prevailing landholding castes by ties of patronage. In some places, however, the manufacturers enjoyed more than local fame and their products found markets across the subcontinent and even in other Asian or Middle Eastern countries. One such area was Bidar in central India, which rose to prominence during the rule of the pre-Mughal Muslim kings of the Deccan, and flourished under the Mughals and the later princes of Hyderabad. C.A.B.

PROVENANCE: Purchased at Christie's, 23 May, 1966 (139) from the D.S. Rice collection.

LITERATURE: Skelton 1976, p.134, pl.609.

31 Glass huqqa bowl

Mughal, 17th-18th century
Green glass with gilt floral decoration
Height 25 ($9\frac{3}{4}$)
The Trustees of the British Museum, Department of Oriental Antiquities (1961-10-16-1)

The huqqa has a compressed spherical body, broad neck and a kink in the base. The decoration is a broad frieze containing poppy plants with narrow horizontal borders. Four single flowers decorate the neck. Tobacco appears to have been introduced to the Mughal court at the end of Akbar's reign. Tobacco cultivation was an important source of peasant income in eighteenth-century and British India. C.A.B.

PROVENANCE: Bequeathed by Louis C.G. Clarke, 1961.

LITERATURE: Ashton 1950, p.233, no. 1236 (b); Pinder-Wilson 1962, pp.91-4; Zebrowski 1981, fig.204; *CEHI*, i, 261-307; Stronge 1986, pp.111-17.

EXHIBITION: London, Victoria and Albert Museum, *The Indian Heritage* 1982 (387).

31

32

32 Ewer

Mughal, 18th century
Cobalt blue glass with painted gold decoration
Height 28.2 ($11\frac{1}{10}$)
The Trustees of the British Museum, Department of Oriental Antiquities (S343)

The decoration of flowers within foliate cartouches is in horizontal registers between narrow borders which consist of two thin bands containing triangles or lozenges, themselves containing stylized leaves or leaf sections. C.A.B.

PROVENANCE: Bequeathed by Felix Slade, 1868.

LITERATURE: Nesbit 1871, ill. pl. XI; Harden, Painter, Pinder-Wilson and Tait 1968, no.163.

EXHIBITION: London, Victoria and Albert Museum, *The Indian Heritage* 1982 (393).

Mughal Textiles

Though European traders were drawn to India by the lure of profits in the spice trade, textiles quickly became their chief export from India. Textiles were produced in every part of the country in an enormous diversity of styles, fabrics and patterns. As in the case of metalware and other artisan industries, hereditary castes of weavers, printers and dyers in all the major centres produced predominantly for local consumption and for locally resident aristocracy. But some localities achieved fame throughout the subcontinent and other Islamic lands. They sold their wares through markets dominated by intermediary merchants who gave cash 'advances' to the weavers to secure their production. No less than 150 different words for cotton goods are mentioned in the first ten years of the English factory records alone. The main varieties were calico, a stout cloth, and muslin, which was much thinner. The best long cloth came from the northern Coromandel coast and north India; muslin came from the Deccan and Bengal (the finest from the city of Dacca); the best painted cloth came from southern Coromandel; and fabrics of mixed cotton and silk came from Gujarat. Silk production was also particularly well developed in Bengal, which had drawn on Chinese precedents to establish its own silk producing industry. Very large quantities of finer and intermediate quality Indian goods were exported to other Asian and Middle Eastern markets, especially to Southeast Asia and to Persia and the Ottoman empire. But the Europeans quickly broadened the markets for Indian producers: the Dutch found a market for Indian silk in Japan, for instance, and the English began to export Indian raw silk to Europe. 'Guinea' or 'Negro' cloth – long cloth in stripes or checks – was exported by the Portuguese for the use of slave owners in West Africa and Brazil.

During the late seventeenth and eighteenth centuries, European companies and free merchants gradually won control of the international and inter-Asian trade in Indian textiles. The English Company began to dominate production by squeezing out the Indian middle-men. Though India's exports to Southeast Asia and the Middle East continued into the nineteenth and even the twentieth century, the value and quality of her produce plunged after the Company became a territorial ruler in India. After 1815 local producers lost the custom of their European purchasers and their external trade as European manufactured goods invaded their markets. C.A.B.

LITERATURE: *CEHI*, i, pp. 269–307.

33 Chintz palampore

Made for the Dutch market, Coromandel coast (northern region), *c.* 1750–75
Painted and dyed cotton, 330 × 213.3 (129 9/10 × 84)
The Trustees of the Victoria and Albert Museum (IS 2–1937)

LITERATURE: Irwin and Brett 1970, p.75, no.23.

34 Shawl

Kashmir, 19th century
Woven wool or fleece (*pashmina*), 169 × 160 (66½ × 63)
The Trustees of the Victoria and Albert Museum (IS 18–1971)

Kashmir shawls were an important item of special trade within the Mughal empire. The wool was worked up by

36

weavers in the mountainous province of Kashmir and shawls formed part of the taxation levied on the area by the Mughal emperors. The finest went into the imperial wardrobe (*Toshkhana*), where they were carefully graded according to their quality and the auspiciousness of the day on which they were presented to the emperor. Until the nineteenth century shawls remained a kind of honorific currency, given by great men as a sign of favour in their durbars. Shawls also continued to be a prize export from India in the nineteenth century, when other sectors of India's textile industry had declined. Scottish manufacturers in Paisley, however, took over the distinctive cypress tree motif – originally redolent of the burial places of learned and holy men in the Muslim tradition – and began their own manufacture. C.A.B.

LITERATURE: Irwin 1973.

37

35 Boy's coat

Kashmir, late 18th – early 19th century
Shawlcloth (*pashmina*), length 91.5 (36)
The Trustees of Victoria and Albert Museum (IM 286–1932)

Long clothes of this sort were particularly favoured during the winter months at the courts of Awadh and Hyderabad. C.A.B.

EXHIBITION: London, Victoria and Albert Museum, *Indian Heritage* 1982 (259).

36 Mughal carpet (fragment)

Indian, mid-17th century
Knotted cotton and silk, 94 × 79 (37 × 31$\frac{1}{10}$)
Keir Collection, Ham (60)

PROVENANCE: Acquired in Paris, 1971.

LITERATURE: Spuhler 1978, p. 125, no. 60, ill. p. 122.

37 Tent hanging

?Jaipur, 18th century
Red cotton and coloured silks, 175 × 135 (68$\frac{3}{10}$ × 53)
The Trustees of the Victoria and Albert Museum (IM 62–1936)

38 Idris giving instructions to mankind on the art of weaving

Mughal, *c.*1590
Gouache, 31 × 18.3 (12$\frac{1}{4}$ × 7$\frac{1}{4}$); page 41.5 × 29 (16$\frac{1}{4}$ × 11$\frac{1}{2}$)
India Office Library and Records (Johnson Album 8, no.5)

Here Idris, scientist and astronomer (identified with the biblical Enoch), gives instruction to mankind. The style is typical of the early Mughal period and the rounded faces betray a continuing Persian influence. Idris was credited with introducing both the use of the pen and of woven garments to humankind.

38

In no. 38 courtiers bring rolls of cloth to him, while weavers in the foreground wash, dry and spin, skein and weave the wool. For Muslims the wearing of woven and sewn garments was a sign of superior civilisation. Muslim weavers were seen as pious and skilled artisans living under the special protection of Idris, and of the Mughal nobility. India's textile producers, however, were both Hindus and Muslims, and enjoyed relatively high social status. They ranged from quite affluent men who employed piece-workers and apprentices to poor weavers who received wages or loans from merchants. Though some instances of near-factory production are recorded in European centres or at Mughal courts, wage labouring and central control did not develop rapidly in pre-colonial India. Since production was both highly localized and highly specialized, artisans' residential quarters were located near to the textile markets or *aurungs* of towns and villages. The intricacies of local production are recorded by an English factor or agent at Fort William, Calcutta, who wrote, 'Fabric of every aurung having its peculiar qualities, will not permit of being packed in one and the same bale.'

The social life of Muslim weavers was based on community mosques and on the tombs of venerated Sufi mystics (*pirs*). Large outlays were made for pious works and at the time of Muslim festivals such as Muhurram and Bakr-Id. Weaving communities fiercely resisted exactions by outside rulers and merchants or acts thought to insult their religion; they perfected the art of the strike and the boycott. It was this community solidarity which gave the weavers their reputation for 'fanaticism' and 'bigotry' in modern times.

C.A.B./K.P.

PROVENANCE: Purchased by present owner in 1807 as part of the Johnson Collection.

LITERATURE: *CEHI*, i, pp. 282–4; Archer and Falk 1981, p.47, no.4, ill. pl.30.

The English East India Company and its Precursors

The Portuguese were the first Europeans to establish themselves as a major power on the Indian scene. Though they were sometimes forced to trade under the protection of the Mughals, the Portuguese also created a compact territorial empire around the port of Goa which they vigorously defended against neighbouring powers. The English followed suit when they received Bombay from the Portuguese Crown in 1661 as part of King Charles II's dowry from Catherine of Braganza. In Bombay neither the Mughals nor any other Indian power had even residual sovereignty, as they did in other settlements. In most respects, however, it was the Dutch East India Company (Verenigde Oost Indische Compagnie or VOC) that provided the model for the English. Like the Dutch Company (though not the Portuguese), it had a degree of independence from the metropolitan government by virtue of its charter, and it raised and paid for its own armed forces.

As in the Dutch case also, the scale of the operations of the English Company soon made it a key part of the domestic financial structure. The seventeenth century Company periodically had to advance money to the Crown; the eighteenth century Company was an important agent in managing national debt. Ministers were therefore at the forefront of the move to unite the 'Old' Company and its rival, the 'New' Company, which had tried to dissolve the Old Company's monopoly of Oriental trade in the heady days of trade expansion that followed the Revolution of 1688. Union, in the shape of the United East India Company, was finally achieved in 1708.

Despite domestic alarms and excursions, the Company was highly efficient and well capitalized by the beginning of the eighteenth century. Its local 'factories' in Calcutta, Masulipatnam, Madras, Surat, Bombay and elsewhere were each ruled by a president or governor, sometimes with the aid of a council. Company servants were designated Factor, Writer or Merchant, according to their status. The servants provided advances to Indian weavers and monitored the quality and design of their chintz (printed fabrics), silks and other cloths. They then made arrangements for the consignment of the annual 'investment' (or commodities purchased) on the famous East Indiamen. Goods were sold by auction in London, and investors paid their dividends out of the profits made. The Company was governed by an elected Court of Directors presided over by a Chairman.

While some of the early governors and presidents had made dubious fortunes or had become entangled in fruitless wars with Indian powers, the Company was a remarkably successful business enterprise until about 1740. Thereafter, it lost the commercial initiative to its own servants, who were to benefit from the rich pickings left after the decline of the Mughal empire.

C.A.B.

39 Portuguese atlas of the world

Diego Homem, 1558
Vellum book, 60 × 90 ($23\frac{6}{10} \times 35\frac{4}{10}$) (open)
The British Library Board (Add. MS 5415.A)

In his search for spices and Christian converts, the Portuguese admiral Vasco da Gama reached Calicut in south-western India in May 1498. For a time the Portuguese made enormous profits in the trade in pepper, cinnamon and cloves because it was able to undercut the prices paid for spices which came overland, via Damascus or Cairo, and through the Mediterranean to western European markets. Voyages were organized through an India House (Casa da India). The Crown appointed a Viceroy to govern the Estado da India (Portuguese Indian State) which had been created between 1500 and 1515 by the seizure of a number of fortified seaports on the Indian, East African, Persian Indian and, later, Southeast Asian coasts. Though the Portuguese established small colonies of settlement at Malacca, Colombo, Macao and notably at Goa, their territorial ambitions were limited and their military edge over Indian states very slight. Outside Goa, the Portuguese 'seaborne empire' had virtually disappeared by the eighteenth century, having been battered to extinction by Indian powers, the Dutch and the English. However, the Catholic converts of mixed race who lived in the old Portuguese stations were to play a intermediary role between Europeans and Indians under the British Raj. They became prominent in educational institutions, the railways and government offices throughout the subcontinent.

This atlas was prepared by Diego Homem, a cartographer employed by the kings of Portugal and privy to confidential Portuguese geographical information. The atlas was made for Mary I of England as a gift for Philip II of Spain, but was left incomplete on her death in November 1558; it is therefore interesting as a record of how the English gained access to information about Portuguese discoveries in the Indian Ocean and elsewhere. C.A.B.

40 *Commentarios*, vol. 1, frontispiece, Lisbon, 1774

Affonso d'Albuquerque
Printed book, 18.2 × 12 ($7\frac{2}{8} \times 4\frac{6}{8}$)
India Office Library and Records (T36581)

D'Albuquerque (1453–1515) is commonly regarded as the founder of Portuguese India. Between 1504 and 1515 he captured what were to become the major centres of Portuguese naval power from local rajas and sultans and provided the seaborne empire with its capital at Goa (1510). Portuguese squadrons patrolled the Oriental seas, forcing Arab and Hindu Gujarati traders to pay for passes (*cartazes*) in an attempt to centralize trade on Portuguese settlements. Though the Portuguese operated very much like a predatory Asian power, Portuguese settlers (*casados*) went into commercial partnerships with local merchants and contributed to the development of trade within Asia. As late as 1770 Portuguese was the dominant European language in British Calcutta, and powerful Portuguese-Asian trading houses operated from Madras to Manila and Southeast Asia. The shrine of St Thomas at Mylapore near Madras was a major focus for Portuguese missionary efforts and Indo-Portuguese soldiers were employed as gunners and artillerymen in Company and Indian armies.

Having captured the important port of Hormuz in the Persian Gulf, D'Albuquerque died at Goa, crushed, it was said, by the ingratitude of the Portuguese king who had promoted an enemy over his head. His illegitimate son, Affonso, who inherited his estate, later published a selection of his father's papers. These *Commentarios do Grande Affonso D'Albuquerque* were periodically republished and became popular again in England in the 1770s when empire-building in India became the vogue.

C.A.B.

LITERATURE: Rohatgi 1982; Diffie and Winius 1977.

41

41 Headquarters of the Dutch East India Company at Hughly

Hendrik van Schuylenburgh, 1665
Oil on canvas, 203 × 316 (80 × 124½)
Rijksmuseum, Amsterdam (A4282)

The Reformation and the Dutch revolt against the Spanish Crown (which had by now absorbed Portugal) brought this powerful northern maritime nation into conflict with the Iberian Catholic powers. The Dutch fleet penetrated the Eastern seas, easily outnumbering and outgunning the weakened Portuguese. J.P. Coen, Captain-General of the Dutch East India Company, planned the seizure of the major Portuguese fortresses in the East. By 1622 the Dutch had replaced the Portuguese domination of the spice trade with one of their own, which they maintained with even greater rigour. Though the Dutch were little more interested than the Portuguese in establishing a territorial empire in India, they built up a lucrative triangular trade between the Mughal realm, their own headquarters at Batavia in Java and the Far East.

The success of the Dutch in the East was a consequence of their large, well-equipped navy and merchant fleets, which already dominated the carrying trade in northern European and Baltic waters and had a large slice of Mediterranean trade. At the same time they pioneered new forms of financial management which were later sedulously copied by the English. Unlike the Portuguese, the Dutch East India Company raised capital on the open market like a modern company. It had regular accounting and auditing systems and included the cost of military operations in its calculations of profit and loss. In a sense, therefore, it created the first 'capitalist empire'. But in the East the Dutch, like other Europeans before and after them, tended to use less sophisticated methods, extirpating rival traders and producers by military force.

The Dutch developed more fully the system of 'factories' (fortified trading posts) inaugurated by the Portuguese. The English were to copy this institution also. Hughly in lower Bengal, the major Mughal port in the region, was the site of the 'factory' from which the Dutch exported silk and muslin to Europe and Southeast Asia in exchange for silver and copper from Japan.

The English settlement of Calcutta was founded quite close to Hughly in 1690. The picture shows Dutch shipping at Hughly, the warehouses, gardens and fortifications of the factory and a camp, possibly that of a visiting Indian ambassador, outside the walls. C.A.B.

LITERATURE: Scammell 1981; Prakash 1985; Losty 1990, p. 12.

The Founding and Organization of the English East India Company

Throughout its commercial life the East India Company was a joint stock company, that is, its members pooled their resources for joint trade rather than trading on their own account, the costs and the risks of Asian trade making it virtually impossible for individual merchants to operate on their own. The Company was founded in 1600 with 219 members. By the mid seventeenth century there were more than 1,500 shareholders, the number nearing 3,000 by the end of the eighteenth century. These shareholders formed what came to be called the General Court of the Company (no.48). Merchants were always the main investors, but the Company also attracted a wide range of gentry, nobility, professional people and, especially in the eighteenth century, foreign investors, mostly from the Netherlands. Detailed management of the affairs of the Company was devolved by the shareholders on a Court of Directors whom they elected annually. Under their governor, or chairman (no.45), the twenty-four directors met once a week or more. The directors were usually substantial businessmen in the City, joined in the eighteenth century by an increasing number of men who had returned from India. The directors were served by what became an elaborate staff of secretaries, clerks and accountants, who arranged the procurement of cargoes for Asia, the dispatch of ships and the sale of the return cargoes and who maintained an increasingly voluminous correspondence with the Company's servants posted in Asia.

The Company's premises were in the City of London. From 1648 it occupied a site in Leadenhall Street, originally the town house of a nobleman to which adjoining properties were added. A drawing of about 1711 (no.42) shows the site before major rebuilding took place from 1726 to 1729. Theodore Jacobsen was the architect for the rebuilding, the result of which is depicted in a drawing of about 1760 (no.43). Another major rebuilding took place in the late 1790s.

Until the 1740s the business conducted at Leadenhall Street was almost entirely commercial. Thereafter the Company also had to direct military operations and supervise the way in which Indian provinces were ruled. The shareholders and the directors had no obvious qualification for their new responsibilities. For a time the Company appeared to break up into factions struggling to distribute the wealth of India among themselves in the form of increased dividends or lucrative appointments in India. Nevertheless, partly as a result of government intervention, the structure of the trading company evolved into a passable imperial bureaucracy that was to last until 1858. After 1784 the Company was required to submit to the supervision of a government body called the Board of Control, but the routine administration of Indian affairs from Britain remained the responsibility of the directors of the East India Company. P.J.M.

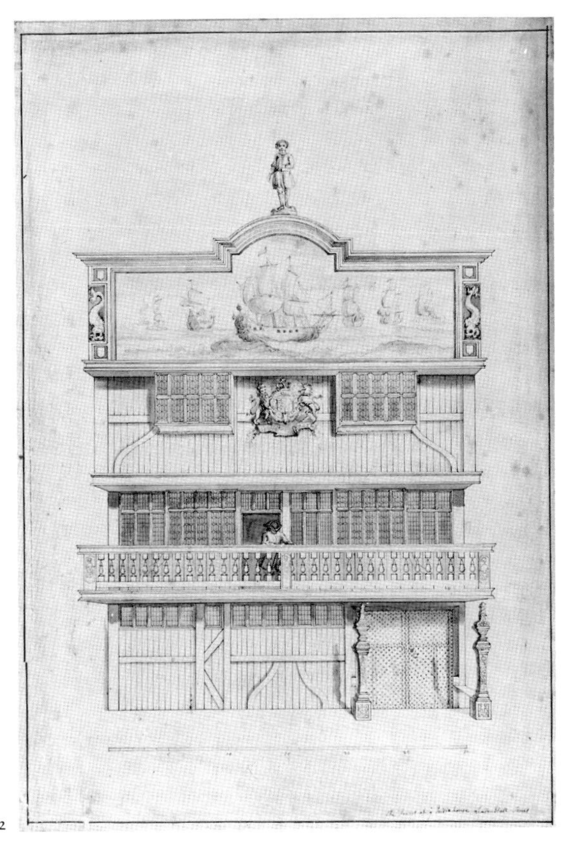

42

42 The Old East India House, Leadenhall Street, London

George Vertue, *c.*1711
Pen, ink and wash 45 × 31 ($17\frac{3}{4} \times 12\frac{1}{4}$)
Inscribed on front, in ink (probably Vertue):
The Front of India House Leadenhall Street
India Office Library and Records (WD 1341)

It has been proposed by S. Rowland Pierce that this drawing may be a copy of another Vertue drawing in the Society of Antiquarians by Vertue's brother-in-law, David Chandler (see Archer 1969, II, p.639), although Foster thought this drawing was by Vertue himself. B.A.

PROVENANCE: Presented by Sir William Foster.

LITERATURE: Archer 1969, II, pp.638–9, no.1341, ill., I, pl.I.

43

45

43 The East India House, Leadenhall Street, London, before the rebuilding by Richard Jupp and Henry Holland in 1796–99

Thomas Malton, *c.* 1795
Watercolour, 65.5 × 92 ($25\frac{6}{8}$ × $36\frac{1}{8}$)
India Office Library and Records (WD 2460)

See no. 42.

44 Wall clock

c. 1730
Enamelled dial, painted and gilded case, *c.* 150 × *c.* 90 (59 × $35\frac{1}{2}$)
India Office Library and Records

PROVENANCE: Formerly in the Marine Department, East India House.

LITERATURE: Birdwood and Foster 1909, p.57; Britten 1911, p.571; Foster 1924, p.53; Jourdain 1929, ill. fig. 9 ; Hardy 1982, pp. 11–12, 46, no. 89.

44

45 Chairman's seat

*c.*1730
Upholstered in crimson velvet, with the East India Company's coat of arms embroidered in coloured silks and silver gilt thread, 155 × 75 (61 × $29\frac{1}{2}$)
India Office Library and Records

PROVENANCE: Made for the Directors' Court Room; in 1858 it became the seat of the Secretary of State for India.

LITERATURE: Birdwood and Foster 1909, pp. 65–6; Foster 1924, p. 134; Jourdain 1929, p. 241; Archer 1965, p.403, ill.fig.5; Hardy 1982, p.18, no. 8.

46 The charter of the United East India Company

1708–9
Ink on parchment with large wax seal, 72.5 × 82 ($28\frac{1}{2}$ × $32\frac{1}{4}$)
India Office Library and Records (A/1/59)

The East India Company owed its existence to grants by the national government, the terms of which were set out in its charters. The charter establishing the Company was approved by the Privy Council of Elizabeth I and dated 31 December 1600. The Company was given a monopoly of trade to Asia for fifteen years. It received concessions over customs payments and was allowed to export bullion to a stipulated quantity.

The charter was renewed at intervals, each renewal being an occasion on which the Company tried to maintain or to extend its privileges, thus emphasizing its need for close relations with the national government. In the late seventeenth century the Company successfully ingratiated itself with both Charles II and James II, leaving it vulnerable to its enemies after the Revolution of 1688. A rival group seized the opportunity to obtain a charter for a new company in 1698. After prolonged negotiations, the two companies agreed to unite and formally became the United East India Company in 1709. The charter of the United Company was based on that of the new company, granted in 1698. The charter renewed the monopoly, defined the powers and composition of the General Court and the Court of Directors and confirmed the Company's authority over its 'forts, factories, and plantations in India'. This charter was the basis of all subsequent renewals until the trading monopoly was broken in 1813. P.J.M.

LITERATURE: Foster 1919, p.2 and introduction. This volume contains copies of letters between Elizabeth I, James I and various minor rulers; lists of 'adventures, commissions and instructions' for voyages; navigational notes; chronological index. Also printed in Birdwood and Foster 1893.

48

47 East India Court Minute Book

Published by G. Birdwood, assisted by W. Foster in *The Register of letters &c., of the Governor and Company of Merchants of London leading into the East Indies, 1600–19*, London, 1893, p.2
Leather-bound volume, 39 × 25 (15½ × 10)
India Office Library and Records (B/2)

The second entry records a commission from Queen Elizabeth I to Captain James Lancaster (d.1618) for the Company's first voyage, which took place on 24 January 1601. Lancaster, born probably in Basingstoke, had previously commanded a merchant ship in Drake's fleet against the Armada in 1588. In the early 1590s he took the same ship on the first English voyage to the East Indies. In this royal commission of 1601 he was instructed to 'set forth to the East Indies with a convenient number of shipps and pinnaces'. Upon his successful return to London in 1603 he was knighted and he settled down to shore life as a director and one of the principle advisors of the young company. C.A.B./K.P.

LITERATURE: Markham 1877; Foster 1919, p.2 and introduction.

48 The General Court Room, East India House, Leadenhall Street with a meeting of the Court of Proprietors in progress

Thomas Hosmer Shepherd, *c.*1820
Watercolour, 14.6 × 20.3 (5¾ × 8)
Inscribed on image: *T. H. Shepherd* and on mount: *The General Court Room, East India House*
India Office Library and Records (WD/2466)

A meeting of the Court of Proprietors is in progress. The chairman and directors are seated at the long table on the right. The niches contain statues of Clive, Pocock and Stringer Lawrence. By the time this painting was made, the Company's monopoly was already crumbling under assault from the apostles of Free Trade. Since there is no sign of the statue of Warren Hastings, which was erected in 1829, this drawing must date from *c.*1820. B.A./C.A.B.

PROVENANCE: Purchased 1902.

LITERATURE: Birdwood and Foster 1909, pl.43; Foster 1924, p.142; Archer 1969, II, pp.633–4, no.2466.

49

49 Ballot box

c. 1730
Mahogany with amboyna wood, brass inlay, 42.5 × 35 × 22 (16$\frac{3}{4}$ × 13$\frac{3}{4}$ × 8$\frac{6}{8}$)
Painted on lid: *Yea/Nay*
India Office Library and Records

LITERATURE: Hardy 1982, p.18, no.7.

50 Seal of the East India Company

Cornelian mounted in silver, diameter 7 (2$\frac{4}{5}$)
Inscribed in Roman and Persian characters commemorating the grant of Bengal, Bihar and Orissa in 1180 AH (1766–7 AD) by the Emperor Shah Alam
The Trustees of the British Museum, Department of Oriental Antiquities (1973 3-9.1)

51 An English East Indiaman, bow-view

Peter Monamy, *c.*1720
Oil on canvas, 99 × 82.5 (39 × 32.5)
National Maritime Museum (BHC 1011)

Ships trading to Asia were among the largest and most expensive merchant ships in the world. They had to be able to undertake voyages round the Cape of Good Hope, lasting six months or more, and had to be armed to defend themselves. Some of the English East India ships of the later seventeenth century were over 1000 tons. The Company was not itself a shipowner. It hired ships built specially for it, which were allowed to make four voyages to Asia before being replaced. P.J.M.

PROVENANCE: Acquired 1947.

52 The East Indiaman *Princess Royal*

John Clevely the Elder, 1770
Oil on canvas, 73.5 × 117 (29 × 46)
Signed and dated 1770
National Maritime Museum (BHC 3564)

52

On her first voyage the *Princess Royal*, under the command of Captain Robert Ker, left Deptford in December 1769 with a crew of 117. She reached Madras on 28 June 1770. After a stop there, she sailed on through the Straits of Malacca to Canton, where she anchored on 23 September. After taking on board a cargo of tea, she was back in England the following July. B.A.

LITERATURE: India Office Records (L/MAR/B/405/D.).

PROVENANCE: Acquired 1931–2.

53 India House, the sale room

J.C. Stadler after Thomas Rowlandson and Charles Augustus Pugin, *c.* 1808–10
Aquatint, 23 × 28 (9 × 11)
India Office Library and Records (P1571)

The Company disposed of the goods which it imported from Asia at quarterly auction sales held at its Leadenhall Street warehouses. Buyers came to these sales from all over Europe as well as from Britain. It was the Company's policy to attempt to maintain stable prices. It therefore provided potential purchasers with a full list of the commodities which it proposed to put up for sale at each auction, together with an indication of the prices at which it expected bidding to begin. Stadler's aquatint, shown here, was based on a drawing by Rowlandson and Pugin. It was published in Ackermann's *Microcosm of London* (3 vols., 1808–10), for which Rowlandson and Pugin had been commissioned to do the lively illustrations. In the 1840s Charles Knight looked back to the ten auctions of the Company's monopoly days, recalling the 'quite frightful' uproar of the proceedings. The 'howling and yelling', in spite of thick walls, 'frequently was heard by frequenters of Leadenhall Market' (Knight 1843). P.J.M./K.P.

LITERATURE: Knight 1843, vol. 5, p. 59; St Aubyn 1985, pp.114–5.

53

54

54 East India Company coat of arms

*c.*1730
Carved wood, painted and gilded, 130 × 152 (51¼ × 60)
India Office Library and Records

The East India Company after 1709 adopted the arms granted to the 'New' Company in 1698: the royal arms and the cross of St George. The motto *AUSPICIO.REGIS.ET.SENATUS.ANGIAE* (By right of the king and senate of England) refers to the grant of the charters by act of Parliament. P.J.M.

PROVENANCE: Originally surmounted canopy behind Chairman's seat in Directors' Court Room; sold, 1861; presented to the Secretary of State for India by Mr Louis Forbes, 1891.

LITERATURE: Birdwood and Foster 1909, p.27; Hardy 1982, p.18, no.6.

East Indian Forts and Factories at Work

55 Nakd Ali Beg, envoy from Persia

Richard Greenbury, 1626
Oil on canvas, 213 × 129.5 (84 × 51)
India Office Library and Records (F23)

Nakd Ali Beg arrived in England from Persia in February 1626. He had been sent by Shah Abbas of Persia, who, like the Mughal Emperor Jahangir, was being cultivated by the East India Company. Sir Thomas Roe had carried out an embassy to both these rulers. The Company's diplomatic and commercial offensive was not directed exclusively at India. It wished to break into the whole sector of southern Asian trade which ran from Persia to the Indonesian archipelago and the China Seas, where the Portuguese and Dutch had hitherto had matters their own way. Roe's negotiations regarding trade in Persia had been more successful than those in India. In time the Company had established factories on the southern Persian coast through which it imported raw silk and exported English woollen goods. The directors were also keen to take a big part of the trade between the Asian countries and, as the century advanced, the English began to export the fine printed cloths of Masulipatnam on the east coast of India to Persia and through it to Afghanistan.

Nakd Ali Beg's embassy was not a happy one: he had a violent quarrel with Sir Robert Shirley, who also claimed to be an ambassador from Persia. Charles I ultimately had both men taken back to the East by his own envoy to Persia, Sir Dodmore Cotton. But Nakd Ali Beg poisoned himself before the ship put in at Surat, where he was later buried. The envoy is here shown wearing a flowing mantle of Isfahan brocade woven with figures over a long gown of lighter material. Greenbury was a versatile artist who painted portraits and copied old masters; he painted in enamel and was also a goldsmith and gilder of frames. In 1631 he was appointed portrait painter to Queen Henrietta Maria. C.A.B.

PROVENANCE: Commissioned by the East India Company, 1626.

LITERATURE: Archer 1986, pp.28–9, no.33, pl.iii.

56 *Some Yeares Travels into Africa and Asia the Great*, London, 1638

Thomas Herbert
Printed book, 29.1 × 40 (11⅜ × 15½)
The British Library Board (c.55.g.8)

Thomas Herbert (1606–82) accompanied Sir Dodmore Cotton on his mission to Shah Abbas, the King of Persia, in 1627 (see Herbert 1928). This engraving, which depicts a woman dancing before a man who sits cross-legged, holding a ewer in one hand and a cup in the other, was copied from an Indian miniature, possibly one brought home by Herbert. It is interesting that the depiction of Indian 'types' began so early in the history of the English connection with the country. C.A.B.

LITERATURE: Herbert 1928; Hind 1955, iii, pp. 162, 164.

57 *A Voyage to Suratt, giving a large account of that city and its inhabitants and of the English factory there*, London, 1696

John Ovington
Printed book, 22 × 28 (8⅝ × 11)
The British Library Board (981.d.19)

The work of John Ovington, Chaplain to William III, epitomizes the new interest in Eastern trade which resulted from economic expansion in the late seventeenth century. Surat (no.18) was the major port of India's west coast and an outlet for Ahmedabad's fine textiles and for the indigo of Bayana near Agra. An English factory and Presidency was founded there in 1614; in 1664 it was stoutly defended by Sir George Oxenden against Shivaji (no.87). Ovington's detailed description of the city's inhabitants contained much that was to become clichéd over the next 250 years: the Bania merchants were 'innocent, obsequious, humble and patient to a miracle' (p.275), and Muslim 'faquires', or ascetic devotees, resembled the 'Romish mendicants' (p.203). The Towers of Silence, the burial place of the Parsis, was 'the most horrid prospect in the World' (p.379). But by the late seventeenth century Surat's days of prosperity were numbered. The effective centre of British power was beginning to move to Bombay, whose fort and Company warehouse are shown here. As Surat's security declined after 1700 its wealthy merchant communities, including the Parsis, migrated to Bombay. The exhibited engraving shows 'the Fort of Bombay in AD 1688'. C.A.B.

LITERATURE: Das Gupta 1979.

58 *An Essay upon the Nature and Qualities of Tea*, London, 1699

John Ovington
Printed book, 17.7 × 21.6 (7 × 8½)
The British Library Board (1038.b.44)

In the late seventeenth century new elements were breaking into the dealings of the 'Old' Company. Men such as Ovington sketched in the details of new maritime trade routes to Surat in western India, while English ships began to take an increasing percentage not only of the India-Europe trade but also of the local trades in the Persian Gulf, the Red Sea and the Indian Ocean. To the east, the Company's trade with the Chinese and the Southeast Asian commercial world unearthed a new commodity – tea. Samuel Pepys was one of the first to consume this novelty, writing on 25 September 1660, 'I did send for a cup of tea, a china drink, of which I never had drunk before'. At first, Chinese teas were brought by junk to Madras and Surat where they were purchased by the Company. Later, direct purchases were made at the port of Amoy and through the Company's new factory at Canton. Though the East India Company traded in tea, it is ironic that tea for export was not produced in its Indian territories until after 1830, during the last few years of its existence.

Ovington's essay touched on the cultivation of tea and on 'the several virtues for which it is famed', notably that men might be 'chearful with sobriety and witty without the danger of leaving their senses'. C.A.B.

LITERATURE: Furber 1976.

59 *An Account of the Religion, Manners, and Learning of the People of Malabar*, London, 1717

Mr Phillips
Bound book, 16.5 × 10.2 (6½ × 4)
Private Collection

European interest in India was further stimulated by a fascination with Indian

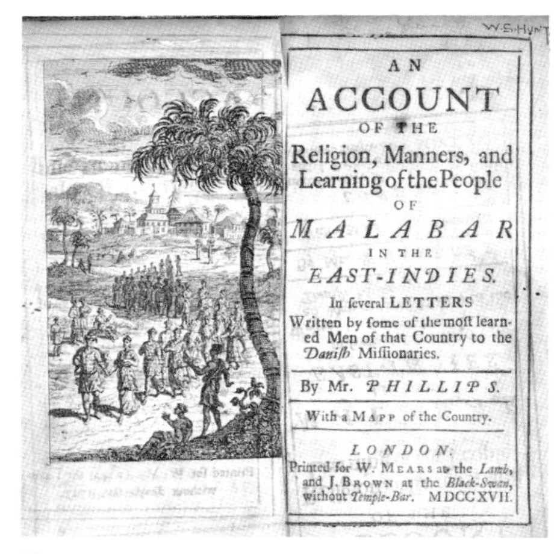
AN
ACCOUNT
OF THE
Religion, Manners, and
Learning of the People
OF
MALABAR
IN THE
EAST-INDIES.
In several LETTERS
Written by some of the most learned Men of that Country to the Danish Missionaries.
By Mr. PHILLIPS.
With a MAPP of the Country.
LONDON:
Printed for W. MEARS at the Lamb, and J. BROWN at the Black-Swan, without Temple-Bar. MDCCXVII.

59

religions which burgeoned with the Enlightenment. However, from its earliest days the Company was wary of being seen to promote missionary activities or missionary investigations. Chaplains accompanied Company ships and were attached to factories, but they were to minister to the Company's servants only. Anglican and Nonconformist proselytising amongst Indians was rare until the early nineteenth century. Before this the English got much of their information about Indian religions from other European missionary endeavours. This book contains what purported to be a series of letters from a Brahmin of Tanjore to Danish missionaries established on the coast of this principality. It recounts the main features of Hindu belief and traces the supposed slow acquiescence of the Brahmin to Christian principles. The engraving shows a procession of the 'King of Tanjour' to the sea, an annual royal pilgrimage. C.A.B.

60 Account books and cloth registers from the Company factory at Dacca, July 1792

Manuscript, ink on paper, 29 × 26 ($11\frac{1}{2} \times 10\frac{1}{2}$)
India Office Library and Records (IO 4026.f.21)

Cloth remained the staple of the Company's exports from Bengal, and from India in general, until the early years of the nineteenth century when the increasing competition of English manufactured products began to be felt. Yet as late as 1802 the directors still believed that 'a quantity of callicoes far exceeding our most exalted order' could find an outlet. Dacca (Dhaka) was an ancient centre of fine muslin production which had been patronized by the Mughals and by the Nawabs of Bengal (no.83). The Company's power in Dacca had severely damaged the industry by the end of the eighteenth century. Competitors were excluded and the stringent policies of the factory had reduced many weavers to the status of wage labourers on small remuneration rather than independent producers. C.A.B.

LITERATURE: Marshall 1988, pp. 106–8.

61

61 Fort William in the Kingdom of Bengal

After Jan van Ryne, 1754
Engraving, 24 × 39 ($9\frac{2}{5} \times 15\frac{3}{10}$)
The India Office Library and Records (P462)

Though it was to become the 'second city of the British Empire', Calcutta had an inauspicious start, founded in the swamp lands near Hughly by Job Charnock in 1690. Madras and Surat were both more important than Calcutta until the 1710s and 1720s, but the extraordinary productivity of Bengal's weavers and the opportunities for lucrative inland or 'country' trade up the rivers Ganges and Jumna soon began to work in Calcutta's favour. By 1760 the city's population was probably well over 100,000 and in the 1770s it became the seat of the Governor-General and of the major army and naval commands.

Van Ryne's engraving shows shipping on the River Hughly and the old Fort William which was soon to fall victim to Siraj-ud-Daulah's attack in 1756 (no.98). The fort, the landing stage with a crane and the factory building can be seen. The Governor's private residence has an avenue of trees down to the river. St Anne's Church, to the left of Government House, is shown with a wooden bell-cote (the spire had fallen during a cyclone in 1737). Van Ryne (1712–*c.*1760) settled in London about 1750. He had not visited any of the sites in this series, which depicted the same places as the Lambert and Scott paintings (no.62), together with the Dutch headquarters of Batavia. C.A.B.

LITERATURE: Harrold 1974, p. 10–11; Losty 1990, pp. 28–9.

62

62 Bombay

George Lambert and Samuel Scott, 1732
Oil on canvas, 81.3 × 132 (32 × 52)
India Office Library and Records (F48)

In the nineteenth century Bombay was to become the great centre of British commerce in India, but before 1818 it was a small and often embattled station which the Company considered giving up more than once. Surat was still officially the commercial headquarters of the British in western India. But as early as 1652 the Company was considering purchasing the Portuguese settlement to the south to avoid constant conflict with the Mughal governors of Surat. In 1661 King Alphonso VI of Portugal gave Bombay to King Charles II as part of the dowry of his sister, Catherine of Braganza. In 1668 it was rented by the Crown to the Company for £10 per annum and Sir George Oxenden, President of Surat, became its first Governor.

The City's early history was chequered (in 1683–4, for instance, it was occupied for nearly a year by English mutineers and 'pirates'), but its fine deep-water harbour and access to the Indian Ocean and coastal trade routes soon helped to build up the commercial community. Portuguese *casados* (householder-settlers) were joined by members of the Muslim trading communities of the Arabian Sea (Khojas, Bohras and Memons), by the rich Gujarati Hindu traders and, after the 1740s, by enterprising Parsis from Surat who worked as shipwrights and chandlers, and helped to build up the powerful Bombay mercantile fleet. By the 1780s, when the Maratha threat had been contained and the city had begun to act as an entrepôt in the opium and raw cotton trades to China, Bombay's rise to prosperity was assured.

Lambert was an architectural landscape and scene painter; Scott was a landscape and marine painter. Their six paintings of the Company's Indian settlements and places en route were commissioned by the Company in 1732. Their purchase for 15 guineas each is recorded in the Company Minutes for November 1732. George Vertue noted later in 1732 that the pictures were installed in the East India Company house in Leadenhall Street.

Elizabeth Einberg has plausibly suggested that the commission may have been promoted by the Child family, who played a prominent part in the Company's affairs and who employed Lambert extensively at their grand Palladian mansion, Wanstead. Since the artists did not visit India it is assumed that they worked from early eighteenth-century plans of the settlements, although liberties were certainly taken over some architectural details. There are also indications that their sources were topographically out of date. It has been suggested that the topography may derive from a common Dutch source since one of the paintings in the set, *The Cape of Good Hope*, corresponds closely to Arnould Smit's pictures of the same subject.

In this view of Bombay the large white building in the centre, with the high gateway surmounted by a coat of arms, is probably that marked in Grose's map of *c.*1760 as 'The Blunder of Company's Warehouse'; on the right the Union Jack can be seen flying from the bastion of the castle. Among the shipping in the foreground is a large vessel with a triangular sail flying the Company's colours with their red and white horizontal bars. John Bowles published two sets of prints from the six pictures soon after their completion, which suggests that the images were extremely popular (Kingzett 1982, pp.69–70).

C.A.B./B.A.

PROVENANCE: Commissioned by the East India Company in 1732.

LITERATURE: India Office Library 1732; Vertue 1933–4, p.63; Walpole 1766, ii, p.334; Foster 1924, pp. 24–5, no.48; Grant 1926, I, p.43; Whitley 1928, I, p.204; Wittler 1928, p.36; Finberg 1942, p.201; Mitchel 1952, p.xvi; Waterhouse 1953, p.104; Archer 1965, p.403; Einberg 1970, p.14; David 1973; Kingzett 1982, pp.69–70; Conlon 1985, pp.181–208; Archer 1986, pp.69–70, pl.XVII, p.169.

EXHIBITIONS: London, Guildhall Library and Art Gallery, *Samuel Scott Paintings & Drawings*, 1955 (53); London, Victoria and Albert Museum, *Arts and the East India Trade*, 1970.

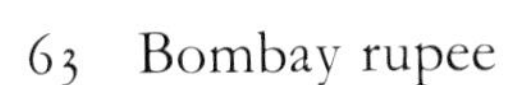

63 Bombay rupee

East India Company, Bombay Presidency, minted at Bombay, 1678
Silver
Obv: *1678 BY.AUTHORITY.OF. CHARLES THE SECOND*

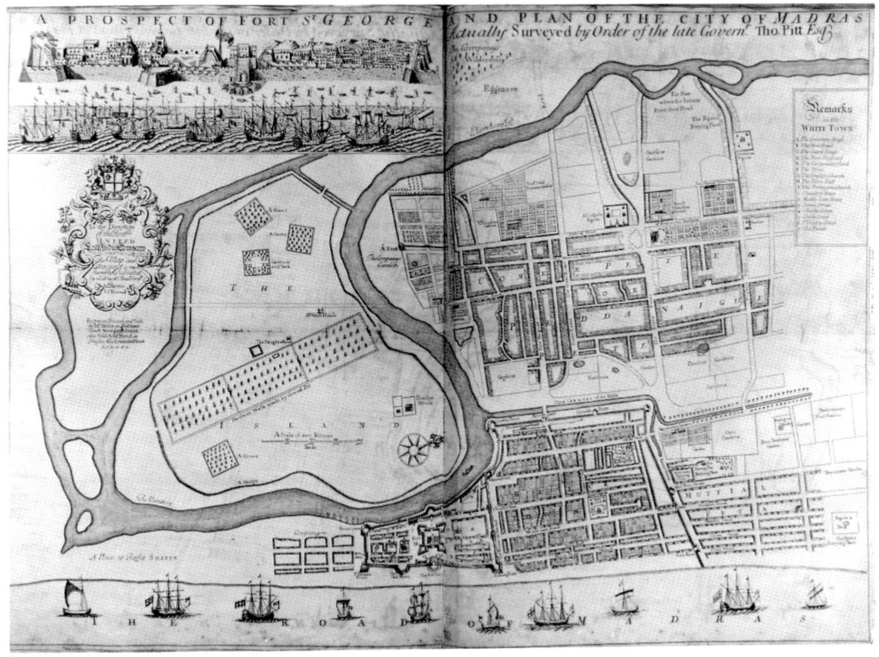

64

Rev: Royal shield of arms, crowned, *KING.OF. GREATBRITAINE.FRANCE.AND. IRELAND*
The Trustees of the British Museum, Department of Coins and Medals (OR 5198)

As a British possession rather than a settlement working within Mughal territory under a *farman*, Bombay minted in the name of the British Crown. C.A.B.

64 Prospect of Fort St George and plan of the city of Madras

John Harris for Thomas Pitt, *c.*1730
Engraving on paper, 70.6 × 103 ($28\frac{3}{4}$ × 42)
Bodleian Library, Oxford (Gough Maps 41°, no.138)

Madras was sited to take advantage of the skilled weaving communities of the Tamil country and the possibilities for export to Southeast Asia. It was founded in 1639 on a grant from the Nayak of Kalahasti, final legatee of the sovereignty of the now vanished Hindu empire of Vijayanagar. By the early eighteenth century Madras boasted a population of about 100,000. Fort St George stood at the centre of the fortified town; to its south were the Company offices and St Mary's Church (where Clive was later to be married); to its north were the houses of European merchants. Further to the north, over a fortified ditch, stood the Black Town, dominated at that time by Hindu merchants from the Tamil and Telugu country, with some Armenian merchants and a few remaining business houses of the Indo-Portuguese.

Until the Peace of Paris of 1763 Madras was never really safe from French and Indian invasion (it was taken by the French in 1746 and again besieged by them in 1758). Hereafter the Nawab of Arcot moved his court to the city, thus adding northern Muslim immigrants to its already heterogeneous population. C.A.B.

LITERATURE: Love 1913.

65 Sir Josiah Child (1630–99)

After John Riley
Engraving, 14.5 × 14 ($5\frac{3}{4} \times 5\frac{1}{2}$)
India Office Library and Records (P1461)

Josiah Child was a Director of the East India Company almost continuously between 1674 and his death in 1699. For most of the period from 1681 to 1690 he was Governor or Deputy Governor of the Company. Although he had made his fortune supplying the navy during the Interregnum, Child succeeded in bringing the Company into very close alliance with the court under Charles II and James II.

In the seventeenth and early eighteenth centuries the East India Company was permanently divided in its attitude to war and conquest in India. 'Men on the spot', seeking security and private fortunes, often urged war on their masters in London. But the Company had before it the dismal spectacle of the Portuguese (and apparently now the Dutch), whose commercial performance was sinking under the weight of military expenditure. But even in England there were some who urged a move from an open trading policy to more aggressive empire building. Child had ambitious designs for building up the population and trade of the Company's Indian settlements and for making them militarily secure. In 1686 Child asserted that, without territorial power and revenue, 'it is impossible to make the English nation's state firm in India upon a sound Political Basis, and without which, we shall always continue in the state of meer merchants subject to be turned out at the pleasure of the Dutch and abused at the discretion of the natives' (Chaudhuri 1978, p.454). He encouraged Company servants in India to use force in obtaining trade concessions, a policy which led to a disastrously unsuccessful war waged by the Company against the Mughal Emperor Aurangzeb in western India and in Bengal in 1689. In the eighteenth century changing political circumstances and the aggression of the Company's agents in India confirmed the ultimate wisdom of Child's admonition.

Child was also a notable writer on economic affairs. A contemporary summed him up as 'a man of great notions as to merchandise . . . he applied himself chiefly to the East India trade, which by his management was raised so high, that it drew much envy and jealousy, both upon himself and upon the Company' (Henning 1986).

C.A.B./P.J.M.

LITERATURE: Chaudhuri 1978; Rohatgi 1982, p.41; Henning 1986.

66

66 Indian textile workers and weavers from the Malabar coast

Henry Tresham, *c.*1780
Pen, ink and watercolour, 45 × 64.5 ($17\frac{5}{8} \times 25\frac{3}{10}$)
India Office Library and Records (WD 4038)

These weavers were probably Tamils. At this time the term 'Malabar' was used to mean coastal south-east as well as south-west India. Company policy towards weaving communities in both north and south was mixed. On the one hand it welcomed the settlement of refugee weavers from the wars of the Indian states. But on the other hand weavers were often ruthlessly oppressed to hold down the prices of their products, and Indian textile merchants were elbowed out of business. In Bengal there were even a few cases where Company officials or representatives cut off the thumbs of weavers to prevent them from working for rival companies of merchants. It was common practice for the Company and Indian states to uproot communities and settle them in their own territories. Given their status as a kind of economic football in eighteenth-century India, it is not surprising that weaving communities appear to have declined dramatically in numbers and status well before industrial products from British machine mills began to be imported into the country. The Irish-born painter, poet and collector Henry Tresham moved to England in 1775. He travelled in Italy around 1776 and stayed on the continent for fourteen years. On his return to England in 1789 he exhibited no.66 at the Royal Academy.

C.A.B.

PROVENANCE: Purchased 1983–4.

LITERATURE: Arasaratnam 1978; Hossein 1979.

EXHIBITION: London, Royal Academy, 1789 (522).

An Exchange of Fabrics and Styles

67

67 William Feilding, 1st Earl of Denbigh (*c.* 1582–1643)

Sir Anthony van Dyck, *c.* 1633–4
Oil on canvas, 247.5 × 148.5 ($97\frac{1}{2}$ × $58\frac{1}{2}$)
The Trustees of the National Gallery (5633)

William Feilding (*c.* 1582–1643) obtained Royal favour by virtue of his marriage to Susan Villiers, the sister of James I's favourite, the Duke of Buckingham. Feilding was created Master of the Great Wardrobe and Earl of Denbigh in 1622. He held a number of naval commands and after Buckingham's assassination in 1628 he commanded the abortive expedition to relieve La Rochelle. From 1631 to 1633 he visited Persia and India with letters of introduction from the King, travelling on the East India Company's ships. Van Dyck's portrait was almost certainly commissioned to commemorate the trip. Lord Denbigh returned to England on 26 August 1633 and it seems probable that this portrait was executed soon afterwards, before Van Dyck's departure for the southern Netherlands in 1634.

According to family tradition the Earl is shown being led to safety by a native boy after he had lost his way, but it is more likely that he is shown out hunting and exploring.

This is one of Van Dyck's most spectacular English portraits and, as Sir Oliver Millar has pointed out, it is as ambitious a portrait of a full-length figure in a landscape as the celebrated portrait of the King '*a la chasse*', painted in 1635 and now in the Louvre. The picture is one of the earliest depictions of an English sitter wearing oriental-inspired dress. The Earl's striking costume of rose-pink silk with a narrow gold stripe is particularly interesting. Many travellers and merchants in India during the seventeeth century adopted native dress in one form or another for reasons of comfort or protection, and the outfit worn here by Denbigh represents a combination of Eastern and Western styles. His long trousers, fastened by a cord at the waist, are based on the Indian 'paijama' but are worn with European shoes. His coat is longer and looser and of much simpler cut than the contemporary doublet, but the manner in which it is buttoned tightly over the chest and is worn with the lace-edged shirt collar turned down over the neck creates a distinctly fashionable appearance. As souvenirs of his visit to India, the Earl brought back with him jewels, some pieces of 'Mesopotamia' cloth and an old 'pagan coat'. C.A.B./B.A./J.S.

PROVENANCE: Probably commissioned by, or given to, the Marquess of (later Duke of) Hamilton, the sitter's son-in-law, in whose collection it is recorded in the 1640s; sold by Trustees of the late Duke of Hamilton, Christie's, 6 November 1919 (72) bt. Amor for 6300 guineas; The Rt. Hon. Viscount Feilding sale, Christie's, 1 July 1938 (127) bt. Colnaghi; Count Antoine Seilern by whom given to National Gallery in 1945.

EXHIBITIONS: London, Royal Academy, 1873 (135); Edinburgh, Royal Scottish Academy, *Old Masters and Scottish National Portraits* 1883 (394); Grosvenor Gallery, 1887 (100); London, National Portrait Gallery, *Van Dyck in England,* 1982–3 (16).

LITERATURE: Smith 1831, vol. III, Van Dyck, no. 551; Bruce 1863; Cust 1900, p. 273, no. 64; Martin 1970, pp. 52–55, no. 5633; Larsen 1980, pp. 110–111, no.779; Millar 1982; Hall 1986, pp.236–7; Larsen 1988, II, p.326, ill.p.512.

68 Bodice

Indian, *c.*1805–10
Muslin, embroidered with flattened silver wire, length (from shoulder) 26 ($10\frac{1}{4}$); waist 65 ($25\frac{1}{2}$)
Cheltenham Art Gallery and Museums (1956.98.29)

This unusual and charming bodice of fine white muslin embroidered with flattened silver thread is one of a pair. Both the muslin fabric and the embroidery technique are of Indian origin but the style of the bodice suggests that it was made for the European market. White muslin, creating a draped, antique effect, was fashionable for ladies' gowns from the 1790s and the high-waisted cut of this bodice and its low, square neckline indicate a date of *c.*1805–1810.

References in contemporary ladies' magazines testify to a vogue for Indian-inspired ornamentation in female fashions around this time, apart from the general popularity of Indian muslin, and demonstrate how motifs from other cultures were readily incorporated into the prevailing neo-classical style. J.S.

PROVENANCE: Whinyates family collection.

EXHIBITIONS: Cheltenham, Pittville Pump Room Museum, *Indian Summer*, 1985.

69 Fabric length of Indian muslin

1806–15
Muslin, embroidered with flattened silver wire, 39 × 144 ($15\frac{3}{4} \times 56\frac{3}{4}$)
Cheltenham Art Gallery and Museums (1956.98.38)

This length of silver-embroidered Indian muslin forms part of the Whinyates Collection at Cheltenham Art Gallery and Museum, a group of costume and textile items brought back

68

69

70

to England by members of a prominent local family who lived in India between 1780 and 1842. It may have been worn by Mrs Whinyates or one of her daughters as a fashionable accessory, perhaps a stole or a sash. Although apparently unconnected with no. 68, it is embroidered in flattened silver thread with repeating motifs and a grape-vine border which exactly match those on the bodice, and comparison of the two suggests that the fabric for the bodice may have originally been cut from a piece such as this. J.S.

PROVENANCE: Whinyates family collection.

EXHIBITIONS: Cheltenham, Pittville Pump Room Museum, *Indian Summer*, 1985.

70 Shawl

Indian, *c.*1840
Pieced wool, hand-embroidered in silk in chain and stem stitch, 19.6 × 18.6 (77 × 73¼)
Cheltenham Art Gallery and Museums (1907.G.7)

This shawl, donated to Cheltenham Art Gallery and Museums in 1907, was originally presented to Lord Ellenborough by an Indian potentate during his term as Governor-General of India between 1842 and 1844. It is constructed from pieces of Kashmir-type wool and its central pictorial design has been entirely hand-embroidered using multi-coloured silk threads. The regular exchange of presents was an established custom amongst the Mughal nobility and luxury textiles such as shawls and sashes remained standard gifts in this period.

J.S.

PROVENANCE: Given by Mrs E.L. Danberry.

EXHIBITIONS: Cheltenham, Pittville Pump Room Museum, *Indian Summer*, 1985.

71 A page in European clothes undressing a lady

Probably Persian or Indo-Persian artist, *c.* 1640
Pen, ink and body colour, 11.9 × 21.6 (4½ × 8½)
The Syndics of The Fitzwilliam Museum (M.40.f.38)

Just as Europeans in the east sometimes adopted Indian clothes, so Indians some-

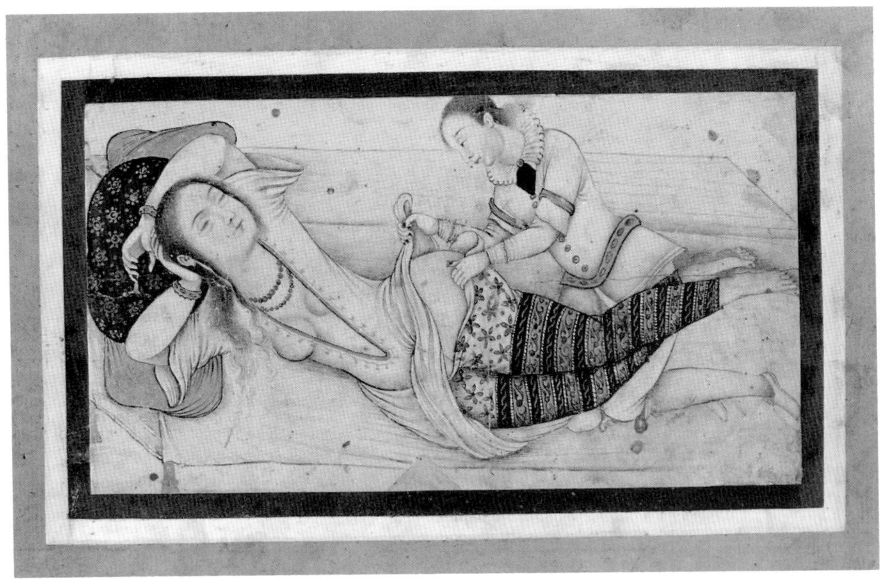

71

times adopted European dress. This was particularly true of the coastal areas where the Portuguese and people of mixed Portuguese and Indian race were settled as householders or *casados*, or where Dutch and later English textiles were imported: Gombroon and Hormuz on the Persian Gulf; Goa, Diu and Daman in western India; and Tuticorin and Masulipatnam in eastern India, all of which were linked by a lively 'country trade'. The doublet, hose and ruff appear to have been adopted as a dress for pages (male and female) in Persian circles, and in areas influenced by them, such as the Deccan kingdoms (no.19). This clothing style survived well beyond the period of its demise in Europe. Here a 'page' in European costume is busily undressing a lady who is lolling on a cushion (which may well be of Indian fabric and style). In India European styles often appear to have been associated with bibulous and erotic themes, an idea which has also survived into the contemporary world, and parallels the Western association of Eastern clothes with the luxurious pleasures of the harem. C.A.B.

PROVENANCE: Marlay Bequest, 1912.

EXHIBITIONS: Victoria and Albert Museum, *Persian Miniature Painting*, 1967 (90).

72 The Earl of Northampton

Mughal School, *c.* 1630/50, copy of engraving by T. Cockson, *c.*1599
Pen and ink, 29.8 × 23.5 ($11\frac{3}{4} \times 9\frac{1}{2}$)
The Syndics of the Fitzwilliam Museum, Cambridge (3447)

Indian rulers and nobles employed Europeans as gunners and miners. They began to purchase European weapons and armour through the major ports, but it was not until the later eighteenth century that European technology and uniforms began to be widely adopted. This English portrait, which was carefully copied and set within an Indian-style border by the Mughal artist, was perhaps one of those images of great men which were exchanged by the respective kingdoms during acts of diplomacy (see no.3). The subject is identified on the back of the copy. C.A.B.

PROVENANCE: Given by Sir Frank Brangwyn R.A., 1943.

72

Mughal Decline and the Struggle for Succession, *c.* 1700–1800

During the eighteenth century there was a dramatic change in the local circumstances in which the English East India Company worked. After the death in 1707 of the last great Emperor, Aurangzeb, Mughal power waned until in 1803 it barely extended beyond the city of Delhi, the imperial capital. Mughal power was assaulted from the north by a Persian invasion in 1739 and a series of Afghan attacks, especially damaging from 1759 to 1761. In 1757 the British conquered Bengal, technically a Mughal province, and in 1759 they became dominant in Surat in the west.

However, it was internal changes which spelled the end of imperial power. Aurangzeb had overstretched himself in trying to conquer the Deccan. The imperial treasury was empty. Worse, the system of checks and balances which moved imperial officers around the country was breaking down and powerful magnates were establishing virtually independent dynasties in the richest provinces. By amalgamating the offices of revenue-manager (*diwan*) and governor, and then making them hereditary within their own families, Mughal officials created what amounted to new kingdoms in Awadh and Bengal in the north, and in Hyderabad and Arcot in the south.

At the same time declared enemies of the Mughals established a firmer grip on power while the imperial armies melted away. These enemies were the Hindu Marathas of western India, the Sikhs of the Punjab and the Jat peasants around Delhi. These non-Muslim revolts represented a reaction by the countryside against the pressures of Mughal tax gatherers and officials.

The struggle for succession in eighteenth-century India was bitter, but all was not anarchy. Trade and agriculture continued in many areas and flourished in some. New cities such as Lucknow, Hyderabad and Poona grew up as Delhi and Agra declined. Architecture, music and miniature painting prospered under the patronage of the new rulers. The British, waiting on the fringes, capitalized on the successes of the Mughal successor regimes as much as they exploited their conflicts. C.A.B.

73 Farrukhsiyar receiving Husain Ali Khan

Mughal, 1712–19
Gouache and gold, 33.8 × 20.7 (13$\frac{1}{5}$ × 8)
Inscribed on reverse: *Farrukhsiyyar padshah m'a vazir Husain Ali*
India Office Library and Records (Johnson 18/5)

Here Husain Ali Khan, the great noble, approaches the Emperor Farrukhsiyar who sits formally enthroned under a canopy on a garden terrace. The brightness of the imperial 'halo' is a reminder that after the death of Aurangzeb, emperors began to insist once again on their superiority to the Muslim doctors of law and their nearly supernatural status as the 'Shadow of God'. Despite the inscription, Husain Ali Khan was Amir-ul-Umara ('Lord Chamberlain'); it was his brother Abdullah Khan who was the Vazir, or chief minister. The strangling of Farrukhsiyar in 1719, following a plot by these two brothers, who were members of the Barah Sayyid community of Saharanpur near Delhi, was a devastating blow to imperial authority. It signalled the beginning of a period of faction during which the Vazir became increasingly independent of the monarch and savage battles ensued between Indian-born nobles like the Barah Sayyids and the great commanders of Iranian and Central Asian origin. Ultimately, several of the latter, such as Burhan-ul-Mulk and Asaf Jah, deserted the centre altogether and opted to concentrate on power bases in the provinces. So began the 'decentralisation' of imperial power which was to lead to the fragmentation of the Mughal empire into many smaller kingdoms, and which materially aided the British rise to power. Husain Ali Khan himself was assassinated in 1720, his faction having been dominant in Delhi for a decade. C.A.B.

LITERATURE: Archer and Falk 1981, no. 156; Alam 1986; Chandra 1958.

74 The Red Fort, Delhi – a bird's-eye view from the East, showing the Emperor entering the Diwan-i-Khas on the right

Unknown artist, Lucknow, *c.*1780–90
Gouache with gold, black border, 29.2 × 41.5 (11$\frac{1}{2}$ × 16$\frac{3}{8}$), page 32.5 × 44.5 (12$\frac{3}{4}$ × 17$\frac{5}{8}$)
Inscribed in Persian on reverse: *529*
India Office Library and Records (Add.Or.948)

The bird's-eye view looks west from the wall overlooking the Jumna river. It shows the domed Musamman Burj, the balcony window where the Emperor displayed himself to the public, and the Hall of Public Audience (*Diwan-i-Am*). Emperor Shah Alam approaches the Hall of Private Audience (*Diwan-i-Khas*).

After Aurangzeb's death in 1707 the Mughal realm diminished almost as fast as it had expanded 150 years previously. In 1719 the Emperor Farrukhsiyar was murdered and the Red Fort at Delhi became a hotbed of intrigue among groups of Indian-born and Iranian or

73

74

Central Asian grandees. After a debilitating period of minorities Muhammad Shah, who reigned from 1719 to 1748, gained a loose hold on power. But his reign was a long catalogue of defeat and failure. The Vazir (chief minister) and other great nobles became increasingly independent. Enemy states flourished and the country was beset by Persian and Afghan invasions. By 1770 the effective sway of the Mughals was reduced to an area within about 100 miles of the Red Fort. In 1788 a Rohilla Muslim chief seized the Emperor Shah Alam II and blinded him. The dizzying fall of the royal house continued apace until the Red Fort and the Emperor fell under the direct protection of Lord Lake's East India Company armies in 1803. European visitors found the pathetic 'tinsel sovereign' forlornly carrying out the royal ceremonies amongst the emaciated ladies of his harem. C.A.B.

PROVENANCE: Purchased June 1959.

LITERATURE: Spear 1951; Archer and Falk 1981, p.160, no.343, ill.p. 446; Spear 1975, p.29.

EXHIBITION: London, Victoria and Albert Museum, *The Indian Heritage* 1982 (95).

75(i) The private pleasures of Raja Ram Chand

Bhura, Bikaner (?), *c.*1680
Gouache and bodycolour, 27 × 19.5 ($10\frac{1}{2} \times 7\frac{3}{5}$)
The Syndics of the Fitzwilliam Museum, Cambridge (PD 205–1948)

75(ii) The private pleasures of Raja Har Birval

Bishen Ram, Bikaner (?), *c.*1680
Gouache and bodycolour, 27 × 19.5 ($10\frac{1}{2} \times 7\frac{3}{5}$)
The Syndics of the Fitzwilliam Museum, Cambridge (PD 206–1948)

The depiction of sexual positions here perhaps owes something to Hindu traditions of works such as the *Kama Sutra* and to illustrations to yogic texts. Mughal influence on the architecture is strong. But this does not necessarily point to a direct Mughal model for the paintings. Bikaner was one of the most 'Mughlai' of the Rajput courts. Its first raja married one of his daughters to the Emperor Akbar; his successors in the later seventeenth century campaigned for the Mughals in the Deccan during the wars against the Marathas.

Their artistic excellence aside, these miniatures appear to have the satirical purpose of portraying contemporary rulers and officers of state as idle voluptuaries. The theme of the moral decay of the Mughals and their satellite kingdoms was developed by Muslim writers long before eighteenth-century European writers began to expound on the 'malign influence of the harem'. Muslim theologians such as the famous Shah Waliullah of Delhi argued that there was a need for an inward regeneration of Islam before it could be restored to political power in India. Denunciations of luxury and decadence often went hand in hand with the view that Mughal government and Mughal manners had become too closely associated with Hindus and Hindu customs.

There is some dispute about the provenance of the series of forty erotic miniatures from which these works are taken. Apart from the reference to Hindu erotic texts, they clearly seek to satirize important people of the seventeenth-century political world, including Mughal emperors, contemporary Rajput princes and even 'the Portuguese commander' (Viceroy of the 'Estado da India'). They have been ascribed variously to nineteenth-century Hyderabad and seventeenth-century Jodhpur, but the most likely attribution is to Bikaner (the western Rajput kingdom) in the late seventeenth century, where a lively indigenous style of Rajput-Deccani painting was coming under the influence of more formal Mughal court painting. C.A.B.

LITERATURE: Goetz 1950; Comfort 1964; Rizvi 1980; Archer and Falk 1981, no. 160.

76 Nadir Shah, King of Persia 1732–47

Unknown Persian artist, c.1740
Oil on canvas, 127 × 99 (50 × 39)
India Office Library and Records (F44)

Nadir Shah, the Persian tyrant, sounded the deathknell of the Mughal empire. The Mughals' internal enemies, the Sikhs, Jats and Marathas, did more lasting damage to Delhi's economy and its revenues, but the humiliating defeat of the Indians by the Persians in 1739 accelerated the major provinces' drive for effective autonomy and encouraged *zamindars* (landholders) in all quarters to 'raise their heads in revolt'. Nadir Shah had come to power in a Persia which had been invaded by ferocious Afghan rebels and which was suffering the same 'end of empire' malaise that beset India.

75(i)

75(ii)

He put together an alliance of Turkish, Afghan and Persian soldiers and invaded the subcontinent in search of glory and booty. He wished to buy support in his own realm which had been impoverished by the disruption of its once lucrative exports of raw silk. The Mughals were crushed on the plains near Delhi, and Nadir Shah entered the helpless city. Thirty thousand, perhaps more, of Delhi's citizens were massacred when they attempted to repulse the Persian soldiers before the Shah acceded to the pathetic entreaties of Muhammad Shah and called a halt to the slaughter. Nadir left India later that year, taking with him a vast quantity of precious stones, plate and bullion along with the famous Peacock Throne. The contemporary value of the treasure was estimated at between £8 and £30 million. Apart from fighting, the things which Nadir most enjoyed were 'the melons of Balkh and Herat and ... a good horse' (Lockhart 1938, p.274).

While at Delhi, Nadir had two portraits painted of himself, one of which was presented to the British Governor of Madras in 1740. This may be no.76, which was acquired by Henry Vansittart (Governor of Bengal 1760–7), whose son passed it to the East India Company in 1822. The technique of the painting is Persian, but heavily influenced by European models, a style developed under the later Qajar dynasty. C.A.B.

PROVENANCE: Presented by the Rt. Hon. Nicholas Vansittart, 1822.

LITERATURE: Durand 1908, ill. frontispiece; Sykes 1915, p.346; Lockhart 1938; Archer 1986, pp. 83–4, no.115, ill. pl.XXVIII.

Successor States to the Mughal Empire: Regional Muslim Dynasties

77 Shuja-ud-Daulah, Nawab of Awadh, holding a bow

Tilly Kettle, Faizabad, *c.*1772
Oil on canvas, 127.25 × 101.75 ($50\frac{1}{8} \times 40\frac{1}{8}$)
Yale Center for British Art, Paul Mellon Collection (B 1976.7.48)

The Awadh dynasty was one of the most important to arise out of the fragmentation of the Mughal empire. Until its richest areas were annexed by the British in 1801 it commanded the fertile plains of the rivers Ganges and Jumna and controlled a population of perhaps 20 million people. It formed the main artery of trade from Delhi to Murshidabad – and in time, to the burgeoning British centre of Calcutta. In the 1720s and 1730s the founder of the dynasty, Burhan-ul-Mulk, a noble of Persian origin and Vazir or prime minister of the empire, had gradually established an independent base of power in the lands around Faizabad. He skilfully exploited conflicts between the great

77

nobles and the emperors and amalgamated the functions of governor and *diwan* which became hereditary within his family.

Shuja-ud-Daulah succeeded to the Nawabi in 1754 and gradually expanded his realm, coercing the Hindu Rajput lords of the countryside and annexing the richer parts of surrounding states. But Shuja made one fundamental error. In 1763 he joined with Mir Kasim of Bengal and the son of the Mughal Emperor against the British, whose influence he wished to confine to Bengal. Defeat at the Battle of Buxar in 1764 led to a long and debilitating relationship with the Company (see no.139). Nevertheless, before his death in 1775, Shuja had reconstituted his army along Western lines and embellished his two great cities of Lucknow and Faizabad. He passed to his son Asaf-ud-Daulah a prosperous but vulnerable kingdom.

This picture apparently belonged to Henry Chicheley Plowden, who served with the East India Company in Bengal from 1773 to 1819 (see no. 9). It is not known how he acquired it but he possibly purchased it from the artist, Tilly Kettle, in Calcutta soon after his arrival. The Nawab is shown three-quarter length holding a bow in his right hand. Seen through the window in the background are a canopied garden pavilion and a group of attendant Indians.

Tilly Kettle (1735–86) was the first significant British painter to go to India. The son of a house painter, he trained in London and began to produce portraits in the style of Joshua Reynolds. He landed at Madras in 1769 and proceeded via Calcutta to the north. This is one of the finest of the large number of portraits of the Nawab, his family and other notables which Tilly Kettle painted or began during his stay in Faizabad in 1772 (see Archer 1979, p.75 and pls.28, 29 for further details).

B.A./C.A.B.

PROVENANCE: H.C. Plowden, Newtown Park, Lymington, Hants; Sabin Galleries Ltd 1970; purchased by Paul Mellon in 1970 and given to Yale in 1976.

LITERATURE: Archer 1979, p.78, pl.30; Barnett 1980; Alam 1986.

EXHIBITIONS: New Haven, Yale Center for British Art, *The British View of India: Selected English Paintings from the Paul Mellon Collection*, 1978 (un-numbered).

78

78 Asaf-ud-Daulah, Nawab of Awadh, Lucknow (1775–97)

Johann Zoffany, 1784
Oil on canvas, 127 × 101.5 (50 × 40)
Inscribed on a note attached to reverse: *Joh Zophany painted this Picture at Lucknow*, AD *1784, by order of His Highness the Nabob Vizier Asoph ul Dowlah, who gave it to his Servant Francis Baladon Thomas*
India Office Library and Records (F106)

Johann Zoffany (1733–1810) is regarded by many as the finest portrait painter to have worked in India. He was born in Frankfurt and, after training in Rome, went to London where he was patronized by David Garrick who commissioned several theatrical conversation pieces from him. During the 1770s his standing as a fashionable painter increased in England, Austria and Italy. Then Zoffany fell out of favour with the Queen (he had delayed too long on a canvas for her) and his reputation and commissions began to diminish. His decision to go to Bengal in 1783 at the age of fifty appears to have been made as much to find new and stimulating experiences as to 'repair his fortune'. Following an intensely productive stay in Calcutta where he painted many of the elite of the British community, he moved to Lucknow. Here also there was a large European population of Company officials and private traders, subsisting on the huge perquisites and profits to be made from breaking into the trade and wealth of Awadh.

Under Asaf-ud-Daulah, Awadh's dependence on the British became more and more onerous. The original 'subsidiary treaty', which had been made in 1765 following the Battle of Buxar, had bound the ruler to pay for contingents of Company troops to be deployed on his territories. The sums demanded were very large (on some estimates up to half of the total revenues of the kingdom). Asaf quickly fell irreparably into the Company's debt, as did the Nawab of Arcot labouring under similar terms in the south. He borrowed from local bankers and rural magnates who 'farmed' the revenues for him. His position was constantly imperilled by the activities of his ministers and others who played politics with successive British Residents, and with the various factions of Company officials vying for influence in Calcutta. The British and their Indian clients disliked Asaf, regarding him as shifty, degenerate and 'addicted to frivolity'. His physical appearance no doubt encouraged this view of him. Yet some recent historians have interpreted Asaf's vacillation and deceit as an elaborate ploy to maintain the independence of his realm and hide its real revenues from British eyes. Certainly his subjects appear to have favoured him; quatrains were still heard in nineteenth-century Awadh praising his munificence and lauding the aid he gave to the people during the great famine of 1783–4.

B.A./C.A.B.

PROVENANCE: Purchased February 1906.

LITERATURE: *The Journal of Indian Art*, vol. 12, no. 107, July 1909, ill. pl. 165; Manners and Williamson 1920, p.207; Foster 1931, p.82; *Journal of the Royal Society of Arts*, LXXIX, 1931; Webster 1976; Archer 1979, pp. 130–77,140–9, ill.pl.89; Barnett 1980; Archer 1986, p.49, ill. pl. XI.

EXHIBITIONS: London, Whitechapel, 1908 (8); London, Royal Academy of Arts, *The Art of India and Pakistan*, 1947–8 (914); London, National Portrait Gallery, *Johann Zoffany*, 1976 (102).

79 Palace of Nawab Shuja Daula, Lucknow†

Thomas and William Daniell, July – October 1789
Folio aquatint, from *Oriental Scenery*, vol.III, plate 16, London, 1790–2
India Office Library and Records

The great palace of the Nawabs of Awadh demonstrated the wealth and sophistication of this post-Mughal state, and it attracted many European visitors including the Daniells and William Hodges. Both contemporary and modern sources contest the palace's origin. While the Daniells attribute it to Shuja, Hodges says that only 'a small part' was raised by Shuja. The most authoritative recent study (Tandan) concludes that the building on the right next to the Panch Mahal Gateway (no.80), the Panch Mahal Palace, was probably built by the Sheikhzadas, the great landed patrons of Lucknow, in about 1600. It was a variety of the great pillared hall; there are other examples: the palace of Tirumala Nayak at Madurai (no.21) and in Bihar and Rajasthan. The larger building next to the Panch Mahal may have been partly constructed by Shuja, but it was greatly extended and changed in style by Asaf-ud-Daulah when he came to Lucknow after 1775.

C.A.B.

LITERATURE: Tandan 1979, i, pp. 158–61; Archer 1980, no. 60; Godrej and Rohatgi 1989, pl. 6, p. 50; cf. Hodges 1794, pp. 100–1.

80 Punj Mahalla (Panch Mahal) Gate, Lucknow

Thomas Daniell, July – October 1789
Watercolour 45.7 × 61.1 (18 × 28¼)
P & O, Art and Memorabilia Collection (21)

This is the gateway to the Panch Mahal Palace shown in no.79. The style suggests early Mughal architecture and it too was probably constructed by the Sheikhzadas, the old landed family which controlled Lucknow before the emergence of the Nawabi, and contested the rise of Burhan-ul-Mulk and the Awadh ruling family. The upper storey is a *naubat khana* on which a drum band played ceremonial salutes to entering dignitaries; in Mughal culture the right to construct *naubat khanas* was a recognition of one's prestige and dignity. The Nawabs are known to have rented the land on which the gateway and palace stood from the 1740s and it was perhaps at this time that the distinctive fish emblem of the Awadh dynasty (*macchi* or *machli*) was added. This paint-

80

ing was the original for the fifth print in the third volume of *Oriental Scenery*.

C.A.B.

LITERATURE: Tandan 1978, i, p. 159; Archer 1980, no.62.

81 Garden House in the Aisbagh, Lucknow

Thomas Daniell, July – October 1789
Watercolour, 30.5 × 50. 8 (12 × 20)
P & O, Art and Memorabilia Collection (22)

Both Shuja and Asaf-ud-Daulah beautified the city of Lucknow with many *baghs* or gardens. One such was the Aisbagh, probably constructed in the 1770s, which contained a 'pavilion' or *baradari* (from *barah* meaning 'twelve' and *dwara* meaning 'door', i.e. a building with twelve doors). This one is in the typical early Nawabi style, based on Mughal originals and as yet little influenced by European designs like the greater and more ornate *baradaris* built in the early nineteenth century. C.A.B.

LITERATURE: Tandan 1979, i, p. 206.

81

82 Pavilion in the Palace, Allahabad

Thomas Daniell, November 1789
Watercolour, 51.4 × 77.5 ($20\frac{1}{4}$ × $30\frac{1}{2}$)
P & O, Art and Memorabilia Collection (28)

82

Allahabad, the commercial town and pilgrimage centre at the confluence of the rivers Ganges and Jumna, was the site of one of the four great fortresses (the others were Agra, Delhi and Lahore) built after 1574 by the Emperor Akbar when he was consolidating his rule. This building was a hall of private audience where the Emperor received his ministers and intimate advisors. Little of the building now survives as it was destroyed in a gunpowder accident during the Company's rule. Control of Allahabad was an important strategic and commercial advantage for the emerging Awadh regime. When the Emperor Shah Alam fled from Delhi and made an alliance with the British, the city became his residence briefly between 1772 and 1774 and hosted a minor revival of Mughal authority. Its security was enhanced by the presence of a British garrison stationed there under the terms of the subsidiary treaties between the British and the Nawabs, which had come into effect after 1765 (nos. 82, 139, 140). Because it was a trans-shipment point and home to a small British population, it was natural that the Daniells should have gone there and seen buildings in 'the grandest style of Mahommedan Architecture'. This was the original for the sixth print in the first volume of *Oriental Scenery*. C.A.B.

LITERATURE: Hardie and Clayton 1932; Archer 1980, no.64; Godrej and Rohatgi 1989, pl.6, p. 50.

83

83 A Nawab Holding Court, probably Alivardi Khan

Unknown artist, Murshidabad, Bengal, *c.* 1760
Opaque watercolour and gold, 42 × 57 ($16\frac{1}{2} \times 22\frac{1}{2}$)
The Trustees of the Victoria and Albert Museum (D 1175–1903)

In Bengal a powerful regime emerged, based on Murshidabad, when Murshid Quli Khan amalgamated the offices of governor (*subahdar*) and revenue manager (*diwan*) and reorganized the landholders of the province. Alivardi Khan, who ruled from 1740 to 1756, was the last effective Nawab of Bengal before the British established a dominant influence there. In spite of being a usurper who seized the throne by violence, Alivardi quickly consolidated his power within Bengal. During his reign, Bengal was frequently attacked from beyond its borders and the Nawab was obliged to fight off a very damaging series of raids by the Marathas into western Bengal. At high cost, both in money extracted from his subjects for the war and in the cession of the southern province of Orissa, Alivardi brought the Maratha attacks to an end in 1751.

Alivardi ruled a province whose links with the Mughal empire had become tenuous. Under him they were further attenuated. The new Nawab sought confirmation of his title from the Emperor and made some payments to him, but regular remittance of tribute from Bengal, the essential duty of a loyal provincial governor, seems to have stopped. Nevertheless, Alivardi still tried to follow Mughal patterns of rule. He was admired for being 'so moral a character'. He 'treated the nobility and the grandees with so much deference' and showed 'so much attention to the oppressed'. It is unlikely that European trading companies figured very highly in his view of the world, but during his reign relations with the British remained relatively untroubled, except when Calcutta was called upon for extra payments. The situation was to change radically with the accession of his grandson Siraj-ud-Daulah (d.1757) in 1756. The kneeling figure, second on the right of the Nawab, is sometimes identified as Siraj-ud-Daulah.

Though 'Murshidabad painting' remains close to the Mughal imperial style, the subtle pastel colouring and the presence of the river Ganges in many of these paintings gives it a distinctive regional quality. P.J.M.

LITERATURE: Skelton and Francis 1979, no.68; Marshall 1988.

84 Asaf Jah, Nizam-ul-Mulk, 1st Nizam of Hyderabad

Unknown artist, Mughal, 18th century
Gouache, album 30.5 × 25 ($11\frac{4}{5} \times 9\frac{3}{4}$)
The Trustees of the British Museum, Department of Oriental Antiquities (BM 1936.1–11.029)

One of the most renowned of the great kingmakers of eighteenth-century India, Nizam-ul-Mulk Asaf Jah founded the dynasty which was to rule in Hyderabad until the end of the British empire. Asaf Jah himself was a Turanian noble, that is to say of Central Asian origin. He was one of Aurangzeb's most trusted officers, and after the Emperor's death in 1707 he pursued an increasingly independent line during the factional struggles and the weak reign of Muhammad Shah. By the early 1730s he had begun to concentrate his resources in the Deccan, building on the tradition of service to the old Sultanate of Golconda and basing himself in the new model city of Hyderabad. Asaf Jah waged almost perpetual campaigns against his Maratha foes to the west and the independent-minded Telugu-speaking warrior chiefs of the plateau. He brought in Muslim cavalry soldiers and administrators and Hindu financiers from the north to build up his state, but before his death in 1748 he and his officers had begun to take loans from French officers and merchants who held a string of fortresses and factories along the Nawab's south-eastern boundary. Asaf Jah had wanted to extend his influence to the south, famed for its rich cloth products and the wealth of its rice-growing river valleys. His nominal subordinate, the *subahdar* (governor) of the Carnatic, the southern Telugu- and Tamil-speaking lands, had begun to create yet another Mughal-style state in this rich territory. Yet the southern expansion of Muslim power was to become fatally entwined with the duel between the British and French East India Companies on the Coromandel coast. C.A.B.

LITERATURE: Khan 1936.

85 Bending of the Bow, illustration to the *Ramayana*

*c.*1780
Gouache, 19.5 × 28.7 ($7\frac{7}{10} \times 11\frac{3}{10}$)
The Trustees of the British Museum, (BM 1948–10–9–0124)

With the decline of the Mughals, many small Hindu kingdoms enjoyed a brief but brilliant flowering in the eighteenth century. In the Punjab hills, especially the state of Kangra, trade from the north-west also vitalized a number of small fortress kingdoms which guarded the passes. A colourful style of painting emerged, blending Hindu and Mughal themes. The illustration represents a famous scene in the great Hindu epic, the *Ramayana*, where the hero Ram asserts his power over his rivals. The King of Videhas had announced that whoever could bend the bow of Shiva would have the hand of his daughter, Sita. Rama not only bent, but broke the bow. Here Sita is putting the emblem of victory, a long garland, on Rama's shoulder. To the right, bearded and wearing a white turban, stands the King; to the left, Rama's brother Lakshmana and the sage Vishvamitra. While the styles of architecture and dress represented are predominantly Mughal, the underlying philosophy and 'elegant idealism' (Archer 1952) are Hindu. C.A.B.

LITERATURE: Archer 1952, pp.2–5.

85

Non-Muslim Successor States to the Mughals

86 Group Portrait of Sikhs – Servants and Favourites of the Patalia Court

Unknown Delhi artist, *c.* 1815–20
Watercolour, 30.6 × 22.1 ($12 \times 8\frac{7}{10}$)
Inscribed along top of painting with numbers 1–8, corresponding with identification of portraits on accompanying sheet
The Trustees of the British Museum (BM 1988–10–20–01)

The Sikhs had arisen as a distinct religious group in India in the late fifteenth and early sixteenth centuries. They drew on the traditions of Indian Muslim Sufism and Hindu *bhakti* (devotionalism) and found their adherents in

86

both the trading and agricultural castes of the Punjab. The community grew in numbers and strength under the leadership of a line of Gurus, or teachers, the last of whom, Guru Govind Singh, died in 1708. By this time a large section of the Sikhs had constituted itself as a military brotherhood (the Khalsa), following bitter warfare with the Mughal governors of the Punjab who regarded the growing sect as a threat to their position. Guru Govind Singh said, 'I shall always be present wherever five Sikhs are assembled'; a final testimony which enabled the community to exist independently of a sovereign. Hereafter the Guru Granth Sahib, the collected sayings and traditions of the Gurus, became the Sikhs' ultimate authority. After the Persian and Afghan invasions of India they regrouped and wrested the rich province of the Punjab from the Mughal governors. The Golden Temple of Amritsar became their supreme centre of worship. In 1799 the leader of one of the main Sikh war bands, Ranjit Singh, took the town of Lahore and began to unite the Punjab once again under his rule. Other smaller kingdoms, such as that of Patalia, grew out of the roving warrior bands which had been characteristic of the Punjab in the eighteenth century.

This watercolour illustrates the variety of caste groups from which the Sikh community and state was constructed. William Fraser identified the figures in this portrait group which include 'Ruttun Singh, the Jat Zemindar' (Jats were a landholding caste), 'Manick Chund, a Chuttree, native of Puttealeh', or Khattri (Khattris were a commercial caste – the Sikh Gurus came from this background) and 'Gohur Goojur Cheenchee' (Gujars were pastoralist people). There are very few representations of Sikhs from before this date. As a Company servant in the Delhi Territory, William Fraser (1784–1835) collected portraits by Indian artists in the western style, encouraged by his artist brother James Fraser (1783–1856).

C.A.B.

PROVENANCE: Purchased from the Fraser Collection.

LITERATURE: Singh 1965; Archer and Falk 1979; Grewal 1990 (forthcoming).

87 Portrait of Shivaji

Deccani (Golconda), *c.*1680–7
Gouache and ink, on decorated album page, album size, open, 17.5 × 29 ($6\frac{4}{5} \times 11\frac{3}{10}$)
Inscribed on border: *Sieúwagie gewezen Maxatise voxSL*
The Trustees of the British Museum
(BM 1974-6-17-011 [12])

By far the most powerful group of resurgent Hindu kingdoms in eighteenth-century India was that of the

87

Marathas. Along with Mysore, they were to mount the fiercest opposition to British expansion in the subcontinent. Shivaji (1627–80) was the founder of Maratha political independence and also its greatest icon. A minor chieftain caught up in the wars and disruption which marked the Mughals' conflicts with the Deccan sultanates in the 1660s, Shivaji welded together a powerful alliance of local Hindu warrior chieftains, Kunbi peasants and pastoralist castes to pose an intense challenge to the Emperor Aurangzeb. The Mughals nearly succeeded in destroying the Maratha guerrilla armies after Shivaji's death, but the Marathas' strength in the western Deccan countryside fuelled a strong recovery after 1707.

In the early eighteenth century the reins of power in the Maratha state were seized by a family of Chitpavan Brahmins, members of whom had served Shivaji's successors as Peshwa, or chief minister. Hereafter power shifted to the new city of Poona and the Marathas began regularly to describe themselves as the 'Brahmin kingdom'. Despite their long duel with the declining Mughals, the Marathas adapted many Mughal forms of statecraft and land-revenue management. In the later eighteenth century great Maratha war chiefs such as the Scindias (no.91), Bhonsles and Holkars emerged alongside the Peshwas' Brahmin family. This Maratha 'confederacy' was to fight three fierce wars with the East India Company for control of peninsular India.

Shivaji is shown here in the prime of life, in Deccani costume, but with a distinctly martial character. The mailed gauntlet is an unusual feature to be displayed in contemporary miniature portraiture. C.A.B.

PROVENANCE: Transferred from Or.MSS (Add.22,282).

LITERATURE: Sen 1928.

88 Shivaji Rides Out

Poona, 20th century
Bazaar oleograph 45.5 × 32.4 ($17\frac{7}{8} \times 12\frac{3}{4}$)
Private Collection

Shivaji furnishes an ideal icon for the regional identity of Maharashtra. As a ruler who outwitted the Muslim Mughals and besieged the English and other meddling foreigners in their factories at Surat, he could hardly be bettered. Shivaji together with the Maratha form of the elephant-headed god Ganesh (Ganpati in western India) became the symbol of B.G. Tilak's 'extremist' challenge to British power in the 1890s. More recently they have provided rallying points for the Shiv Sena, the powerful political party which claims to represent the ethnic interests of Maharashtrians. Large equestrian statues of Shivaji have been erected in recent times

88

fronting the Gateway of India in Bombay, a prime monument to the British empire, and also in Delhi. C.A.B.

89 Maharaja Pratap Singh of Tanjore

Company School, Tanjore, late 18th century
Gouache, gold and beetlewing, 43 × 35.5 ($16\frac{9}{10} \times 14$)
Inscribed on reverse: *Pretaup Sing Maha Rajah of Tanjour*
The Clive Museum, Powis Castle (Powis Estate Trustees) (182)

The western Indian plateau where the Marathas originated was not a rich agricultural region. Maratha stability and prosperity therefore depended on expansion northward into the fertile lands of the Ganges-Jumna plains and southward towards the rice-growing valleys of the southern rivers. Before the end of the seventeenth century a kinsman of Shivaji had established himself as monarch of the small but highly productive kingdom of Tanjore on the river Kavery. A Maratha aristocracy ruled over Tamil- and Telugu-speaking subjects, whose social and agricultural life was dominated by the great Hindu temples of the Kavery delta. Naturally, this rich little kingdom was eyed enviously by powerful neighbours. The French, Dutch and English Companies struggled for a hold on the coast; Danish missionaries were established at Tranquebar (no.59). In 1749, the then ruler Pratap Singh was involved in a skirmish with Major Lawrence (no.95) and lost the coastal town of Devikottai to the British. In 1773, Muhammed Ali of Arcot (no.142) tried to absorb Tanjore in alliance with his European creditors. British intrusiveness continued until towards the end of the century, under Raja Sarabhoji (Serfoji), the kingdom became a Company protectorate and the royal family was left to concentrate on ceremonial and cultural functions.

From the mid-eighteenth century, Indian artists in Tanjore began to adapt their techniques to the taste of European patrons, so evolving a distinctive school of 'Company painting' to stand comparison with those that developed in the north at Patna, Lucknow and Delhi. Depictions of royal processions during the Dussehra festival and sets of paintings of 'tribes and castes' were favourite themes. This picture, showing the ruler beneath a canopy and holding a rose-water sprinkler, displays little 'Company' influence. It was presented to the Collector of Tanjore by Maharaja Sarabhoji in 1800. C.A.B.

LITERATURE: Archer 1972; *CHI*, v, p. 125, n. 129; Appasamy 1980, ill. pl. 14; Archer, Rowell and Skelton, 1987, p. 125, no.182.

90

90 The Battle of Panipat, 13 January 1761

Faizabad artist, *c.* 1770

Drawing with some colour; on paper backed with cloth 51.7 × 65.8 (20⅗ × 26)

Inscribed with the names of the principle combatants in Persian characters

India Office Library and Records (J.66.3)

Many of the fiercest conflicts of the eighteenth century were between Indian and Indian rather than between Indians and Europeans. The regional states which emerged from the Mughal decline all fought one with another, but the greatest duel of all was between Afghans and Marathas over the inheritance of the Mughal empire. Under Peshwa Baji Rao II, the Marathas had decided to make themselves a north Indian power and to fill the vacuum created by the Mughal decline. The Afghans under a new and powerful ruler, Ahmed Shah Durrani, came to India, as had their forbears and Nadir Shah's Persians, with the more immediate aim of seizing the legendary treasures of the north Indian cities. Ahmed Shah was encouraged in his venture by offers of Indian Muslim aid to prevent the victorious Brahmin idolators sweeping across north India. The Marathas, however, made numerous tactical mistakes. They were laden down with a vast army of camp-followers, many of whom were women intending to go on pilgrimage to the holy places of the north. The Maratha cavalry was virtually wiped out by Ahmed Shah's massed guns on the field of Panipat, north-west of Delhi, a field which had seen the decisive moment of two earlier invasions of India. It is generally believed that the defeat at Panipat ended the Maratha bid for supreme power in eighteenth-century India, so perpetuating a vacuum which the British later filled. But even if they had won, it seems unlikely that the Marathas could have maintained their cohesion. Tensions had already arisen between the Brahmin Peshwas and the Maratha war-leaders.

Ahmed Shah Durrani, the Afghan king and victor, is seen on a chestnut horse to the centre; on the left are his allies in the Muslim alliance, Ahmed Khan Bangash and Hafiz Rehmat Khan, the Rohilla chiefs from the lands north of Delhi, and Shuja-ud-Daulah of Awadh. On the right, the defeated Maratha general, Shadashiva Bhao, is helped from his horse while guns and a cavalry charge pound his lines. The Marathas had been forced to adopt a static, defensive sort of warfare, as this drawing implies. This was their undoing. A Maratha chronicle bewailed: 'Had any of them [Marathas] ever dug entrenchments all around and remained in them this way?... The old Maratha system of war, followed from ancient

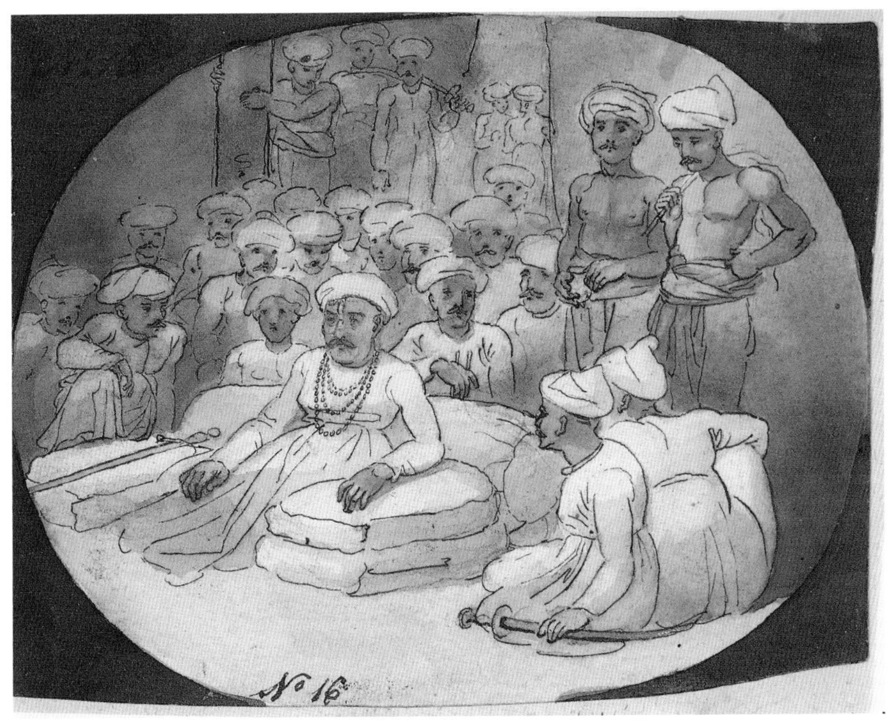

91

times, had been to fight only when the occasion was fair and otherwise to flee' (Raeside 1984, p.95). The rich little town of Panipat, once a key entrepôt on the overland trade route from Delhi to Kabul, Iran and Central Asia, is depicted as the scene of pillage and rapine. C.A.B.

LITERATURE: Archer and Falk 1981, no. 293; Raeside 1984.

EXHIBITION: London, Hayward Gallery, *Exhibition of Indian Drawings*, 1982.

91 Mahadji Sindhia in his Tent

Robert Mabon, *c.*1792
Pen, ink and watercolour, 10 × 13.2 (4 × $5\frac{1}{4}$)
Inscribed on image in ink: *No.16*
Yale Center for British Art, Paul Mellon Collection (B 1977.14.22385)

Mahadji Scindia was one of the last great Maratha war leaders. Though formally subject to the young Peshwa, and often opposed by his powerful minister Nana Phadnis (no.172), Mahadji dominated much of north India in the 1770s and '80s, becoming Deputy Regent of the Mughal empire and protector of the cities of Agra and Delhi. He founded the dynasty that ruled at the town of Gwalior in central India until 1947. His state was an example of the fragmentation of the Maratha confederacy after the defeat at Panipat and also of the tendency of Maratha powers to try to establish themselves in the richer lands of the Gangetic plain, a development which brought them into inevitable conflict with the British.

James Wales arrived in Bombay in 1791 and quickly began to receive commissions for portraits. Later, he met Sir Charles Warre Malet, British Resident at the court of the Maratha Peshwa in Poona, who invited Wales to visit him there. Wales employed Robert Mabon, a former Company soldier with considerable artistic talent, to accompany him. It was on this journey that Wales painted his well-known set of portraits of the Maratha rulers, but it was Mabon who made the preliminary sketches including this work.

A three-quarter length portrait in oils of Mahadji Scindia by James Wales is in the India Office Library (see Archer 1986, p.46, no.61, pl.x). B.A./C.A.B.

LITERATURE: Sen 1928; Archer 1979, p.351, pl. 255.

The French 'threat' to India

The French were late-comers to trade with Asia, but from the 1720s to the 1740s their trade, predominantly at Pondicherry on the Coromandel coast and at Chandernagore in Bengal, grew significantly. As the impact of wars between Britain and France spread around the world in the eighteenth century, it became increasingly difficult for the English and French East India Companies not to become involved, although it was not necessarily in the interest of either to do so. In Bengal a strong Indian government was able to prevent any outbreak of hostilities until 1757. On the Coromandel coast, however, Indian authority was weaker and local pressures escalated into war. The Royal Navy took a number of French ships in 1745, to which the enterprising Governor of Chandernagore, Joseph-François Dupleix (1697–1763), retaliated by taking Madras in 1746.

At the peace signed in Europe in 1748, Madras was restored to the British, but whatever happened in Europe, war continued in India. Dupleix decided to use his troops on behalf of claimants to power in disputed successions in the Carnatic, the coastal area surrounding both Madras and Pondicherry, and in the great state of Hyderabad. As a reward the French were to be granted additions to their territory. Dupleix was seeking extra financial resources, rather than consciously aiming at a French territorial empire, but aggrandisement of the French settlements was unacceptable to the British. They too sought Indian allies and backed their claims against the clients of the French. In 1751 and 1752 British forces under Clive (no. 100) and Lawrence (no.95) successfully struck inland from Madras to Arcot and Trichinopoly. Having failed to win successes that would have justified the cost of his adventures, Dupleix was recalled. A temporary peace was patched up, but in 1756 European war spread to India.

Both sides reinforced the forces of the Companies with increased quantities of royal troops and warships. A French offensive against the settlements failed and after a major defeat at Wandiwash in 1760, the French were blockaded in Pondicherry, which surrendered in 1761.

The main bodies of troops had been deployed on the Coromandel coast, where the major battles were fought. In Hyderabad the French maintained a controlling influence over the ruler's government for some years, until they were forced to withdraw in 1758. In Bengal neutrality ended with a British assault on Chandernagore in 1757, part of the great upheavals of 1756–7, which gave them mastery over the province (see nos.95–105).

At the European peace of 1763 the French were restored to their settlements, but their trade, already in serious difficulties before the wars, did not recover significantly. Even so, the French government remained convinced that the British could be seriously damaged by an offensive in India. During the American War of 1778–83 further close fought battles were instrumental in repelling French expeditionary forces to the Coromandel coast. P.J.M.

LITERATURE: Sen 1958.

92 *Levée du Siége de Pondicherry*

J. F. L. Sergent, 1789
Hand-coloured engraving, 24.5 × 16.5 ($9\frac{1}{2} \times 6\frac{3}{4}$)
India Office Library and Records (P1439)

In retrospect, Joseph-François Dupleix attained the status of a colonial military hero in France similar to that enjoyed by Clive in England. 'Imperial patriotism' and its art was boosted in both nations by the Seven Years War (1756–63) and the War of American Independence (1778–83). In 1748 Dupleix had distinguished himself in defending Pondicherry against the British for 52 days, but as in so many similar incidents, fighting here was brought to an end by the belated news of European peace. By 1789, as this engraving shows, Dupleix was being lamented as a man 'who would have been capable of founding an empire in India.' No. 92 shows Dupleix issuing instructions to the French troops as the siege ends. C.A.B./P.J.M.

92

93 The Surrender of Pondicherry to Sir Eyre Coote

Francis Hayman, early 1760s
Oil on canvas, 121.9 × 152.4 (48 × 60)
Melanesia International Trust Company Limited (Melitco T312)

British magnanimity in victory is the theme of this picture. It is possible that this was a *modello* for a proposed larger picture, perhaps intended as part of the decorative scheme for the annexe to the Rotunda at Vauxhall Gardens. However, unlike Hayman's similar picture of *Lord Clive's meeting with Mir Jaffir* (no.107), this was never worked up into a larger picture. It is possible that the proprietor of Vauxhall Gardens, Jonathan Tyers, felt that a second Indian subject as part of his scheme (see pp.28–33) would create an imbalance in the iconography. More likely, as the war progressed, the events at Pondicherry were overshadowed by events in Canada like the siege of Montreal, which was chosen by Tyers as the subject of one of the other Vauxhall pictures painted by Hayman. Sir Eyre Coote was not entirely excluded from this pantheon at Vauxhall, however, since he appeared in the large allegorical painting of *Britannia distributing laurels to the Victorious Generals*, now lost.

On Clive's recommendation, Coote had been given command of the newly raised 84th Regiment at Madras in October 1759. Within months he had led his troops to victory over the French at both Wandiwash and Arcot. The final reduction of French power in India was achieved by the siege of Pondicherry where, on 16 January 1761, after a blockade lasting eight months, the French surrendered.

Hayman depicts the moment when the victorious Coote, mounted on horseback, is about to receive the sword of the French commander, the Comte de Lally, who gestures towards the humiliated Nawab (?) and his wife/or daughter. Lally is flanked by a corpulent French priest, an image which recalls Hogarth's overfed monk in *Calais Gate, The Roast*

93

Beef of Old England of 1748 (Tate Gallery, London). In the background behind Coote are the ordered ranks of the victorious 84th Regiment, facing the heavily fortified ramparts of Pondicherry. Hayman's rendering of the scene was presumably based on descriptions given to him by those present, although it is very unlikely to be an accurate representation of the event.

Hayman appears to have painted over an earlier composition since a large area of *pentimento* – including a couple of large birds perched on branches – is clearly visible through the two towers to the upper right of the canvas. B.A.

PROVENANCE: Probably acquired or commissioned by Sir Eyre Coote (?); by descent to Michael Coote-Kaye Esq; in store at Queenborough Old Hale, Leicestershire; on loan to National Army Museum.

LITERATURE: Allen 1987, pp.68, 123–4.

94 Ruins of the citadel in Pondicherry after the attack by the British; McClean shown sketching in the foreground. 8th September 1762

John McClean, 1762
Pen, ink and wash on paper, 41.2 × 50 (16 × 19½)
Inscribed on front in ink: *To the Honorable George Pigot Esq. President of the Council & Governor of Fort St.George, this view of the Ruins of the Citadel in Pondicherry is respectfully presented by John McClean, Practioner Engr, Sept 8th 1762*
India Office Library and Records (WD 1293)

The artist went to India as an Ensign in the Madras Engineers in 1762. He was killed at Tingricottah in Madras on 12 February 1768. Drawing, or musing, in the ruins of fallen empires was an evocative theme for the emerging European romantic imagination. B.A.

PROVENANCE: Purchased 14 June 1958.

LITERATURE: Archer 1969, I, p.247, no.1293, pl.5.

Victory in Arcot and Bengal 1752–65

Since the time of Sir Josiah Child (no.65) some Company servants had harboured plans for territorial conquest in India, but the Directors had been cautious. After 1748 the Anglo-French war and skirmishes with the newly-powerful French East India Company in the subcontinent provided the justification and military means for territorial acquisitions. But the politics of Indian states were the prime cause for the expansion of the British empire.

With the death of the Nizam of Hyderabad in 1748 (see no.84) a further struggle over succession erupted in south India, and the British and French supported rival claimants. Ultimately, it was the British and their client, the Nawab of the Carnatic, who triumphed. However, Robert Clive, the most successful commander in this southern war, was soon required in Bengal. Here the young Nawab, Siraj-ud-Daulah, was trying to assert his authority over interests which had gradually been eroding the state's power: the English East India Company, cartels of Indian financiers and regional landholders. A clash with the company led to the Nawab's occupation of Calcutta and the famous incident of the Black Hole. Clive's expeditionary force recaptured Calcutta in January 1757, and on 23 June 1757 defeated the Nawab's armies at the Battle of Plassey. Clive had done a secret deal with the Nawab's internal enemies, with Mir Jafar, his dissident commander-in-chief and the Indian financiers who feared for their property.

The commercial and political power of the Company proved too corrosive for the Bengal state. After a war with their erstwhile client, Nawab Mir Kasim, in 1763, the British took possession of the revenue management (*diwani*) of Bengal from the Mughal emperor in 1765. The British Indian empire had truly begun. The new imperial themes were mirrored in the vogue for dramatic paintings of historical events and personages which spread from Britain and North America to the East during the Seven Years War.

C.A.B.

LITERATURE: Spear 1975; Marshall 1988, pp. 70–92.

95 Stringer Lawrence (1697–1775)

Thomas Gainsborough, *c.* 1774–5
Oil on canvas, 75.9 × 62.6 ($29\frac{9}{10}$ × $24\frac{3}{5}$)
National Portrait Gallery, London (777)

Lawrence was an officer in the regular army who was recruited by the East India Company in 1748 to take charge of its forces opposing the French on the Coromandel coast. The Company had chosen wisely: for the next ten years or so Lawrence was largely responsible for the success of the Company's resistance to the French. During that period he played a large part in the reorganization of the East India Company's forces into an effective army.

In 1748 the Company's troops consisted of companies of Europeans employed on garrison duty and Indian soldiers who were essentially auxiliaries, serving in their own formations under their own commanders. By the time Lawrence left India, the Company had an army at Madras capable of operating

95

94

effectively far inland. The Europeans had been grouped into a regiment and the Indians into new sepoy regiments under European officers, armed and trained to the highest European standards.

As an operational commander, Lawrence distinguished himself in the campaign around Trichinopoly in 1752 (see no.96), but generously allowed Clive much of the credit, and again in the defence of Madras between 1758 and 1759. Clive began his military career under Lawrence and acknowledged that he owed much to him; the East India Company erected a monument to him in Westminster Abbey.

This portrait was probably painted *c.* 1774–5, many years after Lawrence's return from India in 1759 and not long

96

before his death. For details of the many portraits of Lawrence see Kerslake 1977.

B.A./P.J.M.

PROVENANCE: (probably) Robert Palk, Governor of Madras 1763–7, 1st Baron Haldon 1782 (Stringer Lawrence was godfather to Palk's son); anon. sale (Lady Haldon), Christie's, 29 July 1887 (172); presented to National Portrait Gallery in 1888 by Colonel (afterwards Sir Henry) Yule, a member of the Council of India.

LITERATURE: Waterhouse 1958, p.78 (432); Kerslake 1977, I, pp.164–5, II, pl.457.

96 The Rock at Trichinopoly, Madras, with the barracks

Francis Swain Ward, *c.* 1770
Oil on canvas, 71 × 109.5 (28 × 43)
India Office Library and Records (F24)

Dupleix (no.92), Governor of the French settlement of Pondicherry, and his lieutenant, Bussy, had become protectors of Salabat Jang, Nizam of Hyder abad and successor of Asaf Jah (no.84) who had died in 1748. The Nizam and his French allies tried to mop up their factional opponents, including Muhammed Ali Wallajah (no.143), claimant to the province of the Carnatic. The French and Salabat Jang supported instead Chanda Sahib, a member of the famous Nevayat family who had supplied governors, administrators and soldiers to the Carnatic earlier in the century. But Muhammed Ali made two key moves which ensured his ultimate success in becoming Nawab of the Carnatic (sometimes called Nawab of Arcot, after the major town in his domains). First, he allied himself with the British who were aghast at the new lease of life which Dupleix had given their French rivals. Secondly, he seized the great rock fortress at Trichinopoly which dominated the valley of the river Kavery and controlled the irrigation channels which watered the paddy lands of Trichinopoly and Tanjore. The rock had been a place of human settlement from prehistoric times. In the early centuries of the Christian era rock-hewn Pandya temples were constructed here and it became a sacred place as well as a fortress for both Hindu and Muslim dynasties.

The British succoured Muhammed Ali in the Trichinopoly fortress during 1750 and 1751. Robert Clive, a bright young commander of the Company's Madras army, was able to defeat the French and their allies in a series of skirmishes around the fortress of Arcot. Then he and his experienced senior, Major Stringer Lawrence (no.95), moved against Trichinopoly, raised the siege and outmanoeuvred the French General Law. Chanda Sahib, the French protégé and claimant to the Nawabi of the Carnatic, was betrayed and beheaded in the shadow of the great rock. His grave still exists, recently embellished by a pious Frenchman. By this stroke, the British denied the French dominance in south India and paved the way for their own authority which was fully established by the time of the Peace of Paris between Britain and France in 1763.

Francis Swain Ward (1736–1805) trained as an artist but joined the Madras Army of the East India Company, sailing for India in 1757. Although promoted to Lieutenant in 1763, he resigned a year later in controversial circumstances when passed over for further advancement in the army. Returning to London he became for a time Secretary of the Incorporated Society of Artists and exhibited at the annual exhibitions of that body between 1768 and 1773. Failing to make a decent living he persuaded the East India Company to reinstate him as a Captain, and on his appointment presented them with ten landscapes of India of which this is one. These were almost certainly all done in England, based on sketches made by the artist in India before 1764. Ward was rewarded with 200 guineas by the Company and a further sum of 1,000 pagodas when he returned to Madras.

B.A./C.A.B.

PROVENANCE: Presented by the artist to the East India Company in 1773.

LITERATURE: Harcourt 1910, ill.; Foster 1924, p.12, no.24; Spear 1975; Archer 1986, p.78, no.107.

97 Three officers with the Rock of Trichinopoly in the background (possibly the surrender of the French Commander Law to Major Stringer Lawrence)†

Attributed to Edward Penny, *c.*1760s
Oil on canvas, 96.5 × 143.5 (38 × 56½)
Victoria Memorial Hall, Calcutta (R2183)

This picture has been implausibly attributed for many years to Thomas Daniell but can be attributed with confidence on stylistic grounds to Edward Penny. It is thereby one of the first Indian subjects painted by a British artist. It was probably painted *c.*1760, soon after Lawrence's return to England in 1759 and at about the same time as Francis Hayman's pictures of Clive and Coote (see nos.107, 108).

It was first suggested by Thomas Sutton that the scene represented here is the surrender of the French under Law to Major Stringer Lawrence at Pondicherry in 1752. Since one of the officers wears the blue coat of the French army this seems to be a likely interpretation of the subject.

B.A.

PROVENANCE: Mrs George Lyell, by whom presented in December 1932 to present owners.

LITERATURE: Sutton 1954, p.22, n.32.

98 John Zephaniah Holwell, Governor of Bengal

Unknown artist, 1760
Platinotype print, 53.5 × 43.8 ($21\frac{1}{10}$ × $17\frac{1}{5}$)
India Office Library and Records (P587)

In 1756 Alivardi Khan was succeeded as Nawab of Bengal by his grandson, Siraj-ud-Daulah. With the new reign, conflict broke out between the Nawab's government and the East India Company. The potential for conflict had existed for some time, as growing British trade and the rise of Calcutta posed a serious challenge to the authority of the Nawab. Siraj-ud-Daulah forced the issue by making demands on the Company,

98

which were rejected. An attack on Calcutta followed. The senior Company servants abandoned their posts during the siege, leaving John Zephaniah Holwell in command. He surrendered to the Nawab's troops and with other European prisoners spent the night of 20 June 1756 in the Black Hole.

After his release, Holwell returned briefly to Britain, where he published his account of the event (no.99). Back in Bengal in 1758, he was for a short time temporary Governor until he left India for good in 1760. During his brief administration he was largely responsible for engineering the change of Nawab from Mir Jafar to Mir Kasim (see no.112). In retirement in Britain he wrote extensively: polemical works about his Indian career and a study of Hinduism which enjoyed something of a vogue in Britain and Europe before genuine Sanskrit texts became available. Holwell seems to have been an intelligent man and was a vigorous writer, especially in advertising his own merits, but he aroused dislike and mistrust in most of his contemporaries.

P.J.M.

99 *A Genuine Narrative of the Deplorable Deaths of the English Gentlemen and others who were suffocated in the Black Hole*, London, 1758

Bound book, 20.5 × 27 (8 × 10$\frac{6}{10}$)
The British Library Board (1093.e.59)

On his way back to Britain in 1757 Holwell (see no.98) wrote a short account of his experiences on the night of 20 June 1756 in the Black Hole. He described how 146 people had been crammed into a space that he estimated to be about eighteen feet square. He believed that 123 of the 146 were dead by the morning and listed about half of their names. Holwell's *Genuine Narrative* evidently appealed to the eighteenth-century taste for the horrific and attracted much attention. It was frequently reprinted.

In time interest in the story of the Black Hole seems to have waned. A monument which Holwell put up in Calcutta in memory of the victims was allowed to fall into disrepair and was taken down in 1821. By the end of the nineteenth century, however, the events that had launched British rule in India were attracting renewed attention, this time with strong political overtones. With what seems to have been a genuine concern for restoring the past, the Viceroy, Lord Curzon (see no. 480), insisted that the Holwell monument should be repaired. With characteristic insensitivity, he brushed off warnings from the India Council in London against 'parading our disasters and the consequences that ensued' (Ronaldshay 1928, II, p.158). On 19 December 1902 Curzon unveiled his new Holwell memorial with a speech in which he paid tribute to the 'martyr band' (Raleigh 1906, pp. 442–8). This gesture was not well received by nationalist opinion in Calcutta. In 1915 an article in an impeccably scholarly journal called *Bengal Past and Present* suggested that Holwell's account of the Black Hole was a 'hoax' and that most of those whom he listed as having died there had in fact been killed in battle in the siege of Calcutta (Little 1915, pp.75–104). Holwell's mendacity became an article of faith in nationalist circles until, in 1940, Subhas Chandra Bose organized a *satyagraha*, or non-violent strike, against Curzon's monument. Bose called it an 'unwarrantable stain' on the memory of Siraj-ud-Daulah as well as 'a symbol of our slavery and humiliation' (Bose 1962, p.824). The monument was tactfully removed to a Christian churchyard. A modern investigation suggests that less than half the number Holwell claimed to have been in the Black Hole were actually there: 64 people, of whom 21 survived (Gupta 1966, p.78).

P.J.M.

100 Robert, 1st Baron Clive (1725–1774)

Nathaniel Dance *c.* 1770
Oil on canvas, 127 × 101.6 (50 × 40)
The Clive Museum, Powis Castle (H.M. Treasury and the National Trust) (215)

Robert Clive was the son of a Shropshire country gentleman. He was appointed to the East India Company's civil service at Madras in 1743, a short time before the outbreak of war on the Coromandel coast. In 1747, being said to be 'of a martial disposition', he transferred to the military service. He distinguished himself in 1751 in command of an attack on the fort of Arcot and in withstanding a prolonged siege. In 1753 he returned to Britain with a considerable reputation and was sent back to India in 1755 as the military commander of an expedition that was to destroy the west coast fortress base at Gheria, from which raids were launched against British shipping. Victorious at Gheria, the expedition went on to Madras. There Clive was put in charge of the land forces that were being sent up to Bengal when Calcutta fell to Siraj-ud-Daulah in June 1756.

In Bengal Clive was to win fame and an immense fortune. He recovered Calcutta in January 1757 and forced Siraj-ud-Daulah to agree to a restoration of the Company's trade and settlements. Within a few months Clive became aware of yet higher stakes for which to play. The Nawab had antagonized powerful interests within Bengal (see no.104), who wished to see him deposed and were prepared to pay lavishly for the British army to be used for the purpose. Clive took the gamble of marching his army up to Plassey, where the conspirators ensured the Nawab's defeat and his death.

In this painting by Nathaniel Dance Clive wears the Order of the Bath and behind him is a battle scene, presumably intended to represent Plassey. At least eight copies or versions of this work are known.

P.J.M./B.A.

PROVENANCE: Painted for Clive; by family descent; H.M. Treasury from 1963.

LITERATURE: Steegman 1957–62, I, p.266, no.48; Goodreau 1973, pp.303–4; The National Trust, *Powis Castle, Powys*, p.9, n.4.

EXHIBITIONS: London, *National Portrait Exhibition*, 1866–8; Milan, Palazzo Reale, 1975; Kenwood, Iveagh Bequest, *Nathaniel Dance 1735–1811*, 1977 (32).

101 Margaret, Lady Clive

Attributed to Nathaniel Dance, 1772–3
Oil on canvas, 127 × 101.6 (50 × 40)
The Clive Museum, Powis Castle (H.M. Treasury and the National Trust) (P/5)

Margaret née Maskelyne married Robert Clive (no.100) on 15 March 1753 at Madras. Sister of Clive's friend Edmund Maskelyne, a writer for the Company in Madras and later his aide-de-camp, Margaret went to India in 1752 to join several members of her family already in the East. She married Robert Clive in St Mary's Church, Madras, and later bore him two sons. She was a solid support for him in his later days when he was dogged by nervous problems and by political controversy. B.A./C.A.B.

PROVENANCE: Painted for Clive; by family descent; H.M. Treasury from 1963.

LITERATURE: As no.129 except Steegman 1957, no.50; Goodreau 1973, p.303.

EXHIBITION: Kenwood, Iveagh Bequest, *Nathaniel Dance 1735–1811*, 1977.

102

102 Admiral Charles Watson (1714–57)

Edward Fisher after Thomas Hudson
Mezzotint engraving, 39.3 × 29 ($15\frac{3}{10} \times 10\frac{4}{5}$)
India Office Library and Records (P673)

Watson exemplified the naval dominance of the British in Indian waters which was such a critical aspect of the Company's overall success. In 1756, Watson planned and executed an attack on the fort of Gheria on the western Indian coast, which had become a base for the armed Maratha ships that harassed British sea lanes. Clive had his first experience of 'joint operations' on the expedition, important preparation for the following year when Clive and Watson were ordered to co-operate in the joint action to recapture Calcutta from Siraj-ud-Daulah. The expedition consisted of a few ships of the line and one frigate, 800 Europeans and 1,500 Indians. Watson's skilful seamanship was a major reason for the rapid recapture of the city in January 1757.

Edward Fisher's mezzotint is based on the full-length portrait by Thomas Hudson in the Victoria Memorial Hall, Calcutta. In the Calcutta picture Watson is shown with his son Charles, and according to E. Miles (see Literature) it may have been painted in or after 1760, the year the boy was created baronet in recognition of his father's achievements. In no.102 the shadow of the boy's figure has been retained, even though he is not actually present. C.A.B./B.A.

PROVENANCE: Presented by Sir William Foster, April 1905.

LITERATURE: Smith 1883, II, p.507, no.59; Foster 1924, p.30, no.79; Miles 1976, II, pp.192–3, ill.pl.250.

103 The Ghost of Omichund

1773
Engraving, 13.9 × 8.9 ($5\frac{1}{2} \times 3\frac{1}{2}$)
The Trustees of the British Museum, Department of Prints and Drawings (Political Satires no. 5101)

The Punjabi Omichund (d.1758) was one of a number of merchants from other parts of India who were drawn to Bengal in the first half of the eighteenth century. He became extremely rich doing business with the Nawabs of Bengal and with the British, at the fringe of whose settlement at Calcutta he lived in great state. When the Nawab attacked Calcutta in 1756, the British suspected Omichund's loyalty, but, like most Bengal notables, he turned against Siraj-ud-Daulah and joined in the plots against him. He became the go-between for the British with Mir Jafar on the eve of the Battle of Plassey.

For his services Omichund expected to be paid handsomely. The British regarded his terms as extortionate, but were afraid to alienate him at a time when he could betray the plot. They therefore resorted to what Clive later called 'art and policy, warrantable in defeating the purposes of such a villain' (Hill 1905, III, p.315). A false treaty with Mir Jafar was fabricated, guaranteeing

103

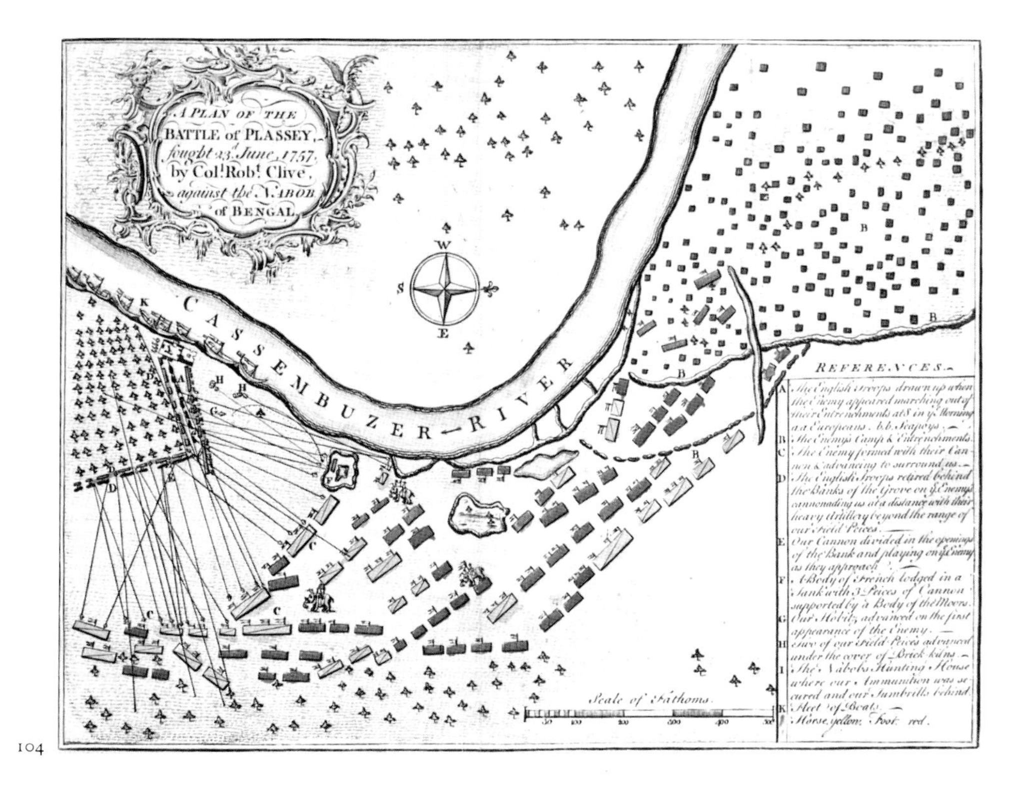

104

Omichund his reward. When the high-minded Admiral Watson (no.102) of the British naval squadron refused to be a party to the fraud, others appended his signature for him. The news that he had been duped was said to have driven Omichund insane and to an early death. The story of insanity seems to be false, but the Omichund episode showed Clive in a very discreditable light. P.J.M.

PROVENANCE: Published in *Westminster Magazine*, January 1773, i.67.

LITERATURE: George 1935, V, pp. 110–11; Hill 1905; Sinha 1956–62, I, p 244; Spear 1975, III, p. 90.

104 Plan of the Battle of Plassey, fought 23 June 1757 by Col. Robert Clive, against the Nabob of Bengal

1760
Engraving 16 × 24 ($6\frac{1}{5} \times 9\frac{4}{5}$)
India Office Library and Records (P1437)

The Battle of Plassey on 23 June 1757 has traditionally been cited as the beginning of British territorial empire in India. Against this it can be argued that the battle was little more than a skirmish, that some kind of British economic 'take-over' of Bengal had begun long before and that much more serious battles, like that at Buxar in 1764, lay ahead. While these points are substantially true, the Battle of Plassey still deserves much of its fame. Contemporaries rightly described it as bringing about a 'revolution', which established British political mastery over the Nawabs of Bengal. After 1757 the complete collapse of the Nawabs was to follow very quickly, whatever the British may have intended.

Having recovered Calcutta from Siraj-ud-Daulah in 1757 (see no.107), Clive was drawn into a further adventure by news that a powerful conspiracy had been formed against the Nawab involving the court nobility, bankers and merchants and the large *zamindars*. Mir Jafar, a prominent military leader, emerged as the Nawab's rival. He promised valuable concessions to the Company and huge rewards to individuals. A treaty was signed and the army marched to Plassey. The outcome was only in doubt so long as those disaffected to the Nawab did not show their hand. Once they had done so, Siraj's forces disintegrated with little bloodshed. He was left to the mercy of the conspirators, who killed him. P.J.M.

LITERATURE: *The London Magazine*, January 1760, ill.

EXHIBITION: London, The British Library, *Calcutta*, 1990.

105(i) Elephant armour

Mughal, early 17th century
Weight 118 kg (originally *c.* 159 kg)
Royal Armouries, H. M. Tower of London (XXVI.102.A)

PROVENANCE: Acquired in India between 1798 and 1800 by Lady Clive, wife of Edward, 2nd Lord Clive; brought back to England, 1801, and displayed at Powis Castle in the Elephant Room; transferred to the Tower Armouries in 1952 in lieu of death duties.

LITERATURE: 'List of items for transport back to England', Powis MS *c.* 1801; Evans 1809, p.879; Robinson 1967, pp.120–1; Archer, Rowell and Skelton 1987, pp.29,72.

105(ii) Armour of mail and plate (*zirah bagtar*)

Mughal, 17th century
Royal Armouries, H. M. Tower of London (XXXVI.23A)

105(iii) Helmet of mail and plate (*kulah zirah*)

Mughal, early 17th century
Height 67.5 ($26\frac{1}{2}$)
Royal Armouries, H. M. Tower of London (XXVI.16A)

105

105(iv) Elephant-goad (*ankus*)

Lahore, 19th century
Royal Armouries, H. M. Tower of London (XXVI.6M)

Elephants were used as shock troops in India from early historic times, and featured largely in the Mughal armies of the sixteenth and early seventeenth centuries. They were occasionally provided with armour and this example seems to be a unique survivor of that tradition.

The armour in its present state lacks the front and rear panels of the three, on the right side. It is displayed with its rear left panel at the front right purely for visual effect. The armour was also provided with swords of iron which were attached to the sawn-off tusks of the elephant; these survive in the collection at Powis Castle.

The *mahout* wears armour of mail and plate of contemporary Mughal style, and carries an elephant-goad (*ankus*) for guiding his mount. The helmet has an early provenance, having formed part of the 'Norman Crusader' figure which came from Tong Castle in Shropshire about 1780. T.R.

106 Silver medal commemorating Lord Clive's victory at Plassey

John Van Noost the Younger and 'C.G.', 1766
Silver, diameter 4.4 ($1\frac{3}{4}$)
Obv: *ROBERT. CLIVE. BARON. OF. PLASSEY*, signed with initials *I.U.[V].N.F.*
Rev: *1757.|Feb. 5 NABO|BS.|CAMP.| DESTRO|YED|JUNE.23| VICTORI|OUS. AT.|PLASSEY. 1765| ESTABLISH|ED. PEACE.| IN.BENGAL.|AND.MADE.| OMRA. 58 OF. THE.|EMPIRE;* inside the double rim lettered: *HONOUR. THE.|REWARD. OF. MERIT*, and below rule, *ANNO 1766|CG*
National Portrait Gallery, London (1688)

PROVENANCE: Purchased from Spink & Son, December 1912.

LITERATURE: Grant 1936–7; Little and Kahrl 1963; Kerslake 1977, p.59, ill. pls. 162,163.

107 Lord Clive meeting Mir Jafar, Nawab of Murshidabad, after the Battle of Plassey

Francis Hayman, *c.* 1761–2
Oil on canvas, 101.6 × 127 (40 × 50)
Inscribed lower left: *Lord Clive and the Nabob of Arcot 25th June 1757 Battle of Plassey*
National Portrait Gallery, London (5263)

Although described in 1979 as 'English School *c.* 1795–1800' and previously wrongly ascribed to Mather Brown, this is a preliminary design for a much larger painting of the subject (now lost) which was placed in the annexe to the Rotunda at Vauxhall Gardens in 1762, during the Seven Years War. It was identified on the basis of its close correspondence to a lengthy description of the larger picture published in 1762 (quoted in Allen 1987) when the picture appeared for sale in 1979. In an earlier, and much cruder, preliminary sketch (Fig. 11) Hayman had introduced a number of Indian servants carrying gold vessels filled with bullion on their heads. These absurdly inaccurate figures, who looked more like Egyptians, were removed in favour of Mir Jafar's son and a particularly inept elephant was much improved for this version.

Despite its inaccuracies Hayman's picture, or at least the lost larger version, which was seen by the thousands of visitors who flocked to Vauxhall Gardens, was one of the very earliest depictions of Anglo-Indian history. Painted within five years of the event and before the conclusion of the Seven Years War, it was amongst the first pictures of its kind to rouse the public spirit.

The incident which gave rise to this painting was a consequence of the growing belief of Clive and others in Bengal that the cessation of hostilities with Siraj-ud-Daulah during the first half of 1757 would not last. Clive invoked the 'prime law of self-preservation' to plot with Siraj's commander Mir Jafar and the financial magnate Jagat Seth to overthrow the Nawab. Watts concluded a treaty with

107

Mir Jafar and the Nawab was defeated at Plassey. Mir Jafar was to become Nawab, but he was to assign certain lands and treasures to the English Company; he was also bound to prevent the 'resettlement of the French in these Provinces'. Clive actually met Mir Jafar two days after the battle. He wrote: 'Next morning he [Mir Jafar] returned my visit, when after a good deal of discourse on the situation of his affairs, I recommended him to consult Juggutseat [the banker] on all occasions, who as a man of sense and by far of the greatest property among all his subjects, would give him the best advice for settling the kingdom in peace and security ... solemn engagements were then entered into by the three parties for a strict union and mutual support of each others interests' (Sinha 1957, pp. 232–4). In this way an armed European trading Company plotted with a rebellious Muslim commander and the Bengali financial community to put the British on their road to territorial power in India. C.A.B./B.A./P.J.M.

PROVENANCE: Col. John Harvey, Biggleswade; Maharaja Bahadur Sir Prodyt Coomar Tagore, Calcutta; private collection; anon. sale, Christie's, 22 June 1979 (162) as 'English School *c.* 1795'; purchased 1979.

LITERATURE: Foster 1931, p.234; *Bengal Past and Present*, XLIV, 1932, ill. p.182; Sinha 1957 pp. 226–34; *The Times*, 4 April 1959; Spear 1975; Archer 1979, p.419, pl.333; National Art-Collections Fund, *Annual Report*, 1979, p.28; National Art-Collections Fund, *Newsletter*, Christmas 1979, p.18; Allen 1987, pp.68–9, fig.40.

EXHIBITIONS: New Haven, Yale Center for British Art and Kenwood, The Iveagh Bequest, *Francis Hayman*, 1987 (49).

108

108 General Sir Eyre Coote (1726–1783)

Henry Morland, *c.* 1763
Oil on canvas, 74.9 × 61.6 ($29\frac{1}{2} \times 24\frac{1}{4}$)
National Portrait Gallery, London (124)

Coote (see no. 92) was a member of the Protestant Irish gentry who provided so many of British India's great soldiers. Unlike the British army before the Napoleonic Wars, the East India Company also recruited Irish Roman Catholics, though their representation among officers was not strong. Coote had played a major part in the defeat of the French and their allies during 1760 and 1761. His most glorious campaign, however, was his last against Haidar Ali and Tipu Sultan from 1782 to 1783, when he virtually saved the Madras Presidency from destruction. Despite age and infirmity and the tortuous system of 'dual government' which pitted the officials of the Nawab of Arcot against those of the Company, Coote managed to mount a credible defence at a time when the powerful Mysore army had penetrated deep into the southern Presidency. Coote is displayed in the typical straightforward style of British military portraits, the painting of which became a major industry during the Seven Years War. The artist has captured his plain and rugged personality. C.A.B./B.A.

PROVENANCE: Purchased 1861.

LITERATURE: Wilson 1982, pp.97–103.

109 Robert Orme (1728–1801)

Joseph Nollekens, 1774
Plaster, height 59 (23)
India Office Library and Records (F406)

Robert Orme went to Calcutta in 1742 for a mercantile firm and later became a writer with the Company. He was active in private trade, having a partnership with Clive, and was a member of the Madras Council from 1754 to 1758 when his Indian career ended with charges of extortion. He supported Clive's appointment to Bengal, but their relationship cooled after Plassey. He returned to England and published the first volume of his famous *History of the Military*

109

Transactions of the British Nation in Indostan from the year 1745 in 1763. He was appointed official historian to the Company in 1769. His works, which were heavily mined by Macaulay at a later period, attempted to chronicle the Company's rise to power through a meticulous day-by-day account.

C.A.B./B.A.

PROVENANCE: Presented by John Roberts, 14 April 1801.

LITERATURE: Orme 1805, ill. frontispiece (engraving); Archer 1986, p.100, ill.pl. XXX.

110 Robert Clive to Warren Hastings, 8 October 1758

Autograph manuscript, 24 × 19 (9½ × 7½)
The British Library Board (Add MS. 29131, f.29)

Here Clive writes to Warren Hastings telling him to pay Mir Jafar a *lakh* (i.e. 100,000 rupees). This communication between the founder of British India and the man regarded as its consolidator took place at a time when Clive was trying to strengthen his position in Bengal while warfare with the French was still continuing in both north and south. Mir Jafar had entered into a treaty with the British before Plassey, but now he was disillusioned both by the constant pressure on the revenues of Bengal exerted by the Company, which was trying to finance its wars, and by Company servants attempting to make private fortunes. At one point, Mir Jafar was suspected of making alliances with the Marathas, a desperate measure indeed. Warren Hastings was at this time the Company's agent at the Nawab's capital, Murshidabad, and this letter was part of an immense correspondence about the intricate financial relations between Nawab and Company. Mir Jafar ultimately proved too independent for the Company. In 1760 he was replaced by the initially more malleable Mir Kasim, and he died in 1765. C.A.B.

LITERATURE: Spear 1975, pp.97–100.

111 Lord Clive (1725–1774) receiving from the Nawab of Bengal [*sic*] the grant of the sum of money which was later used to establish the charity known as 'Lord Clive's Fund' for helping disabled soldiers as well as widows of those dying in the Company's Service

Edward Penny, 1772
Oil on canvas, 137 × 122 (54 × 48)
India Office Library and Records (F91)

In this painting Clive is receiving Mir Jafar's grant from his son Nawab Najim-ud-Daulah (?), while pointing to a group of destitute soldiers.

The Court Minutes of the East India Company for 3 February 1773 record a vote for £150 to be paid to Penny for this picture, but the artist appears to have considered the sum insufficient and replied accordingly. Penny's plea led to him being paid a further £60, making a total payment of 200 guineas.

Penny had been appointed Professor of Painting at the newly established Royal Academy in 1768, and when this picture was exhibited at the Academy's exhibition in 1772 the critic of the *Morning Chronicle* (see Literature) noted that while 'want and disease in the faces of the invalids, are likewise very powerfully marked' the figure of Lord Clive is 'neither expressive of *humanity* or *dignity*, at the same time 'tis reckoned an excellent likeness'. *The Middlesex Journal* commented on the soldiers being 'excellent pictures of distress'.

Penny's reputation as a history painter rested on the success of similar pictures showing the distressed being relieved like *The Marquis of Granby relieving a Sick Soldier*, a version of which was exhibited at the Society of Artists in 1765, and *The*

111

Generous Behaviour of the Chevalier Bayard, exhibited in 1768. With the Parliamentary enquiry of 1772–3 into Clive's amassment of his fortune, it is possible that the East India Company's decision to commission the painting and its public exhibition were intended to bolster Clive's reputation. B.A./C.A.B.

PROVENANCE: Commissioned by East India Company, for Military Fund Office, 1772.

EXHIBITIONS: Sydney and Melbourne, *British Painting 1600–1800*, 1977–8; London, The British Library, *Calcutta*, 1990.

112 Lord Clive receiving from the Mogul the Grant of the Duanney (*Diwani*)

Benjamin West, *c.*1795
Oil on canvas, *c.* 292 × 457 (115 × 180)
The Earl of Plymouth

This painting captures one of the most critical incidents in the Company's rise to power in India, one recognised as such only some time after the event. It represents the Treaty of Allahabad, signed on 12 August 1765, when the Mughal Emperor appointed the East India Company his *diwan* (or chief financial manager) of the provinces of Bengal, Bihar and Orissa. For after the destruction of Mir Kasim the Company had no option but to assume direct rule. The grant ultimately impelled the British to institute under Lord Cornwallis (no.152) a system of government and revenue collection at district level which largely excluded Indian agency. But though the British used the grant of the *diwani* as a legal basis for much of their subsequent activity in India, they did not yet aspire to the ultimate sovereignty. Until 1858 this was held by the Mughal Emperor, however degraded his real power.

As Von Erffa and Staley have recently pointed out (see Literature), this is not an accurate reconstruction of the event, which actually took place in Clive's tent rather than in the much grander setting shown here. In reality an armchair placed on Clive's dining table served as a throne! A drawing in the British Museum, signed and dated 1774, shows figures in European and Indian dress meeting in a tent and may be an earlier and more historically accurate record of the event. A published key to the picture identifies six Englishmen in addition to Lord Clive: General John Carnac, Captain Archibald Swinton, Major Pearson, Sir Henry Strachey, Thomas Kelsall and Anselm Beaumont. Mark Bence-Jones (see Literature) claims that two of them, Kelsall and Beaumont, were not with Clive at Allahabad in 1765.

Around 1771 Clive began to seek West's advice about buying Old Masters and he commissioned from West a series of large canvasses depicting the most important events from his Indian career to decorate the Eating Room at Claremont, the house in Surrey that he purchased in 1769. An interesting drawing by Capability Brown, the architect of Claremont, shows a design for one of the walls of the room with this picture in place. Other drawings suggest that there would have been a second, equally large, painting on the opposite wall plus

112

other pictures (see Literature: Stroud 1950). The scheme was abandoned as a result of Clive's suicide in 1774 and this picture seems to have been the only one of West's paintings for Claremont that was begun, although West may have left it uncompleted until shortly before its exhibition at the Royal Academy in 1795. One review of the exhibition stated that the picture had 'long been upon his hands, though touched up for the present exhibition'.

Another slightly smaller but much later version, exhibited at the Royal Academy in 1818, was presented to the East India Company by the 1st Earl of Powis in 1820 (Von Erffa and Staley 1986, no.103). C.A.B./B.A.

PROVENANCE: Commissioned by 1st Baron Clive; by family descent to the present owner.

LITERATURE: *Morning Chronicle*, 6 May 1795; *Public Characters of 1805*, 1805, p.563; *La Belle Assemblée or Bell's Court and Fashionable Magazine*, IV, 1808, supplement, p.15; Galt 1820, appendix II, p.222; Stroud 1950, p.63, fig.6; Croft-Murray 1962, 1970, II, pp.69, 291; Bence-Jones 1971, p.1448; Farington 1978–84, II, pp.331–2 (28,29 April 1795) and XV, pp.5162–3 (25 February 1818); Dillenberger 1977, p.158; Von Erffa and Staley 1986, pp.216–7, no. 101; Haslam 1990, p.157.

EXHIBITION: London, Royal Academy, 1795 (28).

The East India Company Arms

113 Troops of the Bengal Army

Unknown native Company artist, *c.*1785
Watercolour, 23.5 × 43 ($9\frac{1}{4}$ × 17)
Lent by permission of the Director, National Army Museum, London SW3 4HT (8003–22)

At Plassey in 1757 there was a single Indian battalion trained in the European manner and raised in Calcutta called the Lal Paltan, or Red Battalion. Influenced perhaps by Scottish and Irish models, the Company decided in the aftermath of Plassey to build up an army of high caste peasant soldiers in preference to the previous practice of enlisting members of the Mughal military classes. Such peasant soldiers could be taught to regard the Company as their sole protector and employer and could be duly rewarded with grants of land and other privileges following a relatively lucrative service. The decision was made to give them a suitably modified European-style uniform rather than to continue with Mughal-style dress (a tactic employed, for instance, in irregular units such as Skinner's Horse; nos.180–81). Some of the recruits came from the districts of Bengal proper, but, increasingly, they were drawn from the Benares region and from southern Awadh where the higher castes of whole villages soon developed a tradition of serving in the Company's army. Most of these men were from rural Bhumihar (landholding) Brahmin or Rajput families, and the wealth and prestige acquired by service safeguarded their status in the villages, where their landholdings were shrinking as a result of constant partition. Called 'Purbiyas' or 'easterners' by the Mughals, these Hindu soldiers formed the backbone of the Company's army until 1857, when the vast majority mutinied, believing that both their religion and status were imperilled by military reform.

113

No.113 shows a *golandar* ('ball-man') of the Bengal Artillery, in blue a sepoy of the Bengal Native Infantry and a *subahdar* (Indian officer) of the Governor-General's Bodyguard. C.A.B./S.A.

PROVENANCE: Purchased from Childs Gallery.

LITERATURE: Mollo 1981, pp.13–14.

114

114 One of the Native Cavalry in the Service of the English (Sowar of Bengal)

Unknown native artist, *c.* 1780
Watercolour, 17 × 21 ($6\frac{7}{10}$ x $8\frac{3}{10}$)
Lent by permission of the Director, National Army Museum, London SW3 4HT (6404–18)

The cavalry wing of the Company's army remained quite weak until it encountered Indian enemies which had powerful light cavalry, such as the Marathas and Mysores. Thereafter more attention was paid to recruitment and training and to horse breeding. Arab stallions were brought from Europe, the Middle East and southern Africa and government breeding farms were established. The Company also paid close attention to the horse trade and to horse fairs, hoping to control the flow of animals to its potential enemies. Most of the Company's Bengal Cavalry had originated in Awadh, raised under the terms of the subsidiary alliance of 1765, but then converted into the Company's regiments. C.A.B.

PROVENANCE: Bequeathed by Major V.C.P. Hodson.

LITERATURE: Mollo 1981, pp.14–15; Alavi 1990 (forthcoming).

115

115 Model of Fort William

Colonel Wood, *c.* 1775
Ivory, *c.* 24 × 16 ($9\frac{1}{2}$ × $6\frac{3}{10}$)
The Royal Artillery Historical Trust (Class XXVI/3)

The fortification of Fort William, the seat of British power, was greatly enhanced after the Maratha invasions of Bengal in the 1740s. After Siraj-ud-Daulah's occupation of the citadel in 1756, a huge new fort was built at a cost of £2 million. Eighteenth-century French and British military engineering greatly improved upon the defensive capabilities of Mughal-style fortresses. Among Indian rulers, the Mysore sultans were the most single-minded in introducing new concepts of fortification.

C.A.B.

116 An Officer of the Madras Army, said to be Captain George Jolland

Attributed to Tilly Kettle, *c.* 1770
Oil on canvas, 75 × 61 ($29\frac{1}{2}$ × 24)
Lent by permission of the Director, National Army Museum, London SW3 4HT (5710–44)

This is probably one of the earliest portraits painted by Tilly Kettle when he reached Madras. It is typical of contemporary British military portraits, though the uniform of green and red facings is unusual. The regiment was created in 1759 in the face of the French threat to Madras. Until that date the Presidency Army was composed of about 3,000 men under Indian officers, mainly drawn from the local warrior castes (Maravas, Kallars and others). The total size of the native infantry was fixed at 6,300 in 1761 and the number of battalions was then ten. By 1767 there were nineteen battalions, ten of which were paid for by the Nawab of the Carnatic. This force proved unreliable both in the Seven Years War and the later wars with Mysore. Divided command encouraged factions and treachery while the troops regularly mutinied because of arrears of pay. C.A.B.

LITERATURE: Wilson 1888; Mollo 1981, p.14.

116

Trade and Territorial Expansion: The Rise of the Port Cities

After the Battle of Plassey, British trade in India expanded rapidly, buoying up the cities of Calcutta, Madras and Bombay. It was not so much the Company as such which benefited from the new wealth as its own servants, its military officers and other private traders, who retired to Britain with huge fortunes which had often been gained by oppression and corruption.

The unfettered expansion of European trade and the intrigues of Company servants with their subordinates was one pressure bearing down on vulnerable Indian kingdoms. Another was the cost of their alliance with the British. Rulers such as the Nawabs of Awadh and Arcot already had to pay huge sums of 'protection money' to the Company under the guise of alliances, which located Company troops on their territory. Under the Governor-Generalship of Warren Hastings (1772–85) the Company's influence and territories expanded inexorably. Sometimes Indian princes revolted against the financial demands placed on them, were defeated and lost all; sometimes they acquiesced in these demands and handed over territories in lieu of tribute payments.

The British authorities were by no means pleased by the actions of their agents in India. Not only was the government forced to bail out the Company as its debt was swelled by war and the decline of its trade, but there were also persistent rumours of fraud, oppression and gross mismanagement. As much as one third of the whole population of Bengal was thought to have perished in the famine of 1769–70, a disaster to which the policies of the Company indirectly contributed. The pressure to bring the Company to account became irresistable. Pitt's India Act of 1784 streamlined authority in India and established a ministerial Board of Control in London. Warren Hastings was impeached in Parliament for injustice and misgovernment. Lord Cornwallis was sent out as Governor-General in 1786 with a brief to 'clean-up' the Company. He reorganized the administration, laying the foundations of the Indian Civil Service as a *corps d'élite*, and 'settled' the chaotic revenues of Bengal on a permanent footing.

This was the period when British

painting on Indian themes reached its apogee. The wealthy European 'nabobs' wished to capture the opulence of their Oriental lives, while the Indian nawabs portrayed their fading glory to the world through the medium of some of the best portrait painters of the day. C.A.B.

117 The *farman* granted to the East India Company by the Mughal Emperor Farrukhsiyar in 1717 for freedom of trade in Bengal, Bihar and Orissa as recorded in the Diary of the Surman Embassy

Ink on paper, 46.5 × 31.5 (18 × 12$\frac{3}{10}$)
India Office Library and Records (Home Misc. 69ff. 130–31)

In the struggles between Mughal nobles after the death of Aurangzeb, Farrukhsiyar (no.73) showed himself to be friendly towards the East India Company. When he became Emperor in 1712, all three Presidencies decided to push for greater trading privileges, an idea which had originated with Governor Pitt of Madras in 1708. A mission was sent to Delhi under John Surman. It reached Delhi in 1714, but negotiations were so protracted that no documents were forthcoming until the middle of 1717. Surman was aided in his efforts by the doctor attached to the mission, William Hamilton, who managed to cure the Emperor of a painful disease. In these documents the Company was confirmed in its existing right to trade free of all dues in Bengal, Bihar and Orissa, subject to a payment of 3,000 rupees per annum. Similar concessions were made in the south. Perhaps more importantly, the Company was allowed to increase significantly the lands it rented around Calcutta, Vizagapatam and Madras. Though it had great difficulty in inducing local Mughal officials to recognize these *farmans* as absolute grants of any sort, the British saw in them the basis for an inalienable legal right to both trading privileges and territorial revenue in India. C.A.B.

LITERATURE: Dodwell 1929.

LITERATURE: Dodwell 1929.

Calcutta and Madras

The 1740s and 1750s had been a dire time for Calcutta, threatened first by the Marathas and then captured in 1756 by Siraj-ud-Daulah. But British investment had become so great in the port that the city had to be defended at all costs – a lesson learned from 1756 and the Black Hole incident. The boom in private trade after Plassey swelled the population to more than 150,000 people and a large garrison was placed at the New Fort William after 1757. The Esplanade (no.119 [iii]) and Chowringee Road became the seat of great private 'houses of agency' which managed the funds of Company servants and private traders. In 1772 government offices moved from the Nawabi capital of Murshidabad and the Writers, Building (no.119 [v]) became the centre of expanding official business. Yet Calcutta was first and foremost an Indian city. Early agents and contractors for the British, often men from humble background (Tantis, Seths and Bysaks), rose to prominence. Later, men from upper caste families with literate traditions worked with the British as agents or *banians*, and began to fill the burgeoning public offices. Still other rich men in Calcutta were local agents of the *zamindars* or landholders who were to rule the Bengal countryside for the colonial power. These all built themselves townhouses and embellished the city with temples (nos.119 [i], 119 [ii]). By 1780 Calcutta could already be described as 'that scattered and confused chaos of houses, huts, sheds, streets and lanes, alleys, windings, gutters, sinks and tanks, which jumbled into an undistinguished mass of corruption, equally offensive to human sense and health' (cited in Mitra 1951, VI, iii, p. 8 and Marshall 1988, p.160).

Madras, a somewhat more salubrious but equally heterogeneous city, was only slightly smaller in population by 1780. It had come into existence by the gradual assimilation of Fort St George (no.119 [v]) into the mass of the Blacktown (no.119 [vii]) inhabited by Tamil- and Telugu-speaking merchants, Armenians and Indo-Portuguese whose centre was the nearby St Thomas's Mount with its shrine to that martyr of eastern Christianity. After 1763 the Brahmin town of Triplicane and the palaces of the newly-resident Nawab of Arcot were also gradually reduced to the status of suburbs of the new Madras. Until the turn of the nineteenth century the city continued to flourish as an exporter of fine Madras cloth to Southeast Asia and to Europe. Thereafter, it was more a centre of government and of local and coastal trade, losing to Bombay the pre-eminence which it had held before 1800.

C.A.B.

LITERATURE: Love 1913; Marshall 1988, pp.159–60; Losty 1990.

118

118 View of a House, Manufactory and Bazaar in Calcutta

F. Jukes, London, 1795, after an original picture in the possession of James Stewart
Coloured engraving, 50.5 × 62.5 (19$\frac{7}{10}$ × 24$\frac{2}{5}$)
Inscribed: *published by F.Jukes and Colnaghi & Co London 1795*
India Office Library and Records (P2382)

PROVENANCE: Purchased 1982.

119(i) Black Pagoda

Thomas Daniell
Colour etching with aquatint, 40.5 × 53 ($19\frac{7}{8} \times 20\frac{7}{8}$)
India Office Library and Records (P91(i))

119(ii) House of Bengal Merchant on Chitpur Road, Calcutta

Thomas and William Daniell, 1792
Watercolour, 30.5 × 50.8 (12 × 20)
P & O, Art and Memorabilia Collection (54)

119(iii) View on the Esplanade, Calcutta

Thomas and William Daniell, 1792
Folio aquatint, 55 × 75 ($21\frac{7}{10} \times 29\frac{1}{2}$)
Syndics of Cambridge University Library

119(iv) Writers' Building, Calcutta

Thomas and William Daniell, 1792
Folio aquatint, 55 × 75 ($21\frac{7}{10} \times 29\frac{1}{2}$)
Syndics of Cambridge University Library

119(v) Government House, Fort St George, Madras

Thomas and William Daniell, 1792
Folio aquatint, 55 × 75 ($21\frac{7}{10} \times 29\frac{1}{2}$)
Syndics of Cambridge University Library

119(vi) Armenian Bridge, near St Thomas Mount

Thomas and William Daniell, 1792
Folio aquatint, 55 × 75 ($21\frac{7}{10} \times 29\frac{1}{2}$)
Syndics of Cambridge University Library

119(vii) Western Entrance of Fort St George of Blacktown

Thomas and William Daniell, 1792
Folio aquatint, 55 × 75 ($21\frac{7}{10} \times 29\frac{1}{2}$)
Syndics of Cambridge University Library

119

120 John Mowbray

Attributed to Thomas Hickey, *c.* 1790
Oil on canvas, 104 × 84 ($41 \times 32\frac{3}{4}$)
India Office Library and Records (F638)

John Mowbray was a partner in the private firm of Graham, Mowbray and Skirrow. Thomas Graham, the best known of the group, was a Bengal civil servant and resident at Benares between 1777 and 1780. He later became a member of the Board of Revenue. The whole firm illustrated in miniature the intermeshing of 'public' and private interests in the Company's business before Lord Cornwallis tried to separate the two and prohibit Company servants from making fortunes in private trade. Since the servants were virtually prohibited by the Company's charter from participating in the intercontinental trade, they augmented their salaries by investing them (and other illegal perquisites and presents) in internal trade. This trade was managed by Indian agents (*banians* in the north or *dubashes* in the south), who in turn carried on their own private trade along with that of their masters. Huge fortunes were made by both the Europeans and Indians, and the former often went home to become the infamous 'nabobs' (no.147). But their activities distorted and undermined the policies of the Company itself. While it is clear that private traders and Company servants with private trade by no means welcomed the onset of direct Company administration, they did create a powerful and often disruptive 'interest' in Indian states. Indian rulers resented the freedom to trade without duties which Europeans and their Indian agents secured under the Company's aegis. Private trading interests often favoured local magnates at the expense of the authority and revenues of their overlords. Issues such as these became a potent cause of conflict between the British and the Indian authorities and led in some cases to warfare and direct annexation.

Hickey here shows Mowbray between his servant and his *banian* who holds the typical style of Indian commercial ledger (*bahi khata*). Such *banians* were sometimes from the traditional commercial castes, but in Bengal more often than not were drawn from the ranks of the literate gentry (*bhadralog*). Some of the greatest landowners and magnates in

120

Calcutta in the nineteenth century, including the Tagores, were from families who had acquired fortunes in this way and invested in land. It appears from the map on the wall that the firm traded in Bihar and Tibet, which probably means that the commodities involved were cloths, saltpetre and perhaps fine Himalayan wools.

Hickey was at the height of his powers when he painted Mowbray. Following the death of his wife and relative failure in his native Dublin, Bath and London, he went to India in 1780 and was one of the few British artists to reside there more or less permanently until his death, aged eighty-three, in 1824.

This picture was, quite implausibly, attributed to Zoffany and exhibited as such for many years until Mildred Archer published it in 1979 as a work by Hickey, mainly on the basis of a convincing stylistic comparison between it and other works by him. C.A.B./B.A.

PROVENANCE: Presented by Mrs J. Bull, 1938.

LITERATURE: Marshall 1976; Archer 1979, pp. 205–34.

121 Madras scroll showing a European farmer supervising the cutting of a drainage ditch

Copyprint after original in the Victoria and Albert Museum

Before 1800 the British found themselves playing the role of trader, soldier and administrator in India. The number of actual settlers was quite small. Neither the Company nor the British government was keen to see the growth of a large settlement colony of Europeans with rights over land and labour, even less a 'miscegenated' Eurasian community, which it was felt would antagonise the Indians as well as proving disloyal to the government. Europeans were, it is true, established in the management of indigo factories in north India. The British followed Dutch precedents in the south in constructing spacious houses on their estates and drafting in Indian labour to produce garden fruits and other luxuries. Generally, though, they continued to work through Indian agents and overseers. C.A.B.

Servants and Dependents

The very large salaries paid to the British in India made it possible for them to employ as many house-servants and retainers for travel as did Indian princes, for whom status was designated by the number of their attendants. Immigrants came from as far away as the hills of Orissa and the plains of Benares to seek work as watchmen and palanquin bearers in Calcutta, while Indo-Portuguese butlers and retainers from the Malabar coast sought employment in Madras. The Daniells themselves seem to have travelled with several dozen aides and servants. The drawing and painting of Indian servants by amateur British artists was a tradition that survived until the end of the Raj.

Nayars (no. 122 [i]) were the warrior ruling caste of the Malabar coast, or what is now the state of Kerala. Organ ized into many small kingdoms, Kerala, a rich pepper-producing territory, was subject to intervention first by the Sultans of Mysore and then, after 1792, by the British who wished to protect their own profits from local competitors.

C.A.B.

122(i) A Nair (Nayar) with a Shield and Sword

Thomas and William Daniell, *c.* 1786–93

Pencil, 26.3 × 18 ($10\frac{3}{10} \times 7\frac{1}{10}$)

India Office Library and Records (WD 1876)

122(ii) Four Portrait Heads of Young Indian Men

Thomas and William Daniell, *c.* 1786–93

Pencil, 17 × 12 ($6\frac{7}{10} \times 4\frac{7}{10}$)

India Office Library and Records (WD 1881–1884)

122(iii) Four Studies of Indian Men, three standing, one squatting

Thomas and William Daniell, *c.* 1786–93

Pencil, 17 × 11.4 ($6\frac{7}{10} \times 4\frac{1}{2}$)

India Office Library and Records (WD 1896–1899)

122(i)

PROVENANCE: By descent to ? Thomas Daniell's niece from whom purchased by Sir Henry Russell, *c.* 1840–8; sold by the Russell family to Walker's Gallery, 1931, from whom (or through Sotheby's) purchased, 1961/1962.

LITERATURE: Foster 1931, pp.20–3; Hardie and Clayton 1932; Sutton 1954; Archer 1958, pp. 150–1; *Journal of the Royal Institute of British Architects*, 1960, pp. 439–44; Smithsonian Institute 1962; *Apollo*, November 1962, pp. 689–92; *The Connoisseur*, March 1963, pp. 171–5; *Journal of the Royal Society of Arts*, October 1967, pp. 863–79.

123 The Auriol and Dashwood Families

Johann Zoffany, 1783–7
Oil on canvas, 142 × 198 (56 × 78)
Inscribed in a later hand with the names of the sitters
R.H.N. Dashwood Esq.

One of the best and most famous of the Anglo-Indian 'conversation pieces', this picture is evidence of the growing sophistication of British life in Bengal in the generation after Buxar. The Auriol, Prinsep and Dashwood families were closely related and active in the administrative, mercantile and military life of the Presidency. James Peter Auriol had come to India in 1770 and in 1782 had become Secretary in the General Department and Agent for Supplies to the other Presidencies. His brother John followed him to India in 1776. His sister Sophie Elizabeth married John Prinsep, who had come to India as a cadet, but resigned to become an Alderman of the Mayor's Court in Calcutta and Assistant Superintendent of Company Investments. He cultivated indigo near Calcutta. James Auriol's other sister Charlotte married Thomas Dashwood, another Company servant who came to India in 1781.

The scene is set under a huge jack-fruit tree, possibly in the grounds of the Prinseps' indigo estates. Charles Auriol, a Captain in the British Army, John Auriol, First Assistant to the Secretary, Financial Department, and John Prinsep talk together. In the centre Charlotte Dashwood and Sophia Prinsep sit drinking tea.

Zoffany arrived in Calcutta in September 1783; James and Charles Auriol probably sat for their portraits at this date, with the other sitters being incorporated into the composition later. The carefully rendered silver teapot is still in existence and is hallmarked 1785. It could not have arrived in India before the end of that year when Zoffany is known to have been at Lucknow. Therefore the picture must have been finished in the sitters' place of residence – Calcutta – during Zoffany's stay there in 1787. As Mary Webster has pointed out, were it not for the exotic landscape and the Indian servants Zoffany's composition would be indistinguishable from his conversation pieces painted in England.

Displaying his customary talent for representing drapery and fine costume details, Zoffany gives the different members of this family group and their Indian servants an animated yet elegant appearance. Except for Captain Charles Auriol on the left, who wears a King's Army uniform, all the English men are dressed in fashionable, plain-coloured frock coats and white waistcoats, and, like the ladies, have their hair dressed in the lightly-powdered, curled styles which were popular during the 1780s. Both Charlotte Auriol's turquoise silk gown, set off by delicate silk and gauze scarves, and the shining cream silk gown with a vandyke collar worn by Sophia Auriol are elaborate and stylish and reflect the great interest in dress and personal appearance which prevailed among British women in India.

C.A.B./B.A./J.S.

PROVENANCE: By descent.

LITERATURE: Manners and Williamson 1920, pp. 189–90.

EXHIBITIONS: London, Royal Academy, *Old Masters*, 1881 (41); London, 25 Park Lane, *Loan Exhibition of English Conversation Pieces*, 1930 (13); London, National Portrait Gallery, *Johann Zoffany 1733–1819*, 1976 (100).

124

124 Captain John Foote (1718–1768)

Sir Joshua Reynolds, 1765
Oil on canvas, 123.2 × 99 (48½ × 39)
York City Art Gallery (216)

Captain John Foote of the Honourable East India Company was a neighbour and early friend of Reynolds at Tor Grove, near Plymouth. In the eighteenth century British personnel in India often adopted Indian dress in private. Those who married Indian women, or had extended diplomatic duties at Indian courts, sometimes appeared in Indian costume in public. English serges and woollens were generally expected at formal occasions, and in the nineteenth century adopting 'native' dress became a sign of eccentricity, even a cause of discredit.

The sky in this picture has turned green from Reynolds's use of copper carbonate, known as 'blue verditor'. This resulted, as the artist explained in a letter written to Lord Barrington in 1780, from 'a blunder of my colourman, who sent blue verditor (a colour which changes green within a month), instead of ultramarine, which lasts forever'. The Foote family, however, recorded that Reynolds regarded this portrait as one of his favourite pictures and afterwards retouched it with the paints of his pupil, James Northcote, saying the work would last after many of his other portraits had faded. B.A.

PROVENANCE: Rev. J.S. Foote; Captain George Foote R.A. of Tor Grove by 1856; Rev. H.G. Rolt; Mrs Rolt; Captain A.E. Pickard-Cambridge; sold Puttick & Simpson, 27 November 1929 (147); bought by Agnew; purchased by York Art Gallery in 1950.

LITERATURE: Cotton 1857, p.353; Graves and Cronin 1899–1901, I, p.231; Waterhouse 1941, p.56, pl. 107; York Art Gallery, *Preview*, 10 April 1950, p.113; *National-Art Collections Fund Report*, 1950, p.25; Penny 1986, p.65.

EXHIBITIONS: London, Royal Academy, 1877 (36); Dijon, 1957 (8), ill. pl. III; Birmingham, City Museum and Art Gallery, *Reynolds*, 1961 (144).

125 *Jama, patka* and shawl

Indian, 18th century
Natural cotton with embroidery in silks and flattened-gold strips
York City Art Gallery

By the mid-eighteenth century most Europeans in India followed contemporary western fashions as far as possible and did not feel the need or inclination to adopt native clothing for daily wear. It was, however, fashionable among British sitters who wished to have their Indian connections commemorated by being painted wearing the costume of the country, and Reynolds's portrait of Captain John Foote is particularly interesting as the handsome Indian outfit worn by Foote has survived. The main item is an authentic Indian *jama*, or surcoat, a full-length cotton gown comprising a voluminous skirt tightly gathered onto a fitted, side-fastening, cross-over bodice with narrow, elongated sleeves. It is embroidered with traditional Indo-Persian floral motifs known as *buta* in dark blue and yellow silks and silver-gilt thread. The accompanying waist sash, or *patka*, is of yellowish cotton with deep, elaborate end pieces embroidered in coloured silks on a bright ground of

125

flattened silver-gilt wire and edged with gold fringing. The elegant shawl worn by Foote in the portrait has not survived but a long, narrow cotton sash with embroidered bands may also have been purchased by him in India. J.S.

PROVENANCE: As for no.125.

LITERATURE: NACF *Annual Report* 1950, p.25; City of York Art Gallery, *Catalogue of Paintings* 1963, ii, p.72; Archer 1979, p.411 (incorrectly described as belonging to Foote's descendants); Baines 1981, pl.131.

EXHIBITIONS: Birmingham, City Museum and Art Gallery, *Reynolds* 1961 (un-numbered); London, Victoria and Albert Museum, *Art and the East India Trade*, 1970.

126 William Hickey with a bust of Edmund Burke

Thomas Hickey, *c.* 1790
Oil on canvas, 84 × 61 (33 × 24)
National Gallery of Ireland (310)

William Hickey (1749–1830) is almost certainly the single British individual in India in the East India Company's period about whom most is known, largely because on his return from India in 1808 he wrote a very long memoir of his life, extensive parts of which have been published.

The son of an Irish lawyer in London, Hickey too was trained for the law. He lived the life of a young rake about town to the point where his father decided he must be packed off to a place where he could do less harm. After attempts to get him to India and to the West Indies, he finally went out to Bengal in 1777 as an attorney, or solicitor, to practise in the Calcutta Supreme Court. He stayed there, except for a short return, until his retirement. His memoirs are the most vivid picture of the life of the European elite in Calcutta. Hickey himself was a hedonist and so, it would seem, were most of his friends. They lived in grand neo-classical houses with huge retinues of servants, ate sumptuously and drank heavily, and kept Indian mistresses: Hickey was devoted to his 'Jemdanee', who bore him a son. Even Hickey had his serious side: through his father he was much attached to Edmund Burke and his family, and clearly regarded it as an honour to be painted with a bust of the man who was so stern a critic of the British in India.

Burke's bust was by John Hickey, the painter's sculptor brother, presented to William Hickey by William Burke before the latter left Calcutta for Madras in February 1789. Thomas Hickey may have painted the portrait on his return to Calcutta from Madras before he left for Europe. B.A./P.J.M.

PROVENANCE: Purchased from a member of the Hickey family in 1888.

LITERATURE: Spencer 1913–25, III, p.349; Breeze 1973, pp.117–8, n.105; Archer 1979, pp.214–5, pl.134; National Gallery of Ireland, *Illustrated Summary Catalogue of Paintings*, 1981, p.217, no.310.

126

127 Hicky's *Bengal Gazette* 1780

Bound newspaper, open, 37.5 × 51 ($14\frac{3}{5} \times 20$)
India Office Library and Records (Vol.I, no.27)

James Augustus Hicky, a printer by trade, founded the first Calcutta news paper in 1780. He was a fierce and abusive critic of Warren Hastings, the Governor-General, and of Sir Elijah Impey, the Chief Justice (no.128), with whom he had several bruising encounters. He made no secret of the fact that he regarded them both as petty tyrants and himself as spokesman for the unofficial community in the city and as guardian of the liberties of 'freeborn Englishmen'. The *Bengal Gazette*, the country's first regular newspaper, began publication on 29 January 1780 as a salvo in this war against the authorities. In March 1782 the paper was forced to cease publication as a result of a succeessful private prosecution.

C.A.B.

LITERATURE: Carey 1964.

128 Sir Elijah Impey (1732–1809)

Unknown artist after Johann Zoffany
Platinotype print, 52 × 32.2 ($20\frac{1}{2} \times 12\frac{3}{4}$)
India Office Library and Records (P694)

Impey was first Chief Justice of the Calcutta Supreme Court, which had been established under the Regulating Act of 1773 in an attempt to bring the affairs of the East India Company more closely under the control of the Crown in Parliament. The Court consisted of a Chief Justice and three puisne judges, but the field of jurisdiction, the law to be administered and the relations between the Calcutta Council and the Court were left 'unhappily vague'. Serious conflicts soon broke out between members of the government and the Court; the extent of the Court's jurisdiction over Indians also came under constant challenge. Impey,

128

however, was chiefly remembered for the role he played in the trial and hanging in 1775 of Raja Nandakumar, an agent of government who had been accused of forgery. Warren Hastings was suspected of complicity in his execution because the Raja had previously accused the Governor-General himself of bribery. This was later one of the charges in the impeachment of Hastings and the proceedings against Impey. Whatever the truth of the matter, and it was still debated with ferocity more than 100 years later, the execution had considerable effect on Indian sentiment, bringing about one of the first *hartals* (general strikes) known to Calcutta, a city later famous for them. As Edmund Burke stated:

> The Raja Nundcomar [*sic*] was, by an insult on everything which India holds respectable and sacred, hanged in the face of all his nation, by the judges you [Parliament] sent to protect that people, hanged for a pretended crime, upon an ex post facto Act of Parliament, in the midst of his evidence against Mr. Hastings.

Kettle and Zoffany both painted Impey, an important figure in the English circles of Calcutta, who is here seen as the embodiment of justice. C.A.B.

LITERATURE: Dodwell 1929 pp. 234–7; Archer 1979.

129 Sir Henry Russell Bt. (1751–1836), Chief Justice of Bengal

After George Chinnery, 1807
Aquatint, 72 × 52 (24 × 12)
The Honourable Society of Lincoln's Inn

Russell's career marked the maturing of a British Indian judiciary which was now much more distant from the political interests of the Company's government than it had been in Impey's time, and also more inclined to intervene in and modify Hindu and Muslim judicial practice. He was born at Dover, educated at Queen's College, Cambridge and Lincoln's Inn, was called to the Bar in 1783 and in 1797 was appointed Puisne Judge in the Supreme Court of Bengal which was established in 1774. It had jurisdiction over the city of Calcutta and all British subjects residing in the Bengal Presidency under the protection of the Company. Soon after his arrival Russell became Chief Justice of Bengal. In 1808 he gave a famous judgement against a Company servant who had set fire to an Indian's hut with the words 'The natives are entitled to have their character, property and lives protected'. Lord Moira, Governor-General, wrote of his 'able, upright and dignified adminstration of justice'. Having retired to England he became a Privy Councillor in 1816, but three of his sons entered Company service, including Sir Henry Russell, who was a celebrated Resident of Hyderabad. He married Anne, daughter of Sir Charles Whitworth, who was his second wife: she died in 1813.

Chinnery's portrait was painted as a commission from the Indian residents of Calcutta who wanted it to hang in the new Town Hall there. It occasioned the artist's move from Madras to Bengal where he was to spend much of the rest

129

of his life. It is a typical legal portrait of the period, replete with symbols of justice, but transformed in the original by Chinnery's use of bold colour and his interest in drapery. Russell must have liked sitting for artists; Home, Romney and Jackson also painted him. C.A.B.

LITERATURE: Archer 1979, pp. 365–7.

130 Sir Henry Russell's Account Book

Ink on paper, in a limp-bound notebook
Open, 18.5 × 26.5 ($7\frac{1}{5} \times 10\frac{3}{10}$)
The Bodleian Library, Oxford (MS. Eng. Misc. e. 1634)

During the period of the Napoleonic Wars, the British population in Calcutta became larger, but less idiosyncratic. Indianised manners were discountenanced, the political tone became more patriotic and royalist, and European news and events more central to social life. This account book contains details of Sir Henry Russell's income and expenditure 1768–1809, including his period as a judge in Bengal between May 1798 and 1809. In 1805 Russell recorded a bet (which he lost) to the effect that Bonaparte would not be in power a year from then. C.A.B.

PROVENANCE: Purchased from Dr. J.H. Baker 1983.

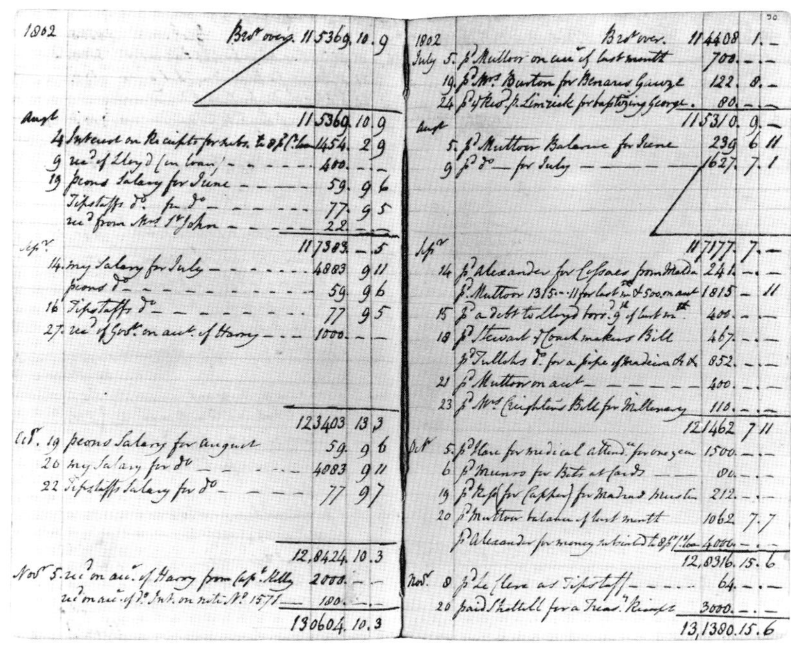

1802	Brt over	115369	10	9
Augt		115369	10	9
4	Interest on Receipts for subs. @ 8 p Cent	1454	2	9
9	recd of Lloyd (on loan)	400	–	–
19	Peons Salary for June	59	9	6
	Tipstaffs do for do	77	9	5
	recd from Mrs St John	22	–	–
Sepr		117303	–	5
14	my Salary for July	4883	9	11
	Peons do	59	9	6
16	Tipstaffs do	77	9	5
27	recd of Govt on acct of Harry	1000	–	–
		123403	13	3
Oct 19	Peons Salary for August	59	9	6
20	my Salary for do	4083	9	11
22	Tipstaffs Salary for do	77	9	7
		12,8424	10	3
Novr 5	recd on acct of Harry from Capt Kelly	2000	–	–
	recd on acct of do Int. on note No 1571	180	–	–
		130604	10	3

1802	Brt over	114408	1	–
July 5	pd Muttoo on acct of last month	700	–	–
19	pd Mrs Burton for Benares Gauze	122	8	–
24	pd the Revd Mr Limrick for baptizing George	80	–	–
Augt		115310	9	–
5	pd Muttoo Balance for June	239	6	11
9	pd do for July	1627	7	1
Sepr		117177	7	–
14	pd Alexander for Cossaes from Malda	241	–	–
	pd Muttoo 1315..11 for last mth & 500 on acct	1815	–	11
15	pd a debt to Lloyd borrd 9th of last mth	400	–	–
18	pd Stewart & Coachmakers Bill	467	–	–
	pd Tullohs do for a pipe of Madeira A & C	852	–	–
21	pd Muttoo on acct	400	–	–
23	pd Mrs Creighton's Bill for Millenary	110	–	–
		121462	7	11
Oct 5	pd Hare for medical attendce for one year	1500	–	–
6	pd Munro for Bets at Cards	80	–	–
19	pd Ross for (Capper) for Madras Muslin	212	–	–
20	pd Muttoo balance of last month	1062	7	7
	pd Alexander for money subscribed to 8 p Cent loan	4000	–	–
		12,8316	15	6
Novr 8	pd Le Clerc as Tipstaff	64	–	–
20	paid Shottell for a Treasy Receipt	3000	–	–
		13,1380	15	6

130

131 Lady Russell's Diary†

Autograph manuscript, 18 × 25 ($7 \times 9\frac{7}{8}$)
The Bodleian Library, Oxford (MS. Eng. Misc.e.1635)

Warren Hastings: The Diplomatic Web

During Warren Hastings's period as Governor-General, the East India Company remained a curious hybrid. In Bengal it retained many features of Indian government, notably Indian agency and the 'farming out' of revenues. Warren Hastings himself tried to emphasize the Indian aspect of his government: he promoted the study of classical and modern Indian languages and law and encouraged the orientalist tradition which began to flower with the foundation of the Asiatic Society of Bengal in 1784. Nevertheless, during Hastings's rule Indian institutions and states were relentlessly eroded. Revenues were held high in Bengal, despite the disaster of the famine of 1769–70, and there were widespread agrarian disturbances. In external policy Hastings declared the intention of protecting rather than increasing the Company's territories, but the burden of paying for Company troops under the terms of subsidiary alliances drew Indian powers more closely into the British orbit. The authority of the Nawabs of Awadh and Arcot dwindled even as Tilly Kettle and Johann Zoffany painted them in their glory. C.A.B.

LITERATURE: Feiling 1954; Marshall 1970.

132 Warren Hastings (1732–1818)

Sir Joshua Reynolds, *c.* 1768–9
Oil on canvas, 127.5 × 102 (49¾ × 39¾)
National Portrait Gallery, London (4445)

132

Warren Hastings (1732–1818) was represented in a vast number of images throughout his long life and he is one of the few men to have been painted by Reynolds, Romney and Lawrence. Most of these portraits show the sitter in later life – at least from his time in India in the 1780s, or later. Reynolds seems to have attempted to keep in touch with Hastings after the latter's return from India, apparently, according to Reynolds's nephew, sending a copy of one of his 'Discourses' to him in 1775.

Hastings was appointed Governor of Bengal in 1772 and was confirmed as Governor-General by Act of Parliament in 1773. It was hoped that he would be able to provide the effective administration so conspicuously lacking since Clive had acquired the *diwani* (see no.112). Within a few years, however, allegations of malpractice, military aggression and financial difficulties were to recur, leading to a fresh round of state intervention in the 1780s and to personal attacks on Hastings which were pressed with even more persistence than those against Clive. Nevertheless, for all the recriminations about him, Hastings did succeed in setting up administrative machinery that was to endure.

Hastings was a well-educated man of scholarly tastes, who had served for fifteen years in Bengal before he was appointed Governor. In discharging the responsibilities of the *diwani*, that is in ensuring that the revenue was collected, that the law courts functioned and that the authority of government was maintained, Hastings found it impossible to limit British intervention to the degree that Clive had envisaged (see no.107). Yet under Hastings British administration in Bengal had as much in common with the methods used by the independent Nawabs as it did with the more formal bureaucracy of the period of Lord Cornwallis (no.152). Indian intermediaries still had an essential role in the East India Company's government.

State intervention not only gave Hastings the office of Governor-General; it also gave him colleagues appointed directly from Britain, with whom he quarrelled bitterly. Philip Francis (1740–1818) was by far the most pertinacious of Hastings's opponents, denouncing both his personal conduct and his principles of government. In defending himself against what he regarded as undeserved attacks, Hastings could act ruthlessly, as he showed in his involvement in the prosecution of Nandakumar, one of the Indians who had made allegations against him.

This ruthlessness was more obvious in the later years of his administration, when the Company was entangled in war, first of all against Indian opponents, and then against a new French offensive in India during the American Revolution. In organizing the Company's war effort, which he did with success, Hastings was less than scrupulous about extracting funds from Indian allies and dependents of the Company. Both involvement in what seemed in Britain to be unnecessary wars and the dubious expedients used to finance them were held against him. When he returned to Britain in 1785 he faced not the hero's welcome that he had expected but investigation and ultimately a long trial (see no.151). It was his misfortune that he had outraged the conscience of Edmund Burke, a man of much higher moral and political standing than any of Clive's opponents (see no.148). B.A./P.J.M.

PROVENANCE: G. Watson Taylor 1823; his sale, Christie's, 25 July 1832 (148), bt Newton; 2nd Lord Northwick; by descent to Capt. E. G. Spencer Churchill; acquired by H. M. Government and allocated to National Portrait Gallery 1965.

133 Mr and Mrs Warren Hastings†

Johann Zoffany, *c.* 1783–7
Oil on canvas, 119.5 × 90 (47 × 35½)
Victoria Memorial Hall, Calcutta (C1310/R1436)

Warren Hastings is shown here with his wife Marian (1747–1837), in the grounds of their house at Alipore (in the background), accompanied by an *ayah*. The compositional formula is entirely English in feeling and has a venerable tradition in the conversation piece genre.

Although Zoffany sent Hastings a bill for the picture in February 1785, the work was begun just before Mrs Hastings returned to England in January 1784. It was perhaps not completed until at least the end of 1787, when Hastings's private secretary and attorney Nesbitt Thompson wrote to him noting that he had not received 'the small full-length picture of yourself and Mrs Hastings.'

The Governor-General is elegantly dressed in a fashionable frock coat, short waistcoat and matching breeches, while the Indian servant wears her own native garments and carries her mistress's plumed beaver hat. However, it is Hastings's wife who dominates this elegant group. Her gleaming, gold-coloured silk gown, edged with gold fringing and complemented by a delicate gauze collar and stole, is stylish and exotic, reflecting both her own personal tastes and the prominent social position which she enjoyed in India.

Mrs Hastings's manner of dressing was much commented upon by her contemporaries: her lavish expenditure on clothes and her notorious love of jewels, especially the diamonds which she wore in great quantities, were condemned by some as over-ostentatious; others regarded her appearance as eccentric, such as the way in which she wore her long auburn hair in loose, unpowdered curls, as here. Some women, however, admired her, for example, the author of the contemporary novel *Hartly House, Calcutta*, who described her as 'the great ornament of places of polite resort, for her figure is elegant, her manners lively and engaging, and her whole appearance a model of taste and magnificence'.

B.A./J.S.

PROVENANCE: Painted for Warren Hastings; by descent to Miss Marrion Winter who bequeathed it to Lord Curzon, through whom it was acquired by the Victoria Memorial Hall.

LITERATURE: *Hartly House, Calcutta* 1789; *Bengal Past and Present*, XVII, 1918, p.126; Manners and Williamson 1920, ill. p.97; Feiling 1954; Webster 1976; Archer 1979.

EXHIBITION: London, National Portrait Gallery, *Johann Zoffany* 1976 (99).

134 Warren Hastings in European court dress

Mughal, unknown artist, *c.* 1782
Gouache, 17.5 × 11 ($6\frac{7}{8} \times 4\frac{4}{10}$)
The British Library Board (Or. 6633, f.67a)

134

135 Warren Hastings's Diaries

Bound book, open, 18 × 28 (7 × 11)
The British Library Board (Add. MS. 39878)

136 Colonel Mordaunt's Cock Match

Richard Earlom, 1 May 1792, after Johann Zoffany's painting of *c.* 1786
Mezzotint engraving, 47.8 × 66.7 ($18\frac{1}{2} \times 26\frac{1}{4}$)
India Office Library and Records (P158)

136

One of the most famous 'conversation pieces' of the eighteenth-century Anglo-Indian record, this picture came to epitomize the luxurious ease of the kingdom of Awadh in the later eighteenth century, where Company officials and soldiers had adopted Indian ways in the glittering court of Asaf-ud-Daulah. The principle figures are Colonel Mordaunt, who stands to the left of the central group, and Asaf-ud-Daulah, who has risen from his seat on a dais and advances towards Mordaunt with his arms outstretched. Between them, counting on his fingers, is Salar Jung, Asaf-ud-Daulah's uncle, and behind them is Hasan Reza Khan (no. 140).

Mordaunt was Commander of the Bodyguard to Asaf, who had maintained the European-style military force established by his father, Shuja. This office was held on the very large salary of 8,000 rupees per month, an indication of the level of reward which attracted Europeans, including artists, 'up country'. Mordaunt appears to have been the regular master of ceremonies at fights at which the Nawab, his Indian and European officers, and members of the Company's Residency came together for gossip and intrigue.

Amongst the European spectators are Colonel Martin (see no. 138) seated on a dais, talking to Mr Wheeler, who holds a cock. Behind Colonel Martin is John Wombwell, with a *nargila* pipe, and Zoffany himself, holding a pencil. The painter Ozias Humphry stands with his hand on Zoffany's shoulder. The seething crowd of Indian spectators, including musicians and dancing girls, gives the composition a remarkable vivacity.

Zoffany appears to have painted one version of this picture (now lost) for Asaf and one (the Daylesford version) for Hastings, who attended a match when visiting the Nawab in April 1784. The theme of cock-fighting was very popular with English travellers and the public at home, possibly because it was rapidly vanishing as a 'respectable' pastime in the face of the growing tide of evangelical disapproval.

The interesting variety of costumes helps to identify the diverse characters present. The several groups of Indians are distinguished generally by their long, flowing garments which differ in their details according to sex and caste. The clothing of the European spectators ranges from military uniforms to various forms of fashionable dress, with or without powdered hair or hat, and the case of Colonel Mordaunt himself who, for freedom of movement apparently wears a cotton, sleeved waistcoat but no outer coat – a rare glimpse of undress. Westerners in India often adopted comfortable, oriental-style slippers for indoor wear. C.A.B./B.A./J.S.

LITERATURE: Manners and Williamson 1920, pp.84–92; Foster 1931, pp.82–3; Webster 1973, pp. 588–9; Webster 1977, pp. 77–8; Archer 1979, pp.148–54, pls.94, 95.

137 An Indian Dancing Girl with a Hookah

Tilly Kettle, 1772
Oil on canvas, 193 × 119 (76 × 47)
Inscribed: *Kettle Pinxit 1772* on base of column to right
Yale Center for British Art, Paul Mellon Collection (B1981.25.385)

The Awadh Court, which moved from Faizabad to Lucknow and back, soon gained a reputation as the most luxurious and refined of the late Mughal courts. It attracted soldiers, administrators, learned men and artists from the declining centres of Delhi and Agra. After the signing of the subsidiary alliance with the Company in 1765 a wealthy group of British and European merchants, soldiers and officials also arrived, luxuriating in what became known as the 'silver age' culture. Temple dancing by girls given to the gods (*devadasis*) was common in the south where Tilly Kettle had first

137

worked. But dances in the fluid north Indian style, Bharat Natyam, were a favourite entertainment for the Mughal artistocracy and proved of particular fascination to European travellers in search of the exotic. Dancing girls often achieved considerable celebrity and even power. They were often literate and made their way as courtesans, or even wives of notables. Until the final collapse of the court culture in 1856, some celebrated women presided over salons at which poets and literati would air their works. B.A./C.A.B.

PROVENANCE: Sold Christie's, 24 July 1959 (46); sold Sotheby's, 10 March 1965 (105) ill.; Gooden and Fox from whom purchased by Paul Mellon, March 1967; given to Yale Center for British Art 1981.

LITERATURE: Archer 1979, p.79. ill. pl.1 and fig.31; Cormack 1985, ill. p.134.

EXHIBITIONS: New Haven, Yale Center for British Art, *The British View of India Selected Paintings from the Paul Mellon Collection*, 1978 (un-numbered).

138 Colonel Polier with his friends†

Johann Zoffany, 1787
Oil on canvas, 137 × 183.5 (54 × 72½)
Victoria Memorial Hall, Calcutta

The painter Zoffany is seen here in the centre of the composition working on a canvas of a group of Hindu devotees seated under a banyan tree. With him are three of his Lucknow friends: on the left is Colonel Antoine Polier (1741–95); standing to the right of the table is Colonel Claude Martin (1735–1800), who is pointing out to the seated figure of John Wombwell, son of the Chairman of the East India Company (1777–9), and by this date the Company's Paymaster at Lucknow, features of a watercolour of his house, the Farad Baksh on the River Gumti. This drawing may be his own work since he holds paintbrushes in his right hand. Wombwell holds a book, probably indicating his literary interests. Behind them a servant is giving a banana to a pet monkey. On the left, Polier points to the basket of produce brought to him by his gardener and instructs his cook. The Oriental manuscripts and a portfolio, presumably containing prints, on the table are clear indications of Polier's interests. All four men are shown enjoying pictures in Polier's house where Zoffany may have been living at this time. The artist, however, seems to have intended the real subject of the picture to be himself. His presence is reinforced by the paintings on the wall behind him, which also appear to be his work.

The oval picture in the centre shows elephants being washed by their keepers in a river set against a mountainous backdrop. The picture to the left depicts a Hindu *sati* scene and that to the right shows pilgrims bathing in a river. The two small circular paintings depict, on the left, a disturbance involving a Muslim warrior on a white horse in the company of red-coated soldiers. In no other work from his India period does Zoffany make so clear a statement of his interests in Indian life. To Europeans, Lucknow offered exoticism and freedom from some of the social constraints of the principal Presidency cities, and Polier and his friends were all deeply interested in Eastern culture. Polier followed many Indian customs, including the adoption of full native dress on occasion, and in this portrait wears an elaborately frogged coat, a fur cap which may be of Afghan or Central Asian origin and a drooping, Oriental-style moustache which hint at his taste for the exotic. B.A./J.S.

PROVENANCE: Probably Edward Strachey (second assistant to the Resident at Lucknow, 1797–1801); given by his son Captain Henry Strachey to Robert Henry Clive (in payment of a debt); by descent to his nephew Viscount Bridgeman; sale, Christie's, 28 June 1929 (75).

LITERATURE: Manners and Williamson 1920, p.108; Webster 1977, pp. 79–80; Archer 1979, pp.154–6, pl. 96, col. pl. VII.

EXHIBITION: London, National Portrait Gallery, *Johann Zoffany 1733–1810*, 1976 (105).

139 Nathaniel Middleton with Nawab Asaf-ud-Daulah and his ministers†

Tilly Kettle, *c.* 1784
Oil on canvas, 152 × 137 ($59\frac{3}{4}$ × 54)
Private Collection

This group portrait commemorates Nathaniel Middleton's assumption of charge as Resident of Lucknow in December 1776, after the death of Shuja-ud-Daulah in 1775. Middleton returned to England in 1784. The new Nawab of Awadh was Asaf-ud-Daulah, shown here seated with Middleton. The two figures standing behind them are two newly appointed ministers, Haidar Beg Khan and Hasan Reza Khan (no. 140). Although this event happened some time after Kettle's return to London (in November 1776), he had painted the three Indians at Faizabad and probably still had drawings from which he was able to reconstruct this group portrait.

Middleton, who had previously been civil officer to the Court of Awadh at Faizabad (1773–5), took up his duties as Resident at Lucknow in December 1776. As emissary of Warren Hastings, Middleton's main task was to make sure that the Nawab kept up regular payments of the sums he owed the Company under the subsidiary alliance. In consequence, the Company became even more deeply entangled in the affairs of Awadh, private individuals made huge sums through graft and trade monopolies, and in 1781 Benares and a large part of southern Awadh erupted in revolt. Middleton himself was involved in the unsavoury affair of the 'Begums of Oudh' (later to be one of the charges of impeachment against Hastings), when sums of money were extracted from female relatives of the Nawab to offset the financial pressures on the state. But there was a more attractive side to his career. Middleton was one of a circle of Orientalists who collected Indian manuscripts and paintings and patronized Tilly Kettle and other artists.

After Hastings's departure from India a more moderate policy was adopted towards Awadh, and a trade treaty of 1788 restricted British commercial dealings in the territory. It was not until the crisis of Wellesley's wars (1801–2) that the Company took direct control of its most valuable divisions.

Kettle painted the picture after both he and Middleton were back in Britain. B.A./C.A.B.

PROVENANCE: Middleton Collection, Bradford Peverell House, Dorchester.

LITERATURE: Archer 1979, pp.87, 94–5, pl.2; Barnett 1980; Llewellyn-Jones 1985; Cole 1986.

140 Hasan Reza Khan

Johann Zoffany, 1784
Oil on canvas, 127 × 101.5 ($49\frac{1}{2}$ × 16)
Inscribed: *Joh.Zophany* painted this Picture at *Lucknow, A.D. 1784, by desire of Hussain Reza Caun, Nabob Suffraz Ul Dowlah, who gave it to his friend Francis Baladon Thomas**
(*surgeon to the Lucknow Residency, dismissed 1784)
India Office Library and Records (F108)

Hasan Reza Khan, a chief minister (technically *Naib-i-Kull* or Absolute Deputy) of Nawab Asaf-ud-Daulah, was painted by Zoffany during his highly productive stay at Lucknow in 1784. There are also paintings of him by Tilly Kettle, Ozias Humphry and Charles Smith, an indication of the wealth of the Awadh court and the fashion for employing European artists. Hasan Reza Khan was a devout Muslim of the Shia sect from an old established family. He served Asaf as superintendent of his extensive private kitchen, but he also supervised the accounts of the East India Company's revenue assignments in Awadh, thus gaining the favour of British Residents, notably Nathaniel Middleton (no.139). Hasan Reza Khan was deeply implicated in the tortuous games of administrative bluff and counter-bluff by which the Nawab tried to exclude the British from direct access to, and control of, revenues in what was still nominally an independent state. Whereas Hasan Reza Khan tended to ally with the Resident against his opponents at court during Warren Hastings's period, in the 1790s

140

he was found taking a more forceful line against further British penetration of the province. B.A./C.A.B.

PROVENANCE: See Foster 1924; purchased February 1960.

LITERATURE: *The Journal of Indian Art*, XII, no. 107, July 1909, pl. 166; Manners and Williamson 1920, p. 207; Foster 1924, no.108; Sutton 1970, p. 90, fig.4; Archer 1979, pp. 146–7, pl.90; Barnett 1980; Archer 1986, pp.49–50, no.66, pl.XI.

EXHIBITIONS: London, Royal Academy, *The Art of India and Pakistan*, 1947–8 (914); London, National Portrait Gallery, *Johann Zoffany 1733–1810*, 1976 (103).

141

141 George Pigot, Baron Pigot (1719–77)

George Willison, 1777
Oil on canvas, 67.3 × 56.5 ($26\frac{1}{2} \times 22\frac{1}{4}$)
Signed and dated: *Geo. Willison pinxit 1777*
National Portrait Gallery, London (3837)

Tilly Kettle had begun this picture in London and brought it with him to Madras in 1769, perhaps hoping to sell it to the local authorities. Pigot had a long, though ultimately tragic career in the Presidency. He had been a redoubtable Governor of Madras during the stormy years from 1755 to 1763, when the Presidency only just survived its long duel with the French and their Indian allies. In December 1775, the Directors reappointed him Governor of the Presidency. They were concerned that members of the Madras Council under the influence of Nawab Muhammed Ali and Paul Benfield, his enormously wealthy creditor, had connived in the invasion and looting of the rich principality of Tanjore (no.89), and that this would bring the Company into conflict with other Indian powers and saddle it with further unwanted territories. The returning Governor was determined to reinstate the Tanjore Raja on his throne. But the faction in Madras with an interest in the servicing of the 'Nawab of Arcot's debts' – if necessary through territorial expansion – was more powerful than Pigot. He was outvoted and, on 24 August 1776, kidnapped by the majority on his own Council led by George Stratton (who was probably acting under the influence of the Nawab, and Benfield). He was interned at St Thomas's Mount, where he died 'under restraint' but not before George Willison had painted him once again.

The incident illustrates the importance of the role of the 'man on the spot' in the territorial expansion of British influence, even when this was directly opposed by the home authorities. On the other hand, it was events like the deposition of Pigot, along with the charges against Warren Hastings, that led the British Government to intervene and reorganize the Company's administration under the India Act of 1784.

C.A.B./B.A.

PROVENANCE: Purchased 1952.

LITERATURE: Archer 1979, pp.67, 104–7, pl.62; Ramaswami 1984.

142 Prince of Arcot House

John Smart, 1788
Watercolour on ivory, oval 5.7 × 4.2 ($2\frac{3}{16} \times 1\frac{5}{8}$)
Signed and dated in black, br: *JS/1788/I*
Syndics of the Fitzwilliam Museum, Cambridge (PD 16–1948)

The British in Madras never had the sort of violent showdown with the Nawabs of the Carnatic that they had with those in Bengal. What became the Madras Presidency was still ruled by the 'divided government' of Company and Arcot servants until 1802. After the failure of the Tanjore intervention in 1776, however, the Nawabs of the Carnatic gradually forfeited any real control over events in the south. Large areas of territory were taken over temporarily by British officials during the Mysore war of 1780–3 because the Nawabi officers could not, or would not, provide resources and monies stipulated under the terms of their subsidiary alliance with the Company. After the fall of Mysore in 1799 (no.109), treasonable letters from Azim-ud-Daulah, Nawab of Arcot, were allegedly discovered in Tipu Sultan's papers. This gave the Company the excuse to seize the whole of the Carnatic and pension off the Arcot house to a suburban palace in Madras. The princely glories of Muhammed Ali shone brighter even as his power waned. He introduced learned Muslim teachers from the north, patronized mosques and Hindu temples with catholic generosity, and employed the great British artists and miniaturists to paint him and his family.

Smart was one of the finest British miniaturists to have visited India and he made several portraits of members of the family of Muhammed Ali, along with numerous portraits of the Madras civil and military establishment. The sitter wears a white turban with gold ornamentation and a white robe, over which there is a white gauze garment with green edging and gold embroidery (*kalabatun*). There are problems with identification. This is possibly a study of Azim-ud-Daulah (no.144) in his youth (Smart painted his father); or perhaps of Umdat-ul-Umara's son Taj-ul-Umara, who refused to succeed to the Nawabi on the terms set out by Wellesley's government in 1801–2 (see no.144).

C.A.B.

PROVENANCE: Leicester family, by descent to Sir Peter Leicester; his sale, Christie's, 24 May 1948 (84), where bought by the Friends of Fitzwilliam Museum, by whom given, 1948.

LITERATURE: Reynolds 1952, p. 153; Foskett 1964, pl.XVII, fig. 64; Archer 1979, pp. 390–3; Ramaswami 1984; Bayly 1989.

142

143 Muhammed Ali Khan, Nawab of the Carnatic (1717–95)

George Willison, *c.* 1774
Oil on canvas, 240 × 147.5 (93 × 58)
Inscribed on column: *Nabob Waulaujah ummeer ulhind omdat ul mulk ausuph uldowlah behauder Zupherjung sepah saulaur soubahdar of the Carnatick etc 1775*
India Office Library and Records (F12)

The serene and majestic Muslim prince of Willison's portrait is better known as Muhammed Ali Walahjah (1717–95), Nawab of the former Mughal province of Arcot in southern India. The son of a north Indian soldier-adventurer, Muhammed Ali strove to establish himself as an hereditary dynast in this land of few Muslims and an ancient Hindu cultural heritage. The patronage of European artists like Willison was an important feature of Muhammed Ali's battle to secure his realm. Like the building of mosques and palaces in the key cities of his domain, the commissioning of portraits helped to identify Muhammed Ali as a true ruler, a visible embodiment of princely dignity and pious excellence, and as a consumer of suitably aristocratic goods and services. Artists such as Willison helped to transmit these messages to the Nawab's south Indian subjects, and also his English creditors in Madras: their high-priced loans entangled the Nawab in a debilitating spiral of indebtedness and reduced him to the status of a dependent pensioner of the East India Company.

143

In February 1775 Muhammed Ali Khan sent two almost identical full-length portraits of himself to England, one for George III (now in the Victoria Memorial Hall, Calcutta) and this version for the East India Company. As Mildred Archer has pointed out, the composition is borrowed unashamedly from Tilly Kettle's portrait of 1770, Willison simply reversing the pose. The two paintings were part of a group of six family portraits commissioned by Muhammed Ali in 1774 and 1775, and in the years that followed Willison produced further portraits of him and his sons (see Archer 1979, pp.102–3).

Willison (1741–97) arrived in India in 1774 and Muhammed Ali was easily his most important and extravagant patron. In 1775 Willison visited Bengal but was back in Madras by 1777. He sailed for England in June 1780 and worked in London for a few years before settling in Edinburgh. C.A.B./B.A.

PROVENANCE: Presented to the East India Company by Muhammed Ali Khan, 1775.

LITERATURE: Love 1913, II, p.620; Foster 1924, p.6, no.12; Foster 1931, pp.78–9; Sutherland 1952; Millar 1969, I, p.147 (cf.no.1192); Gurney 1973; Archer 1979, pp.98–107, pl. 57; Archer 1986, p.48, no.64, pl.XI.

EXHIBITION: London, Royal Academy, *The Art of India and Pakistan*, 1947–8 (913).

144 Azim-ud-Daulah, Nawab of Arcot, and his son Azam Jah

Thomas Hickey, 1801–2
Oil on canvas, 227.9 × 137.2 (89 × 53½)
Powis Castle (The National Trust) (210)

This is one of the portraits done by Hickey during his second and highly productive visit to India, during which time he made a dramatic record of many of the people connected with the fall of Mysore and the end of the Arcot state. After 1781 the East India Company gradually trenched on the rights and privileges of its ally the Nawab of Arcot on the grounds that he was failing in his duties to provide troops during the conflict with Mysore. During the war of 1780–84 substantial territories were taken over and run by the Company, but the Directors and the British Government forced the Madras authorities to hand them back. Gradually, Nawab Muhammed Ali, saddled with enormous debts to his British creditors, allowed his remaining powers to melt away. He still presided over a grand court which constructed great mosques and brought learned religious men from the north. After his death in 1795, Muhammed Ali's eldest son, Umdat-ul-Umara, of whom the British had long been suspicious, took the throne. After the fall of Seringapatam in 1799 (no.169) allegedly treasonable correspondence between Umdat and Tipu Sultan was discovered.

The finding of a British board of enquiry was anticipated by the death of Umdat in 1801. His son Taj-ul-Umara, alias Ali Hussain, refused the British terms for succession, though the authorities were keen to pass him over because of the trouble that his Shia leanings might bring. Accordingly, Muhammed Ali's nephew, Azim-ud-Daulah (son of Amir-ud-Daulah, his second son) became Nawab. The line continued with Azam Jah (reigned 1819–25, or 1820 according to some sources) seen here, but the Nawabs were little more than pensioners providing ceremonial centres for a vanished realm. Their descendants are still allowed princely honours by the government of India, the only former ruling family to be so recognized.

When the 2nd Baron Clive retired as Governor of Madras in 1803 he brought Hickey's portrait home with him and it has been at Powis ever since. The painting unfortunately tends to confirm Lord Valentia's description of the sitter (quoted by Archer 1979, p.228) as 'very fat and dark, with a stupid countenance, and not the least appearance of a prince in his manners.'

A copy of the portrait was made by Thomas Day in 1820 at the request of the Court of Directors of the East India Company, who presented it to the Nawab of Arcot. This is now at the Fort St. George Museum, Madras.

B.A./C.A.B.

PROVENANCE: Presented by the sitter to 2nd Baron Clive (son of Robert Clive, 1st Earl of Powis) when he retired as Governor of Madras in 1803; by descent.

LITERATURE: Nainar 1950; St John Gore 1972, p.8; Breeze 1973, p.1590, no.177; Archer 1979, pp. 228–9, pl.155; Ramaswami 1984.

Bringing the Company to Book

The corruption associated with the Nawab of Arcot's debts and the arbitrary acts allegedly committed by Hastings and his minions in Bengal and Awadh built up Parliamentary pressure for a review and rationalization of the Company's whole government. This need was only highlighted by the Company's behaviour during the wars of 1778–83, when it was defeated by the Marathas, nearly lost Madras to Haidar Ali and Tipu and was faced with a rash of revolts in Bengal and the north. William Pitt's India Act of 1784 laid the groundwork for closer Parliamentary control over a less capricious Indian government.

C.A.B.

145 Shah Allum in Distress

1773

Engraving, 16.5 × 10 ($6\frac{1}{2}$ × 4)

Inscribed, centre: *The India-man wrecked. L12*

The Trustees of the British Museum (Political Satires no.5100)

The acquisition of the *diwani* of Bengal by the East India Company in 1765 led to high public expectations that wealth would flow into Britain from India (see no.112). These expectations were not fulfilled. The *diwani* revenues were less than Clive and others had anticipated, the Company's new provinces were increasingly costly to defend, and the Company's trading operations in Britain were seriously disrupted by a general collapse of credit. During the autumn and winter of 1772 the Company was in deep crisis: the price of its stock dropped sharply, payment of a dividend was put off and the Company had to appeal to the British Government for immediate financial help. In these apparently dire circumstances it was natural to seek culprits on whom to lay the blame. The servants in India were of course accused of embezzling and squandering the Company's resources, but the Directors at home also came in for much abuse. As this print shows, Sir George Colebrooke (1729–1809), the chairman, was the main target. He had tried to make a great fortune by cornering the world supply of alum, an essential material in the manufacture of textiles (hence 'Shah Allum', a pun on the title of the Mughal emperor, Shah Alam). His own business had failed and he was accused of deliberately misleading the public about the East India Company's problems so that he could sell out his own holding of stock on favourable terms. George Johnstone (1730–87), an enemy of Clive and an active MP, is shown as Colebrooke's main critic.

145

The print also draws attention to what was to be the major outcome of the 1772 crisis: the Government was to intervene much more closely in the Company's affairs. Intervention had already begun in 1767, when Parliament claimed for the state a stake in the supposed riches of the *diwani*, an annual payment of £400,000. This had of course added to the Company's difficulties. In 1772 the Company had to ask the state for assistance. The price of this assistance was a degree of state supervision in the way

146

147

that the Company conducted its affairs, embodied in the Regulating Act of 1773.

P.J.M.

PROVENANCE: Published in the *Westminster Magazine*, January 1773, i.41.

LITERATURE: George 1935, p.110; Spear 1975, p.191.

146 The India Directors in the Suds

Engraving, 9 × 17 ($3\frac{1}{2} \times 6\frac{7}{10}$)
The Trustees of the British Museum, Department of Prints and Drawings (Political Satires no.5102)

This satirical print, like no.103, is directed at Clive while he was under examination by a committee of the House of Commons in 1772 and 1773. Clive is called 'the Jaghire Factor' because he had obtained for himself the grant of a *jagir* or allowance for the support of a dignatory of the Mughal empire, worth £27,000 a year. 'The Black Merchants' haunting him no doubt included the dead Omichund, but were probably also a reference to two Armenian merchants who had come to London to pursue a case against his successor, Harry Verelst, who was accused of disrupting their trade. The Armenians were patronized by Clive's enemies and their grievances were investigated by a Parliamentary committee.

The Directors of the East India Company, under their Chairman Sir George Colebrooke (see no.145), are also a target in this print. In addition to denunciations of the Company's rule in India, they were facing serious financial crisis and pressures from the Government for reform (see no.151). P.J.M.

147 'Count Roupee' in Hyde Park

H. Humphrey, 1797
Hand-coloured engraving, 26 × 35.6 ($10\frac{1}{4} \times 14$)
Inscribed: *published June 5th 1797 by H. Humphrey, 27 St James's Street.*
India Office Library and Records (P1742)

'Nabobs', Company servants who had returned home richer than they ought to have been, were prominent figures in the demonology of late-eighteenth-century England. Rumours of the vast wealth acquired by Britons in the aftermath of Plassey raised fears that an 'East India interest' might influence Parliamentary elections and throw its weight behind a 'ministerial tyranny'. While it is true that East Indian fortunes were spent lavishly, in the construction of a country house at Sezincote, Gloucestershire, for instance, the real size of the East Indian interest was greatly exaggerated. Fewer than thirty MPs could sensibly be included in any such computation during the 1780s. The 'Nabob scare' was part of a more general concern that new money was corrupting society and edging aside aristocratic, landed wealth. The dramatic events of the Warren Hastings impeachment (no.151) gave it a new lease of life, even though Pitt's 1784

India Act had reformed the Company's government and put the scandals behind it. C.A.B.

148 Edmund Burke (1729–97)

Studio of Sir Joshua Reynolds, *c.* 1771
Oil on canvas, 75.6 × 62.9 ($29\frac{3}{4} \times 24\frac{3}{4}$)
National Portrait Gallery, London (655)

Edmund Burke was the first major British politician to become deeply involved with Indian affairs, although he never went there and, as was inevitable in the eighteenth century, his sources of knowledge were often distorted and partisan. But the seriousness of his commitment and the intensity of his concern for Indian people under British rule are beyond question. For nearly all his political career Burke was in opposition to the government of the day. He therefore had very little practical responsibility for the way in which British India was ruled. Apart from drafting one major piece of legislation, which never got through Parliament, his efforts were concentrated on criticism of what was being done and on efforts to bring to punishment a single individual, Warren Hastings (see no.132).

In the early part of Burke's political career India was not an issue of significance. Indeed, in a way that was inconsistent with his later views, Burke at first appeared to be a defender of the East India Company from state interference. In the mid-1770s, however, he became convinced that the Company was ruling India in a scandalous way. His immediate source of information, a not very creditable relative and Hastings's inveterate opponent, Philip Francis, was not always disinterested, but Burke quickly imposed his own vision on what he learnt. He believed that Indian civilization was being barbarously despoiled, that the East India Company must be rigidly restrained and that its servants must be punished for their misdeeds. His codes to retrain the Company were embodied in Fox's India Bill of 1783. When this was rejected Burke was left with punishment as his sole remedy for abuses. He embarked on the impeachment of Warren Hastings, which was to absorb him for most of the rest of his lifetime, and with Hastings's acquittal in 1795 (see no.151), to end in defeat. P.J.M./B.A.

PROVENANCE: Purchased 1882.

LITERATURE: Waterhouse 1941, p.59 (as studio copy).

148

149 William Pitt the Younger

James Gillray, 1789
Watercolour on paper, 22.9 × 17.1 ($9 \times 6\frac{3}{4}$)
Signed in ink: *Js. Gillray* (pencil sketches on back inscribed *William Pitt, drawn by Jas. Gillray (?) 1789*)
National Portrait Gallery, London (135a)

Pitt's interest in imperial affairs was inherited from his father, the great Earl of Chatham, who had been responsible for the successful campaigns against the French colonies during the Seven Years War (1756–63). During the last years of Lord North's administration the near loss of southern India had provided plenty of material with which young Whigs like Pitt could damn the Ministry. For there was a strong (and not unjustified) suspicion that insubordinate interests in Bombay and Madras had inadvertently created a nearly fatal combination against the beleaguered Governor-General, Hastings. Pitt's India Bill (reinforced in 1784) therefore sought to create a clearer command structure in India and subordinate it directly to the British Government. The Governor-General in Calcutta was to have executive power over the Governors of Madras and Bombay. He was also given a decisive voice in his own council where Warren Hastings had often found himself outvoted by a hostile majority. In London a new Board of Control for Indian Affairs was to be set up and its

President, a member of Cabinet, was empowered to override the Court of Directors except in the matter of patronage in jobs. Over the next twenty years Pitt and Henry Dundas, Lord Melville (no.150), worked in tandem on Indian affairs. They were partly successful in bending the Company's policy to their

149

150

will. But in the heat of the wars with Revolutionary and Napoleonic France after 1793, they also allowed a rapid extension of British territory in the subcontinent.

This drawing seems to relate to the contract between Gillray and the publisher S.W. Fores, dated 26 June 1788, in which they agreed to share any profit and loss on an etched plate of Pitt. The plate appeared in February 1789 but, as a result of a quarrel between Fores and the artist, the contract was cancelled. John Hains eventually published the etching in April and May. C.A.B./B.A.

PROVENANCE: S.W. Fores; sale of Fores' caricatures, Puttick and Simpson 1859, bt by H.W. Martin and given by him to present owner in 1861.

LITERATURE: Hill 1965, pp.31–3, pl.24; Walker 1985, I, pp.391–2, II, pl.940.

EXHIBITIONS: London, Arts Council, *Gillray*, 1967 (96); Dublin, *The Disestablishment of the Church of England*, 1970 (66); Yorktown, *Virginia Bicentenary*, 1976.

150 Henry Dundas, 1st Viscount Melville (1742–1811)

Sir Thomas Lawrence, *c.* 1805–10
Oil on canvas, 76.3 × 63.8 ($30 \times 25\frac{1}{8}$)
National Portrait Gallery, London (7846)

Dundas was a scion of a Scottish landed and legal family. He had been Lord Advocate of Scotland (1775–83) and flourished in Parliament because of his skill in managing Scottish constituencies. His administrative ability was recognized by Pitt who made him President of the Board of Control for Indian Affairs in 1784. He built up an unrivalled knowledge of the subject and proved a powerful advocate of a consolidated, even expanded Indian empire, which he saw as a great commercial bonus for the British empire. His connection with Richard Wellesley, Lord Mornington, during his period as Governor-General was close, though sometimes abrasive. But Dundas's most long-term influence on Indian affairs came about through his subtle use of patronage. During his Presidency of the Board, the number of Scots in the Company's services swelled greatly until they were as prominent in the civilian service created by Lord Cornwallis (no.152) as Anglo-Irishmen were in the Company's military.

Despite its uncertain early provenance, this portrait seems to be from Lawrence's own hand. It appears to be a reduced version of the three-quarter length portrait formerly at Melville House and now in the Rosebery collection at Dalmeny, which was exhibited at the Royal Academy in 1810.

B.A./C.A.B.

PROVENANCE: Lawrence himself or Lord Melville (?); anon. sale, Christie's, 11 July 1885 (70); bt Hon. Edward Stanhope MP; from him by present owner.

LITERATURE: Gower 1900, p.149; Armstrong 1913, p.151; Garlick 1964, p.141.; Walker 1985, I, pp.337–8, no.746, II, col. pl. XVII, pl. 816; Garlick 1989, p.236 (see lit. no.554).

151

151 The Trial of Warren Hastings before the Court of Peers in Westminster Hall, 13 February 1788

R.G. Pollard, 1789, after E. Day
Coloured aquatint, 39.8 × 65 ($15\frac{7}{10} \times 25\frac{3}{5}$)
Dated: *1789, London*
India Office Library and Records (P2376)

Burke's work on a Parliamentary committee in 1782 and 1783 convinced him both that Bengal and its neighbouring provinces had been grossly misgoverned and that Hastings was personally responsible for this to a high degree. When Hastings returned to Britain in 1785, Burke called for an inquiry into his conduct. This took the form of an impeachment, that is, of a trial by the House of Lords on charges brought by the House of Commons. First, the House of Commons had to approve Burke's charges. Since Burke was a member of an opposition facing a strong government, it seemed that he was unlikely to succeed. In 1786 and 1787, however, the House of Commons showed that it was prepared to be convinced by the eloquence of Burke and his assistants that there was substance in the case against Hastings; he was therefore sent to stand trial in the Lords.

The impeachment opened in 1788 in great state in Westminster Hall. To begin with it was a much admired public spectacle attracting highly fashionable audiences, but interest soon waned as proceedings became increasingly protracted. Burke and his friends made no real attempt to present a precise judicial case, while Hastings's lawyers were content to demolish much of the prosecution's case on strict interpretations of the rules of evidence. By the time the Lords gave their verdict on Hastings in 1795, the political atmosphere of a world war against Revolutionary France was entirely different to the high moral and reforming tone which the House of Commons had adopted in 1786 and 1787. The trial seemed to be an anomalous persecution of a deserving man, and Hastings was easily acquitted.

In retrospect, there can be no doubt that there was a case to be answered. Hastings had on occasions been high-handed and unscrupulous, but it would be hard to argue that he, or indeed Burke, deserved a nine-year prosecution. B.A./P.J.M.

PROVENANCE: Purchased 1982.

152

152 Charles, 1st Marquess Cornwallis (1738–1805)

Thomas Gainsborough, 1783
Oil on canvas, 74.9 × 62.2 ($29\frac{1}{2} \times 24\frac{1}{2}$)
Inscribed and dated 1783
National Portrait Gallery, London (281)

Lord Rawdon (afterwards Marquess of Hastings and Governor-General of India) and Lord Cornwallis were sitting alternately at Gainsborough's studio at Schomberg House in Pall Mall at the beginning of 1783. Each had requested Gainsborough to paint his portrait for presentation to the other, and the Cornwallis portrait was intended for exhibition at the Royal Academy in the spring. A very similar Gainsborough portrait of Cornwallis of the same size and date was painted for the Prince of Wales and is still in the Royal Collection.

Lord Cornwallis was one of the founders of British India. Seeking a soldier loyal to the ministry to install in the newly augmented office of Governor-General, Pitt appointed a man whose career appeared to have been severely damaged during the American War of Independence. But on his arrival in India in 1787, Cornwallis acted with energy and decision. His tenure of office saw the creation of a body of salaried district collectors and magistrates, the prototype for the Indian Civil Service of the nineteenth century. He 'settled' the land-revenues of Bengal in perpetuity in 1793, a move which he hoped would both stabilize British revenues during the time of war and bring forth in Bengal a class of 'improving landlords'. He also galvanized the sleepy Presidency of Madras in his capacity as Commander-in-Chief of the Company's forces and inflicted a heavy, though not decisive, defeat on Tipu Sultan of Mysore. Otherwise, Cornwallis was cautious about further extensions of British territorial power in India. On his return to England in 1794 he was immersed in Irish affairs, but in 1805 he briefly resumed the office of Governor-General, dying at Fattehgarh on the Ganges in that year. B.A./C.A.B.

PROVENANCE: Painted for Lord Rawdon (Marquess of Hastings); his heirs' sale, Philips, 26 February 1869 (215); bt Graves for NPG.

LITERATURE: Whitley 1915, pp.194–5; Waterhouse 1953, p.24; Waterhouse 1958, p.61, n.168; Millar 1981, p.130, no.281.

EXHIBITION: London, Royal Academy, 1783 (45).

SECTION II

COMPANY SUPREMACY AND INDIAN RESISTANCE

1800–58

From Company to Crown. Nineteenth-Century India and its Visual Representation

C. A. BAYLY

The East India Company Paramount

By 1818 British power was firmly established on the Indian subcontinent. The Maratha states of western India were now defeated tributary kingdoms. Tipu Sultan's resistance was a fading memory, revived from time to time by autobiographies, novels and history paintings such as David Wilkie's depiction of the discovery of the Sultan's body. Of the great Indian principalities, only the Punjab, ruled by the Sikh Maharaja Ranjit Singh, could boast any significant independent military power. Yet the Company's Raj was to be beset by intractable difficulties until its final abolition in the aftermath of the Indian Rebellion of 1857. Military dominance did not bring a respite from war. Over this half-century British power continued to be engaged in costly clashes on the frontiers, and in piecemeal annexations of new territory. The earlier promise of great wealth seemed to have been blighted and the rural economy staged only a fitful revival. After 1793 the Company had tried to bring stability to the Indian countryside. British district collectors and magistrates, now better trained and more honest than their forebears of the eighteenth century, wrestled with the details of the system of land-revenue management inherited from the Mughals. Dependent on Indian clerks and subordinate officials, and beholden to Indian landholders or peasant leaders, the conquerors were strictly limited in what they could achieve, for to a great extent the British empire in India remained an empire run and garrisoned by Indians. That is not to say that British rule was superficial. The open warfare of the eighteenth century was suppressed and new courts of justice were established. Yet, on the other hand, Indian living standards do not seem to have risen very much, if at all, and the Company's budget was generally in deficit. As Kipling later remarked, the British had always worked with defective tools in India.

Still, the subcontinent was safe from outside threats, despite the onward march of the Russian empire beyond the Hindu Kush. The Company's dominion was underwritten by its army. By 1820 this was the most formidable fighting force in Asia. With a strength of about 300,000, it was also one of the largest European-style standing armies in the world. It was used to maintain internal security and to guard the expanding frontiers of British India. But units were often despatched to further outposts of British power: to Egypt in 1801, to Burma from 1824 to 1826 and in 1852, to Afghanistan (with fatal results) between 1838 and 1842, to Malaya periodically and to China in the 1840s and '50s. This oriental army was in fact, thanks to its maintenance by local taxation, a huge hidden subsidy for the British taxpayer.

The Company was careful to keep its European troops (and associated King's Regiments of the British Army) in control of artillery. The regular army was also officered by Europeans. But the European total rarely numbered more than 40,000 men before 1857. The Company was, therefore, deeply dependent on its Indian fighting men. These were the troops portrayed by Indian painters of the Company School and by the British amateur artists who went 'up the country'.

Varieties of Company troops

We can distinguish three broad categories of Company soldier. First, there were the 'armed peasants', the men of the rural high castes (Brahmins and Rajputs), recruited mainly from the plains between Benares and Lucknow, but also from peasant communities in western and southern India. These are the mustachioed redcoats who took to military service to supplement their vulnerable agricultural incomes (nos. 113–4). Lord William Bentinck (Governor-General from 1828 to 1835) called them 'proud men of high caste and character, of respectable connections and proverbially faithful to their salt'.[1] Yet the north Indian sepoys among them were to mutiny with explosive consequences in 1857.

Next, there were the 'tribal' people of the high passes, jungles and hills both of the north and the south, from whom the Company had recruited since its earliest years. These were groups who were distinguished by religion, language, race or occupation from the settled Hindu or Muslim farmers and townsmen of the plains. They began as bowmen, pikemen and guards for British parties in difficult terrain. Later some of the tribal regiments distinguished themselves so greatly in guerrilla warfare that they were drawn into the heart of the regular army, where the Gurkhas, their most famous exemplars, still remain (see no. 183).

Thirdly, there were those communities whose menfolk had long supplied cavalry and swordsmen for the Mughal and post-Mughal kingdoms of north

Fig. 14 Seven Mewatis, unknown artist of Delhi, *c.* 1815–27; watercolour (India Office Library and Records; no. 182)

and central India. They went by such names as Sheikh, Sayyid, Rohilla ('men of the hills' of Pathan origin; no.190) and Mewatti (men of Rajput origin but now converted to Islam; Fig. 14; no.182). In the early nineteenth century a number of Company allies among princes of the Delhi region and officers of mixed race, notably Colonel James Skinner, formed new battalions of auxiliary troops from the men of these warrior communities. The employment they offered compensated villages for the ravages of war and for the loss of the employment which had once been offered them by the Mughal nobility. The pageantry and ritual of the courts and durbars of grandees such as Skinner and Begum Samru (no.192) massaged the esteem of the local leaders who deplored the decline of the Mughal emperors. The racial and cultural mixing that these irregular forces encouraged also gave the Company access to deeper levels of Indian life, now that the expatriate European society was separating itself to form exclusive racial enclaves in the major cities.[2]

The native states

Another pillar of Company power was the expert diplomatic and political system which managed relations with the 'native states'. By 1818 the East India Company had established what came to be called 'Paramountcy' within India. This meant that the British were recognized as supreme rulers by the remaining semi-independent Indian states. Yet the authority of the Company and, through it, of the British Crown coexisted ambiguously with that of the Mughal ruler until Delhi was conquered following the Rebellion of 1857. Those Indian kingdoms, such as Hyderabad, Hindu Mysore and the truncated Awadh, which had survived the final wars of annexation, were penned in by British garrisons and saddled with subsidiary military alliances. These bound them to accept – and to pay for – Company's troops stationed in their territories. British residents (resident ministers) at Indian courts controlled their foreign policy and advised on internal affairs.[3]

Though these 'princely states', as they came to be known, controlled about 30 per cent of the land mass of the subcontinent and 25 per cent of its population, their rulers were politically neutered. Princely rights and dignity were relentlessly eroded. The decline of European painting of Indian rulers and court scenes after the glories of Willison, Zoffany and Tilly Kettle is witness to the dwindling prestige and incomes of these sovereigns. One important exception to this was the series of paintings made in the 1840s of the Sikh court in the Punjab by the Hungarian artist August Shoefft (see no.206–7). He was painting the aristocracy of the last independent and rich Indian kingdom left in the subcontinent; this too was to fall prey to the strategic fears and financial cupidity of the Company after 1845.

Company authority and its image

Revealing, too, is the dearth of European and Indian representations of the new British rulers. After Wellesley's brief attempt to establish a 'Regency' style of empire – the new government house, the grandiose titles, and the rituals of court modelled on those of the Lord-Lieutenant of Ireland – Governors-General were more circumspect. Lord William Bentinck was painted as an enlightened Whig grandee; Dalhousie as a Peelite reformer. But the public and artistic representation of Company power stood uneasily poised between the Mughal, the Royal and the flat ritual of the chartered company. The workaday 'military engineers'' style of architecture prevailed. Indians complained that the Company constructed nothing but courthouses and jails, where once the Mughals had built fine palaces, mosques and tombs. Only the new hybrid Eurasian creation, the bungalow, bore witness to architectural creativity on the British side. This dull uniformity in architecture and the public representation of power was not dispelled until after the mid-century when Indian neo-Gothic and neo-Saracenic styles of architecture flourished and the first Viceroys, as the Governors-General now became, reinvented the Mughal *darbar* and fused it with the panoply of the British Imperial Crown.

For Indians the power of the Company was now unassailable, but its legitimacy as ruler was still masked. Strictly, it remained no more than the revenue manager (*diwan*) of Bengal on behalf of the Mughal emperor. Artists still portrayed Hindu and Muslim rulers as the centres of illustrious courts and the pivot of splendid religious ceremonies and of royal pilgrimages to places of sanctity. Ironically, these actually increased in numbers and opulence under the Christian rulers. Some of the most striking pictures of the period – the Delhi scroll (no.201) or the Mohurram celebrations of the Nawab of Dacca – were painted at Indian courts whose power had been extinct for a generation. It is almost as if there was an inverse relationship between the glory of the ceremonial and the real authority of these protected rulers. The British appear in the pictures as redcoated sepoys or as *topiwalas* ('hatmen', a term which referred to the distinctive headgear of the Europeans). Their presence seems to add to the glory of the Indian ruler, like the retinue of one of his great nobles, but it is Indian royalty which remains central. Much of the literary and textual evidence of this period coming from Indian sources gives the same impression. Whatever their private frustrations, the chroniclers were portraying an India still ruled by its own royalty, and only the brutal drama of the Rebellion of 1857 was to shatter this illusion.

Fig. 15 A raw cotton bulking point, central India; modern photograph by C.A. Bayly

Social change and Company painting

In fact, the careful preservation of the outward forms of the old order under the East Indian Company concealed the changes which British rule had already brought to the country. India's economy had been significantly changed (some historians would say distorted or damaged).[4] Peasant farmers tilled the soil and Indian merchants and bankers still controlled much of the internal trade. European capital and commercial farming had been only fitfully successful. Yet by the mid-century, India had ceased to be the exporter of fine quality artisan cloth that she had been a hundred years earlier. Now she exported increasing quantities of agricultural raw materials such as opium, indigo and raw cotton to markets in Europe and the Far East (Fig. 15). She had also begun to import large quantities of Lancashire-manufactured cotton cloth. The colonial cities of the coast, Calcutta, Bombay and Madras, along with some entrepôts of the hinterland such as Mirzapur or Cawnpore (Kanpur) had grown apace, while the old Mughal centres had declined or stagnated. The British had raised and made more rigorous the collection of the cash land revenues which had supported the Mughals and their successors. Cornwallis and his generation had been solicitous of the indigenous landholding class, the *zamindars*, in part because this was fiscally prudent, but also because they hoped a class of Indian improving landlords like those of England would consolidate itself in due course. However, the new landlords were generally rack-renters not 'Turnip Townsends'. Even on the fringes of arable society, the nomads, pack-bullock drivers, hill and jungle tribes felt the harsh edge of Pax Britannica and found their realms invaded by money-lenders and loggers. The stresses caused by these social changes were to be furiously released during the Rebellion of 1857.

The deeper penetration of British officials, businessmen and soldiers into the texture of Indian life during the early nineteenth century was most revealingly displayed not in the great set pieces of British painting, nor by the traditional Indian miniaturists, but in the occasional drawings of amateur British artists and by the Company School of Indian painters. The drawings of Sir Charles D'Oyly or Emily Eden show their picturesque appreciation of the variety of the Indian scene grappling now with the details of Indian people and places. Paintings of the Company School were made by Indian artists who adapted their styles, mainly for the growing European market in Indian memorabilia. Among the favourite subjects were numerous and minute representations of Indian 'types', organized by caste and occupation: Brahmins and Rajputs, washermen and water carriers. This attempt to record and classify Indians visually went hand in hand with the official effort which created the revenue survey maps of India, the early gazetteers of districts, tribes and castes and the great topographical works such as those of Francis Buchanan or Walter Hamilton. The British wished to 'know their India' for political and financial purposes, but also to organize their own experiences in the categories of genre painting which were now common in Britain.

This effort at the classification of types had its effect on the way in which Indians perceived themselves. The caste system had existed in one form or another for many centuries. It was a complex pattern of ritual and social ranking based on birth and reinforced by ideas of the relative purity and pollution of different types of humans. But many historians now argue that the policies of the East India Company emphasized and made more rigid some aspects of caste. British law courts, paradoxically, tended to reinforce the most orthodox Brahmin interpretations of Hindu custom in matters of inheritance and marriage; people became more aware of caste identity and made attempts to become more 'orthodox' in their social lives. Institutions such as the army consolidated orthodox religion and life-styles (Fig. 16). The painting of the presentation of Colours ceremony (no.191), for instance, shows that the Brahmin priest has virtually reproduced the role of the Protestant chaplain in the Indian regiment. In an earlier period religious practice in Indian war bands would have been more varied and syncretic, with Hindu and Muslim, folk and orthodox religion all represented, but in the private quarters of the sepoys. The classifications of the hundreds of Indian types in the 'Company paintings' fixes an important moment in the British understanding of India, and in the social history of India itself. By emphasizing caste and occupational specialization, the exotic and picturesque, these paintings, it has been argued, present an unchanging view of traditional society.[5]

The great public issues of the early nineteenth century in India reflect this

Fig. 16 Brahmins mounted on the temple 'chariot' bless the crowd, Mylapore, Madras; modern photograph by C.A. Bayly

tendency among Europeans to see religion, caste and tradition in everything, and so to consolidate them. Women and crime, in particular, became focuses of debate between British officials or commentators and the Indian public figures. For the first generation of Indian reformers were beginning to organize and to conduct pamphlet debates in the cities of Bombay, Calcutta and Madras. The missionaries who began to come to India with more freedom after 1813 (when Parliament emended the Charter of the East India Company) saw what they called the 'abyss of female degradation' as a root cause of India's alleged moral degeneration. Officials joined them in deploring female infanticide, child marriage, the interdict against the remarriage of widows among the orthodox, and above all *suttee*.

Suttee (or *sati*) was the practice of self-burning by a widow on her husband's funeral pyre, and it was officially outlawed by Lord William Bentinck in 1829, with the support of some Hindu reformers such as Raja Ram Mohan Roy.[6] There was much more to the debate on *sati* than the suppression of a practice that was abhorrent to rationalists, both British and Indian. For one thing, widow burning was not very widespread, yet it seemed to symbolize what Europeans increasingly represented as the heathen barbarism of India. The thousands of pages of Parliamentary Papers and pamphlets devoted to the issue contrast sharply with the sparse coverage of famine and disease which killed millions during the same period. These were generally portrayed as purely natural events, unrelated to the policies of the rulers. Painters and writers also gave great attention to the issue. While Tilly Kettle and Johann Zoffany in the eighteenth century saw *suttee* as a species of classical virtue (no.278), missionaries and pamphleteers in the nineteenth emphasized the horrors of the custom. Ironically, a few Indian publicists of today claim to see *suttee* (which is a crime under the Indian Penal Code) as an honourable reflection of the country's glorious traditions.

The robbery and strangling of wayfarers, thuggee (*thagi*), was another issue which received much attention from amateur and professional artists. Hollywood and the studios of Hammer Films have continued to be fascinated by it. Highway robbery and murder certainly took place on a large scale in India in the aftermath of the wars of conquest. But most historians now doubt that it was organized by a single religious sect or that it was suppressed singlehandedly by William Sleeman and his Thuggee and Dacoity Department. Many 'thugs' were probably laid-off soldiers or poor migrants who tried to keep alive by murdering and stealing from other wayfarers. The 'Thug scare' tells us as much about the tendency of the British to see India in terms of arcane religious knowledge, and their fear of wanderers and unsettled people, as it does about Indian society.[7] The Thuggee establishment also proved to be a useful tool with which to overawe native princes who were accused of harbouring thugs; pressure could be exerted without going to the expense of directly administering their territories.

The Rebellion of 1857 and its visual representation

By 1857 the East India Company had some achievements to its credit. It had begun road, canal and railway building in the subcontinent. It had suppressed open warfare, though not local rebellion. It had imposed a uniform system of justice, administration and weights and measures and had tied India closely to the world economy as an exporter of agricultural raw materials. The Company had not, however, been able to revive India's vast internal economy, and the country's once prized cloth exports were dwindling. The people's standard of living was at best stagnant, and for all the talk of reform the European administration was not large, resourceful or deeply-seated enough to effect revolutionary economic changes. When the Rebellion of 1857 finally blew away the Company and replaced it with the direct government of the Crown, many already saw the Company as a spent force.

Indians were driven to rebellion in 1857 by a host of resentments and hardships which had become acute by the mid-century. Petitions spoke of 'the tyranny and oppression of the infidel and treacherous English'.[8] Indian princes felt deprived of honour and glory as the administration stepped in to regulate their internal and foreign policy or to absorb their states into British India. Maladministration was the justification for the invasion and annexation of Awadh, the most important of the semi-independent Indian states, in 1856. Landowners and peasants in north India were oppressed by the rigid administration of the land tax and also by the differences of wealth and status which became onerous as the new exports of cash crops benefited some and impoverished others. There was also great resentment at the close relationship which was thought to exist between the civil administration and Christian missionaries who were felt to threaten both Hindu and Muslim beliefs.

Fig. 17 Indian prisoners grinding corn, Benares, during the Rebellion, Egron Lundgren; drawing (Windsor Castle, Royal Library; Indian Sketches Album)

The Mutiny of the Bengal Army in May and June 1857, was the catalyst which gave these tensions an explosive release. The Company's soldiers believed that the gathering pace of military reform was threatening both their livelihood and their way of life. In addition, European troops were so heavily concentrated in Bengal and the Punjab that, when revolt came, they were unable to suppress it rapidly. In the event, however, neither the mutinous army nor the old princely families could provide a coherent leadership to weld together the revolt in the towns and villages. Using their strength in the Punjab, south India and Bengal, the British were able to outflank and surround the rebels, who were suppressed with relative ease, though with great savagery, before the end of 1859.[9]

Most drawing and painting concerning the Rebellion, both at the time and in the later Victorian years, was of military engagements or atrocities perpetrated against British women and children by the mutinous sepoys. Indian 'bestiality' and the treachery of the once loyal natives was taken as proof of their low degree of humanity, and emerging racial stereotypes were hardened. In reality Indian atrocities often followed news of outrages committed by British troops, or were equalled by them. The famous massacre of British women and children in the station of Cawnpore, for instance, was matched by General Neill's executions of civilians in nearby districts. The destruction of British lives and property by rebellious town and country mobs also reflected the deep hatred of many poor and dispossessed people for a regime which they saw as alien, Christian and exploitative. But the full-blooded participation of many peasants and of the urban poor is hardly represented at all in the pictures and drawings (the work of the Swedish artist Lundgren is a partial exception to this; Fig. 17). British visual representation followed the view of the Indian Civil Service in the region, which held that this was nothing more than a mutiny. The Bengal military, however, were clear that the grievances of rulers, landlords and peasants played an equally important part, while Disraeli himself posed the question of whether the empire was not witnessing 'a great national revolt'. For its part, the Rebellion was so firmly suppressed that Indian representation of these events is virtually non-existent until the radical nationalists of the 1900s began to parade icons of the famous rebel leaders in their processions and demonstrations. Today, however, the rebellious warrior queen, the Rani of Jhansi, has achieved the status of an Indian Joan of Arc.

The New India and the British Crown

The Rebellion ended the East India Company and gave the British Crown and Parliament a more direct role in the governance of India. Other changes were also recasting the links which bound Britain to India. The Suez Canal, opened in 1869, and the railways, which extended rapidly over the subcontinent after 1853, tied India more firmly into the international economy (Fig. 18). Her exports of raw cotton, wheat, jute, tea and coffee were matched by a surge in imports of British manufactured textiles and machinery. A new range of rich merchant families, both British and Indian, grew up in the major centres, notably Bombay. The electric telegraph and rapid spread of the printing press revolutionized India's government. It also provided a potent means of communication for the Raj's opponents among the new generation of younger men who had had the benefit of an English education in the small number of government schools and larger number of private schools which were founded after 1857.

Fig. 18 Choo choo gari: late 19th-century mural on a *haveli* in Nawalgarh, Shekhavati district; modern photograph by G.H.R. Tillotson

New voluntary associations and political clubs sprang up, and in 1885 these came together in Bombay for the first meeting of the Indian National Congress.[10] Indian lawyers and educationalists, along with their supporters among businessmen, demanded that the Government provide protection for infant Indian industries by raising tariffs against British imports. They also pressed for the expansion of representative institutions of government and for easier access by Indians to government employment. The rulers made some concessions by extending the representative element in municipal and provincial legislative councils; but these were not enough to assuage the growing restiveness of young India. The new educated class, denounced as a 'microscopic minority' by the rulers, seemed to be making little headway against the bureaucracy of the Indian Civil Service, and saw itself surrounded by mass poverty which it believed had been deepened by the economic developments of the nineteenth century. By the first years of the next century

Fig. 19 The Indo-Saracenic Style: Mayo College, Ajmer, designed by Charles Mant, 1875–85; modern photograph by G.H.R. Tillotson

some Indians were making radical demands for total independence, and a few were prepared to press for freedom with terrorist violence.

These great changes in Indian society were mirrored by, in some ways reinforced by, a change in representations of power and wealth. The British Crown now finally supplanted the Mughal throne as the centre of political authority. Queen Victoria became Empress of India. Great Imperial assemblies or durbars were held in 1877, 1903 and 1911 at which English feudal ritual was mixed promiscuously with Mughal grandeur.[11] Governors and Indian princes expressed their power in styles of architecture and public ceremonial – coronations, investitures and tiger-shoots – following the practice of European and Indian royalty. The grand neo-Gothic buildings of Bombay served the merchant princes of Bombay well. But a new style, Indo-Saracenic, which blended Gothic and medieval Muslim features seemed to match the pretentions of Victoria's Raj even better.[12] The new middle class of Indian lawyers, businessmen, estate managers and educationalists also sought to represent themselves. They usually hit on an Indian version of English and Scottish Victorian civic virtue. Indian public men had themselves painted, and now photographed, as enlightened leaders of local communities, wearing Indian dress modernized with reference to Western fashion. They built municipal clock towers and neo-Gothic civic buildings alongside the temples, mosques and wells which their ancestors had constructed. Even as

European historical painting and drawing in India fell into decline, photography, architecture and public ritual achieved a more distinctive character (Fig. 19).

Of course, this Westernization of public style and of representation was generally limited to the élite. Older arts and crafts persisted, though artists in the bazaars adapted some Western techniques such as aniline dyes or electroplated rather than solid gold thread. Anglo-Indians and radical Indian aesthetes, drawing on the Arts and Crafts movement in Britain and fearful for the survival of India's heritage, actually gave artisan industries a boost at the end of the nineteenth century. But it is easy to overestimate the extent to which the mass of Indian society or art was influenced by the West before 1947, particularly as British sources tend to exaggerate that impact. Well before Gandhi had pioneered the return to Indian dress and Indian languages within the Indian National Congress, the radical politicians of the 1900s were emphasizing their Indian roots. Mother Kali, the terrible goddess of destruction, became the patroness of the fight of Bengal's young radicals against Lord Curzon's attempt to partition their Province in 1905. In western India Shivaji, the warrior hero of the seventeenth century who resisted the Mughals, and the elephant-headed god Ganesh became potent symbols for Bal Gangadhar Tilak's call for *purna swaraj* or complete independence. His political and personal style contrasted quite sharply with the liberal rhetoric and Westernized way of life of many of the leaders of the 'moderate' wing of the Congress.[13] These symbolic battles between icons, styles of dress and styles of self-representation were to go right to the heart of the struggle to define a new India.

NOTES

1. 'Evidence of Lord William Bentick' in *Parliamentary Papers, 1836, xl, paper 319, 10*, cited in Embree 1962, p. 238. See also Sleeman 1844, repr. 1973, pp. 641–3.
2. For information on this subject I am indebted to Miss Seema Alavi of St Catharine's College, Cambridge. See her forthcoming Ph.D dissertation, 'North Indian military culture in transition, 1770–1830'.
3. Thompson 1943 remains the best older study. See also Jeffrey 1978.
4. See Kumar 1983. The controversy over the effects of British rule in India is discussed in Charlesworth 1982.
5. Amin 1972: introduction in his edition of Crooke 1879, repr. 1989; Archer 1972, introduction.
6. Kopf 1969, Mani 1985 in Sangam and Vaid 1989.
7. For the older view, see Sleeman 1933. For revisions, see Nigam 1987. I have also benefited from discussions with Ms Radhika Singha of Darwin College, Cambridge; see her forthcoming Ph.D thesis 'The introduction of English criminal law into north India, 1770–1838.'
8. The Azimgarh Proclamation, appendix to Mukherjee in De 1976.
9. Metcalf 1964. Two recent books on the Rebellion are Stokes 1986 and Mukherjee 1984.
10. For the later nineteenth century see Seal 1968 and McLane 1977.
11. Cohn in Ranger and Hobsbawm 1983.
12. Metcalf 1989; Tillotson 1989.
13. Cashman 1974.

The Indian Picturesque: Images of India in British Landscape Painting, 1780–1880

G. H. R. TILLOTSON

The representation of India in British landscape painting is a unique artistic achievement: at no other time has one country been so extensively and minutely observed by artists from another – despite various other fashions for antique and exotic lands. And yet this artistic episode lasted in strength for only a century. The East India Company had begun trading operations as early as 1600, but it was only after the full establishment of an English landscape school in the mid-eighteenth century that India was first visited by a professional landscape painter: William Hodges arrived in 1780. By that time, the expansion of the Company's activities in India, and the increased number of permanent British residents there, had created both a market for pictures within India and an interest in that country at home. In the ensuing decades, the number of British artists visiting or taking up residence in India was never large, but it remained steady.

That succession effectively came to an end with the departure of Edward Lear in 1875. The reason usually given for the demise of landscape painting in India is the rise in popularity of photography as a method of depicting and conveying information on the country. Another factor may have been the increasing lure of other areas, such as the Near East, which were closer to hand but less well known. The demise was not of course definitive: after 1875, India was visited by artists of the calibre of Mortimer Menpes, and more recently by artists such as John Nankivell. But in spite of these individuals, a continuity of tradition had ended.

Until that tradition began, the British public had no visual idea of India. Some earlier depictions existed, but were known to be fanciful. The supply of large numbers of detailed depictions of India by artists who had been there therefore became a powerful force in shaping British perceptions of India's physical aspects. But the painters themselves were not naïve recording instruments. They were creative artists, and they took with them to India their training and a well-defined aesthetic. They also took certain expectations about what they would find, and although a traveller's expectations may be overturned, they generally determine what he looks for. Through much of the century in question, English landscape painting was dominated by that complex aesthetic known as the Picturesque. Indeed the very inception of a full-bodied English landscape tradition was itself a part of the wider process of the formulation of the Picturesque, so that this aesthetic was bound to prove a profound and durable influence. Among its many effects was that it coloured how English artists and their audiences saw India.

The idea of the Picturesque began to acquire its distinctive form in the mid-eighteenth century. Originally, it was a vogue for looking at the natural landscape in a manner informed by principles derived from paintings, notably from the works of such seventeenth-century masters as Claude Lorrain, Salvator Rosa and Gaspard Poussin. The influence of Dutch painters such as Jacob van Ruisdael offered some adjustment to these principles. Later, through the writings of Richard Payne Knight, Uvedale Price and Humphry Repton, this vision was directed towards a new style of landscape gardening; and, having thus found its way on to the country estate, it subsequently exerted a powerful influence on British architecture. But however widely it was applied, the idea always entailed an appeal to pictorial values; and so it could be turned back on the art of landscape painting itself. And this was done explicitly by William Gilpin and Alexander Cozens in the 1780s.

What the Picturesque required of the artist in practice was, first, that his painted landscape should be generally harmonious and coherently composed, including a good depth of field, preferably divisible into three grounds. It was to be, in other words, frankly artificial. In addition, the classically approved but now ridiculed 'smoothness' was rejected in favour of a certain 'roughness', which offered a greater variety of form and line. There was a preference for abrupt shapes such as irregular hills and buildings. There was also a strong predilection for intricate detail, especially in the foreground, which could be littered with stones or plants or broken statuary. The work should contain some reference to man's presence in the landscape: a wandering traveller or toiling peasant, perhaps; or a ruin that was both picturesquely irregular in itself and a reminder of man's transience. This kind of treatment had begun to appear in British landscape painting by the middle of the century as a result of direct and individual stylistic influences, such as that of Ruisdael on Thomas Gainsborough, and that of Claude on Richard Wilson, his greatest British imitator. But from the 1780s onwards the essentials of the Picturesque were analysed and propagated in the writings of the aesthetic theorists, and by this means became common currency among all who were engaged in, or even talked about, painting.[1]

From the start, travel was an important element. As a sensibility, the Picturesque encouraged the aesthete to travel in search of landscapes to admire; while as a painterly method, it sent the artist in search of new subject-matter. Initially, both routes led to the wilder parts of the British Isles, including the Lake District. But soon, mass travel to such accessible places jaded the appetite, and the field of discovery was broadened to include continental Europe, especially such dramatic regions as the Alps. Thus foreign topography became part of the stock-in-trade of the Picturesque. The extension of Picturesque travel to India (as to other parts of the colonial East, and even China) was an easy step; it required no change in principle or inspiration, merely a widening of the ambit.

The first professional British landscape painter to visit India was Wilson's pupil, William Hodges. He arrived in Madras in February 1780, but as the war with Haidar Ali prevented him from travelling in the interior of the country, he moved on to Calcutta the following year. From there, he made three tours westwards; starting each time along the River Ganges and visiting towns of historical and architectural interest, he reached as far as Agra on his

Fig. 20 The Taj Mahal, William Hodges, 1783; grey wash with pen and grey ink over pencil (Yale Center for British Art, Paul Mellon Collection)

Fig. 21 The Pagodas at Deogur, William Hodges, *c.* 1787; oil on canvas (Private Collection)

third and most extensive tour (Figs 20 and 21). He finally returned home from Calcutta in September 1783. He had visited Benares on his second tour in August 1781. His depiction of part of the city (no.246) bears many of the hallmarks of the Picturesque treatment, notably in the varied and irregular outline formed by the buildings, further enlivened by tufted trees; in the sense of movement created by small, scattered details, such as the figures and boats at the *ghats*; and in the broken stabs of colour.

Earlier in his career, Hodges had accompanied Captain Cook's second expedition to the South Seas (1772–5). This experience exposed him to landscapes of a kind entirely unfamiliar to the eyes of European painters, and to the company of men who looked at atmospheric effects in an acute, objective manner. It has often been argued that Hodges consequently discarded the classical formulae of his training in favour of a more impressionistic style; and that he later approached the Indian landscape with the same frank observation.[2] While some of his sketches made in the South Seas are indeed strikingly immediate, this assessment is not generally borne out by his finished oils, least of all those of Indian subjects. Most, like no.246, display a treatment that is firmly rooted in the new English tradition. Some time after Wilson's death, Hodges wrote an article on his former master, praising 'the classical turn of thinking in his works, and the broad, bold and manly execution of them'.[3] Just these qualities characterize Hodges's own work and – as his remark makes clear – they were part of an artistic inheritance.

Hodges was in fact preceded by the curious figure of Francis Swain Ward, who is not generally counted a professional painter of India since he travelled there in the service of the Madras army. It was only when he resigned his commission and returned to England in 1764 that he resumed his earlier career as an artist, producing several canvases of Indian subjects. Ten of these, including *A Choultry* (no.245), he presented to the Company in 1773, perhaps as an inducement to allow him to rejoin the service in that year and return to India. The picture shows a travellers' shelter of a type once common in southern India, set in an idealized landscape.

The most famous British landscape painters to visit India were undoubtedly Thomas Daniell and his nephew William. They landed at Calcutta early in 1786, and in the course of the next seven and a half years travelled extensively in the subcontinent. Their first long tour took them westwards along the Ganges and through neighbouring regions, in the footsteps of Hodges. This itinerary was dictated partly by the convenience of starting in areas under British control, and partly by the Daniells' determination to emulate Hodges. Eventually they penetrated a good deal further, reaching Delhi and pressing on into the Himalayan foothills, where they became the first Europeans to visit Srinagar in Garhwal. It was on their way back on this tour that they stopped (as Hodges had seven years before) at Sasaram in Bihar, to visit the majestic tomb of the Emperor Sher Shah Sur (no.249). Their last stopping place before returning to Calcutta at the end of 1791 was the ancient deserted city of Gaur in Bengal (no.248).

Among the friends made by the Daniells – whose hospitality they enjoyed at provincial stations – was Samuel Davis, a Company servant and amateur draughtsman. Though at this period stationed at Bhagalpur, Davis had earlier accompanied the embassy of Captain Samuel Turner to Tibet in 1783. In the event, Davis was refused entry into Tibet itself, and so spent his time instead recording the landscape and architecture of Bhutan (no.247).

After a tour in the south in 1792 – visiting temples and the hill-forts that had featured in the recent war against Tipu Sultan – the Daniells visited Bombay. There they met the artist James Wales, who was engaged in making an extensive survey of the rock-cut temples of the region. The Daniells joined him in his explorations for a while, before beginning their long voyage home

Fig. 22 The Composition Piece, a capriccio of Indian architecture, Thomas Daniell, 1799; oil on canvas (Private Collection)

Fig. 23 Mausoleum of Nawaub Asoph Khan, Rajemahal, Thomas and William Daniell; aquatint from *Oriental Scenery*, volume III, 1803

in the autumn of 1793. After Wales's premature death in 1795, they used his sketches to produce a series of aquatint views of the temples of Ellora, published in 1803 (no.250).

The attraction of these temples for Wales and the Daniells was not just their strange and exotic aspects, nor only their Arcadian setting. As is evident from the aquatints, the artists had a serious archaeological interest too. The plates were intended to appeal to the scholarly as well as the aesthetic impulses of connoisseurs, to offer them a thorough and exact source-book on early Hindu architecture. The same spirit pervades most of the Daniells' work. Their numerous oils and the magnificent aquatints of the six volumes of *Oriental Scenery* (published after their return home, between 1795 and 1808) constitute a detailed record of many aspects of Indian architectural history

(Figs 22, 23). Similarly, Davis's views of Bhutan are not merely picturesque scenes but topographical illustrations of a previously unexplored region of the subcontinent. Indeed, in general the work of the late eighteenth century is imbued with a spirit of intellectual enquiry.

This period was also marked by considerable examination of India by British scholars. As visually, so intellectually, the British had been largely ignorant of India; but through the pioneering work of scholars such as Sir William Jones and Sir Charles Wilkins, they began to acquire some knowledge of the country's religions, laws, customs and literature. This scholarly movement was given focus and impetus by the establishment in 1784 of the Asiatic Society of Bengal. It is clear that artists saw themselves as contributing in their own manner to a more general process of discovery. Thomas Daniell explicitly compared his work with that of naturalists and philosophers.[4] Hodges, too, described his work in these terms. Part of the attraction for Hodges of Benares was its importance in Hinduism. He visited the city in the company of his patron, Warren Hastings, who was also a patron of the Asiatic Society and – through the foundation of a Persian college – of local traditions of learning. Both men urged a cultural pluralism that would open their compatriots' eyes to the wealth of India's artistic and intellectual heritage.[5] Like other contemporaries, they saw themselves as pioneers in the huge task of examining this newly-discovered store; and in their enthusiasm they assumed that prejudice was the fruit only of ignorance and would be dispelled by study.

If artists were to play a part in this high-minded movement, it was essential that the information they conveyed should be accurate. Consequently, we find in their writings frequent assurances as to the faithfulness and authenticity of their depictions; and such qualities became the most common criteria of criticism. Thus the young William Daniell – piqued that he and his uncle had been anticipated by Hodges – sought to disparage Hodges's work, not by saying that it was badly executed or ugly, but by insisting that it was inaccurate. The slightly later traveller Lord Valentia chastised particular works of both Hodges and the Daniells for giving false impressions of places; and the Daniells' views of Benares were famously dismissed by Lear on the same grounds (see no.261).[6]

The artists were of course bound to invite such charges, because their aim at fidelity was seriously undermined by the power of the Picturesque aesthetic. The Picturesque involved an act of interpretation; it was a method of portrayal which quite frankly altered or rearranged parts of a subject from how they were to how they ought to be, according to criteria that were quite alien to Indian soil. In many of these paintings there is a palpable tension between the informative intention and the Picturesque treatment. And here the comparison of such work with the scholarly investigation of India is reinforced; for Western students of India's religions could seldom resist the temptation to compare Hindu mythology with the classical myths that formed much of their own education, and such comparisons led easily to misunderstandings of India. Similarly, the artists, while professing to be true to their subjects, offered a view of India through a lens – and one which was also ultimately inherited from a classical European tradition.

The Picturesque treatment was frequently at odds not only with the quest for truth, but also with the exotic nature of the subject. Whatever their other concerns, a part of the lure of India for these artists was always its strangeness. Indeed, a fascination with the exotic was a part of the Picturesque repertoire: so much so that one of the effects of the work of Hodges and the Daniells was to indulge this Regency taste, encouraging the Picturesque movement at home to new flights of eclectic fancy. An Indian vogue in architecture arose in England, permeating country houses such as Sezincote in Gloucestershire (1805), and culminating in the Royal Pavilion at Brighton, as remodelled by John Nash between 1815 and 1818. In Brighton and Sezincote the Picturesque and the exotic were complementary. And yet, paradoxically, the treatment of real Indian subjects with a Picturesque painterly method tended to temper, rather than exaggerate, their exoticism, by making them conform to a set of supposedly universally applicable values, derived from European art.

A further kind of tension arises where the subject is a building and therefore itself a work of design – a tension between the Picturesque and the Indian aesthetic involved. The Muslim tomb at Gaur depicted by Thomas Daniell, for example (no.248), is of a type in which the plan and the arrangement of architectural volumes are governed by a rigorous formal geometry. But Daniell has depicted it in a manner which suppresses that quality: we see it obliquely, with its symmetry disrupted, so that it becomes a Gothic folly in an Arcadian park. The English vision that these artists transferred to India may have been unavoidable. But they made no effort to avoid it; on the contrary, they declared the Picturesque as their manifesto. And so their pictures often remain unresolved, as the Picturesque competes not only with the Indian aesthetics of their subjects, but with their own efforts towards authenticity and exoticism.

Their work nevertheless laid the foundations for what was to follow, and particularly with regard to the continuing obsession with Indian architecture. Henry Salt travelled in India for two years, starting in 1803, with his patron Lord Valentia. On his return he used his sketches (no.251) to produce a series of aquatints similar in format to, and intended to compete with, those of the Daniells. Colonel Robert Smith of the Bengal Engineers developed a profound interest in Indian architecture, especially the Mughal monuments of Delhi, which he helped to restore (no.257; Fig. 24). Another enthusiast was his namesake, Captain Robert Smith of the 44th Regiment. Among the latter's work are some watercolours depicting sites along the Ganges that he visited on a tour made in 1832–3. In his view of Allahabad (no.258), the cattle and rocks in the foreground and the agitated cloudy sky follow so closely the Picturesque formula as proposed by Gilpin that the scene might at first glance be mistaken for Aldershot.

The taking of the cities of Delhi and Agra by British forces under Lord Lake in 1803 made Mughal architecture more accessible to the British, and artists were not its only admirers. Many who could not produce drawings themselves commissioned views from Indian draughtsmen, especially those who had trained with British engineers and so had mastered the Western technique of perspective drawing and could depict buildings realistically. There thus arose a genre of Company painting devoted to measured and precise drawings of Mughal buildings and their decorative details (no.256).[7]

Fig. 24 The Kila Kona Masjid in the Purana Qila, Delhi, Robert Smith, *c.* 1823; oil on canvas (Yale Center for British Art, Paul Mellon Collection)

In spite of the British influence, these Indian works were unaffected by the Picturesque and show a different interpretation of the architecture.

James Baillie Fraser was a Calcutta businessman, though his greater gifts lay in art. In 1815 he accompanied his brother on a tour of the Himalayan foothills, and subsequently published twenty aquatints of *Views in the Himala Mountains* (no.255). Like Davis's views of Bhutan, these prints revealed a lesser-known margin of India at a time when it had become a focus for British political and commercial ambitions. Like Salt's, Fraser's aquatints follow the pattern established by the Daniells, indicating the force of their stylistic influence. The publication of such views as prints ensured that they reached a wider audience. But another advantage of the aquatint was that this medium had long been thought especially suitable for the Picturesque landscape, as it was capable of imitating in print the effects of watercolour. It was used in this manner in England by many artists, including Paul Sandby and Philip de Loutherbourg; and it became even more popular following the dramatic improvements in the technique made by the Daniells. By about 1830, however, great volumes of aquatints were no longer produced, and their place was taken by more modest illustrated travel books, using lithography, a less spectacular but simpler form of reproduction.[8]

While Salt and Fraser were sustaining the intellectual ambitions and grandiose schemes of an earlier age, some other artists were looking at previously unnoticed aspects of Indian scenery, aspects that were less dramatic but also less relentlessly inspiring, more amenable and pleasant. The dominant figure among them was George Chinnery, who worked in India between 1802 and 1825, when he departed for Macao (see no.265). Much of his work was portraiture – a more lucrative pursuit – but his real love was for landscape.

Fig. 25 Hut by a Ruined Mosque in Bengal, George Chinnery, *c.* 1810; oil on canvas (Private Collection)

He spent the years 1808 to 1812 based in Dacca, exploring the Bengali countryside and producing vast quantities of drawings of the rivers and their craft, and villages with their huts and cattle (Fig. 25 and no.252).

Chinnery's host in Dacca was the Collector, Sir Charles D'Oyly, a prolific amateur artist. D'Oyly learned a great deal from his guest, and from this period onwards produced numerous small works, in a range of media, evidently influenced by Chinnery's style (no.253). Another pupil of Chinnery's, in Calcutta, was William Prinsep, a member of a large family of businessmen and amateur artists. He too produced views of village life in a style greatly indebted to Chinnery (no.254). Such works show to what extent an artist could be made to see India through another's eyes. It is often observed that British artists in India were never much influenced by indigenous artistic traditions; indeed their style was rarely greatly affected even by the Indian landscape itself (in contrast to that of European artists working in other parts of the East).[9] Works such as these are the extreme case, being not merely guided but dominated by a vision borrowed from another artist, so that reality intrudes only at second hand.

It is perhaps not surprising that imitation characterizes the work of amateurs – which both these pictures are. In fact, the majority of British views of India were made by amateurs; not professional visitors like Hodges or

Salt, but men and women who were resident there for another purpose and filled their leisure hours with drawing. For many the ability to draw was a socially desirable skill, while for engineers like Smith it was acquired in the process of training.

The professional minority, however, were always dominant, and the third quarter of the nineteenth century saw three such visitors, all working chiefly in watercolour. This medium had always been thought suitable for picturesque topography, but it was now the major medium. Aquatint had been priced out of fashion, and under the impact of Romanticism and then the Pre-Raphaelites, oil painting had moved on to other concerns.

William Carpenter travelled in India between 1850 and 1857, especially in the west and north, dividing his attention equally between people and scenery (no.259). William Simpson, who had established his reputation with his views of the Crimea, was sent to India in the wake of the Mutiny of 1857, by the publishers Day & Son, with the intention of producing another great book of views of a region made topical by conflict. The venture failed as the publishers went bankrupt; but between 1859 and 1862, Simpson travelled widely in the country. He concentrated in fact not on scenes connected with the Mutiny, but on subjects with inherent picturesque appeal, and there were none more appealing than the palaces of Rajasthan (no.260). Edward Lear was one of the finest English watercolourists, in whose work the standard (and by now rather overworked) formulae of the Picturesque were converted into a highly individual style (Fig. 26). Yet in some ways, his work in India (which he visited between 1873 and 1875) shows how little had changed. Like Hodges a century before him, he was attracted to Benares as the principal Hindu city, and his vision of it was not radically different (no.261).

Though properly a manner of looking at – and representing – landscape, the Picturesque could be applied also in certain senses to people. This involved simply the representation of people, not as they were, but again in a manner tinged by an aesthetic based in a tradition of European art. And this occurred in India.

One of the earliest artists to set about the systematic portrayal of the Indian population was the Belgian Baltazard Solvyns. Inspired by the vogue in Europe for books illustrating the traditional costumes of various countries, Solvyns began in 1794 to produce a set of two hundred and fifty coloured etchings depicting the manners and customs of the Hindus, doing the printing himself from his own drawings (no.262). In its intention to inform, this project is akin to the architectural studies of the same period by Hodges and the Daniells. But commercially it was not a success. Solvyns's plates were judged to be so faithful to their subjects as to be insufficiently picturesque: he had evidently got the balance wrong in meeting the conflicting demands of his time. But the idea behind his work proved enormously influential; especially on Company painters, and albums depicting types of Indians classified by caste or trade were made in large numbers in the early nineteenth century.

Some of the later works of William Daniell, produced after he and his uncle had completed the volumes of *Oriental Scenery*, also focus on India's people. In those drawings that were engraved as illustrations for the *Oriental*

Annual in the 1830s, and in some of his oils (no.263), we see a somewhat sentimentalized view of Indian women; they have become exotic beauties, not unlike the idealized odalisques of the Orientalist painters. A little later, Emily Eden published her *Portraits of the Princes and People of India* (1844). Eden had accompanied her brother, Lord Auckland, while he was Governor-General (from 1835 to 1842) and this position had given her privileged access to India's royal courts. But it is doubtful whether the Sikh princes would have recognized themselves as the epicene creatures of her plates (no.264).

It might be felt that in depictions of India's people – even more than those of landscape and architecture – the Picturesque treatment is a disturbing misrepresentation, a simple falsehood. It has been argued that this process was wilful, that representations of India by British artists consistently sanitized the subject, showing India as the British wanted to see it; and a recent school of thought links such preferences to Britain's status as an imperial power.[10] Certainly some British art in India (such as George Atkinson's work on the Mutiny) served a clear propagandist purpose. But whether all British artists were deploying the Picturesque in order to contribute to a wider political intention is more doubtful. Where such an intention is not explicit, it must be assumed (by those who suppose it to exist) to have been subconscious, making the theory conveniently untestable.

What is clear is that the idea of the Picturesque, having arisen from discussions about European landscape in the mid-eighteenth century, cannot itself be identified as a part of the imperialist project. Furthermore, it was so fundamental a part of the English landscape tradition that to most artists it was not a consciously adopted instrument but an inescapable artistic vision. Consequently, while it is certainly true that the pictures discussed here show India as Britons wanted to see it, their preferences were inspired primarily by an aesthetic habit. And to the persistence of that habit these pictures are a remarkable testimony.

Fig. 26 A View of Benares, Edward Lear, 1873; watercolour on paper (India Office Library and Records; no. 261)

NOTES

1. Specific reference to painting is made in the works of Gilpin (published from 1782) and Cozens 1785. See also Knight 1794; Price 1794; and Repton 1795. For discussion of the Picturesque among Jane Austen's characters, see Hussey 1927, pp. 1, 231.
2. See for example Archer 1967, p. 869; Stuebe 1979, pp. 2, 18–20, 45–6, 84–5; Smith 1985, pp. 56–8, 76.
3. (Hodges) 1790, p. 404. The anonymous article is generally attributed to Hodges, for example by Stuebe 1979, p. 6.
4. Daniell 1810, Preface.
5. Hodges 1794, pp. iii–iv, 47, 65; see Hastings's introduction to Wilkins's translation of the *Bhagavad Gita* (1785).
6. Daniell comments on Hodges in his journal, published in Hardie and Clayton 1932 – see pp. 43, 46, 64; Valentia 1809, vol. 1, pp. 89, 356; Lear, in Murphy (ed.) 1953, p. 46.
7. See especially Archer 1968.
8. Such as R. M. Grindlay's *Scenery, Costumes and Architecture*, 1830.
9. See MaryAnne Stevens 1984, p. 15, on changes in the technique of European artists in the near East; and Sweetman 1988, p. 135, on Islamic influences in the work of J. F. Lewis.
10. See for example Pal and Dehejia 1986, p. 16.

Company Supremacy and Indian Resistance

The final stage of the British rise to dominance in the Indian subcontinent took place during the war between Great Britain and revolutionary, later Napoleonic, France. The new wave of conquest was justified by appeals to the distant possibility of a French thrust against India, but the true reasons for British expansion lay once again in the subcontinent itself. The Company was still faced by two powerful Indian enemies which were rapidly developing sophisticated military power: the Sultans of Mysore, Haidar Ali and Tipu Sultan, and the Marathas. The British regarded Mysore as 'the most perfect despotism in the world', the Marathas as a dangerous machine for 'freebooting' and plunder. Under Richard Wellesley, Lord Mornington (later Marquess Wellesley), Governor-General from 1798 to 1805, the *coup de grâce* was delivered to Tipu. Then the Marathas were neutralized, finally to be overwhelmed in a later war of 1817–18. Yet these were 'close-run things'. The Indian states put up a valiant defence against British regular troops and the powerful army of men of peasant origin which the Company had drawn from the eastern provinces of Awadh, Benares and Bihar, and from parts of the south and west. Meanwhile, Company armies had overrun the ancient heartland of Mughal power and the Emperor himself had become a pensioner in the hands of the conquerors. As Company power spread north to the Punjab, Sind and the borders of Afghanistan, Pax Britannica was maintained by the subtle arts of the Residents at Indian courts, and by the powers of district collectors and judges in areas controlled directly by the British. The drama of these events and their symbolic importance to a people now defining itself more clearly as a 'conquering race' were magnificently reflected in this, the last great age of Indian history painting in British art. C.A.B.

153 Richard Colley Wellesley, 1st Marquess Wellesley (1760–1842)

J. Pain Davis, *c.* 1815
Oil on canvas, 53.2 × 42.7 ($20\frac{7}{8} \times 16\frac{3}{4}$)
National Portrait Gallery, London (846)

Brother of the famous Duke of Wellington and two other colonial public servants, Wellesley came of an Anglo-Irish family and was educated at Eton and Oxford. He caught the eye of Dundas and Pitt who saw the necessity of giving the Company's government a strong executive at a time when the French remained a mortal threat to Britain's interest both in Europe and overseas. Unlike his predecessors, Wellesley went to India in 1798 with a blueprint for conquest: he had decided to force a showdown with the Marathas and Tipu Sultan and to purge, or if necessary sweep away, the failing Indian governments in Arcot, Awadh and Hyderabad. He achieved his aims while at the same time elevating and glorifying the office of Governor-General, which temporarily attained something like the status the Viceroy was to have in the later nineteenth century. Yet Wellesley's pretensions, and the enormous cost of his wars which had dragged the Company even further into debt, attracted fierce hostility in Parliament. Wellesley was recalled in 1805, before his time as Governor-General was up, and it was not until the 1820s that public opinion began to see in the 'glorious little man' one of the great founders of the Indian empire.

153

Lord Wellesley wears the Ribbon and Star of a Knight of the Garter. The National Portrait Gallery has a pencil and watercolour drawing (847) which the artist's executor, M. Montague Brown, suggests may have been a study from the life for this portrait.

C.A.B./B.A.

PROVENANCE: The artist; bequeathed by his widow, 1890.

LITERATURE: Butler 1970; Walker 1985, vol.I, p.523, vol. II, pl.1312.

EXHIBITION: Brighton, *The British in India*, 1973 (B.11).

154 Hyder Ally Cawn sitting in his Durbar

Unknown artist, *c.* 1793
Engraving, 12 × 15 ($4\frac{4}{5} \times 6$)
India Office Library and Records (P368)

Haidar Ali and his son Tipu Sultan overhauled the revenue administration and built up the military might of Mysore with a vigour which was unparalleled elsewhere in the subcontinent. Haidar Ali had been a cavalry subaltern in the armies of the Nizam of Hyderabad. Between 1761 and 1763 he displaced the Hindu Wodiyar ruling house of Mysore, making himself generalissimo and, ultimately, sole ruler. Haidar carefully cultivated members of the powerful Hindu scribal classes, who ran the revenue administration, and Hindu bankers whom he attracted to his territory with a favourable regime of taxation. The Sultan, who appears to have been a religious sceptic, was careful not to offend Hindu religious susceptibilities and patronized their temples. As early as 1770 Mysore dominated much of the southern uplands of the subcontinent and from here it was able to mount two successful campaigns against the unready authorities of Madras in 1769 and 1781–4. Naturally, Haidar's ability to counter British plans and to use their

154

own weapons of boycott and economic violence against them attracted fierce denunciation. To many he was an 'infamous tyrant', a position which his son filled after his death in 1782 to even greater vilification. Here Haidar wears the typical turban common to southern warrior communities, Telugu, Maratha and Muslim. C.A.B.

LITERATURE: *The European Magazine* 1793; Hasan 1971; Rohatgi 1982.

155 East View of Bangalore, from *Twelve Views of Places in the Kingdom of Mysore*, 1793

R.H. Colebrooke
Printed book, spine 50 ($19\frac{7}{10}$)
Syndics of Cambridge University Library (Harley-Mason Collection)

At its greatest extent, Haidar Ali's kingdom of Mysore was the most powerful southern Indian empire since the fall of the Hindu empire of Vijayanagar in the sixteenth century. It posed a significant threat to British military power in India, not only because it pressed on the borders of the Carnatic, but because it was prosperous and well governed, 'a garden from one end to the other', as Cornwallis himself observed. Bangalore, founded in 1537, was greatly extended by Haidar Ali, who constructed the stone fort and laid out a number of gardens and broad new streets, which can be seen in this engraving. Haidar fostered the trade in cloth and agricultural products which ran from the west to the east coast through Bangalore. The city remained an important military centre under the British regime and is today one of India's greatest industrial centres.

Lieutenant Robert Hyde Colebrooke (1762–1808), a Bengal infantryman and amateur topographical artist, was a member of Cornwallis's expeditionary force against Tipu in 1791–2, which corralled the Sultan into the centre of his territories and put an end to his attempts to become a sea power. In 1793 he published his *Twelve Views of Places in the Kingdom of Mysore*, of which this is one. These went through several editions as the 'Tipu legend' grew in Europe. C.A.B.

LITERATURE: *Imperial Gazetteer of India* 1908; Godrej and Rohatgi 1989.

156 Plan of the Battle of Seringapatam, 15 May 1791

Unknown artist, 1791
Pen and ink with watercolour, 32.5 × 52.5 ($12\frac{4}{5}$ × $20\frac{7}{10}$)
India Office Library and Records (WD 3137)

Lord Cornwallis was concerned above all to implement his plans for 'economical reform' in the government of India. He did not relish prolonged warfare of the sort which had dogged Warren Hastings's later years. But Mysore was a dangerous and determined enemy, and Tipu Sultan's thrust against the Raja of Travancore, which was designed to open up the west coast and its commerce to the 'God-given government', was a direct threat to the Company. Following years of diplomatic cold war, direct conflict broke out in 1789.

General Medows, whose force was later joined by the Governor-General (now also Commander-in-Chief), drove a spring offensive into the heart of Mysore despite his weakness in cavalry. Cornwallis's plans to encircle Tipu's army in front of Seringapatam went badly wrong when they were frustrated by the heavy monsoon rains and over-extended lines of communication. But in the cold weather of 1792 he moved against Tipu's fortress island in the river Kavery (shown at the top of the plan) for a second time and decisively defeated the Sultan.

Cornwallis did not relish a fight to the finish with Tipu and considered that the deposition of a major ruler such as the Sultan would furnish a bad precedent. He therefore negotiated a harsh treaty which deprived Mysore of most of its outlying regions and cut it off from the sea. C.A.B.

PROVENANCE: Purchased 1971.

LITERATURE: *CHI*, V; Moon 1989.

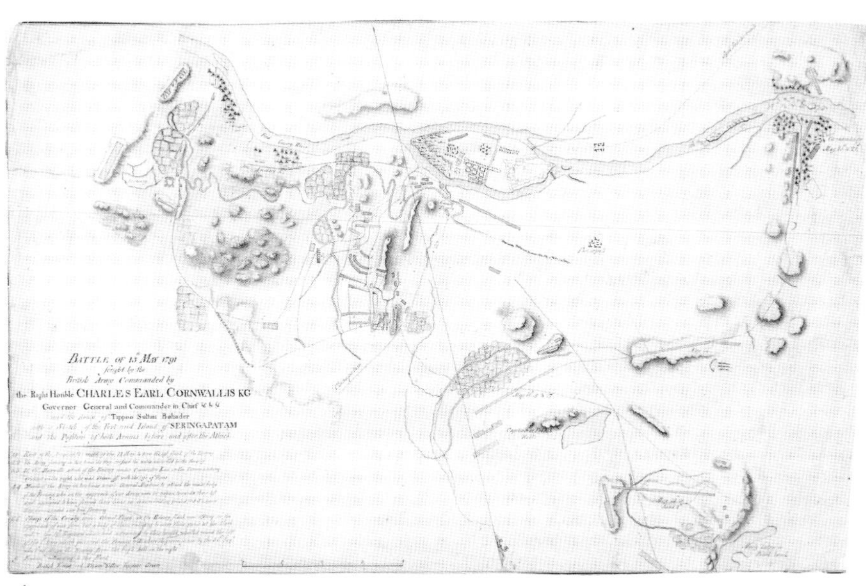

156

157

157 Lord Cornwallis receiving the sons of Tipu Sultan as hostages, Seringapatam, 25 February 1792

Robert Home, *c.* 1792
Oil on canvas, 148 × 201 (59 × 80¾)
Lent by The Director, National Army Museum, London SW3 4HT (7611–86)

Tipu's defeat by Cornwallis in 1792 forced him to pay the Company an indemnity of more than 33 million rupees and hand over half his territories along with all his prisoners. He was also forced to give his sons into Cornwallis's hands as hostages. The two boys, shown here aged about 8 and 10, were held for over two years in Madras. Moon writes that 'Among their entertainments (which they may not have appreciated) was to be taken twice to amateur performances of extracts from Handel's *Messiah*, *Judas Maccabaeus*, and *Esther*' (Moon 1989, p.259). Hostage-taking was common in eighteenth-century politics; indeed, members of the royal family of Coorg had recently suffered this fate at the hands of Tipu. But the good reception afforded the Mysore princes gave British painters and publicists an opportunity to praise British 'benevolence in conquest' and visually to draw attention to antique Roman parallels. By the time Tipu was killed in 1799, the public mood had hardened and the bloody 'death of the tyrant' was emphasized (no.169).

Robert Home was the only artist present at the occasion, but it was not until A.W. Devis arrived in Madras late in the summer of 1793, intending to make sketches on the spot for his large pictures of the surrender of the princes (see Archer 1979, pls. 187, 188), that Home was prompted to make his own record of the event. By October 1794 Home's painting was well advanced and on 28 February 1795 the *Madras Gazette* announced that the picture could be seen at the artist's house and that it was about to be despatched to England (where it was later exhibited at the Royal Academy).

The princes had been borne to the scene on the three elephants which dominate the composition to the right. In the background is the British encampment and to the left Cornwallis's tent, with a carpet spread on the ground. On the extreme left the artist stands cross-legged, with a portfolio of drawings under his right arm. In the centre is Sir John Kennaway, Resident at the Nizam's Court, holding the hand of the elder prince, Abdul Khaliq, while the younger prince, Muiz-ud-din, is handed over to Cornwallis by the lame *vakil* (ambassador) Ghulam Ali Khan supported on his silver carrying chair. Tipu's second *vakil*, Ali Reza Khan, stands beside Ghulam Ali Khan and to his left stand Mir Alam (Mir Abul Qasim), the representative of the Nizam of Hyderabad, and Buchaji Pandit, representative of the Maratha Peshwa.

B.A./C.A.B.

PROVENANCE: Purchased by Major-General Sir Henry Floyd in 1899 and presented by him to the United Service Club (Junior); The United Service and Royal Aero Club sale, Christie's, 20 June 1975 (123), bt Spinks; given anonymously.

LITERATURE: Archer 1979, pp.308–9, pl.213; Marshall 1981; Moon 1989, pp.257–60.

EXHIBITIONS: London, Royal Academy, 1797 (258); London, Victoria and Albert Museum, *Art and the East India Trade*, 1970 (101) as A.W. Devis; London, National Army Museum, *The Armies of India*, 1987.

158 Tipu Sultan on his Throne

Anna Tonelli, Mysore, *c.* 1800
Watercolour, 38.5 × 53.2 (15 × 21)
The Clive Museum, Powis Castle (The Powis Estate Trustees) (213)

The British referred to the Mysore sovereigns as 'usurpers' and officers such as Mark Wilks, later Resident at Mysore, wished to return the territory to what they called the 'ancient Hindoo constitution'. It is true that the Mysore Sultans occupied a rather ambiguous position from the point of Indian sovereignty. This, perhaps, was one reason why Tipu surrounded himself with symbols of kingship. From one perspective the sultans remained servants of the Hindu Wodiyar maharajas (who were to be restored by the British in 1799). But they had also received titles and insignia from the Mughals and could therefore be considered subordinates of the Nizam of Hyderabad, whom they despised. After 1788 the position became critical, for Mysore's arch foes, the British, had now achieved a dominance over the Nizam and the Marathas had the weak and later blind Shah Alam, the Mughal Emperor, in their sphere of influence. This appears to have been one reason why Tipu chose to have himself declared *Padshah*, or emperor, in his own right. Another reason is that Tipu desperately needed foreign support. He became a 'citoyen' of the French Republic, to the fear and fury of the British. He also tried to make alliances among the remaining independent Muslim sovereigns, writing to the Afghan ruler and also to the Ottoman sultan in Constantinople to seek solidarity against the 'swine-eating infidels'. Yet Tipu was singularly ambivalent as a zealous Muslim sovereign. He destroyed temples and churches only when they belonged to his sworn enemies, and patronized them when they belonged to his own Hindu or Christian subjects. He declared Mysore a *khudadad sirkar* or 'God-given state', but gave offerings to the Seringapatam temples. After Tipu's death the throne seen here was broken up. The large tiger head and the *huma* bird on the top of the umbrella (*chatri*) are in the Royal Collection at Windsor; a smaller head is depicted below (no. 159).

C.A.B.

LITERATURE: Miles 1834; Hasan 1971; Archer, Rowell and Skelton 1987.

EXHIBITION: London, Victoria and Albert Museum, *The Indian Heritage*, 1982 (94).

159 Tiger-head Finial from the throne of Tipu Sultan, Mysore (Seringapatam)

1787–93
Gold on wooden core, rubies, diamonds and emeralds; height 8.3 ($3\frac{1}{4}$), base width 4.7 ($1\frac{7}{8}$)
The Clive Museum, Powis Castle (The National Trust)

Tiger symbolism pervaded Mysore under Tipu. The Sultan's troops wore tiger-stripe uniforms, his French-style chairs (no.161[ii]) and throne had tiger-head finials; even the interior of the royal mosque at Seringapatam was decorated with tiger stripes. The symbolism was particularly appropriate. The lion (*sher*), with which the tiger was generally associated in India, was an ancient symbol of Persian royalty which was introduced by the Afghans and Mughals to the subcontinent. But tiger symbolism was already prolific in India, where it was associated with the vengeful aspect of the goddess Kali, and figured prominently in folk religion. In Mysore, the Hindu Wodiyar maharajas often stamped tigers on their coins. Small religious icons made at the time of the southern Indian festivals often depicted lions/tigers devouring kids in much the same way as Tipu's famous tiger in the Victoria and Albert Museum is shown devouring a British soldier. Tipu's symbolism, therefore, announced him as a valiant Muslim sultan, but also conveyed a subtler and less orthodox message to his Hindu subjects.

This was one of the items auctioned in India and acquired by the 2nd Lady Clive, Countess of Powis, who recorded that it was 'given me by Ld. Wellesley'. On the base of the stand is a metal ring inscribed 'Tiger's head which formed part of Tippoo's throne with H.A. Powis's love'.

C.A.B.

LITERATURE: Forrest 1970, pl. 14b; Hasan 1971; *Oriental Art* 1974, XX, 4; Courtney 1980, fig 47; Archer, Rowell and Skelton 1987 (88).

EXHIBITION: London, Victoria and Albert Museum, *The Indian Heritage*, 1982 (346).

160 Tippu Sultan

1920s or 1930s
Oleograph, 50.1 × 37.5 ($19\frac{3}{4}$ × $14\frac{3}{4}$)
National Portrait Gallery, London

Tipu was long an ambiguous figure, and remains so for some on the Hindu right wing. He was undoubtedly unforgiving to his enemies, but the British elaborated the picture greatly and attributed to him a Muslim religious fanaticism for which

160

there is no factual basis. More recently he has become a folk hero in the state of Karnataka, and in 1988 a historical soap opera of his life was being made by Indian television until it was dramatically halted when the set burned down. His status both as a 'proto-nationalist' hero and as a Muslim purist are in hot contention.

This oleograph is of high quality and its style recalls that of Mughal painting.

C.A.B.

161(i) Table

Late 18th century
Ivory and mica, height 70 ($27\frac{3}{10}$)
The Trustees of Sir John Soane's Museum

161(ii) Chair

Late 18th century
Ivory and rattan, height 90 ($35\frac{1}{10}$)
The Trustees of Sir John Soane's Museum

The chair (one of a set of four) and table are said to have been owned by Tipu Sultan and to have been seized from his palace at the fall of Seringapatam in 1799. They were later recorded as being 'Purchased at the sale of General Crewe's effects by Richard Westmacott R.A.', and Sir John Soane probably purchased them from Westmacott in the early 1820s. They were first shown on display in the museum in a drawing of 1823. 'General Crewe' has not been identified as being present at Seringapatam; while there was a huge amount of looting, many pieces from Tipu's art collection, his manuscripts and other possessions were auctioned to the troops.

The inclusion of tiger head motifs on the chairs and table make it highly probable that they were from Tipu's collection (see no.159). Tipu's father was also associated with tiger symbolism (his name 'Haidar' means 'tiger'), but whereas he was not interested in acquiring furniture based on European styles, Tipu frequently commissioned and purchased such furniture, and these items therefore probably date from Tipu's reign (1782–99).

C.A.B.

PROVENANCE: See entry.

LITERATURE: Symonds 1950; Ghose 1976; Ghose 1979.

161

Weapons associated with Tipu Sultan

Haidar and Tipu built up a formidable military power which combined the flexibility of Indian armies with the fire-control learned from their European enemies. Large numbers of Afghan horses and riders, engaged in north India and from among enemies of the Nawabs of Arcot, formed the cavalry. Beda tribal people from the Mysore hills provided sappers and archers. After 1784 Tipu also began to build up his own household cavalry. The infantry was recruited from Arabs, Abyssinians and other military groups who could be counted on for absolute personal loyalty.

Both sultans paid close attention to the purchase and production of modern weapons. A French officer stated in the 1780s that Haidar's army had derived two-thirds of its matchlocks from British sources. But Tipu established several arsenals which could produce weapons according to French patterns. These were usually decorated with tiger motifs and engraved with slogans and Persian quatrains mentioning the maker's name and sometimes the recommended charge of gunpowder. After the fall of Seringapatam these weapons were auctioned to British soldiers and civilians, finding their way back to Britain as Tipu's private weapons, though very few actually came from his personal Cabinet of Arms.

C.A.B.

162(i) Armour of Tipu Sultan (*peti* or breastplate)

Mysore, late 18th century
Royal Armouries (XXVI.139A)

PROVENANCE: Acquired from the collection of Duke of York before 1859.

LITERATURE: Hewitt 1859, class XV, nos. 406–7, p.111; Egerton 1880, no. 587T, p. 124; Dillon 1910, class XV, nos. 477–8; Robinson 1968.

162(ii) Helmet of Tipu Sultan

Mysore, late 18th century
Royal Armouries (XXVI.139A)

PROVENANCE: See 162(i)

LITERATURE: See 162(i)

163 Socket bayonet (*sangin*)

Mysore (Seringapatam), late 18th century
Steel, length 29.1 ($11\frac{2}{5}$)
Royal Armouries (XXVI.28D)

PROVENANCE: From Seringapatam 1799; Major-General Codrington collection; purchased 1863.

LITERATURE: Hewitt 1865, add.no. 353, p. 11; Dillon 1910, class XV, no. 784.

164 Helmet

Mysore, 1782–9
Quilted fabric, lined with velvet
Embroidered inscription inside back flap
The Trustees of the Victoria and Albert Museum (IS 3518)

The inscription states that the helmet has been dipped in the holy well of Zum Zum at Mecca and is therefore impenetrable.

PROVENANCE: Presented to the Indian Museum 'by the besiegers of Seringapatam'.

165 Sword belonging to Tipu Sultan

Mysore, made between 1782–9
Blued steel hilt inlaid with gold; steel blade
Blade: length 70 ($27\frac{3}{10}$); hilt: length 16.5 ($6\frac{2}{5}$)
The Clive Museum, Powis Castle (The National Trust) (34)

The hilt of the sword is covered with Koranic quotations, conveying the fundamental Islamic concepts of victory in war. Tiger-head langets are inlaid with gold calligraphy – the outline of the face, including eyes and nose, is defined by the stylization of the name

162

165

'Ali'. The broad curving blade shows Turkish influence. T.R.

LITERATURE: Forrest 1970, pl.13a; Buddle 1984–5, fig.10.

166 Gold inlaid steel head piece

Height 40 ($15\frac{3}{4}$)
National Museums of Scotland (L 1932.112)

167 Steel spear

Length 168 ($66\frac{1}{8}$)
National Museums of Scotland (1960.273)

168 The Last Effort of Tippoo Sultann in defence of the Fortress of Seringapatam

1802, after a painting by Henry Singleton, *c.* 1800
Stipple engraving, 70.5 × 104.6 ($27\frac{1}{2} \times 40\frac{4}{5}$)
National Museums of Scotland (1952.615)

Deserted by Purniya (no.197) and several of his other commanders, and unable to call on the French allies with whom he was negotiating, Tipu's fate was sealed once the British army had devised a method to protect their enormous baggage train against the Mysorean light cavalry. Once the siege had begun, Seringapatam's defences quickly collapsed under the pounding of British and Hyderabad cannon. The final assault came on 4 May 1799. Major-General David Baird, who had been a prisoner of Tipu's nearly twenty years before, was in command. Tipu fell during the assault on the Watergate, though it was not until nightfall, sometime after the fall of the citadel, that the news of his death leaked out.

These events were dramatized by several British artists, notably Robert Ker Porter, Thomas Stothard and, much later, in 1838, Sir David Wilkie. The Tipu legend was an important justification for the more aggressive 'forward policy' adopted by the British empire in India after 1790. Tipu's 'Mahommedan tyranny' was contrasted

166

167

with the 'ancient Hindoo constitution' supposedly enjoyed by Mysore before Haidar Ali's coup of 1761. The British could thus see themselves as conservators and protectors in India. But the image of the history paintings had changed subtly in the process. The emphasis on 'benevolent' British acts found in pictures relating to the life of Clive, or even the victory over Tipu in 1792, were replaced by scenes of dominion, war and death. Not everyone rejoiced. Radical pamphleteers and, later, James Mill doubted the wisdom of the conquest of Mysore. Members of the public in the 1830s even sympathized with Tipu when confronted by Wilkie's huge canvas. Yet the triumphalist mode of imperial painting remained seductive and it would be given another powerful boost by the Indian Rebellion of 1857.

C.A.B.

LITERATURE: Hasan 1971; Archer 1979, pp. 425–35.

Devis, who had returned to England in 1795, may have been prompted to paint this subject by the appearance in August 1800 of S.W. Reynolds's mezzotint after Robert Ker Porter's version of the subject, now in the Memorial Hall, Calcutta (see Archer 1979, pl.340). Devis produced two versions of the subject in which the compositions are virtually identical, the difference being that this version is horizontal and the other (still in a private collection) is vertical. In both the body of Tipu lies on the ground in the centre while an officer announces its discovery to the assembled throng.

Devis was declared bankrupt during

168

169 Major General Baird and other British Officers finding the body of Tippoo Sahib, the Sultan of Mysore, in the gateway in the north face of the Fort of Seringapatam on the 4th May, 1799

Arthur William Devis, 1799–1802
Oil on canvas, 74.2 × 97.8 ($29\frac{1}{4} \times 28\frac{1}{2}$)
National Museums of Scotland (1990.7)

The discovery of the dead body of Tipu after the fall of Seringapatam became a key theme of British history painting. Major-General Baird had once been imprisoned by Tipu, so that in addition to the pervasive triumphalism of the time this painting depicts the revenge of fate on the tyrant. At another level though the constant return to the theme suggests something more, for here India lies dead at the feet of the British, its darkest recesses now illuminated by the light of civilization.

169

the production of these pictures, but in 1802 he had the good fortune to be befriended by John Biddulph of Ledbury, who took a great interest in his Indian subjects (in 1802 he had exhibited one of his many versions of *Lord Cornwallis receiving the sons of Tipu Sultan as hostages* at the Royal Academy). Biddulph's family may have had some links with India. Between 1802 and about 1810 the Biddulph family supported Devis and his family, advancing him considerable sums of money in return for security against his paintings. B.A./C.A.B.

PROVENANCE: Acquired by the Biddulph family between 1802 and 1810; by descent; anon. sale, Christie's, 17 March 1978 (?); anon. sale, Sotheby's, 21 March 1979 (50); anon. sale, Sotheby's, 24 July 1986 (90).

LITERATURE: Paviere 1950, pp.101–41 (151); Archer 1979, pp.266–7, pl.189.

EXHIBITION: Preston, Harris Museum and Art Gallery, *Lancashire Art*, 1937 (39).

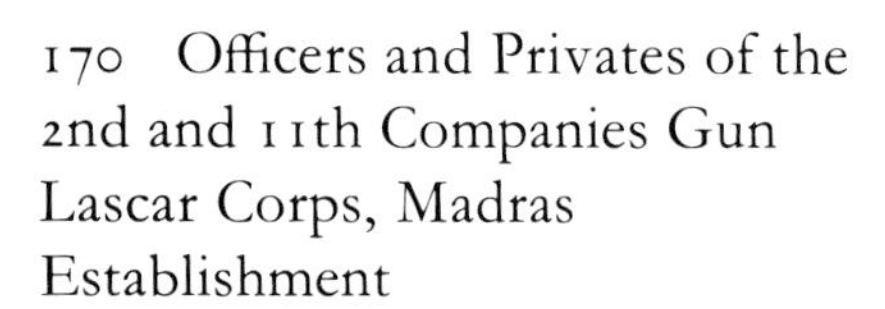

170

170 Officers and Privates of the 2nd and 11th Companies Gun Lascar Corps, Madras Establishment

Attributed to Captain Charles Gold, 1796
Watercolour, pen and ink, 23 × 24 (9 × 9½)
Inscribed b.l.: *Sketched from life at Trichinopoly.1796*
Lent by The Director, National Army Museum, London SW3 4HT (6106–18)

The shock of the near defeat by Mysore in 1781–3 prompted a reorganization of the Madras army and a temporary end to the mutinies and wrangling over pay which had plagued it during Coote's campaigns. However, its cavalry wing remained weak (as had been demonstrated in 1791 before Seringapatam) and it was unable to develop a tradition of regular recruitment from 'army villages' like that fostered by the Bengal army in southern Awadh. Though the Madras army performed better during the second and third Mysore wars, its reputation was tarnished by a serious mutiny at Vellore near Arcot in 1806. Hindu and Muslim troops resented the introduction of European-style headgear and regulations about cutting beards (there were premonitions here of the events of 1857). The underlying causes of this outbreak were, however, very general unease about the coming of a 'Christian' government and the collapse both of the Hindu 'poligars' (*palayakkarars* or warrior chieftains) and of the Muslim sultanate of Mysore. Sympathy for the fallen house of Tipu Sultan was strong. The soldiers here wear the high stiff turban (red for officers, dark blue for NCOs) which was standard dress in the Madras native army. C.A.B.

PROVENANCE: Given by Mrs G. McGowan, 1961.

LITERATURE: Gold 1806, see pl. 38; Wilson 1882; Carman 1969, p.27; Mollo 1981.

171 Medal for Seringapatam

1799
Gold, diameter 4.8 (1⅞)
National Museums of Scotland (L 1935.21)

171

172

172 Madhu Rao Narayan, the Maratha Peshwa, with Nana Fadnavis and attendants

James Wales, 1792
Oil on canvas, 228.6 × 190.4 (90 × 75)
Royal Asiatic Society, London (01.013/89)

During the eighteenth century the Marathas extended their political influence from their homeland in western India into parts of central and southern India, westwards into Gujarat and northwards through Malwa into the Gangetic plain. The organizers of Maratha expansion were the Peshwas Baji Rao I (1720–40) and Balaji Baji Rao (1740–61) who were, in formal terms, the chief ministers of the Raja of Satara, the direct descendant of Shivaji, founder of the Maratha state in the seventeenth century (no.87). The Peshwas' government was based at Poona. Although Maratha expansion was temporarily checked in northern India by the Afghans at the Battle of Panipat in 1761, their fortunes were largely restored by Madhav Rao I (1761–72).

Following Madhav Rao's death, however, Poona became the scene of vicious political infighting. Madhav Rao was succeeded by his brother Narayan Rao, but not without opposition from Raghunath Rao, their uncle. An attempt by Raghunath Rao to seize his nephew resulted in the latter's murder on 30 August 1773. Even so, Raghunath Rao failed to secure sufficient support for himself as Peshwa and his political opponents rallied round Narayan Rao's widow. On 18 April 1774, some seven months after the death of her husband, she gave birth to a son; and on 28 May the baby was installed as Peshwa Madhav Rao II (here called Madhu Rao Narayan). The event signalled not only defeat for Raghunath Rao, but the ascendancy of Nana Phadnis (or Fadnavis) and his party. Nana, as the Peshwa's guardian and chief minister, became the real ruler at Poona for the next twenty years.

Nana Phadnis was born on 12 February 1742 into a family which had

173

powerful connections with government and banking in western India. The office of *phadnis* (chief accountant) had become hereditary in his family and he succeeded to it in 1756 when he was only fourteen years old. He rose rapidly during the reign of Madhav Rao I, becoming recognized as the principal minister in the government. His political position was seriously undermined by the accidental death of Madhav Rao II on 27 October 1795. Nana Phadnis died on 13 March 1800, aged 58 'and with him', wrote Colonel Palmer, the Company's ambassador at Poona, 'has departed all the wisdom and moderation of the Mahratta government'.

Wales worked in London and exhibited portraits at the Royal Academy and Society of Artists between 1783 and 1791. His decision to visit India may have been the result of his friendship with James Earles, who had retired from Bombay. Wales reached Bombay in 1791. His sketches and drawings were the basis of Thomas Daniell's large painting of Malet concluding the treaty with the Marathas (no.173). B.A./G.J.

PROVENANCE: Probably originally painted for the Peshwa; Major-General Archibald Robinson (Resident at the Maratha Court of Satara 1827–31); presented by his widow to present owners, 1854.

LITERATURE: Duff 1826, vol. 3; Carets 1936; Archer 1979, p.343, pl.243; Simmonds and Digby 1979; Gokhale 1988.

EXHIBITION: London, Victoria and Albert Museum, *India Observed*, 1982 (11).

173 Sir Charles Warre Malet, Bt., the British Resident at the Court of Poona, in 1790 concluding a treaty in Durbar with Souae Madarow, the Peshwa or Prince of the Maratha Empire

Thomas Daniell, *c.* 1800–5
Oil on canvas, 181.9 × 278.8 ($71\frac{5}{8} \times 109\frac{3}{4}$)
Signed and dated *1805*
Heim Gallery Ltd, London

At 6 o'clock on the morning of 6 August 1790 ('that unusual hour being fixed as the only auspicious one for several days'), Charles Malet, the East India Company's ambassador at Poona, was received 'in a very full Durbar' and presented the Peshwa with a letter from Lord Cornwallis and the ratified treaty whereby Poona agreed to join forces with Hyderabad and the Company against Tipu Sultan of Mysore. The Company had already declared war on Tipu as a result of his attack on their ally, the Raja of Travancore.

Cornwallis, with a view to protecting the position of the East India Company at Madras, determined to isolate Mysore by drawing Poona and Hyderabad into an alliance against Tipu Sultan. Given the many disputes between these governments, the conclusion of the treaty was a major diplomatic coup. Even though the military campaigns of 1790–2 revealed considerable practical difficulties in co-ordinating effectively the resources and strategies of the allies, the triple alliance was crucial in tipping the scales against Mysore, for the Company was not powerful enough to defeat Mysore unaided.

This large painting was commissioned by Malet himself, who was created a baronet on 24 February 1791 in recognition of the part he had played, soon after his appointment as acting Governor of Bombay.

Thomas Daniell, who had not witnessed this event, based the painting on sketches made by James Wales and his assistant Robert Mabon. Wales had been befriended by Malet in India and the latter became his most important patron. Had Wales not died in 1795 he might have executed the picture himself, but on his return from India in 1798 Malet brought Wales's daughter Susanna back with him, together with many of her father's paintings, drawings and notes, and married her a year later. Soon after his return Malet contacted Thomas Daniell and asked him to complete some of Wales's unfinished schemes, including the 1790 treaty picture. Daniell was occupied with the project for some years and Malet apparently travelled regularly from his Wiltshire house to London to witness the progress of the picture. It was eventually exhibited at the Royal Academy in 1805.

The principal sitters in the painting are, from the left, the seated figure of the Peshwa, Souae Madarow (Madhav Rao II) with his outstretched hand receiving the treaty from Malet; between them are Nana Phadnis, the Chief Minister, and Bahirao Pant Mehendale, the Peshwa's agent for British affairs; then, to the right of Malet, is Joshua Uhthoff, First Secretary of the British Embassy; Nur-ul-din Husain Khan, Malet's assistant; Captain Heirn, Commanding Officer of Malet's bodyguard and Dr James Findlay, the British Embassy surgeon.

Malet is seen wearing a Chellink in his hat. This is a very unusual diamond head ornament presented as an award for gallantry or distinguished service. Wales, after making the preliminary drawings for this composition in 1792, remarked in his journal for 10 September: 'As the people of distinction in India are fond of fine, or rather rich dresses with watches, snuff boxes, rings, etc. etc. introduced, it is no easy matter for an artist to please them without sacrificing the best principles of his art'. Judging from Daniell's painting, he submitted to the demands of the Peshwa and his ministers on this occasion, depicting in minute detail their various weapons, items of jewellery and costume accessories which provide a colourful contrast to the elegant and beautifully tailored but relatively plain clothing of Malet and the Residency staff.

The engraving of the picture by Charles Turner was published in 1807.

B.A./J.S./G.J.

PROVENANCE: Commissioned by Sir Charles Warre Malet, Bt.; by descent to Colonel Sir Edward Malet, Bt.; his sale, Christie's (in conjunction with Lawrence of Crewkerne), 14 April 1989 (86).

LITERATURE: Duff 1826, vol.3; Malcolm 1826, vol.1; Malet 1885, pp.60,141; Ray 1937, vol.3; Sutton 1954, p.84; Archer 1979; pp.352–4; Shellim 1979, p.66, no. TD60, ill.

EXHIBITIONS: London, Royal Academy, 1805 (1); New York, Metropolitan Museum of Art, *Costumes of Royal India*, December 1985 – August 1986, p.9.

174 Arthur Wellesley, 1st Duke of Wellington (1769–1852)

Robert Home, 1804
Oil on canvas, 76.2 × 66 (30 x 26)
National Portrait Gallery, London (1471)

The future Duke of Wellington cut his teeth on Indian warfare. He arrived in India as a Colonel in 1796. He fought against Tipu in 1799 and against the Marathas in central India between 1802 and 1804, winning great victories at Assaye and Argaum, which were among the most difficult of his career. The Marathas had developed sophisticated

174

artillery and infantry which could lay down heavy fire; they also retained a pre-eminence in fast cavalry. Only their leadership seemed weak and vacillating. Here, perhaps, was the main disadvantage of relying so heavily on foreign mercenaries. One reason why the British were able to defeat Scindia, the Bhonslas and other Maratha chieftains was that Wellesley played close attention to supply and drew up a code for managing the Banjaras or itinerant pack-bullock drivers who provided the armies in the field with their supplies. Wellesley became a 'commissary's general', an experience that was to prove vital in his later career in the Peninsular campaigns.

Robert Home's *Register of Sitters in India 1795–1813 with prices in sicca rupees*

(MS in National Portrait Gallery archive) lists fourteen portraits of General Wellesley begun between September 1804 and August 1806. Presumably the single half-length portrait, listed September 1804, is this picture which shows the future Duke with his right hand thrust into his tunic, in Major-General's uniform (he was promoted in 1802), but without the Star of the Order of the Bath which, although awarded in August 1804, did not arrive from England until shortly before he sailed for home in March 1805.

B.A./C.A.B.

PROVENANCE: Mrs Elizabeth Bruce Gordon; bequeathed by her in 1885 to Sir Brooke Kay, Bt. for his life, 1885; then to National Gallery, 1907; transferred 1907.

LITERATURE: Owen 1880; Foster 1924, p.21, cf. no.41; Spencer 1925; Cotton 1927–8; Cotton 1928; Wellesley and Steegman 1935; Archer 1979, p.317; Walker 1985, vol.I, p.525, no.471, vol.II, pl.1314.

175 Battle of Assaye, 1803. The 74th Highlanders attacking the Maratha Lines

Copyprint reproduction after a painting by J. Marshman (1874) in the National Army Museum (7209–20)

The Battle of Assaye, fought on 24 September 1803, was probably Arthur Wellesley's greatest victory in India; he himself thought it was the best in his career. The Maratha chieftains, Scindia, Holkar, and the Raja of Berar had been panicked into war by the treaty of Bassein in 1802 between Richard Wellesley and their nominal overlord, the Peshwa. They expected the conclusion of a subsidiary alliance treaty of this sort to lead to the subversion and collapse of their regimes, a fate which had already overtaken Awadh and Arcot. Wellesley's brilliant five-month campaign with a small force of under 20,000 men was marked by rapid movement and excellent logistical planning. Scindia and the Gaikwad were decisively defeated at Assaye, though the British lost nearly a third of the force actually committed to the battle, about 8,000 men. While the war effectively ended Maratha autonomy, it also terminated Richard Wellesley's career as Governor-General. He was recalled in 1805 after the campaign against Holkar had become bogged down. The Government and Directors had become alarmed at the spiralling India debt and the constant expansion of the Company's frontiers.

The 74th Highlanders held the line against Scindia's forces despite being 'cut up badly by grape', a heroic moment in their regimental history.

C.A.B.

PROVENANCE: Gift from 2nd Battalion Highland Light Infantry, 1956.

LITERATURE: Davidson 1901, p.547.

176 View of Poona (Bombay) with River in the foreground

Henry Salt, October 1804
Wash, 41.8 × 60.4 ($16\frac{3}{10} \times 23\frac{1}{2}$)
India Office Library and Records (WD 1306)

Sir Charles Malet, British Resident at Poona from 1785 until 1797, referred to Poona as 'a large village', while a near contemporary Muslim chronicler had scornfully dismissed the public and private buildings of the Maratha capital as no better than the stables of Mughal palaces. There were, it is true, few great buildings in the city; the Shahnawara palace, the Peshwa's headquarters, was simply a large Maratha fortress containing durbar halls. The Marathas themselves were a hardy peasant warrior caste, given to few luxuries and relishing their time in the saddle. All the same, Poona had become a recognizable urban centre in the course of the eighteenth century. One estimate put its population at 150,000 in 1790. The city was also subtly changing its character. The rise of Chitpavan Brahmins surrounding the Peshwa and administrator Brahmins such as Nana Phadnis was matched by an expansion in the number of endowments for classical Hindu study and orthodox Hindu temples.

Henry Salt had been a pupil of both Joseph Farington and John Hoppner prior to leaving London on 3 June 1802 for a long Eastern tour with George Annesley, Viscount Valentia (afterwards 2nd Earl of Mountnorris), to whom he was secretary and draughtsman. They visited Colonel Barry Close, Resident to the Peshwa's Court at Poona, in October 1804. Salt made many drawings in India and this is the original drawing for plate 13 of *Voyages and travels in India* ... (Annesley 1809). The view of the confluence of the rivers Mula and Mutha reveals the village-like character of Poona, showing the Parvati hill and temple on the left and the older Simagarh hill fortress in the distance. Other drawings were made for Salt's own *Twenty-four views taken in St Helena, the Cape, India, Ceylon, the Red Sea, Abyssinia and Egypt*, also published in 1809.

In January 1809 Salt was sent to Abyssinia by the government to take presents to the king, and this expedition resulted in the publication of *A Voyage to Abyssinia* (1814). In 1814 he was appointed Consul-General in Egypt, where he took an active interest in excavations; the collections he formed were later acquired

175

176

by the British Museum (see Archer 1969, vol. I, pp.43–4, vol. II, p.627).

B.A./C.A.B.

PROVENANCE: Purchased by India Office Library 1958.

LITERATURE: Annesley 1809, vol.II, pp.114–47, pl.13; Archer 1959; Archer 1969, vol.II, p.631, no.1306; Gokhale 1988; Godrej and Rohatgi 1989.

177 A Mahratta Surdar entertaining Brahmins from *The Costume ... and Character of the Marathas*, 1813

T. D. Broughton
Printed book, 45 × 27 ($17\frac{7}{10} \times 10\frac{3}{5}$)
The Syndics of Cambridge University Library (Harley-Mason Collection)

Broughton's despatches from Scindia's camp illustrate the growing body of intelligence which the British were able to amass concerning the recalcitrant Maratha princes who were still smarting from their defeats of 1802–4. His despatches and letters give a vivid picture of Daulat Rao Scindia's huge camp on the move, and the difficulties of holding together an army of Maratha soldiers, Muslims from the north and tribal levies. While Scindia was scrupulous in paying due deference to both Hindu and Muslim festivals and religious figures, the Maratha states had become more and more 'Brahminized' as the years passed. Feeding Brahmins was therefore a meritorious act. Broughton remarked cynically, 'Brahmuns (*sic*) after eating till they are ready to burst will sometimes consent, at the earnest entreaty of their host to cram down a little more, receiving for each successive mouthful an increasing number of rupees, till nature revolts at the oppressive load ...' (p.48).

Significantly, Broughton dedicated his book to Marquess Wellesley, 'The acute detector of Mahratta wiles, the firm repeller of their insolent pretentions, and the formidable barrier to their ambitious projects'. Some years after Wellesley's recall he began to be accorded a heroic status in Britain, partly as a result of a propaganda campaign waged by his old India associates to deflect a wave of criticism in Parliament.

C.A.B.

LITERATURE: Broughton 1813.

178 The Battle of Nagpore

Denis Deighton after Captain Robert Woolf, 1817
Coloured lithograph, 55.5 × 72.5 ($21\frac{7}{8} \times 28\frac{1}{2}$)
Lent by The Director, National Army Museum, London SW3 4HT (7102-33-264)

After Wellesley's recall, Cornwallis, Sir George Barlow and Lord Minto, his successors, pursued a more cautious policy of consolidation. By 1817, however, tension between the Company and the Maratha states had built up once again. The main cause of friction was the activities of the so-called Pindaris, armed horsemen who had been laid off by Indian armies at the end of the previous wars and moved around the countryside looting merchants and settled agriculturalists to sustain themselves. The British accused the remaining inde-

178

pendent Maratha chieftains of giving these raiders succour. The Marathas, fearful of British intentions, flew to arms as soon as Company troops were mobilized on their borders. The outcome of this final conflict was hardly in doubt. The Marathas simply did not have the resources of the Company and were easily surrounded and outgunned. Maharaja Holkar was defeated at Nagpur, the Peshwa at Kirkhi near Poona. The Peshwaship was accordingly abolished and the Company annexed large parts of the Maratha lands. Gwalior (Scindia), Indore (Holkar) and Baroda (Gaikwad) survived as protected native states under British paramountcy.

C.A.B.

PROVENANCE: Transferred from British Museum Crookshank Collection.

179

Recruiting the Company's Army

The East India Company's military successes against its Indian foes between 1790 and 1857 would have been impossible without British naval command of the Indian Ocean and the Arabian Sea and without the regular flows of land revenue to support its expanding forces. Yet the Company also developed a flexible combination of *types* of army which drew on Indian and European precedents. To the regiments of King's and Company's European troops was added a well-equipped and well-trained army of soldiers of peasant origin from the mid-Ganges valley (see nos. 113, 114, 116). The Madras and Bombay armies attempted to create similar 'peasant warrior' forces though with less success. The elite of the Bengal force was the Governor-General's Bodyguard, formed by 1775, which also established a recruitment base in the Benares region.

With the operations against Mysore and the Marathas and control of the huge revenue-bearing areas of north India, the Company needed different types of forces. For this reason 'irregular' cavalry regiments such as those of Skinner, Gardner, Begum Samru and, later, Hodson, began to play a greater role in the Company's army. Skinner and Gardner in particular drew not only on peasant-warrior communities but also on the elite military families, both Hindu and Muslim, which had served the Mughals, the Marathas and other eighteenth-century rulers. The dress and military ceremonial of these troops were less influenced by European patterns and their officers acted as an important bridge between the Company's European enclaves and the mass of Indian society.

C.A.B./S.A.

179 Jacket of Governor-General's Bodyguard worn by Major W.H. Rainey, 1817–20

Scarlet uniform, dark blue facings and silver lace

Lent by The Director, National Army Museum, London SW3 4HT (7805–69)

LITERATURE: Mollo 1981, pp.16–19; Alkazi 1982.

180 Colonel James Skinner with one of his sons holding a Regimental Durbar at Hansi

Ghulam Ali Khan, 1827

Watercolour with gouache, 77.5 × 134 ($30\frac{1}{2} \times 52\frac{3}{4}$)

Signed and dated b.l. in Persian: *Ghulam Ali Khan 1827*

Lent by The Director, National Army Museum, London SW3 4HT (5602–27–3)

Colonel James Skinner (1778–1841) was the most famous of the military 'adventurers' who participated in the expansion of British power in northern India. He was the son of Hercules Skinner, a Scottish captain in the East India Company's service, and a Rajput woman of princely family. After a colourful early life he worked for de Boigne, a French general then serving with the Maratha forces of Scindia. After the defeat of the Marathas by the Wellesley brothers and Lord Lake, Skinner and many of his men joined the British army (he had previously been disdained by the officer corps because of his mixed race). His force, known as Skinner's Horse, served with distinction in the campaigns against the Sikhs in 1809 and the Gurkhas in 1814.

Skinner's main contribution was to build up a strong cavalry force from the military families of the Mughal heartland. But the money and patronage he was able to distribute also helped to settle and pacify the turbulent area, which had suffered with the decline of the Mughal empire. Elaborate durbars of this sort (which after Skinner's death centred on his personal sword) helped maintain the illusion that the old military culture was still alive. Ghulam Ali Khan, a Delhi artist, painted durbar scenes such as this in the formal Mughal style, but used a looser, more European style when painting informal portraits. C.A.B./S.A.

PROVENANCE: Gift of Nicholas Crispin Wood, 1956.

LITERATURE: Archer 1972, p. 171.

EXHIBITION: London, National Army Museum, *The Armies of India*, 1987.

180

181(i)

181(i) Skinner's Horse at Exercise

John Reynolds Gwatkin, *c.* 1840
Oil on canvas, 61 x 76.3 (24 × 30)
Lent by The Director, National Army Museum, London SW3 4HT (6812–31)

181(ii) Skinner's Horse at Exercise

John Reynolds Gwatkin, *c.* 1840
Oil on canvas, 61.9 × 77.2 ($24\frac{2}{5}$ × $30\frac{2}{5}$)
Lent by The Director, National Army Museum, London SW3 4HT (6812–32)

The famous 'Yellow Boys', so called because of their yellow coats, formed the heart of Skinner's force. They are

181(ii)

shown here practising repelling a cavalry charge. Skinner and other irregular cavalry officers of the early nineteenth century preferred to keep a modified form of traditional Indian military dress rather than to press on their men the sort of Westernized uniforms that had led to the Vellore Mutiny of 1806. But even here there seems to have been some innovation. Yellow (or saffron) was the battle colour of the Rajput princes (from whom Skinner was partly descended), while other aspects of style and deportment were more purely Mughal in inspiration. C.A.B./S.A.

PROVENANCE: Both purchased Parker Gallery, 1968.

LITERATURE: National Army Museum Annual Report 1968–9; Mollo 1981, pp.47ff.

EXHIBITION: London, National Army Museum, *The Armies of India*, 1987.

182 Seven Mewatis

Unknown artists, Delhi area, *c.* 1815–27
Watercolour, 25 × 37.8 ($9\frac{3}{4} \times 14\frac{9}{10}$), album spine 43.3 (17).
Inscribed: *Mewattis*
India Office Library and Records (Add. Or. 1262) (Illustrated in colour Fig. 14)

Strictly, Mewatis were an Islamicized section of the Meo caste, a Hindu warrior group of putative Rajput origins, who at least formally acknowledged the Muslim faith. Their main settlements were in the dry Aravalli hill ranges to the south-west of Delhi. Numbering about 100,000 in the 1840s, they practised an 'indifferent and unthrifty' agriculture below the hills, but periodic drought and a martial tradition of fighting for – and against – the Mughals predisposed them to outside military service, or if necessary to plundering the roads and settled agriculture near Delhi. Soon after the British first conquered the area in 1803, we find them paying *banditti* (or Mewatis) 'fees' for protecting the roads in the Aligarh region. Later, recruitment into the forces of Skinner and Begam Samru provided a useful outlet for their energies. But during the bad years of 1833–8 they were once again found plundering the arable land. Though the term 'Mewati' was properly applied to Muslim Rajputs, it was sometimes loosely used to mean simply people from the area of Mewat which was controlled by Mewati warriors. Thus, in this picture two of the men are recorded as Hindu Brahmins and one as a Hindu Gujar, drawn from one of the marginal and nomadic agricultural castes, while the fourth is recorded as being a Muslim, according to a note on a duplicate possessed by William Fraser, Commissioner in the Delhi Territories and friend of Skinner. C.A.B.

PROVENANCE: Colonel James Skinner; by descent to Evangeline Ingram, from whom purchased via Sotheby's, 1 February 1960.

LITERATURE: Archer 1960, pp.608–15; Holman 1961; Archer 1982; Stokes 1986, p.123.

183 Portraits of Gurkha Chiefs with Soldiers standing in a Wooded Landscape

Possibly by Ghulam Ali Khan or another Delhi artist, *c.* 1815–27
Watercolour, 25 × 41.2 ($9\frac{3}{4} \times 16$)
Inscribed: *Ghoorkha Chiefs and Soldiers*
India Office Library and Records (Add. Or.1260)

From the 1760s in Bengal and from the 1790s in the hills of the Malabar region in the south, the British recruited hillmen and 'tribals' to their colours. Warriors of this sort provided skills and knowledge of quite a different kind from those of the peasant soldiers. They helped to control the hill passes and to fight in difficult terrain. By building up an interest in these hill communities, the Company also helped to restrain them from plunder and tied them into the wider British-Indian economy. As they expanded into north India the British came into contact, and conflict, with the Gurkha hill warriors who inhabited what is now Nepal and had control of

183

adjoining parts of the hill region. The British learned to respect their fighting qualities during the Anglo-Nepal war of 1814–16. After peace had been restored increasing numbers of Gurkhas were recruited to British forces, first as irregular 'hill' units and later into the core of the army.

In this picture the dress of the Gurkhas is of great interest, as it is not yet standardized. Only the man on the extreme left (called 'Himmut a Khatree [i.e. Kshatriya or Gurkha] of village Kunoor') is dressed in a manner typical of later Gurkha soldiers and notables. Otherwise, their dress seems to be typical of what might be called the 'Mughal fringe'. In fact, service in the British army appears to have been one of the main influences tending to make groups such as the Gurkhas more homogeneous, not only in dress and deportment but even in religious observation (see also no.191).

Ghulam Ali Khan, the probable painter, was one of the artists employed by William Fraser, the Political Agent in the Gurkha territories. William's brother, James Baillie Fraser, who was attached to a Calcutta Agency House (commercial firm), was himself a skilled artist and painted the same men.

C.A.B./S.A.

PROVENANCE: Colonel James Skinner; by descent to Miss Evangeline Ingram; sale, Sotheby's, 1 February 1960 (200a).

LITERATURE: Archer 1972, p.199, pl.69; Archer 1982.

184 Portrait of Sayyid Mirza Azim Beg and his staff

Possibly by Ghulam Ali Khan or another Delhi artist, *c.* 1815–27
Watercolour, 23.8 × 38 ($9\frac{3}{10}$ × 15)
India Office Library and Records (Add. Or. 1265)

Azim Beg, aged 107 years when this painting was made, was a landowner of Hansi, seat of the Skinner fief and a close associate of his, who helped rule the locality. Azim Beg had served the Irish adventurer, George Thomas, and local Indian rulers; one of his daughters married Skinner. The *vakil*, Dyem Lal, on the left, would have represented his master in the British courts which were becoming increasingly important to the life of the Indian landowner. He would also have appeared at the durbars of local rulers and princes. Roshan Lal, the *munshi* or writer, on the right, would have written letters for Azim Beg and kept his business papers. Both these men were typical of the Hindu members of the Brahmin, Kayastha and Khattri castes who served the Mughals as clerks and accountants and wrote in Persian.

C.A.B./S.A.

LITERATURE: Archer 1982.

185 *Tashrih-ul-Akvam* (Concise Account of the People), 1825

James Skinner
Book, 21 × 14 ($8\frac{1}{4}$ × $5\frac{1}{2}$)
The British Library Board (Add. 27,255,f.260, no.59)

This 462–page volume, profusely illustrated with miniatures of north Indian religious groups and local occupations, was prepared under Skinner's supervision. In many ways it has the form of a typical Persian local history which would discuss the named and holy men, products and fruits of a district. The contemporary Anglo-Indian concern with caste categories and ethnic types also finds its expression, however. In addition, Skinner wrote a gazetteer of

184

local nobility (*Tazkirat-ul-Umara*), various works of military strategy, and his own memoirs. C.A.B.

LITERATURE: Archer 1982.

186

186 An Officer of Colonel Gardner's Irregular Cavalry

Jairam Das of Patna, *c.* 1818
Watercolour, 12.4 × 19.8 ($4\frac{7}{8} \times 7\frac{3}{4}$)
Royal Asiatic Society, London (015. 067/89)

Gardner's Horse, first raised in 1809, was another of the irregular cavalry regiments which were to prove vital to the British success over such mobile enemies as the Gurkhas, Pindari 'freebooters', the Sikhs and the fleetfooted Maratha cavalry.

The Regiment took its name from its founder, William Linnaeus Gardner. The son of a British officer and an American heiress, Gardner was married to the Muslim Princess of Cambay. The Nawab of Cambay was on friendly terms with the Mughal Emperor Akbar II (reigned 1806–1837). Long associations with the Cambay family gave Gardner an understanding of Muslim sensibility and Mughal military culture. Prior to his service with the East India Company, Gardner had served with the Jaipur Irregular Cavalry. This experience had instilled in him an intense admiration for Rajput valour which was reflected in the military tradition which Gardner created for the Company. He recruited local men, mainly Pathans from Hindustan, with a sprinkling of Rajputs and Jats. Regimental loyalty was inspired in them by a symbolic appeal to their sense of valour. The recruits wore a magnificent dress in red and green, the latter a sacred colour for the Muslims, with silver lacing which gave the uniform an air of grandeur. The imagery of military splendour was consciously cultivated by Gardner. It helped to project him as the figure who had 'restored' the recruits to the high status they had enjoyed in the Mughal and Muslim regional states of Rohilkhand and Farrukhabad.

187

This watercolour was number 15 from an album of 36 original drawings, some coloured, by Jairam Das of Patna. It was acquired by Major-General Charles Doyle (1787–1848) during his period in India as Military Secretary to the Marquess of Hastings. The volume is inscribed: 'Thirty six drawings presented to the Royal Asiatic Society by Lieut. Colonel Carlo Joseph Doyle 15th of March 1834'. S.A.

PROVENANCE: Presented to Royal Asiatic Society by Colonel Doyle, 1834.

LITERATURE: Doyle 1911; Head n.d., p.127.

187 Sowar of the Rohilla Cavalry

Unknown artist, *c.* 1820
Watercolour, 15.8 × 8 ($6\frac{1}{8} \times 3\frac{1}{8}$)
Lent by The Director, National Army Museum, London SW3 4HT (6409-4-1)

The Rohillas ('Men of Ruh', in the north-western hills) were among the most celebrated of the warrior groups who served in the armies of eighteenth-century India. Afghans of dubious tribe, or no tribe, they formed themselves into well-organized bands and enlisted under the Mughals at the beginning of the eighteenth century. By 1740 the Rohillas had created a number of rich small kingdoms in the area north-east of Delhi. Farrukhabad and Bareilly were their most important capitals. In the 1770s the Rohillas were expelled from much of their territory by the Nawab of Awadh in alliance with the Company (their treatment provided another of the charges for Warren Hastings's impeachment). But they held on to the state of Rampur and continued to serve in the armies not only of Muslim princes but also of the Marathas. The British were suspicious of these tough cavalry soldiers, though they recruited some of them into the Rohilla Horse, Gardner's Horse, and other irregular units in the North-Western Provinces called Provincial Battalions. These units were formed to face the expected final war with the Marathas and the menace of 'freebooter' Pindaris who roamed in central India. Pious Muslims and military men as they were, the Rohilla gentry found it difficult to adjust to British rule. There was a serious rebellion in the city of Bareilly in 1816 and disenchanted soldiers were held partly responsible. A few years later, Bishop Heber warned of the danger from declining bands of Rohilla mercenary soldiers, many of whom were active in the rebel cause in the Rebellion of 1857. C.A.B.

LITERATURE: Mollo 1981, p.29.

PROVENANCE: Gift of Colonel J. H. Nicholls, 1964.

188 Flintlock Sporting Gun

Mysore (Seringapatam)
Length 135 ($58\frac{1}{8}$)
Dated: *1224M*, (1797/8)
Royal Armouries (XXVI.61F)

PROVENANCE: Transferred from C.O.D. Weedon, 1949.

189 Begum Samru in Old Age

Indian artist, *c.* 1820
Gouache on paper, 90 × 58 ($35 \times 22\frac{3}{5}$)
The private collection of Yasmin and Shahid Hosain

In an effort to cope with cavalry warfare in the area east of Delhi, the East India Company allowed army commanders who wielded political power and authority on military *jagirs*, to continue as 'independent rulers' within its military establishment. Begum Samru was one such figure.

Sardhana, in the modern district of Meerut, was a *jagir* given by the Mughal Emperor Shah Alam to an Austrian military officer Walter Reinhart (popularly known as Samru in India). On his death the estate, which yielded a large annual revenue of about £90,000, was handed over to his wife Begum Samru. In 1803, when the region became a part of the East India Company territory, the Begum was allowed to continue as an 'independent ruler' on her promise of

189

loyalty and military support to the Company.

In Sardhana the Begum recreated the Mughal political ritual of the durbar. She made a lavish display of the symbols and etiquette of high status which prevailed in the upper echelons of Muslim society in Awadh. She observed *purdah* (seclusion), travelled in closed palanquins, used a hookah and donned silk and brocade clothes. But she also adopted Western military technology and routines of discipline.

The Begum was an exotic figure for the many British visitors who halted at her estate on their way to Delhi. They admired her tolerance which embraced a small Catholic church on her estate (she later converted to Roman Catholicism), and the excellence of agriculture at Sardhana. But they also gossiped about the lurid tales of her history, intrigues and autocracy. C.A.B./S.A.

190

190 A Coffee Party. After Parade at a Military Station in India. Horse Artillery; Regular Cavalry; Irregular Cavalry; Infantry

M. and N. Hanhart after Philip Trench
Coloured lithograph, 32 × 46 (13½ × 19¾)
Lent by The Director, National Army Museum, London SW3 4HT (5706–21)

Faced with local revolts in India, the turbulent North-West Frontier, and Russian advances in Central Asia, the Indian Army kept up its fighting strength of over a quarter of a million men throughout the early nineteenth century. It was therefore one of the largest European-style standing armies in the world, and provided an honourable career for the sons of numerous upper- and middle-class families in England, Scotland and particularly Ireland.

The picture shows officers of the Bengal Irregular Cavalry (Indian-style uniform), Native Infantry (red uniform), Light Cavalry (blue-grey uniform) and Horse Artillery (black uniform) in the cantonment after exercises. Irregular cavalry officers had by this time abandoned formal European uniforms to dress in the more picturesque style of their own Indian soldiers. Irregular forces were raised during wartime to supplement regular regiments. C.A.B.

PROVENANCE: Given by Mrs E.M. Fletcher, 1957.

LITERATURE: Mollo 1981, p.55.

191 Hindu Priest Garlanding the Flags of 35th Bengal Light Infantry at a Presentation of Colours Ceremony

Indian artist, perhaps at Lucknow, *c.* 1843
Watercolour, 39 × 48 (15¼ × 18¾)
India Office Library and Records (Add. Or. 741)

Since the 1780s the British had been concerned to accommodate the 'religious prejudices' of their Bengal army of high-caste peasant soldiers. They had paid careful attention to providing a pure Hindu diet for the army and had made possible the celebration of Hindu festivals. After 1836 the authorities redoubled their efforts to create Hindu regimental identities as part of the army reform programme which had begun under Bentinck. Now Hindu priests began to carry out formal functions similar to those performed by the padre of a European regiment. Over several generations the high status (and wealth) furnished by military service does seem to have helped to raise generally the status of the Bhumihar Brahmins of the Benares region and of southern Awadh. Ironically, though, it was the sepoys' feeling that this jealously-guarded status was being treated with contempt by the British in the 1850s which sparked off the Rebellion of 1857.

The regiment became the Light Infantry in 1843 and was given the Governor-General's Order for Kilmarnocks for Sepoys in 1847. The flags bear the battle honour of 'Cabul 1842'. As the troops are wearing Kilmarnocks, and as the regiment was abandoned after the Rebellion, the picture must have been painted between 1843 and 1858. C.A.B./S.A.

PROVENANCE: Purchased by India Office Library, 1957.

LITERATURE: Archer 1972, pp.163–4, no.128(i); Mollo 1981.

Residents and Protected Princes 1800–57

In the early years of the nineteenth century the British perfected the system of Residencies at the remaining independent and semi-independent courts. The work of men such as Charles Metcalfe, Mountstuart Elphinstone and David Ochterloney, coordinated from Calcutta by the Foreign, Persian and Political Departments of the Indian Government, tried to impose peace on north-western India and benefited from the fact that the Punjab, under the Sikh ruler Ranjit Singh, would be a well-governed and friendly neighbour.

The growth of Russian interests in Central Asia and the fear of instability at Kabul combined with the death of Ranjit Singh in 1839 to disturb the fragile equilibrium. Determined to find a stable northern and western border at

191

last, the British occupied Sind and the Punjab. But their attempt to reduce Afghanistan to client status misfired badly, and in the Kabul campaign of 1838–41 the Company suffered one of its worse defeats in Indian military history.

C.A.B.

192 A View of Government House, from the Eastward

Robert Havell after James Baillie Fraser, 1824–6
Aquatint, 90 × 60 ($35\frac{1}{2} \times 23\frac{6}{10}$)
Syndics of Cambridge University Library

The new Government House was completed in 1804 during Wellesley's period of office. Typical of the architectural style developed by Kent, it was much grander than the 'mean counting house' which had preceded it. The house and its grandiose entrance, based on Adam's entrance to Syon Park near London, symbolized a new awareness of the glory of empire, and of the exalted position of the Governor-General, which was a hallmark of Wellesley's period. Wellesley's immediate successors as Governor-General were somewhat embarrassed by the regal style of court ritual and precedence which he had encouraged, but a hundred years later Lord Curzon was delighted with it, particularly as the building was a more or less exact replica of his own family house, Kedleston Hall.

The Indians gathered in front of the gateway represent local merchants and palanquin bearers. By this time many of the bearers were low caste or tribal people from the relatively distant hills of Orissa, an indication of the city's growth as a labour market. Fraser (1783–1856) had come to Calcutta in 1814 and spent his leisure hours sketching. He was employed by a general trading company, or agency house, and was helped in his hobby by George Chinnery. The album *Views of Calcutta, and its environs* was engraved by Robert Havell, Frederick Lewis and Theodore Fielding who developed a more sophisticated aquatint process which eliminated the need for much of the hand-colouring.

C.A.B.

LITERATURE: Archer and Falk 1989; Godrej and Rohatgi 1989.

193 Sir William Rumbold in Fort William

George Chinnery, *c.* 1818
Oil on canvas, 75 × 61.5 ($29\frac{1}{4} \times 24$)
Lent by his widow in remembrance of Sir Anthony Rumbold, Bt.

The Rumbolds were a famous Anglo-Indian family whose most colourful member had been Sir Thomas, Governor of Madras in the 1770s and a celebrated 'nabob'. Sir William Rumbold became involved in loans to the Nizam of Hyderabad through Palmer & Company (see no. 231). The Calcutta skyline with Government House forms the backdrop. The portrait shows Chinnery's formal style during his later but very productive period.

C.A.B.

LITERATURE: Archer 1979, pp.366–86.

193

194 Purniya, Chief Minister of Mysore

Thomas Hickey, *c.* 1801
Oil on canvas, 127 × 100.4 ($50 \times 39\frac{1}{2}$)
Yale Center for British Art, Paul Mellon collection (B. 1973.1.22)

Purniya, a Maratha Brahmin administrator, embodied some of the most important features of the transition to British rule in peninsular India. He had risen to prominence during Tipu's rule, and was typical of the class of *lokika* or 'secular' Brahmins who kept the revenues and administration running smoothly, even in the Muslim states of central and southern India. Purniya was head both of the Revenue Department (*Mir Asaf Kutcheri*) and the Military Department (*Mir Miran Kutcheri*) of Tipu's government. But during the final war of 1799 the British bought him off and he offered only token resistance to their thrust against Seringapatam, thus sealing the fate of the Sultan. As a reward for the betrayal of his master, Purniya acquired a position as chief financial officer (*diwan*) to the restored

194

Hindu Wodiyar rulers, and helped to reconstruct the kingdom as a client state of the Company.

As for the Mughals, control of the chief financial officers in dependent kingdoms was critical for the British empire. Purniya's position was similar to that of Chandu Lal, another Hindu minister in a Muslim state (no.231). In 1809 Purniya offered further critical help to the Madras authorities when he refused to join, or countenance, the so-called 'White Mutiny', a movement of disgruntled European army officers who threatened rebellion against the Company. Naturally, the British liked to laud his sense of 'fair play'. Dr John Leyden, Surgeon to the Mysore Survey, wrote, 'Pournia sprung from Brahma's line./Intrepid in the martial fray/Alike in council formed to shine.' Hickey's picture includes symbols and gestures representing justice and administrative integrity.

Although the identity of the sitter has not been established beyond doubt, Mildred Archer (see Literature) has noted that the costume, caste and emblematic statuette of justice all point to the sitter being Purniya. Hickey had probably drawn Purniya when he was at Mysore in 1801. Significantly, the stylistic conventions adopted by Hickey are overtly European. There is a classical architectural background, the pose is of a type frequently used by artists from Van Dyck to Reynolds, and the allegorical figure of justice is an appropriate emblem for Purniya, renowned as he was for his sense of fairness, at least among the British. Hickey's portrait is a vivid characterization and is one of the most sympathetic and lively portraits of Indian sitters. B.A./C.A.B.

PROVENANCE: Spink & Son Ltd, London; purchased by Paul Mellon and given to Yale Center for British Art 1973.

LITERATURE: Hasan 1971, pp.330–36; Breeze 1973, p.148, no.172; Archer 1979, pp.227–8, pl.153; Cormack 1985, p.114, ill. p.115.

EXHIBITIONS: London, Spink & Son Ltd, *English Paintings*, November-December 1972 (5); New Haven, Yale Center for British Art, *The British View of India Selected Paintings from the Paul Mellon Collection*, 1978 (unnumbered).

195 General Sir Thomas Munro (1761–1827)

Sir Martin Archer Shee, 1819
Oil on canvas, 76.5 × 63.5 (30⅛ × 25)
National Portrait Gallery, London (3124)

195

Munro, one of the greatest of the British Indian civil servants, played a leading role in the creation of the Madras Presidency. Born in Glasgow, the son of a failed 'Virginia trader' in tobacco, Munro left for an infantry cadetship in Madras in 1789. He fought in two campaigns against Mysore and became administrator of the Barahmahal territory taken from Tipu in 1792. Later, he consolidated the initial British settlement of the Kanara District on the south-west coast and the northern districts ceded by Hyderabad (1800–7).

During these years Munro became convinced of the social and economic value of the *raiyatwari* ('peasant-wise') system of land-revenue management. In this system government made a contract with the individual cultivator, basing the state's revenue on the actual productivity of the land. Munro and his colleagues were also favourable to the local Hindu judicial bodies, the *panchayats*, considering that they dispensed better and cheaper justice than the British courts. Munro fought fierce administrative battles against the proponents of the *zamindari* or landlord-based systems of revenue management. In the south he won his victory, becoming Governor of Madras in 1819, but died of cholera in 1827.

Munro revisited England with his family in June 1819 and was promoted to Major-General in August. He was appointed KCB in November 1819, before leaving for India again in December. It was presumably during these six months that Shee painted this portrait, plus its companion piece of Lady Munro (NPG 3124a), exhibiting them at the Royal Academy the following spring.

This portrait is the basis for the grand full-length version painted in 1828 for the Town Hall in Madras. Munro wears a Major-General's uniform, the Star and Badge of a KCB, and a gold medal with a Seringapatam clasp. B.A./C.A.B.

PROVENANCE: By family descent; Torquil Munro sale, Christie's, 25 September 1942 (74), bt Frost & Reed, from whom purchased by NPG, 1942.

LITERATURE: Walker 1985, vol.I, p.352, vol. II, pl.847; Stein 1990.

EXHIBITIONS: London, Royal Academy, 1820 (341); Glasgow, *Scottish Exhibition*, 1911, lent by Sir Campbell Munro.

196 Lieutenant-Colonel James Achilles Kirkpatrick in Indian court costume

Deccani, *c.*1798
Gouache, 55 × 42.5 (21⅝ × 16⅝)
Private Collection

James Achilles Kirkpatrick, Resident at Hyderabad between 1797 and 1805, consolidated the British position in this vital southern state. A pro-French party was gaining influence in Hyderabad at the very time when the final showdown with Tipu was looming; Kirkpatrick outmanoeuvred his enemies and concluded a new subsidiary treaty (1800) and a commercial settlement which drew the Nizam more firmly into the British orbit.

C.A.B.

PROVENANCE: By descent.

LITERATURE: Briggs 1861.

197 Khair-un-Nissa Begum, wife of James Achilles Kirkpatrick

J. Smart, *c.* 1798
Gouache, 22 × 17 ($8\frac{5}{8} \times 6\frac{5}{8}$)
Private Collection

One reason for James Achilles Kirkpatrick's political success (see no. 199) was his marriage to Khair-un-Nissa, a great-niece of the *Diwan* of Hyderabad, Mir Alam. Two children were born of this union but by 1800 official and private opinion was beginning to turn against inter-racial marriage, and Kirkpatrick's advancement in the service was jeopardized by his easy relations with Indians.

C.A.B.

PROVENANCE: By descent.

197

198 Itimad-ud-Daulah's Tomb, Agra

Company artist, Delhi or Agra, *c.* 1820
Ink and watercolour on paper, 55.9 × 83.8 (22 × 33)
British Architectural Library Drawings Collection/RIBA (F/3/8[1])

This graceful monument was built in 1622–28 by the Empress Nur Jahan, wife of Jahangir (no.3), as a tomb for her parents. Mirza Ghiyas Beg was a Persian who had come to India during Akbar's reign to seek employment at the imperial court. He continued in service under Jahangir, with the title 'Itimad-ud-Daulah' or 'Pillar of the State'. The women of his family achieved even greater power and more lasting fame, since his daughter married Jahangir and his granddaughter was the woman in whose memory Shah Jahan built the Taj Mahal. Itimad-ud-Daulah's tomb in some ways prefigures that more famous building, particularly in the enveloping marble facing and the *pietra dura* decoration. The two buildings stand on opposite banks of the River Jumna in Agra.

The capture of Delhi and Agra by the British in 1803 made this and other Mughal buildings more accessible to British eyes. In the early decades of the nineteenth century pictures of them became highly fashionable. Many were painted by Indian artists local to the cities. In an attempt to appeal to the tastes of their new patrons, they modified their style. The large scale, the use of thin watercolour, and the adoption of perspective all suggest the influence of British architectural drawing. In many of these pictures, however, including no.198, the absence of a background to create a real depth, and the use of brilliant colour, are legacies of a more traditional Indian style (see also no.256).

G.H.R.T.

LITERATURE: Archer 1968, p.48.

198

199 Charles Theophilus Metcalfe, 1st Baron Metcalfe (1785–1846)

George Chinnery
Oil on canvas, 27.9 × 21.6 ($11 \times 8\frac{1}{2}$)
National Portrait Gallery, London (5381)

Another of the founding fathers of British India, Metcalfe like many of his generation was trained in Wellesley's briefly flourishing Fort William College, where he learnt oriental languages. He was a literary man and wrote extensively during his time as the Company's envoy to Kabul. His main achievement was

199

helping to stabilize political relations with Persia, Afghanistan and the Punjab. In 1835 he briefly became provisional Governor-General, but a measure to liberate the Calcutta press complicated his relations with the Company from whose service he resigned in 1838. In 1839 he became Governor of Jamaica and later Governor-General of Canada. A philosophical Whig by temperament, Metcalfe had a sceptical view of the British Government in India, whose downfall, he predicted, 'may be short work ... and the world will wonder more at the suddeness (*sic*) with which our immense Indian empire may vanish than it has done at the surprising conquest we have achieved' (Metcalfe to Bentinck, 11 October 1829). C.A.B.

LITERATURE: Kaye 1854.

200 A European smoking a Hookah. Possibly Sir David Ochterloney

Delhi school, *c.* 1820
Gouache, 22.4 × 31.9 ($8\frac{3}{4} \times 12\frac{1}{2}$)
India Office Library and Records (Add. Or. 2)

The British Residents at the Delhi Court such as Sir David Ochterloney, and later Sir Charles Metcalfe, coordinated the British diplomatic and military effort in the whole north Indian region. As in Faizabad and Lucknow a generation before, many of the British in Delhi were fascinated by the Mughal 'silver age' culture which had staged a revival once the city began to benefit from sustained peace. Several European administrators were accomplished students of Persian and the Indian classics; others, as shown here, were partial to the more exotic aspects of Mughal culture, the hookah and the dancing girl. But the growth of evangelical influence and notions of racial exclusiveness doomed the eighteenth-century Anglo-Indian synthesis. Ochterloney (1758–1825), the probable subject of this painting, was the first British Resident at Delhi, first from 1803 to 1806, and then again from 1818 to 1822. He defended the city against resurgent Maratha power in 1804 and achieved significant military successes against the Gurkhas (1814) and during the Pindari War (1817–18). Not long before his death he had a bitter disagreement with the Viceroy, Lord Amherst, over the treatment of the Raja of Bharatpur.

Although the painting is not inscribed, the central figure resembles the other known portraits of Ochterloney, such as the watercolour in the Red Fort Museum, Delhi.

Ochterloney lived in Indian style, and became a celebrated character in Delhi. Here he is depicted by a local artist in Indian dress at home, watching a *nautch* (a dance display) while smoking a hookah. By the nineteenth century it was unusual to find Europeans in India publicly adopting native clothing and those who did so were regarded as eccentric, although lightweight coats and other comfortable oriental-style garments were acceptable for informal wear indoors. C.A.B./J.S.

PROVENANCE: Purchased by India Office Library, 1954.

LITERATURE: Archer 1972, pp.201–2, no.170; ill. colour pl.D.

201 Panorama of a Durbar Procession of Akbar II, Emperor of Delhi, probably at Id or after Ramadan

Delhi school, *c.* 1815
Watercolour, 16 × 229.8 ($6\frac{1}{4} \times 94$)
Inscribed on original tin container: *Native Painting. Durbar Procession Baroda.*
India Office Library and Records (Add.Or.888)

200

201 (detail)

After 1803 the British controlled the city of Delhi, though the authority of the Mughal ruler was allowed to reign paramount within the walls of the Red Fort itself. A series of bruising encounters between British magistrates and military personnel and officials of the court ensued during the next fifty years, complicated by the fact that the Company, for all its real power, was still only the *diwan* or revenue collector of Bengal. Until the early 1840s, however, the Company continued to pay formal respect to the Emperor, and Company officers, including the Resident, played a secondary role in the great royal festivals and processions which seemed to belie the precipitate decline of Muslim authority in Delhi. Here the Emperor is accompanied by his sons, the Resident's party, Indian and British officials, and royal insignia such as umbrellas and 'sun' and 'fish' standards. C.A.B.

PROVENANCE: Acquired by W.S. Boyd, Bombay Civil Service 1818–44, while at Baroda; by descent to E. Lennox Boyd, who presented it to India Office Library, 1903.

LITERATURE: *Journal of Indian Art and Industry* 1912, XV, no.120, pp.77–8; Archer 1972, p.197, pl.58; Gupta 1981.

EXHIBITIONS: London, *Festival of Empire*, 1911; London, Barbican Art Gallery, *Panoramania*, 1988.

202 Emperor Akbar II (1806–37)†

Unknown artist, *c.* 1830
Watercolour on ivory, 5 × 3.8 (2 × 1½)
India Office Library and Records (Add.Or 2609)

PROVENANCE: Presented by F. Lennox Boyd.

LITERATURE: Spear 1953, p. 39–42; Archer 1972, p. 168.

203 Light Six-pounder Gun and Carriage

Sikh, probably Lahore, *c.*1840
Length 3.51m (11ft. 4in.); calibre 9.3 (3⅗)
Royal Armouries (XXIX.329)

It is most likely that this gun is one of the 256 guns captured by the forces of General Sir Hugh Gough (later 1st Viscount Gough, 1792–1869) during the first Sikh War of 1845–6. Although it is not illustrated by R.S. Smythe in *Plans of the Ordnance captured by the Army of the Sutlej* (*c.* 1848), it is close in barrel and carriage form and in decoration to a group of guns illustrated there, one of which (no.45) was cast in Lahore in 1839. Both carriage and barrel are based on British designs, the former in particular on Sir William Congreve's design of 1792 for the British service. T.R.

PROVENANCE: Purchased 1986 from estate of Lord Gough.

204

204 Cavalcade of the King of Oudh (Awadh)

c. 1820
Bronze, height 19.1 (7½)
The Visitors of the Ashmolean Museum, Oxford (1977.25)

This splendid bronze in the north Indian folk tradition is one of the finest (and one of the latest) examples of a style that spread throughout north and south India from the middle of the eighteenth century. The production of these pieces may have been influenced by eighteenth-century French styles of toy soldier, perhaps by indigenous chess pieces.

Until Buxar in 1764, the Awadh army was organized on Mughal principles, but after that date, Shuja put in train substantial reforms which increased the strength of his infantry, introduced western methods of fire-power control and diminished the importance of the old Mughal cavalry class. Nevertheless, the army remained very heterogeneous throughout the remainder of the Nawabi. 'Najibi' swordsmen, Rohilla cavalry and European-trained infantry jostled with armed Hindu *fakhirs* in its ranks. This colourful variety is captured in no. 204. The cavalcade shows the former Nawab, now King of Awadh, the British Resident of Lucknow, cavalry (sowars) dressed in Indian style and probably representing Rohillas, and foot soldiers dressed in European style. The King wears the new-style crown designed for him by Robert Home and indicating his status as an independent monarch of the Shia sect. C.A.B.

LITERATURE: Digby and Harle 1982, pp.9–10; Fisher 1985; Welch 1985 (283); Harle and Topsfield 1987, no.75.

EXHIBITIONS: New York, Metropolitan Museum of Art, *India!*, 1985–6 (283).

205 A British Officer

Rajasthan, Kotah, *c.* 1850
Black line and colour wash on paper, 13.7 × 13.8 (5⅜ × 5⅜)
James Ivory

The many small states of Rajasthan offered the greatest scope for the skills of the British Residents and their military entourages. Colonel James Tod pacified the territory in the 1810s and later wrote its history. His successors, such as this officer, worked closely with the princely families to discipline their recalcitrant vassals. The traditional arts, including painting and drawing, flourished throughout the nineteenth century in Rajasthan. C.A.B.

LITERATURE: Tod 1920.

206 Maharaja Ranjit Singh (1780–1839) listening to the Granth being recited near the Golden Temple. Amritsar

August Shoefft, Vienna *c.* 1850
Oil on canvas, 143.5 × 106.2 (56½ × 41⅞)
Department of Archaeology and Museums, Government of Pakistan

Ranjit Singh was the first Sikh ruler to preside over a united Punjab. From his entry into Lahore in 1799 he strove to unify the Sikh military aristocracy, which had been split into competing war bands in the eighteenth century. He tried to revive the trade and manufactures of the region and built up an effective army with the help of French and Italian officers. Until his death the Punjab was a prosperous and effective buffer state between the British at Delhi and the growing turbulence of central Asia and Afghanistan.

Sikhism was the royal religion of the Punjab, and Ranjit Singh ruled in the name of the Sikh military brotherhood, the Khalsa. He embellished the central shrine of the Sikh faith, the Golden Temple at Amritsar, and attended regular readings of the sacred book, the Guru Granth Sahib, as depicted here. But Ranjit Singh was a tolerant ruler. Hindu Brahmins and Muslims were amongst his closest leaders and he kept Sikh zealots under control. The one-eyed monarch is reported as saying, 'God intended me to look upon all religions with one eye; that is why he took away the light from the other.'

Shoefft (1809–88) was a Hungarian artist working in the Picturesque tradition, who went to India like many before him to paint his way out of poverty. By the 1840s, however, the decline of the independent Indian courts and the obsession of Anglo-Indian purchasers with small watercolours and the products of the Company School of painting made this a more difficult proposition. Shoefft painted this up in Vienna from a sketch made in Amritsar about 1841, three years after the death of the monarch. Ranjit Singh sits on a cushion with the Koh-i-Nur diamond on an amulet around his arm; beside him sit *bhais*, or priests, and members of his family. In the background is the holy Akhal Takht, seat of Sikhism. C.A.B.

LITERATURE: Archer 1966; Aijazuddin 1979, pp.32–3.

207 Maharaja Sher Singh (1807–43) seated, attended by his Council in the Lahore Fort

August Shoefft, Lahore 1841
Oil sketch, 45.8 × 60.1 (18 × 23$\frac{6}{10}$)
Department of Archaeology and Museums, Government of Pakistan

The death of Ranjit Singh was followed by a period of six years of conflict during which factions of the Sikh aristocracy and its powerful army of peasant origin vied for power. The British looked on, attracted by the riches of the Punjab but doubtful about further extensions of their territory. Maharaja Sher Singh, reputed son of Ranjit Singh, briefly ascended the throne and was rapidly assassinated, along with his own son, by a group of competing notables. C.A.B.

LITERATURE: Archer 1966; Aijazuddin 1979, p.51.

208 Maharaja Dalip Singh (1838–83)

Franz Xaver Winterhalter, 1854
Oil on canvas, 203.8 × 109.5 (80$\frac{1}{4}$ × 43$\frac{1}{8}$)
Signed and dated, b.r.: *F. Winterhalter 1854*; on back of canvas inscription giving names of artist and sitter and date, *July 1854*
Her Majesty The Queen

Dalip Singh (1838–83), the youngest son of Ranjit Singh, was formally declared Maharaja of the Punjab in September 1843, shortly after his fifth birthday and the assassination of Maharaja Sher Singh (no.207). In 1846 it fell to him to present the Sikhs' surrender to Lord Hardinge, the Governor-General. In 1849, after an attempt to rule through a Council of Regency with the titular Maharaja, followed by a rebellion of the Punjab army,

208

the British finally annexed the state. They forced Dalip Singh, still only a boy, to resign for himself and his successors 'all right, title and claim to the sovereignty of the Punjab'. Other terms included the surrender of the famous Koh-i-Nur diamond to Queen Victoria. Following his conversion to Christianity Dalip Singh went to England in 1854. He was accepted at Court and became a friend of Prince Albert. But, harbouring a sense of resentment against the British authorities for his poor financial position, he reverted to Sikhism and, following an abortive return to India, spent his final years in unhappy exile in France.

This picture was painted for Queen Victoria. Dalip Singh is shown in Indian dress, standing in a landscape and resting his right hand on his sword. He wears, as Sir Oliver Millar has pointed out (see Literature), several of the jewels he retained when his lands were annexed by the British, including, in his turban, his diamond aigrette and star.

The Queen recorded in her Journal for 10 July 1854 that at Buckingham Palace she 'Went to see Winterhalter painting, when we found the Maharajah in his full dress ... Winterhalter was in ecstasies at the beauty and nobility of bearing of the young Maharajah. He was very amiable and patient, standing so still and giving a sitting of upwards of 2 hours. Winterhalter has got the whole figure beautifully, and the likeness is so good.' On the following day when the Queen was again present she noted that 'The portrait of me, set in diamonds, which he generally wears, was the gift of Lord Auckland to his father, as well as the ring with my signature which he had on today.' During one of the sittings the Maharajah was shown the Koh-i-Nur diamond, presented by the Company to the Queen.

According to Lady Login (quoted by Millar; see Literature) Winterhalter gave Dalip Singh, still short of his sixteenth birthday, the height he assumed he would eventually attain, although he apparently grew no taller.

Winterhalter was paid £300 for the picture in 1854. Although, as Richard Ormond pointed out (Ormond 1987, p.57), Winterhalter's greatest achievements are not usually in male portraiture, he excelled himself in producing this exotic and highly romantic portrait of the boy prince in full regalia, the like of which had not been seen since Sir Thomas Lawrence's impressions of the heroes of the Napoleonic Wars a generation earlier. B.A./C.A.B.

PROVENANCE: Painted for Queen Victoria; placed in the Princesses' Corridor at Buckingham Palace, transferred to Osborne, 1912.

LITERATURE: Login 1904, pp.122–3; Farrer 1908, p.390; Alexander and Anand 1980, pp.44–9; Ormond 1987, pp.57, 197; Millar forthcoming.

EXHIBITIONS: Baden, Kunsthalle, *Winterhalter*, October 1973; London, National Portrait Gallery, *Winterhalter*, 1987 (40).

209 Sir Herbert Edwardes (1819–68)

Henry Moseley, *c.* 1850
Oil on canvas, 249 × 157.5 (98 × 62)
National Portrait Gallery, London (1391)

Sir Herbert Edwardes arrived in India in 1841 as a cadet in the Bengal Infantry, but soon displayed his ability as a linguist in Urdu, Hindi and Persian. An assistant to Henry Lawrence (and later to his brother John) in the famous conquest and settlement of the Punjab between 1848 and 1858, he was typical of the self-reliant men, deeply knowledgeable about the local population, who founded what came to be called the 'Punjab School' of Indian government. Edwardes served as Commissioner of the Peshawar Division and its mountainous dependencies, 'the outpost of the Indian Empire' as Lord Dalhousie, the Governor-General, called it. Edwardes

209

helped secure a period of stability along the Afghan frontier, repairing the damage done by the disastrous campaign of 1838–41. In due course he became Commissioner of the Ambala Division of the Punjab, applying once again the principle of 'knowing the country' and settling it by gaining the trust of the peasant landowners and tribal chiefs. Edwardes was a strong evangelical Christian and his campaign for vigorous and state-supported missionary activity after the Rebellion of 1857 led to a slow parting of the ways with official opinion. A note on the canvas records that this was the Afghan dress that he wore at Bunnoo (Banu) in 1848–9. C.A.B.

PROVENANCE: The sitter; bequeathed by his widow, 1905.

210 Sir Charles James Napier (1782–1853)

Attributed to Samuel Smart, 1840s (?)
Oil on canvas, 35.3. × 28.9 ($13\frac{9}{10} \times 11\frac{3}{10}$)
National Portrait Gallery, London (3964)

Napier (1782–1853) went to India for the first time in 1841, after a distinguished career in the British army. In 1842 he deployed the force that he was moving up to Afghanistan to subjugate the territory of the Amirs of Sind. His campaign ended in annexation in 1843. Napier remained in Sind to establish a new British administration in spite of considerable criticism of the conquest in Britain. He left India in 1847 but was recalled for the last stage of the second Sikh war.

The authorship of this portrait has not been firmly established (Ormond 1973). P.J.M./B.A.

PROVENANCE: Napier family or dealer named Pforzer (see Ormond 1973); E. Kersley, from whom purchased 1955.

LITERATURE: Holland n.d., III, p.28; Lambrick 1952; Ormond 1973, I, p.333, no.3964, II, pl.656.

210

211 Captain Macpherson received at the Durbar of Nawab Muhammad Bahawal Khan of Bahawalpur

Muhammad and Karim Bakhsh, AH 1263/AD 1851
Gouache on canvas, 76.3 × 122 ($29\frac{3}{4} \times 47\frac{1}{2}$)
nasta'liq inscription on top: *amal-i ustah Muhammad Bakhsh wa pesaresh Karim Bakhsh Ahmadpuri naqqash sannat 1263*; other *nasta'liq* inscriptions on painted surface naming each figure
Courtesy of Hosain Books

The inscription states that the work was executed by Muhammad Bakhsh and his son Karim, artists originally from Lahore and later from Ahmadpur, a small city in the state of Bahawalpur, where they worked under the patronage of Nawab Muhammad Bahawal Khan. The inscriptions also name the courtiers seated before the ruler as Sayyid Khwaja Zayn-al-Abidin Shah, Ahmad Khan Afghan, Sayyid Ahmad Shah Jami, Mu'izz-ad-Din Khan Khukuwani and Abd-al-Khaliq Khan. Seated beside Macpherson is Sayyid Surur Shah Bahadur and in the foreground Sultan Ali Quraishi, accompanied by his bodyguards.

The Daudputras, who were the Bahawalpur ruling family, claimed descent from the Abbasid Khalifas of Egypt. They came from Sind and founded an independent state with the break-up of the Afghan empire after the death of Ahmed Shah Durrani, victor of Panipat (see no. 90). With the rise of Ranjit Singh's Sikh state (see no. 209), Nawab Muhammad Bahawal Khan III looked increasingly for British support and in 1833 a treaty was signed between the two powers which guaranteed the independence of Bahawalpur. During the Afghan war the Nawab helped supply the British army and between 1847 and 1848 he cooperated with Sir Herbert Edwardes (no. 209) in an expedition against the Sikhs in Multan, which signalled the occupation of the Punjab.

The pronounced 'halo' emblem around the head of the Nawab symbolizes his family inheritance of the charisma of the Khalifas, the spiritual successors of the Prophet on Earth.

C.A.B.

PROVENANCE: The collection of James Andrew Broun Ramsay, 10th Earl and 1st Marquis of Dalhousie; sale, Sotheby's, 26 April 1990 (99); purchased by present owner.

LITERATURE: Imperial Gazetteer of India 1908.

212

212 Four Portrait Heads of Afghan leaders

Emily Eden, June 1841
Watercolour, 35 × 25.6 (13¾ × 10)
Inscribed on back in ink: *Hyder Khan, Dost Mahomed Khan, Mahomed Akram Khan, Abdool Ghunee Khan.*
India Office Library and Records (WD 1291)

Emily Eden accompanied her brother Lord Auckland to India when he was made Governor-General (1836–1842). An accomplished artist, she had many of her sketches published as lithographs in her *Portraits of the princes and people of India* (see Literature). Her journal, *Up the Country*, also attracted great interest when it was published in 1866.

The heads are those of Dost Muhammad Khan and three members of his family: Haider Khan, governor of Ghazni; Muhammad Akram Khan; and Abdul Ghani Khan. Dost Muhammad Khan ruled Kabul and Ghazni from 1826 and was Amir of Afghanistan from 1836 to 1840, and again from 1841 to 1863. He and his family were Auckland's guests, or rather prisoners, at Barrackpore in June 1841. British involvement in Afghan affairs was a consequence of Lord Palmerston's fears of Russian influence in Afghanistan. Finding Dost Muhammad insufficiently pliable, the British had attempted to replace him with Shah Shuja. But the expeditionary force sent to Kabul in 1838–41 went disastrously wrong and was almost totally destroyed in one of the worst defeats in British military history. A punitive army was later sent to Kabul, but British influence was mortally weakened. Auckland was recalled and his successor, Ellenborough, withdrew from the Afghan 'hornets' nest'.

Dost Muhammad Khan was allowed to resume his rule. The British had been humiliated, like other Europeans were to be after them, by the inhospitable terrain and the implacable resistance of the Afghan tribesmen, who hated the presence of the unbelievers on their soil. Hereafter Afghanistan remained a buffer zone between the British and the Tsarist empires, though two further wars and many minor skirmishes were to be fought between the Raj and the Afghans. B.A./C.A.B.

PROVENANCE: From family collection of Emily Eden's great grandnephew, Captain Eden G. Wallace; purchased by India Office Library, 1958.

LITERATURE: Eden 1844, pl.1; Norris 1967; Archer 1969, I, p.184, no.1291, repr. pl.49.

213 *Sketches in Afghanistan during the campaign of 1839 and 1840 up to the surrender of Dost Mohamed Khan*, London, 1842

J.Atkinson, 1842
Printed book, 20 × 13 ($7\frac{7}{8} \times 5\frac{1}{8}$)
India Office Library and Records (T4845)

214 *Afghanistan Costumes and Views*, London, 1848

J. Rattray, 1848
Printed book, 63 × 46 ($24\frac{6}{8} \times 18\frac{1}{8}$)
India Office Library and Records (X562)

215 Sepoys attacking Baluchi Snipers in the Siri-Kajur pass (Baluchistan)

James Atkinson, *c.* 1839–40
Watercolour, 25 × 36.6 ($9\frac{7}{8} \times 14\frac{3}{8}$)
Inscribed on mount: *The wild pass of Siri-Kagoor*, and in lower left corner *No.5*
India Office Library and Records (WD 2394)

Atkinson, a Renaissance man among the Anglo-Indians, entered the Bengal Medical Service in 1805 and became Civil Surgeon. Later he was Assay Master of the Calcutta Mint and Officiating Deputy Professor of Persian at Fort William College, and he founded the *Calcutta Annual Register*. In 1833 he became Surgeon to the 55th Native Infantry and from 1838 to 1841 was Superintending Surgeon with the Army of the Indus. This was the ill-fated force despatched through the Bolan Pass by Lord Auckland to put Shuja Shah on the throne of Afghanistan.

This is one of sixteen drawings depicting the march of the Army of the Indus from Sind to Kabul in Afghanistan via Quetta and Kandahar in 1839 and 1840. The drawings are part of the original set of twenty-four from which lithographs were made by L. and C. Haghe for Atkinson's *Sketches in Afghanistan* (see Literature). B.A./C.A.B.

PROVENANCE: Presented, with other drawings, by artist's son, Rev. Canon J.A. Atkinson, to India Office Library, 1910.

LITERATURE: Atkinson 1842, pl.6; Foster 1924, p.45, no.151; Archer 1969, I, p.96, no.2394.

216

216 Two Camels with Sindhi riders; a European seated behind one of them

Henry Ainslie, 1852
Watercolour, 26 × 35.8 ($10\frac{1}{4} \times 14$)
Inscribed on back in ink: *Camel travelling in Sindh 1852*
India Office Library and Records (WD2086)

Though the conquest of Sind was effected by 1843, its pacification was a more protracted matter. Anti-British tribal coalitions, often enthused with Islamic fervour, regularly formed in the more remote and desert areas in order to threaten the Indus plain where British control centred on the acquiescence of large landowners.

Major Ainslie (*c.* 1805–79), an officer in the British Army, served in the garrisons at Karachi and Hyderabad, the main towns in the restive province. This is one of a group of eighteen drawings of scenes and antiquities in Poona and Sind executed between 1849 and 1853. C.A.B./B.A.

PROVENANCE: Purchased 16 April 1963.

LITERATURE: Archer 1969, I, pp.91–3, no. 2086, pl.53.

217

217 British Troops crossing the Sutlej (Punjab) by a Bridge of Boats during the first Sikh War

Sir Henry Yule, February 1846
Pen, ink and wash, 17.9 × 25.5 (7 × 10)
Inscribed on front in watercolour: *Bridge on the Sutlej. Feby 1846*
India Office Library and Records (WD 1039)

Sir Henry Yule (1820–89) served in India with the Bengal Engineers from 1840 to 1862, taking part in the first and second Sikh Wars (1845–46, 1848–49). He is probably best known for his glossary of Anglo-Indian colloquial words and phrases entitled *Hobson-Jobson* (1886). B.A.

PROVENANCE: Purchased 12 December 1919.

LITERATURE: Archer 1969, I, pl.355, no.1039, pl.21; Mukherjee and Leach 1970.

The Wheels of Commerce and the British Discovery of India

During the first half of the nineteenth century India was transformed by the decline of Indian weaving and the first wave of British manufactured imports from an exporter of cloth and silks into an exporter of agricultural raw materials. The Company refurbished and extended the Mughal system of land-revenue management and established a deeper control over the countryside in the face of local uprising and revolt. Open warfare had been suppressed, but famines and the heavy weight of taxation continued to bear down on the peasantry.

Forms of British criminal and civil justice were slowly introduced and Indians began to learn English and European sciences in a small number of schools in the major centres. Yet British power and influence was felt very unevenly. It took issues such as widow-burning (*sati*) or the ritual strangling and robbery of travellers (*thagi* or *thuggee*), both of which assumed a symbolic importance in the European mind, to galvanize the thinly stretched colonial authorities into action.

The most far-reaching changes came about as Indians, both Hindu and Muslim, responded directly or indirectly to the challenge of alien rule and foreign ideas. Reforming and revitalizing movements were led by men such as Raja Ram Mohan Roy and Shah Abdul Aziz. The printing press and political debate began to appear in the major cities. C.A.B.

Calcutta and Anglo-Indian Life

By 1820 the European population of Calcutta had reached about 4,000 and the total population was in excess of 350,000, making it one of the largest cities in the British empire. Indian cloths from Bengal and north India continued to be exported through the port. But the British agency houses were exporting increasing quantities of cotton, indigo and opium. Raw cotton from central India was despatched by way of Calcutta to China whose raw cotton supply failed to keep up with its growing population. To the horror of its mandarins, the Chinese empire also imported from India, legally and illegally, growing quantities of opium, a commodity which created its own sinister market. The blue dye indigo, produced in the Agra region and in Bihar, was shipped to China and to Europe. Control of Indian resources thus helped the British to balance their trade with the whole of East Asia. Commercial buildings associated with this burgeoning trade straggled along the Strand and into Lal Bazaar. But the British and Indian elites of Calcutta also prospered with the expansion of the administration which now spilled out of the old Fort William and the area around the Writers' Building into the surrounding streets. A large and opulent European area emerged in Chowringhee, where a large number of Palladian-

218

220

style private houses were erected. The society which inhabited these salubrious suburban quarters was more 'polite' and anglicized than the somewhat louche set portrayed by William Hickey a generation before. Evangelicalism had made its mark and Calcutta's citizens now turned their hands to good works within the European and Indian community.

C.A.B.

LITERATURE: Mukherjee 1970.

218 Servants of Lieutenant-Colonel Gilbert on the Verandah of a Bungalow

Unknown Calcutta artist, perhaps from Murshidabad, *c.* 1825
Watercolour, 46.2 × 64.4 ($18\frac{1}{4} \times 25\frac{1}{4}$)
Inscribed in pencil on front: *Our Old Servants*
India Office Library and Records (Add. Or. 2524)

Lieutenant-Colonel Gilbert (1785–1853) was Commandant of the Ramgarh Battalion at Hazaribagh in Bihar at the time this painting was made. He later served in Orissa. He was married to the sister of Sir Charles D'Oyly's wife and belonged to a circle which was deeply involved in the patronage of both British and Indian painting. The scene on the verandah of a bungalow shows the *ayahs* (nurses), the *khidmatgar* (butler) and other servants dressed in the livery appropriate to a great Anglo-Indian household.

C.A.B.

PROVENANCE: Purchased by India Office Library, 19 March 1963.

LITERATURE: Archer 1972, pp.89–90, ill.pl.31.

219 A European Lady and her Family attended by an Ayah or Nurse

J.H. Clark and C. Dubourg after Sir Charles D'Oyly, 1813
Engraving, 28 × 35 ($11 \times 13\frac{7}{10}$)
The Syndics of Cambridge University Library (Harley-Mason Collection)

The *dhood-dhye*, or wet nurse, was distinguished from the *ayah*, or dry nurse. The text says that the *ayahs* were 'commonly fond of children ... owing to a total deficiency of education ... ' but better than 'our juvenile race of nurses, whose time is commonly divided between the novel and the window seat!'

C.A.B.

LITERATURE: Blagden 1813, ill. pl.XVII.

220 The Emporium of Taylor & Co. in Calcutta

Sir Charles D'Oyly, *c.* 1825–8
Watercolour, 18.1 × 23 (7 × 9)
The Trustees of Victoria and Albert Museum, London (IS-1–1980)

As the number of British women in India grew during the nineteenth century, so shopping facilities improved with the opening of large warehouses which operated along European lines and stocked a wide range of highly-coveted French and English items including silver urns, strings of pearls, hunting saddles, toys and preserves. Instead of sending their servants to the local bazaar, where goods were generally comparable and much cheaper, ladies preferred to shop in person, accompanied by their gentlemen, and this soon became a popular pastime. Here, D'Oyly depicts a group of British men and women wearing the day dress fashionable around 1818–28 and admiring the merchandise in Taylor's Emporium, a well-known Calcutta store which he also described in detail in his satirical poem, *Tom Raw the Griffin*, written in 1824:

> The rooms themselves, as designated prove
> Exceeding long – two hundred feet or more;
> And as, in India, colonnades we love
> A row of pillars cut their very core;
> Of every tasteful article a store,
> On tables heaped, reveal their varied charms.
> Porcelain from France and England glittering o'er
> With gold and flowered patterns .... (1.1873)
>
> And from the ceilings drop stupendous lustres
> And girandoles and chandeliers, that vie
> With wall shades stuck around in sparkling clusters .... (1.1887)

This illustration was omitted from the published version of the poem. J.S.

LITERATURE: D'Oyly 1828; Roberts 1835; M. and W.G. Archer 1955, p.33 ff.

EXHIBITION: London, Victoria and Albert Museum, *The Indian Heritage*, 1982 (105).

222

221 Chowringhee Road

Thomas Prinsep, 1821
Pencil and watercolour on paper, 11.3 × 16.5 (4¼ × 6½)
Signed with initials and dated
Spink & Son Ltd, London

A minor incident of colonial life in 1820s Calcutta is recorded here. Thomas and Thoby Prinsep were two of the sons of the indigo dealer John Prinsep, and brothers of the famous scholar James and the artist William (see no.270). Thoby (1792–1878) had a distinguished career in government service, rising to be a Member of the Supreme Council. At the time of this drawing, he was the Government's Persian Secretary. In the drawing, his brother Thomas (1800–1830) shows himself leaving Thoby's mansion on the fashionable Chowringhee Road. The misfortune that befell him at the gate is described in the accompanying inscription: 'Tom's catastrophe coming out of Thoby's house; a kite pouncing upon the feather of his cock'd hat!' G.H.R.T.

LITERATURE: Archer 1982, p.5, no.12.

222 A Calcutta House surrounded by a Garden with Tank (rain-fed pools) and Out-houses

Shaikh Muhammad Amir of Karraya, *c.* 1845
Watercolour, 45.2 × 64.4 (17¾ × 25)
India Office Library and Records (Add. Or. 488)

This is one of three drawings made for an Englishman in Calcutta, depicting his house, horses, gig and servants, by Shaikh Muhammad, a prolific artist who used to tour Calcutta in search of commissions to paint domestic scenes. His was a particularly charming adaptation of the colours and expertise of animal draughtsmanship associated with Murshidabad Mughal painting (eg. no. 84) to European taste. There were numerous mansions such as this, built to sub-Palladian designs and with watertanks, along Chowringhee Road and also in the suburban settlement of Garden Reach. By the 1840s, however, the sloping-roofed bungalow, an imitation of domestic Bengali rural architecture, was becoming a common type of residence

223

224

for European families. Storks, like the one on the left, were a notable feature of Calcutta's birdlife. They are shown, for instance, perching on the balustrades of Government House in no.195. C.A.B.

PROVENANCE: Purchased by India Office Library, 14 January 1957.

LITERATURE: Archer 1965, no.79; Archer 1972, p.92, ill. col. pl.B; Kling 1976; Welch 1978, no.20.

223 Pony Riding

Shaikh Muhammad Amir of Karraya, Calcutta *c.* 1845
Watercolour, 39.4 × 52.1 ($15\frac{2}{5} \times 20\frac{3}{10}$)
The Marquis of Dufferin and Ava

A European girl in a large bonnet goes riding with the *khansamah* (head servant), the groom and an attendant with a parasol. C.A.B.

LITERATURE: Welch 1978, no.23.

224 Trial of Four British Seamen at Canton, 1 October 1807

Oil on canvas, 71 × 101.5 ($27\frac{3}{5} \times 39\frac{1}{2}$)
National Maritime Museum (1943–30.2; Caird Collection BHC/0581)

The East India Company had been established in Canton since the middle of the eighteenth century, and private British fortunes had been remitted to London via the Canton and Macao establishments of other European nations. After 1784, however, the China trade became even more important to India and to the British balance of payments. In order to purchase valuable china teas, the sales of which were booming in Britain, both the Company and private merchants in Bengal began to import large quantities of raw cotton wool from Gujarat and central India. Many early fortunes, both British and Indian, were made in this trade. At this time the Chinese authorities restricted the commerce of Britain and other European nations to Canton and its own subjects were only allowed to trade with the outside world through a body of registered merchants, the Cohong, some of whose members are shown here. Until 1841 foreigners exercised no kind of territorial jurisdiction in Canton, but on this occasion British sailors accused of an affray were examined by Chinese officials in the Company factory in the presence of Company servants. From the 1810s, however, the Company began to import into China a more noxious product, opium. It was the tension between British and Chinese authorities over the outflow of silver and the social disintegration brought about by this trade which led to the Opium War and the defeat of China in 1842. C.A.B./P.J.M.

LITERATURE: Moore 1926; Greenberg 1958.

225 Indenture to William Cox with Seal of the East India Company, 14 March 1812

38.1 × 49 (15 × 19¼)
Royal Commonwealth Society (MSS 22)

Since the Crown had granted the East India Company a monopoly on trade both within the Orient and between Britain and the East Indies, private merchants and 'free mariners' were compelled to seek the Company's permission to reside and do business in its territories. In no.225 William Cox is licensed to 'peaceably and quietly trade and traffic in the East-Indies' provided that he does not infringe the Company's privileges and obeys its government. As the East Indian trade swelled and became more valuable, however, pressure to modify and even abolish its monopoly built up in Britain. Protagonists of free-trade scored a major success in 1813 when the Company's monopoly was revised, and in 1833, when it lost control over the China trade. In 1833, after another victory for the free-traders, the East India Company lost its commercial character altogether and became little more than an agency of government dispensing the patronage in 'East India jobs', which British ministers were too cautious to take over until forced to do so by the events of 1857. C.A.B.

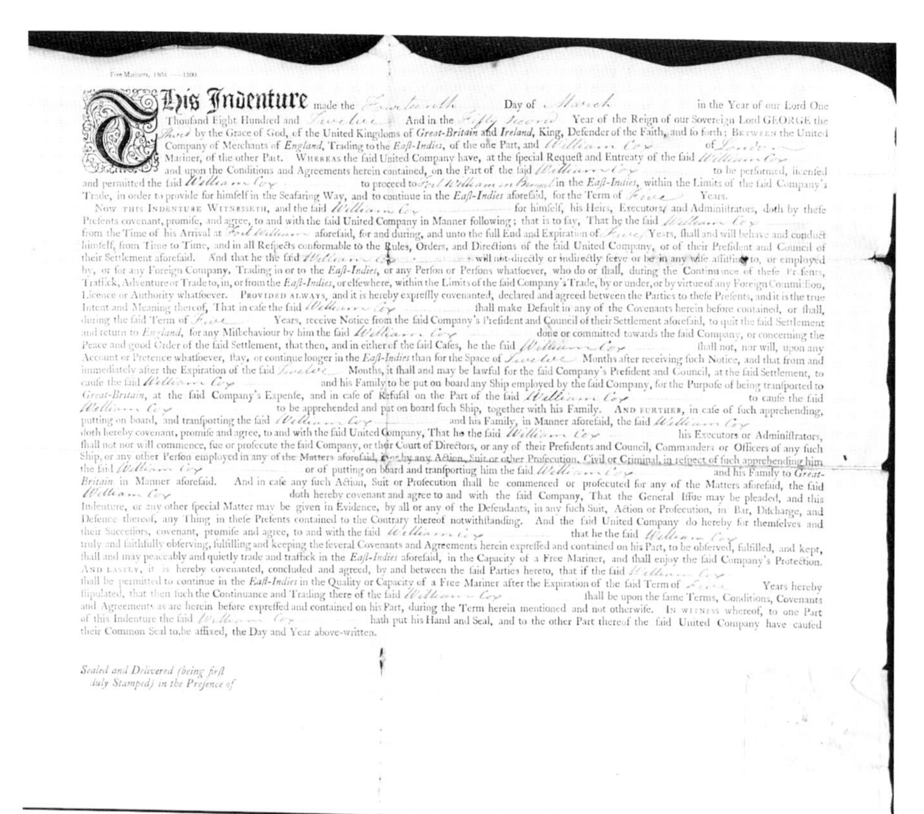
Free Mariners, 1801 — 1100

This Indenture made the Fourteenth Day of March in the Year of our Lord One Thouſand Eight Hundred and Twelve And in the Fifty second Year of the Reign of our Sovereign Lord GEORGE the Third by the Grace of God, of the United Kingdoms of *Great-Britain* and *Ireland*, King, Defender of the Faith, and ſo forth; BETWEEN the United Company of Merchants of *England*, Trading to the *Eaſt-Indies*, of the one Part, and William Cox of London Mariner, of the other Part. WHEREAS the ſaid United Company have, at the ſpecial Requeſt and Entreaty of the ſaid William Cox and upon the Conditions and Agreements herein contained, on the Part of the ſaid William Cox to be performed, licenſed and permitted the ſaid William Cox to proceed to Fort William in Bengal in the *Eaſt-Indies*, within the Limits of the ſaid Company's Trade, in order to provide for himſelf in the Seafaring Way, and to continue in the *Eaſt-Indies* aforeſaid, for the Term of Five Years.

NOW THIS INDENTURE WITNESSETH, and the ſaid William Cox for himſelf, his Heirs, Executors and Adminiſtrators, doth by theſe Preſents covenant, promiſe, and agree, to and with the ſaid United Company in Manner following; that is to ſay, That he the ſaid William Cox from the Time of his Arrival at Fort William aforeſaid, for and during, and unto the full End and Expiration of Five Years, ſhall and will behave and conduct himſelf, from Time to Time, and in all Reſpects conformable to the Rules, Orders, and Directions of the ſaid United Company, or of their Preſident and Council of their Settlement aforeſaid. And that he the ſaid William Cox will not directly or indirectly ſerve or be in any wiſe aſſiſting to, or employed by, or for any Foreign Company, Trading in or to the *Eaſt-Indies*, or any Perſon or Perſons whatſoever, who do or ſhall, during the Continuance of theſe Preſents, Traffick, Adventure or Trade to, in, or from the *Eaſt-Indies*, or elſewhere, within the Limits of the ſaid Company's Trade, by or under, or by virtue of any Foreign Commiſſion, Licence or Authority whatſoever. PROVIDED ALWAYS, and it is hereby expreſſly covenanted, declared and agreed between the Parties to theſe Preſents, and it is the true Intent and Meaning thereof, That in caſe the ſaid William Cox ſhall make Default in any of the Covenants herein before contained, or ſhall, during the ſaid Term of Five Years, receive Notice from the ſaid Company's Preſident and Council of their Settlement aforeſaid, to quit the ſaid Settlement and return to *England*, for any Miſbehaviour by him the ſaid William Cox done or committed towards the ſaid Company, or concerning the Peace and good Order of the ſaid Settlement, that then, and in either of the ſaid Caſes, he the ſaid William Cox ſhall not, nor will, upon any Account or Pretence whatſoever, ſtay, or continue longer in the *Eaſt-Indies* than for the Space of Twelve Months after receiving ſuch Notice, and that from and immediately after the Expiration of the ſaid Twelve Months, it ſhall and may be lawful for the ſaid Company's Preſident and Council, at the ſaid Settlement, to cauſe the ſaid William Cox and his Family to be put on board any Ship employed by the ſaid Company, for the Purpoſe of being tranſported to *Great-Britain*, at the ſaid Company's Expenſe, and in caſe of Refuſal on the Part of the ſaid William Cox to cauſe the ſaid William Cox to be apprehended and put on board ſuch Ship, together with his Family. AND FURTHER, in caſe of ſuch apprehending, putting on board, and tranſporting the ſaid William Cox and his Family, in Manner aforeſaid, the ſaid William Cox doth hereby covenant, promiſe and agree, to and with the ſaid United Company, That he the ſaid William Cox his Executors or Adminiſtrators, ſhall not nor will commence, ſue or proſecute the ſaid Company, or their Court of Directors, or any of their Preſidents and Council, Commanders or Officers of any ſuch Ship, or any other Perſon employed in any of the Matters aforeſaid, in or by any Action, Suit or other Proſecution, Civil or Criminal, in reſpect of ſuch apprehending him the ſaid William Cox or of putting on board and tranſporting him the ſaid William Cox and his Family to *Great-Britain* in Manner aforeſaid. And in caſe any ſuch Action, Suit or Proſecution ſhall be commenced or proſecuted for any of the Matters aforeſaid, the ſaid William Cox doth hereby covenant and agree to and with the ſaid Company, That the General Iſſue may be pleaded, and this Indenture, or any other ſpecial Matter may be given in Evidence, by all or any of the Defendants, in any ſuch Suit, Action or Proſecution, in Bar, Diſcharge, and Defence thereof, any Thing in theſe Preſents contained to the Contrary thereof notwithſtanding. And the ſaid United Company do hereby for themſelves and their Succeſſors, covenant, promiſe and agree, to and with the ſaid William Cox that he the ſaid William Cox truly and faithfully obſerving, fulfilling and keeping the ſeveral Covenants and Agreements herein expreſſed and contained on his Part, to be obſerved, fulfilled, and kept, ſhall and may peaceably and quietly trade and traffick in the *Eaſt-Indies* aforeſaid, in the Capacity of a Free Mariner, and ſhall enjoy the ſaid Company's Protection. AND LASTLY, it is hereby covenanted, concluded and agreed, by and between the ſaid Parties hereto, that if the ſaid William Cox ſhall be permitted to continue in the *Eaſt-Indies* in the Quality or Capacity of a Free Mariner after the Expiration of the ſaid Term of Five Years hereby ſtipulated, that then ſuch the Continuance and Trading there of the ſaid William Cox ſhall be upon the ſame Terms, Conditions, Covenants and Agreements as are herein before expreſſed and contained on his Part, during the Term herein mentioned and not otherwiſe. IN WITNESS whereof, to one Part of this Indenture the ſaid William Cox hath put his Hand and Seal, and to the other Part thereof the ſaid United Company have cauſed their Common Seal to be affixed, the Day and Year above-written.

Sealed and Delivered (being firſt duly Stamped) in the Preſence of

225

226 Babu Dwarkanath Tagore†

G.R. Ward after F.R. Say, London, 1846
Engraving, 74 × 44.5 (28$\frac{9}{10}$ × 17$\frac{2}{5}$)
India Office Library and Records (P1556)

Son of a famous *banian* family of Calcutta, whose members had amassed a fortune servicing the British ships and British traders in the eighteenth century, Dwarkanath was an important figure in the religious and economic life of early nineteenth-century India. He became the most important leader of the monotheistic Brahmo Samaj movement, following the death of its founder Ram Mohan Roy. Under his leadership the Brahmo movement consolidated its position among the leading Bengali *bhadralog* ('gentry') families, propagating a modernized Indian religion to counter the missionary onslaughts on traditional Hinduism. But during the 1840s the movement split, one faction drawing back towards Hindu society and the other maintaining an uncompromising radicalism and even a tendency towards Christianity.

On the economic front, Dwarkanath tried hard to build a niche for Indian entrepreneurs within Bengal's commercial life, founding his own steamship and coal-mining companies and trading on a large scale in indigo. Ultimately, neither he nor other members of Bengal's commercial classes were to have enough staying power. British banks, insurance companies and other institutions tended to favour their own and looked askance at Indian enterprise in the modern sector. At the same time, Dwarkanath and his peers were at the mercy of trade cycles and were too distant from the buying centres 'up country'. Increasingly Bengalis were strangers in their own commercial world, losing out to Britons (particularly Scotsmen) who commanded the European trade, and to north Indian traders, the Marwaris, who had up-country connections.

Dwarkanath's journalistic forays (and criticism of the East India Company) drew him to the attention of the British

227 228

establishment. In 1842 he travelled to England where he met Wellington, Queen Victoria and Prince Albert. Seeking out cultural as well as political leaders, Dwarkanath met the painters Martin Archer Shee and F.R. Say from whom he commissioned the original painting (now in the Victoria Memorial Hall, Calcutta) from which this engraving is derived. C.A.B.

LITERATURE: Cotton 1907, p.777; Kling 1976, p.171.

227 Jamsetjee Bomanjee (1756–1821)

J. Dorman, *c.* 1830
Oil on canvas, 42 × 35.5 ($16\frac{1}{3} \times 13\frac{4}{5}$)
Inscribed: *J. Dorman*
Royal Asiatic Society, London (01.007/89)

Master shipbuilders of the Bombay naval dockyards, Bomanjee and Nourojee were typical of the more successful members of the Parsi community of western India, which adapted well to the challenge of British rule. Parsis, who profess the Zoroastrian religion, had fled in the early Middle Ages from Persia to Surat and other towns and villages of coastal Gujarat where they became woodworkers, boatmakers and artisans. During the seventeenth century some of the most enterprising members of their community struck up relationships with the factors of the English and Dutch East India Companies, and some were employed to repair and provision European ships. As the fortunes of British Bombay rose towards the end of the eighteenth century many Parsi families emigrated to Bombay where they worked in the naval and merchant dockyards and became major provisioners for the East India Company. Parsis also benefited from the boom in cotton sales to China in the early nineteenth century, but though their fortunes waned somewhat after 1860, they remained the most important – and most Westernized – element in Bombay's elite of merchant princes.

The full-length portrait of Jamsetjee Bomanjee shows the shipbuilder, seated on a chair, holding plans of the man-of-war *Minden*. Through the window the ship can be seen in the process of construction. The 74-gun *Minden* was laid down in 1807 and launched in 1810. Bomanjee was master builder in the Bombay dockyard from 1792 until 1821 and was one of the famous Lowjee family of Parsi shipbuilders, active in Bombay since the early eighteenth century. He was the first Parsi to be entrusted by the Lords of the Admiralty with the building of a man-of-war in India, and from 1792 until his death in 1821 he was responsible for the design and building of 16 men-of-war and 40 large ships. This posthumous portrait was probably taken from an original miniature by Edward Nash (Bombay, 1801–10). C.A.B.

PROVENANCE: Probably a gift from Nourojee Jamsetjee to Sir Charles Forbes, *c.* 1830; presented by him to Royal Asiatic Society, 2 July 1836.

LITERATURE: Karaka 1884; Wadia 1955; Head n.d., pp.32–4.

228 Nourojee Jamsetjee (1774–1860)

J. Dorman, *c.* 1830
Oil on canvas, 42 × 35.5 ($16\frac{1}{3} \times 13\frac{4}{5}$)
Inscribed: *J.Dorman*
Royal Asiatic Society, London (01.008/89)

On the death of his father, Nourojee Jamsetjee continued the family's shipbuilding tradition. He is shown seated and wearing a shawl; a plan of the man-of-war *Asia* is on the table. The 84-gun *Asia* was launched in January 1824. C.A.B.

PROVENANCE: See no. 227.

LITERATURE: See no.227.

229(i) Parry cup

Gold, height 16.8 ($6\frac{1}{2}$); width 16 ($6\frac{1}{5}$) at handles
The Trustees of the British Museum, Department of Oriental Antiquities (1983.6–18.1)

229(i)

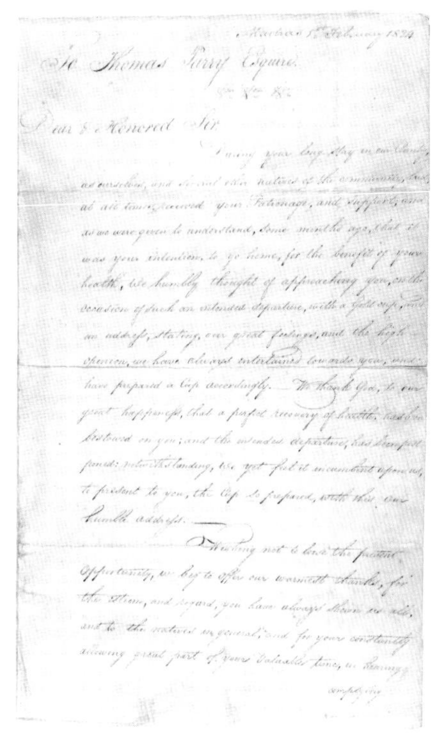

Madras 1st February 1824

To Thomas Parry Esquire

&c &c &c

Dear & Honored Sir

During your long stay in our Country as ourselves, and several other natives of the community, have at all times received your Patronage, and Support, and as we were given to understand, some months ago, that it was your intention, to go home, for the benefit of your health, we humbly thought of approaching you, on the occasion of such an intended departure, with a Gold cup, and an address, stating, our great feelings, and the high opinion, we have always entertained towards you, and have prepared a Cup accordingly. We thank God, to our great happiness, that a perfect recovery of health, had been bestowed on you; and the intended departure, has been postponed: notwithstanding, we yet feel it incumbent upon us, to present to you, the Cup so prepared, with this our humble address.

Wishing not to lose the present opportunity, we beg to offer our warmest thanks, for the esteem, and regard, you have always shown us all, and to the natives in general, and for your constantly allowing great part of your valuable time, in hearing

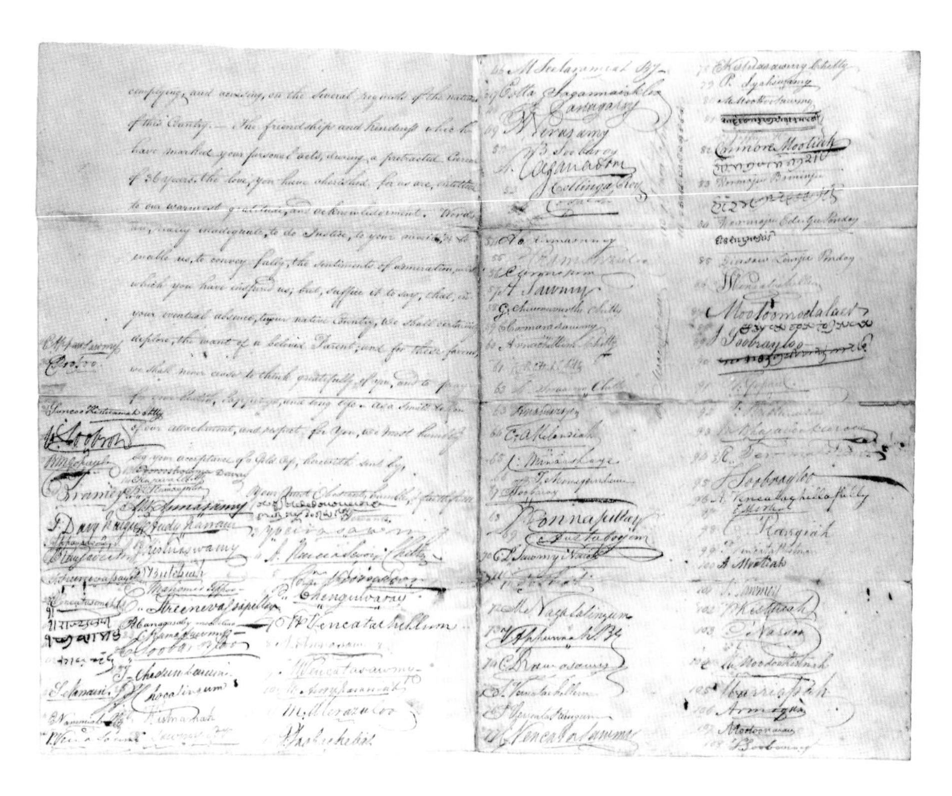

complying, and assisting, on the several requests of the natives of this Country. — The friendship and kindness which have marked your personal acts, during a protracted Career of 36 years, the love, you have cherished for us are, entitled to our warmest gratitude, and acknowledgement. Words are, really inadequate, to do Justice, to your merits, [illegible] to enable us, to convey fully, the sentiments of admiration, with which you have inspired us; but, suffice it to say, that, in your eventual absence, to your native Country, we shall certainly deplore, the want of a beloved Parent; and for these favors, we shall never cease to think gratefully of you, and to pray for your health, happiness, and long life. As a small token of our attachment, and respect for You, we most humbly beg your acceptance of a Gold Cup, herewith sent by

Your most Obedient, humble, & faithful Servants

229(ii)

229(ii) Scroll

Ink and newsprint on paper, 68.5 × 51 ($26\frac{7}{10}$ × 20)

The Trustees of the British Museum, Department of Oriental Antiquities (1983.6–18.2,3)

Parry's was the greatest of the Madras Houses of Agency. These were British commercial companies which acted as general traders and investment agents for the capital of government servants and private traders and investors which they pooled and managed. Parry's was founded in the 1790s and was soon involved in trading in cotton, rice and manufactured goods throughout the Madras Presidency. The firm dominated the commercial life of the region until the 1940s. The cup was to be presented to Richard Parry, founder of the firm, by 'several respectable Hindu inhabitants' on 1 February 1824 before he returned to England. The inscription on the cup testifies to Parry's 'natural humanity and benevolence to assist as much in his power the poor, distressed, and helpless persons among the community'. Some time before the scheduled presentation, Parry decided to stay on in Madras after all, but he was presented with the cup and scroll listing the donors nonetheless. C.A.B.

LITERATURE: Ramaswami and Muthiah 1988, pp.50–1.

Peasant and Money-lender: Coins of the East India Company during its Paramountcy

The Company began to coin in the name of William IV but continued to coin occasionally in the Mughal name until 1857. Silver rupees were the standard coin in the north while the pagoda, worth about three rupees, circulated in the south (no.230 [iv]). The pagoda, so-called after the image it bore of a south Indian temple *gopuram* or tower, was, of course, the origin of the term 'shaking the pagoda tree', which in the eighteenth century came to mean acquiring an illicit fortune in India.

In south India Company policy speeded the process by which cash payments replaced payments in kind throughout the Indian economy, though this 'monetization' had been slowly proceeding for many centuries. The dependence on coin had unforeseen results. The severe agricultural depression felt throughout the subcontinent in the 1820s and '30s was caused largely by the Company's closure of some of its own mints in an effort to cut costs, and by the dwindling supply of silver from Latin America which was in the grip of nationalist revolutions. Money supply was not significantly boosted again until British troops flooded into India after the Rebellion of 1857. C.A.B.

230(i) Double pice coin of Emperor Shah Alam

East India Company, Bengal Presidency, Benares issue minted at Calcutta, 1809
Copper, 12.16
The Trustees of the British Museum, Department of Coins and Medals (1870-5-7-13715)

230(ii) Mohur of Emperor Shah Alam

East India Company, Bengal Presidency (year 19), minted at Murshidabad
Gold, 12.17
Dated: *1198 AH* (AD 1783)
The Trustees of the British Museum, Department of Coins and Medals (BMC 20)

230(iii) Mohur of Emperor Shah Alam

East India Company, Bengal Presidency (year 19) minted at Murshidabad
Gold, 12.19
Dated: *1201 AH* (AD 1786)
The Trustees of the British Museum, Department of Coins and Medals (1935.4–1.12038)

230(iv) Quarter Pagoda

East India Company, Madras Presidency 1808
Silver, 10.61
The Trustees of the British Museum, Department of Coins and Medals (1935.4–1.12293)

230(v) Mohur of Queen Victoria

East India Company, minted at Calcutta
Gold, 11.65
Dated: *1841*
The Trustees of the British Museum, Department of Coins and Medals (1935–4–1–12417)

The Victoria Queen was announced by proclamation in February 1841. The obverse design on this example was introduced in 1850–1 at the mint of Calcutta. The Mughal title had disappeared from most coins by about 1840. V.P.

231

231 Raja Chandu Lal, Minister of the Nizam of Hyderabad (1809–43)

John Goodwin Williams, *c.* 1836
Oil on canvas, 76 × 63.5 (30 × 25)
India Office Library and Records (F16)

The skills of India's financial communities were as important to the functioning of the Company's government in the nineteenth century as they had been during its rise to power. Many of the families of the *dubashes* or *banians* of the earlier period had allowed their trading interests to wither and had bought into land, especially in Bengal where the effects of the Permanent Settlement of 1793 (no.157) had been to force many landowners to sell off parcels of their rights. But other Indian traders and bankers came forward to fill the role of intermediaries between European financial houses and the merchants of the bazaar. Important figures in this commercial world were members of those families who had secured positions as chief financial officers (*diwans*) of the Indian princely states. Such men retained an interest in trades still run by their relatives while at the same time taking 'farms' of land revenues and managing the financial dealings of the state. Chandu Lal was a member of the north Indian Khattri community, famous for

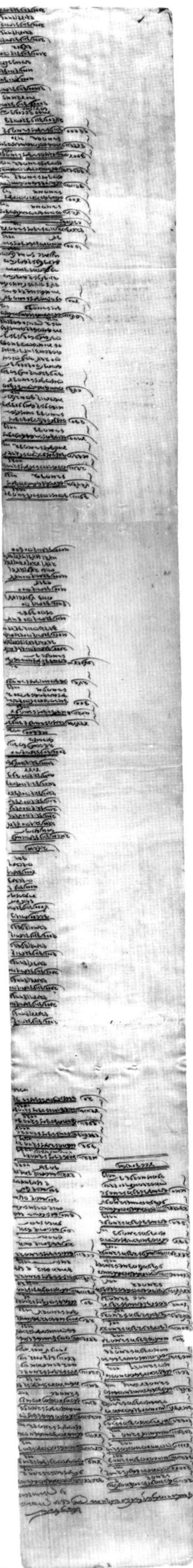

232

producing both traders and administrators. Between 1809 and 1843 he was the pivotal figure in the administration and commerce of Hyderabad, doubling as an unofficial adviser and contact for a succession of British residents who were deputed to report on the financial and political conflicts of this increasingly impoverished state. At the same time, British financial interests, such as the notorious firm Palmer & Company, were able to secure through Chandu Lal important contracts and concessions for the monopoly of Hyderabad's exports, while lending money at high interest rates to its notables. Chandu Lal therefore filled the same sort of function as Purniya, Lord Protector of British interests in his state of Mysore (no.194).

Williams (fl. 1813–37) is a shadowy figure who went to India briefly in 1813, but appeared again as a 'free merchant' in Calcutta and as an 'artist' in Bombay between 1832 and 1837. Chandu Lal is shown wearing the simple and restrained dress of the Indian commercial classes. C.A.B.

PROVENANCE: Presented by Mrs Moore (n.d.).

LITERATURE: Foster 1924, p.8, no.16; Archer 1986, p.47, no.63, pl.XI; Chander 1987.

232 An Indian banker's 'book', Delhi, 1858–9

Copyprint after original in private collection

One reason why the Indian commercial classes were able to survive and even prosper during the colonial period was their highly sophisticated internal organization. From before the Mughal period the more substantial Hindi bankers and traders had employed a double-entry system of commercial accounts, written in a variety of forms of Hindi, Gujarati and Punjabi 'shorthand', often called *mahajani*, or merchant script. Different types of accounts recorded family expenditure, daily cash transactions, the current accounts of major borrowers and the passage of the commercial credit notes (*hundis*) of Indian banking networks. In the eighteenth century the British moved much of their treasure around the country by means of the *hundis*. In the nineteenth century the district treasury system took over most of these functions, but European civil and military officers and private merchants continued to use the good offices of Indian traders and bankers to move their own funds around the country. This is a page from the general account book of the Delhi firm Chunna Mal Saligram, which rose to prominence before 1857 but bought up much 'rebel' property after the conflict. C.A.B.

LITERATURE: Jain 1933; Bayly 1983.

233 Patna City near the Gateway of the Fort. 18 October 1824. From an album of sketches containing 80 drawings and 83 folios of views in Bengal and Behar, executed between January 1823 and May 1825.

Sir Charles D'Oyly, 1824
Pen and ink, mounted in bound volume, 26 × 36.6 ($10\frac{1}{4} \times 14\frac{1}{4}$)
India Office Library and Records (WD2060)

While Calcutta and inland marts such as Mirzapur, which bulked raw cotton and other basic commodities for export, flourished in the early nineteenth century, many older cities which had been important Mughal trading towns declined as a result of the impoverishment of their artisan industries and the diversion of their trade. Murshidabad, Patna and Benares, which had flourished until the end of the eighteenth century, were in this category, though the opium trade saved Patna from complete decline. The picturesque qualities which the British painters such as D'Oyly found amongst their crumbling mosques and great houses sometimes reflected the migration and decline of their magnates and business families.

Sir Charles D'Oyly (1781–1845) returned to India (where he was born) in 1797 and held a number of posts in

Calcutta (see Archer 1962) before moving to Patna in 1821 as Opium Agent. D'Oyly was a prolific artist and published many books with engravings and lithographs from his drawings, including *Indian Sports* (1829) and *Costumes of India* (1830). He imported a lithographic press to Patna which he ran with the help of local Indian artists. Amongst his many achievements was the formation of an art society in Patna in 1824 which was given the rather grand title: The United Patna and Gaya Society, or Behar School of Athens. Under D'Oyly's guidance many Indian painters in Patna adapted their styles to suit European tastes. G.H.R.T/C.A.B.

PROVENANCE: Passed to his brother-in-law or sister-in-law, Sir Walter Raleigh Gilbert or Lady Gilbert (née Jane Ross, sister of D'Oyly's second wife, Eliza Ross) by the artist; purchased by India Office Library, 6 March 1963.

LITERATURE: Archer 1955, pp.33–7; Archer 1969, I, pp.163–8, pl.35.

233

234 Cotton printer block printing a length of fabric

Punjabi artist, Lahore, *c.* 1890

Watercolour, 15.5 × 20.5 (6 × 8); leaf 31 of an album 16.5 × 21.5 ($6\frac{2}{5}$ × $8\frac{1}{2}$)

Album inscribed twice at front: 1) *H.C. Fanshawe May 1896;* 2) *The gift of the late Herbert Charles Fanshawe Indian Civil Service December 1923*

Royal Asiatic Society, London (059.031/89)

Indian textile production did not flourish under the rule of the Company or of the British Crown. Most Indian historians now speak of a 'de-industrialization' of India in the nineteenth century, though few would put it as dramatically as Lord William Bentinck, who wrote of 'the bones of weavers bleaching on the plains of Hindustan'. The great Mughal centres of fine textile production – Ahmedabad, Surat and Dacca – collapsed after 1815. Demand from European markets fell back irrevocably with the gathering pace of British industrialization; the new machine-manufactured items also drove Indian products out of Southeast and East Asian markets in the course of the early nineteenth century. Medium- and low-quality cloths continued to be made in large volumes, particularly in less accessible areas such as the Punjab, Gujarat or Sind.

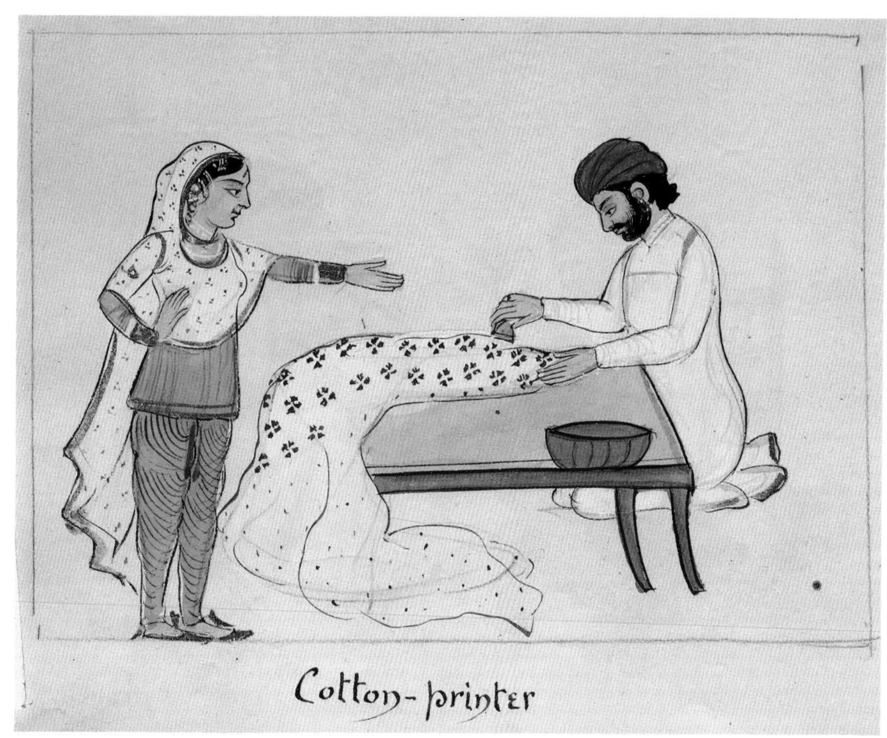

234

PROVENANCE: Album purchased by H.C. Fanshawe of the Indian Civil Service, May 1896; bequeathed to Royal Asiatic Society, December 1923.

LITERATURE: Head n.d., p.356 et passim, no. xxxi.

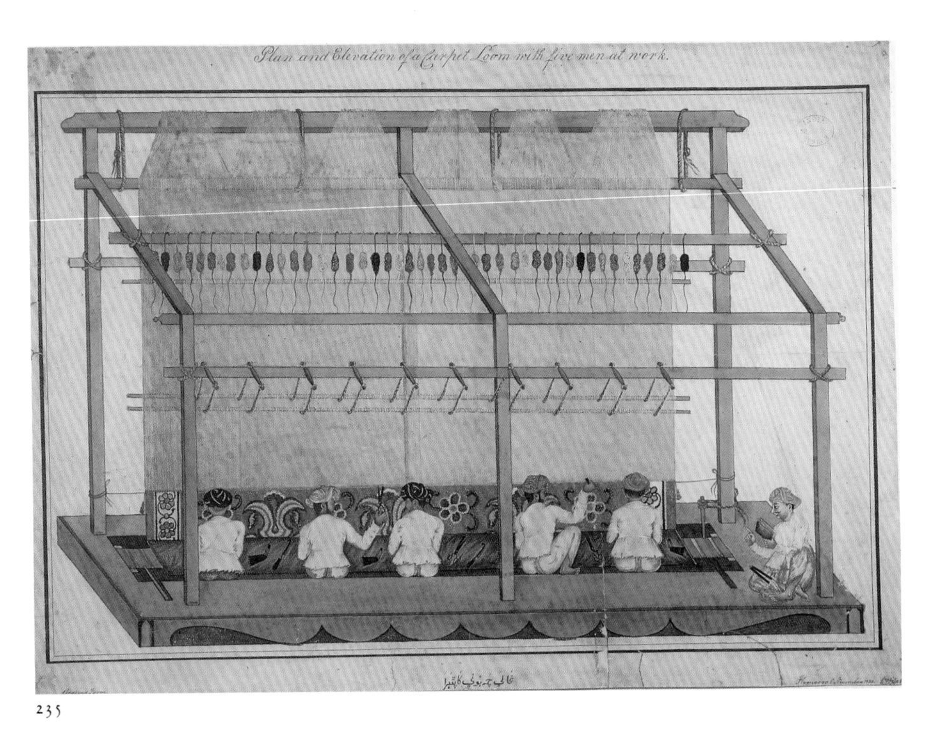

235

235 A Pile-carpet Loom at Hansur

Unknown south Indian artist, Mysore, 1850
Pen, ink and watercolour, 44.7 × 62.4 ($17\frac{1}{2}$ × $24\frac{1}{2}$)
Inscribed in Persian: *qhī līchah būnī (bunnī) kā pathīn*; inscribed in English: *Plan and elevation of a carpet loom with five men at work. Grazing farm. Hoonsoor. 1st November, 1850.*
Indian Office Library and Records (Add.Or.755)

The Company did patronize some indigenous crafts in the early nineteenth century, but only on a small scale and usually only in connection with production for government and military departments. Pictured here is a rug-weaving loom associated with the Amrit Mahal cattle-breeding establishment at Hunsur, on the south-west side of Mysore, adjoining Coorg. The establishment was maintained by the Madras Commissariat and also had a large tannery, blanket manufactory and timber yard. This drawing may have been sent to the East India Company together with a specimen carpet for the Museum. C.A.B.

PROVENANCE: Presented to the East India Company's Museum, 1850.

LITERATURE: Archer 1972, p.58, no.37.

236 A *Shroff*

Delhi artist, *c.* 1910
Watercolour, 13 × 9 (5 × $3\frac{1}{2}$)
India Office Library and Records (Add Or. 3183)

The term *shroff* or *sarraf*, Persian in origin, means 'money-dealer' but was loosely used of members of the commercial castes who bought and sold copper and bullion as well as lending money. In the early nineteenth century, when a large variety of coins issued by different Indian rulers were circulating in the markets alongside Company coins, these people played a vital role in money-changing for which they took *batta* or a commission. From the 1830s onward the British tried to impose a standard coinage and this aspect of the *shroff's* business declined. But Indians still hoarded gold and silver coins, plate

236

and ornaments to sell during bad seasons or to meet unexpected family outlays, so the *shroff* remained a prominent denizen of the bazaar. C.A.B.

237 A *hath* or open market in the Sunderbunds

Thomas Prinsep, *c.* 1825
Pencil and watercolour on paper, 12.7 × 22.9 (5 × 9)
Spink & Son Ltd, London

The Sunderbans are the great jungle swamps of lower Bengal which lie across the many mouths of the River Ganges and its tributaries, comprising approximately 12,000 square miles of wilderness. By tradition a haunt of pirates, *dacoits* (robber gangs) and tigers, the Sunderbans could nevertheless support a surprisingly active trade. As the population grew during the nineteenth century so did the number of settlers who were drawn to the potentially rich rice-growing lands.

The *hath* was a periodic market, held on a specified day and usually in an open space. It was the basis of commerce throughout India (though it was called by different names in other areas). Here the produce of the villages was sold to *beoparies* (small merchants) who brought in metalware, tools, cloth, salt and spices from outside the locality.

Thomas Prinsep (1800–30) was one of the eight sons of John Prinsep (no.237), who went to India in the 1770s and worked as a chintz and indigo merchant. Thomas's brief career, which was ended by a riding accident, was spent in the Bengal Engineers. In the 1820s he became Surveyor of the Sunderbans, where a canal system was being constructed to link the area to the River Hughly. During his visits to Calcutta he almost certainly came into the circle of the professional painter George Chinnery; this is one of a number of landscape sketches which betrays the influence of Chinnery's own studies of the Bengali countryside (cf. nos. 238, 239, 252; and see also no.221). C.A.B./G.H.R.T.

LITERATURE: Pargiter 1885; Archer 1982, pp. 2–3.

238

238 Bengal Village Scene

George Chinnery, *c.* 1820
Oil on canvas, 31 × 39.3 ($12\frac{3}{4} \times 15\frac{1}{2}$)
Birmingham City Museums and Art Gallery (287'43)

No. 238 has been described as a view of Macao but is clearly Bengal. Chinnery's livelihood was mainly derived from portrait painting, but his real love lay in the sketching of the countryside and its people. This painting is a typical product of the Picturesque landscape style, with its small human figures in the foreground, luxuriant foliage and decaying monuments, but it also records some features typical of the villages near the suburbs of Calcutta where Chinnery sketched. The large house is typical of landlords' and moneylenders' houses throughout the Bengal countryside. Such pools provided irrigation water for rice paddies and supported the fish which were such an important part of the Bengalis' diet. The tomb in no.239 is a reminder of the deep penetration of Islam into many parts of the Bengal countryside, particularly in the east of the Presidency.

Bengal's villages changed little in the first half of the nineteenth century. The *zamindars* did not prove to be an active class of improving landholders as Cornwallis had hoped: instead they generally became grasping rack-renters, and absentee landlordism prevailed as many moved into Calcutta. Indigo, silk and later jute cultivation improved the lot of some villagers, but the decay of the river systems and the slow rise in population helped to depress the livelihoods of many more. C.A.B.

PROVENANCE: Purchased by the Birmingham Corporation, 1943.

LITERATURE: Birmingham, City Museum and Art Gallery, *Catalogue of Paintings*, 1960, p.31.

EXHIBITIONS: London, Thos. Agnew and Sons Ltd, *Loan Exhibition of Pictures from the City Art Gallery, Birmingham*, 1957 (41); Milan, Palazzo Reale, *British Painting 1660–1840*, 1975.

239

239 Natives by a Pool near a Temple

George Chinnery, *c.*1820
Oil on canvas, 17 × 23 ($6\frac{3}{5} \times 9$)
Private Collection

See no. 238.

PROVENANCE: Spink & Son Ltd, London; Sale, Sotheby's, 9 March 1988 (84).

240 Indian Villager with Bullock

George Chinnery, *c.* 1810–22
Pen, ink and wash, 28.3 × 35.6 ($11\frac{1}{10} \times 14\frac{1}{10}$)
Inscribed in ink: *Hindoo Costume from Nature Chinnery*
Indian Office Library and Records (WD353)

LITERATURE: Archer 1969, II, p.572, pl.72.

240

241 A Village Scene, Haryana

Unknown artist, Delhi area, early 19th century
Watercolour with gold bottom edge, 31.3 × 41.8 ($12\frac{1}{2} \times 16\frac{1}{2}$)
Inscribed: *No 3*
India Office Library and Records (Add. Or. 4057)

'Up country' in Haryana, conditions were very different from those in Bengal. Here, north-west of Delhi, the land was much drier and more dependent on rainfall, which was calculated as being inadequate once every four years. Here the staple crops were cereals, not the rice of Bengal, and the camel was as much in evidence as the bullock. Quite a large segment of the population was still nomadic, moving around with its herds but cultivating a little dry grain at certain times of the year. It was from villages like these that the Gujars and the Jats were enlisted for the Company's irregular corps (no.182). No powerful class of large landlords had emerged as in Bengal, Bihar or Awadh; the population was too sparse for heavily intensive agriculture, and, besides, powerful landholders could not flourish in the eighteenth century when lands were frequently overrun by Sikh, Mughal, Jat and Maratha war bands. After the wars of 1802–3, when the British began to administer the territories, they made arrangements with the powerful men of the villages rather than territorial *zamindars*, who were few and far between. Villagers suffered badly during the not uncommon famines, which were only ever partially reduced in intensity by British canal systems. From time to time the great village grain pits (*khatas*) were empty. But, paradoxically, this somewhat arid land had a better long-term prospect than the lush acres of Bengal. The population pressed less heavily on resources, and the rugged individualism of the western lands, much freer from landlords and caste hierarchy, encouraged peasant enterprise. Today Haryana is the home of a prosperous, tractor-owning farming community. C.A.B.

LITERATURE: Archer and Falk 1989.

241

242

242 An Indigo Factory in Bengal

William Simpson, 1863
Watercolour, 24.8 × 34.9 (9¾ × 13¾)
Inscribed on front in ink: *Indigo factory. Wm.Simpson,1863*
India Office Library and Records (WD1017)

The blue dye indigo had a chequered history in India. In the seventeenth century it had been one of the great exports from India and had produced much wealth for the Bayana area near Agra, which had been the most specialized centre of production. Bayana's local indigo trade declined, but by the late eighteenth century European- and Indian-owned indigo enterprises were common from Bengal to Delhi, buoyed up by European and Asian demand. Indigo brought benefits to those peasants who produced it for outside markets on their own behalf. But it was a very labour intensive crop and fierce disputes broke out between planters and their workers and also between *zamindars* and planters. Serious anti-planter riots broke out in the 1860s and 1870s in Bengal, and Calcutta's Indian intelligentsia took up the plight of the indigo peasant in numerous publications. In the nineteenth century the British indigo planters had a reputation for brutality which was by no means undeserved. Gandhi was later to organize protest movements against the indigo planters of Bihar. The commodity was a difficult one for both planter and merchant. In the 1820s and 1840s there were disastrous collapses in the market due to overproduction. Before the end of the century German synthetic aniline dyes were beginning to squeeze the vegetable product out of its European markets.

William Simpson (1823–99) is perhaps best known as a Crimean War artist and in particular for his twenty-four views of *The Campaign in the East* (1855). In 1859 the publishers Day and Son commissioned him to make drawings of India. On his return he produced *India, Ancient and Modern* (1867) and this is the original drawing, engraved as plate 38 in that work. He returned to India in 1876 as part of the Prince of Wales's entourage. B.A./C.A.B.

LITERATURE: Kling 1966; M. Archer 1969, p.636.

243

244

243 A Group of Starving Villagers outside the Pilgrims' Hospital, Cuttack

Unknown Cuttack artist, *c.* 1840
Watercolour, 22.5 × 28.5 ($8\frac{3}{4}$ × 11)
Inscribed: *A scene at the Pilgrims hospital during the famine taken from life. This is the way the natives sit down and clean each other's heads and catch game*
India Office Library and Records (Add. Or. 3131)

Cuttack, in common with much of northern and eastern India, suffered severe famines in 1836, 1837 and 1842. The immediate cause was the periodic failure of the monsoon rains, but poor distribution of existing supplies of food and general poverty greatly increased the number of deaths both from hunger and the epidemic diseases which came in the wake of famine. Many British officials at this time were committed to the doctrine of *laissez-faire*, refusing to intervene in the grain market or to redistribute stocks. The results were as dire as in contemporary Ireland. Both public and private agencies provided some relief, however. Government 'relief works' on roads and canals gave able-bodied people a little cash with which to buy grain. This 'Pilgrims hospital' was probably the one run by the Government out of the proceeds of the tax on pilgrims to the Jagganath temple.

The famines of the 1830s, which killed many millions in north India, encouraged the government to begin to speed up the programme of irrigation works, though little money was found in the straightened imperial budgets before 1860. In the later nineteenth century periodic famines continued in most parts of the country, but famine abated in the twentieth century with the exception of the terrible man-made Bengal famine of 1943. C.A.B./K.P.

LITERATURE: Bhatia 1967; Archer 1972, p.96, no.64ii.

244 The Ganges Canal, Roorkee, Saharanpur District

William Simpson, 1863
Watercolour, 25.4 × 35.5 (10 × $13\frac{4}{5}$)
Inscribed on front in ink: *Ganges Canal, Roorkee. Wm Simpson. 1863*
India Office Library and Records (WD 1012)

Mughal canals were mainly extensions to existing rivers, though large areas north of Delhi were irrigated by them. The British slowly began to introduce long dug-canals to irrigate dry but fertile lands. The most celebrated schemes were Sir Arthur Cotton's system in the Kavery Delta in south India, and the north Indian works in the western part of the North-Western Provinces and in the Punjab. Here relatively quick returns were made as acres of new land came under cultivation and rates of land revenue soared. The Ganges canal scheme was planned in the 1830s, but

245

most of the construction was delayed until the 1850s (it was finally opened by Lord Dalhousie in April 1854). Before the Punjab canal colonies were finished later in the century, it was seen as the greatest feat of British civil engineering in India, a status recognized by the statue of an imperial lion near the beginning of its headworks near Roorkee. Though the early canals brought problems of flooding and salinity, they clearly benefited large areas of the north Indian countryside. Many historians of the Indian economy, however, consider that government expenditure on the upkeep and extension of existing small-scale irrigation plants in areas of wet cultivation was inadequate. For William Simpson, see no.242. C.A.B./B.A.

PROVENANCE: Purchased 4 November 1956.

LITERATURE: Archer 1969, II, p.636, no.1012, pl.79; Whitcombe 1970; Stone 1984.

The Indian Picturesque

245 A Choultry or Travellers' Rest House in South India

Francis Swain Ward, *c.*1770
Oil on canvas, 71.1 × 109.2 (28 × 43)
India Office Library and Records (F22)

This is one of the earliest British depictions of Indian architecture and landscape, anticipating the interest in the south that was generated by the Mysore wars of 1780–99. Ward (1736–94) had served in the Company's Madras army in the 1760s, but resigned his commission in protest at his lack of advancement. Failing to make a living as a painter back in England, he donated ten large works (including this) to the Company, and rejoined its service in 1773. After his return to India his military career was more successful, and he stayed until his death in 1794. Aquatints after some of his paintings were published by Edward Orme in a composite work issued in 1805.

Rest houses like the one depicted here were once ubiquitous features in south India, and were intended primarily for the benefit of travelling pilgrims. Ward has observed closely the details of the comparatively undistinguished building, but he has also been concerned to show it in its landscape setting and so to convey the atmosphere of the region.

G.H.R.T.

LITERATURE: Foster 1924, p.11; Reynolds 1950, p.190; Archer 1986, p.79.

EXHIBITIONS: London, Chartered Society of Artists, 1770–3; London, Royal Academy of Arts, *The Art of India and Pakistan*, 1947–8 (912).

246

246 A View of Benares

William Hodges, *c.*1781
Oil on canvas, 68.5 × 91.4 (27 × 36)
India Office Library and Records (F94)

In the centre of this view of part of Benares (Varanasi) stand the palace of Raja Abal and the mosque built on the site of an ancient Hindu temple by command of the Mughal Emperor Aurangzeb. Hodges (1744–97) reached Benares in August 1781 in the retinue of his patron, the Governor-General, Warren Hastings. In his travel memoirs Hodges recalls how excited he was at the prospect of being able to examine the arts and customs of the people of this ancient Hindu city. His studies were interrupted, however, by the infamous conflict between Hastings and Raja Chait Singh.

For some time Hastings had been attempting to extort money from Chait Singh, the Raja of Benares, in excess of the dues paid to the Company under treaty arrangements. It was Chait Singh's refusal to comply that had prompted the Governor-General's visit to the city, and the Raja was now placed under arrest within his own palace. His troops, however, rose to rescue him and massacred the guard of British sepoys. Hastings had not expected this action, and as the Raja's troops prepared to attack the small British force, he and his retinue were obliged to make a swift, undignified evacuation. In the haste, Hodges was forced to abandon 'the whole of my baggage, excepting my drawings, and a few changes of linen' (Hodges 1794, p.52). Subsequently, British reinforcements were summoned and Chait Singh's uprising was ruthlessly suppressed. By the end of September the Governor-General's party was able to return to Benares, and Hodges resumed his dispassionate investigation of its antiquities. This episode was one of the principal matters leading to the impeachment of Warren Hastings in 1787. Hodges, however, always remained loyal to his former employer, and insisted that the conflict arose solely from the 'guilt and perfidy' of the Raja.

This picture is believed by some authorities to have been painted expressly for Hastings and to be the view of Benares listed in the sale of some of Hastings's pictures at Christie's in 1797. Even Stuebe, who questions this assumption, suggests that the work was painted while Hodges was still in India.

G.H.R.T.

LITERATURE: *Select Views in India,* 1787, pl.21; *European Magazine,* October 1788, p.248; Foster 1924, p.33; Foster 1925, p.6; Foster 1930–1, p.42; Reynolds 1950, p.188; W. Archer 1970, p.99; Stuebe 1979, p.206, no.199; M. Archer 1986, p.68.

EXHIBITION: London, Royal Academy of Arts, *The Art of India and Pakistan,* 1947–8 (902).

247 The Palace of Punukka in Bhutan

Samuel Davis, 1783
Watercolour on paper, 45.7 × 67.3 (18 × 26½)
India Office Library and Records (WD3271)

Samuel Davis (1760–1819) was a Company civil servant, not a professional painter, but it was in the capacity of official draughtsman that he accompanied Captain Samuel Turner's expedition to Bhutan and Tibet in 1783. This expedition was made on the orders of Warren Hastings, who wished to maintain the links with Tibet established by an earlier expedition that he had sent, under George Bogle, in 1774. The Tibetan authorities denied the draughtsman access to their country, and Davis was obliged to spend his time in Bhutan.

In his account of the expedition Turner recalled passing the scene shown in Davis's watercolour:

> Punukka is the winter residence of the Daeb Raja, and, as we were informed, his favourite seat: he has lavished large sums upon it. . . . A stern porter kept the inner entrance; and . . . obstinately refused me admittance. . . . We had not the same difficulty in gaining access to the gardens which were extensive, and well stocked, containing the orange, sweet and sour; lemon, lime, citron, pomegranate, peach, apple, pear, and walnut trees (Turner 1800, p.139).

On his return from Bhutan, Davis was appointed Collector at Bhagalpur. At some stage he met Thomas and William

Daniell, and these artists paused in their travels to stay with him at Bhagalpur briefly in 1788, and for a long period in 1790–1. At the end of this second stay Davis accompanied the Daniells on their visit to Gaur (see no.248). It has been suggested that it was Davis's drawings that inspired the Daniells to travel in the Himalayas. It is clear that William at least was impressed by Davis's work: in 1813 he published a set of six aquatints of Davis's *Views in Bootan*; and much later he redrew some of Davis's drawings for engravings in the *Oriental Annual*. G.H.R.T.

LITERATURE: Turner 1800, pl.IX; *Oriental Annual* 1838, pl.22; Aris 1982, p.2.

248 View in Gaur (A Ruined Tomb)

Thomas Daniell, *c*.1791
Oil on canvas, 46 × 63 ($18\frac{1}{8}$ × $24\frac{7}{8}$)
Charles Greig Esq.

Though originally a Hindu city, Gaur was at various times the capital of the Muslim rulers of Bengal following their conquest of the region in AD 1202. The city flourished particularly in the early sixteenth century, when it was embellished with numerous fine mosques and tombs. However, in 1537 it was sacked by Sher Shah Sur (see no.249), and in 1575 it was devastated by plague. In the following year it was annexed by the Mughals, who added some further buildings including – to judge by its style – the now lost tomb depicted here.

By the eighteenth century the city was deserted. The first Briton to make an extensive study of its architecture was Henry Creighton, who in 1786 was appointed superintendent of an indigo factory built among the ruins. The Daniells arrived, with their friend Samuel Davis, late in 1791; they were on their way back to Calcutta at the end of their extensive tour across northern India.
G.H.R.T.

PROVENANCE: W. G. Archer; Dr Maurice Shellim, 1970; acquired by present owner, 1988.
LITERATURE: Shellim 1979, p.45.

249 The Tomb of Sher Shah Sur at Sasaram in Bihar

Thomas Daniell, 1810
Oil on canvas 97.2 × 135.9 ($38\frac{1}{4}$ × $53\frac{1}{2}$)
The Trustees of the Tate Gallery, London (TO 1403)

Sher Shah Sur was descended from an Afghan who had come to India to serve under the Sultans of Delhi. Being more ambitious than his forbears, Sher Shah carved out his own independent state in eastern India, which incorporated parts of Bihar and Bengal, with a capital at Sasaram. The somewhat ineffectual Mughal Emperor Humayun was unable to prevent this expansion, and in 1540 Sher Shah succeeded in dislodging

247

248

Humayun from the throne of Delhi. For the last five years of his life Sher Shah ruled in the Mughals' place, restructuring the administration of their empire and adding splendid fortifications and other buildings to the city of Delhi. His successors lacked his abilities, however, and in 1555 Humayun was able to recapture the empire, and Mughal rule resumed.

Sher Shah's stately sandstone tomb was built in his former capital, probably during his lifetime. The main part of the building is an octagonal hall, surrounded by a veranda and surmounted by a large dome. This pattern has its origin in the tombs of the fifteenth-century Sayyid Sultans in Delhi. But though based on a standard type, Sher Shah's tomb transforms the tradition into something far more noble. It is much larger than its antecedents and it stands on a fortified podium placed in the centre of a vast artificial lake. It is reached by means of a causeway (ruined when the Daniells visited it, but now restored).

In reality, the water setting has the effect of isolating the building from its surroundings so that it appears to float in a void, complete and perfect in itself. Daniell (1749–1840), however, has seen the building in a typically Picturesque manner which relates it to the wider landscape, and obscures the even edge of the tank with a more varied line of ground. The Daniells visited Sasaram in February 1790. They were much impressed by the sober dignity of the tomb, finding that its 'gloomy grandeur ... awakens feelings rather painful than agreeable'. G.H.R.T.

PROVENANCE: Purchased 1971.

LITERATURE: *Oriental Annual* 1834, pl.16; Shellim 1979, p.71.

EXHIBITION: London, Royal Academy of Arts, 1810 (143).

250 The Mountain of Ellora

Thomas Daniell after James Wales, 1803
Plates 1–3 from *Hindoo Excavations in the Mountain of Ellora,* 1803
Aquatint on three sheets, 45.7 × 180.3 (18 × 71)
India Office Library and Records (P 2890–2)

Soon after arriving in India in 1791 James Wales (1747–95) won the patronage of Sir Charles Warre Malet, then Resident at the Court of the Maratha Peshwa in Poona (Pune). Wales painted a number of portraits for Malet and for the Peshwa (see no.172); but he also made a detailed survey of western India's rock-cut architecture. Among these now famous antiquities, the most impressive examples are those at Ellora. There is a sequence of thirty-four caves at Ellora, including Buddhist, Hindu and Jain examples, mostly excavated between the sixth and eighth centuries.

These and other temples of the region had already excited the attention of scholars, but no complete visual record of them had been made. Wales was already engaged on his studies when the Daniells met him in Bombay in 1793. He took them to see some of the rock-cut temples close to the city, including that on the island of Elephanta. The Daniells did not, however, visit Ellora, and Wales himself did not go there until the spring of 1795, after they had left India. Wales was intending to produce a major publication on the caves, with engravings after his drawings; but while working at the Kanheri cave in October 1795 he caught a fever and died before the work was complete.

In 1798 Malet returned to England. He brought with him Wales's daughter, whom he married, and Wales's drawings, which he showed to Thomas Daniell. From these Daniell produced a number of aquatints, including an entire series of twenty-four devoted to Ellora. Published in 1803, this work was complementary to his own volumes of *Oriental Scenery*. Many of the plates illustrate the richly decorated temples in great detail, but the book opens with this panoramic view showing some of the caves as small embellishments in a massive, idyllic landscape. G.H.R.T.

LITERATURE: Archer 1980, nos.149–51.

251 The Temple at Rameswaram

Henry Salt, 1804
Ink and washes on paper, 43.2 × 62.2 (17 × 24½)
India Office Library and Records (WD1302)

As secretary and draughtsman, Henry Salt (1780–1827) accompanied Lord Valentia on his travels between 1802 and 1806. Their eastern Grand Tour was most imaginative in scope, taking in not only India, but Ceylon, the Red Sea, Abyssinia and Egypt. On their return, Valentia wrote a volume of travel memoirs, while Salt published aquatints after his drawings, in imitation of the successful Daniells.

They reached India early in 1803, and after an extensive tour in the north they sailed to Ceylon. From there they visited the south of India, arriving at Rameswaram on 25 January 1804. Immediately after having landed and breakfasted, they examined the town's principal temple. This is of the standard southern type, consisting of a large complex of structures surrounded by an outer wall, and entered through vast pylons or *gopurams*. The size of these pylons particularly impressed Valentia:

> The entrance to the temple was through a very lofty gateway, I should suppose about one hundred feet high, covered with carved work to the summit. It was pyramidically oblong, and ended in a kind of sarcophagus.... This massive workmanship reminded me of the ruins of

251

252

> Egyptian architecture. . . . The whole was well executed, and was the finest specimen of architecture I had seen in the East (1809, vol.1, p.340).

Valentia's comment about Egyptian architecture arose from the temptation felt by all travellers to understand strange scenes by relating them to more familiar ones; this habit can colour our interpretation, and led Valentia to emphasize the temple's massiveness. His draughtsman saw it rather differently, concentrating on the vivacity of the scene. His foreground figures turn a precise study of the temple into animated archaeology. G.H.R.T.

LITERATURE: *Twenty-four Views* 1809, pl.9; Archer 1959, p.890; Archer 1969, p.630.

252 A Woman by a Hut in Bengal

George Chinnery, *c.*1810

Pen and ink on paper, 17.1 × 24.8 ($6\frac{3}{4} \times 9\frac{3}{4}$)

Inscribed in artist's shorthand and numbered *31*

Dr Maurice Shellim

This is one of the very large number of sketches, in a variety of media, made by Chinnery (1774–1852) in the period between 1808 and 1812, when he was living in Dacca as the guest of the collector Sir Charles D'Oyly (see no. 253). Chinnery had arrived in India in 1802; after a few years in Madras he moved on to the more important city of Calcutta and established himself there as a successful portrait painter. Though highly proficient and much in demand in that field, Chinnery was not committed to it: as one client protested, 'He likes landscape painting a thousand to one better than portrait painting.' The invitation to stay with D'Oyly gave him a chance temporarily to abandon portraiture and Calcutta society and immerse himself in the Indian countryside. In fact he produced few finished landscape oils, but he filled many sketchbooks with his impressions of eastern Bengal (now Bangladesh), all drawn in his sure and masterly hand. His interests centre on the region's poorer inhabitants, their villages and their cattle.

Returning to Calcutta in 1812, Chinnery resumed his portrait practice. But though he was always employed, he was a spendthrift and his debts eventually became intolerable; in 1825 he was forced to flee from his creditors, ending up eventually in Macao where he spent the remainder of his life. In the later years in Calcutta he had given instruction to a number of gifted amateur artists, and even after his departure they continued to paint in a manner dominated by his distinctive style. G.H.R.T.

PROVENANCE: Spink & Son Ltd, 1969, from whom bought by present owner.

253 A View in Dacca

Sir Charles D'Oyly, *c.*1810
Oil on canvas, 25.4 × 33 (10 × 13)
Dr Maurice Shellim

In the shadow of a Muslim tomb, a villager draws water from a well and another smokes, while a cow looks on. Although Sir Charles D'Oyly (1781–1845) would have been surrounded by scenes such as this during the years that he was Collector in Dacca (1808–18), his attention was drawn to them particularly by his friend George Chinnery (see no.252). Such subjects form part of the standard repertoire of Chinnery's numerous sketches and watercolours, which D'Oyly had ample opportunity to study. The style and technique of this work, too, owe much to Chinnery's example, although with its somewhat empty centre it lacks the compositional coherence found in the master's work.

The civil servant and baronet Sir Charles D'Oyly was one of the most delightful of amateur artists to work in India. At a later stage in his career (1821–32) he was the Opium Agent in Patna, a relatively undemanding post which enabled him to devote a great deal of time to art. In 1827 he established one of the earliest lithographic presses in India, and he encouraged the activities of Company painters. But in spite of his enthusiasm he was never tempted to take himself too seriously: in a spirit of mock solemnity he christened his circle of like-minded friends 'The Behar School of Athens', and he published, among many other illustrated books, the humorous doggerel *Tom Raw the Griffin* (1828). Much of his work is marked by an urbanity and a self-deprecation typical of the talented amateur of his times. His oils are unpretentious essays in the Picturesque, focusing on rural idylls.

G.H.R.T.

PROVENANCE: Eyre and Greig, 1988; from whom purchased by present owner.

LITERATURE: Shellim 1989, p.9.

253

254

255

254 A Village Scene

William Prinsep, *c.*1820
Watercolour on paper, 25.4 × 35.5 (10 × 14)
India Office Library and Records (WD4028)

William Prinsep (1794–1874) was a member of a great British Indian dynasty, being one of the eight sons of John Prinsep, an important East India Company merchant who traded in indigo and chintz in the 1770s and 1780s. All but one of the sons also worked in India. The most celebrated, James, was a distinguished numismatist and scholar who deciphered the famous Ashokan edicts. The fifth son, William, arrived in Calcutta in 1817 and joined Palmer and Company. When this firm failed in 1830 he and an elder brother established a bank.

Besides being a businessman, William Prinsep was an enthusiastic artist and traveller. He was one of many amateurs who took lessons from Chinnery, and this profoundly influenced both his choice of subjects and his drawing style. Later in his career he travelled to Burma and Macao, where he met up with Chinnery again. On his retirement in 1842 he returned home by means of the newly established Overland Route through the Red Sea and Alexandria, one of the first travellers to do so.

G.H.R.T.

255 Gungotree, the Holy Shrine of Mahadeo

R. Havell after James Baillie Fraser, 1820
Aquatint, 40.6 × 61 (16 × 24)
India Office Library and Records (P48)

Fraser (1783–1856) went to India in 1813 in an attempt to make his fortune and rescue the troubled family estates in Scotland. He soon set up in business in Calcutta; but he was not greatly successful and by the beginning of 1815 he was in need of a change of air. He decided to go and join his younger brother, William, who was in the service of the Company, acting as Political Agent to the army in the Nepal War of 1814–15. At the end of this conflict, soon after the brothers had met up, William was appointed Commissioner of Garhwal in the Himalayan foothills. His first task in this post was to make an extensive tour of the region that he was to administer.

In the summer of 1815 the two brothers travelled through the hill states, and while William negotiated with their rulers, James sketched their dramatic landscape. Towards the end of the tour, James struck out on his own, reaching as far as Gungotree, one of the sources of the River Ganges. Here he bathed in the river:

> The water, just freed from the ice, was piercing cold; and it required no small effort of piety to stay long enough in it for the Brahmin to say the necessary prayers over the pilgrim . . . Afterwards, with bare feet, we entered the temple, where worship was performed, a little bell ringing all the time (Fraser 1820b, p.478).

Later he made a sketch of the scene, and this was one of twenty drawings made on the tour that were published as aquatints in 1820.

In 1824–6 James Fraser published a set of aquatints of Calcutta, to which city he had returned in a second attempt to become a businessman. Recently he and his brother have also become known as the patrons of a most important collection of Company paintings, many of which depict recruits to the irregular force established by William Fraser during the Nepal War (see no.182).

G.H.R.T.

LITERATURE: *Views in the Himala Mountains* 1820, pl.11; Archer 1989, pp.34, 66.

256 The Taj Mahal

Agra or Delhi artist, Company school, *c.*1820
Plate 15 from an album of 82 drawings of Mughal architecture
Pencil, ink and watercolour on paper, 48.3 × 30.5 (19 × 12)
The Syndics of the Fitzwilliam Museum, Cambridge (4033)

This album was bought by W. Wright, the Judge and Magistrate of Farruckabad district, while he and a companion were camping in the outer compound of the Taj Mahal in February 1821. Pictures of architectural subjects

256

257

by Indian artists were highly popular among British patrons in the early nineteenth century, and this album is typical of such work. It contains depictions of numerous Mughal buildings including the Jami Masjid and Safdar Jang's tomb in Delhi, the Taj Mahal and Moti Masjid in Agra, and the Buland Darwaza in Fatehpur Sikri. The majority of its plates show details of the *pietra dura* decoration inside the Taj Mahal. Most of the plates are inscribed in both Urdu, by the artist, and English, by Wright. On the page shown, Wright has identified the subject as the 'Exterior of the Taj itself, with the terrace and minarets', and on the facing page he has stuck a plan of the ground storey.

India's most famous building was constructed on the orders of the Mughal Emperor Shah Jahan as a tomb for his favourite wife, Arjumand Banu Begam, known as Mumtaz Mahal. It was begun after her death in 1631 and took over twenty years to complete. The treatment of the subject by the Indian artist differs markedly from English views of Indian buildings. Attempting to be scrupulously factual, he has delineated every detail, including even the lines between the slabs of marble facing on the dome. But the result is not a greater realism, since such details are inevitably exaggerated; instead, the details are hardened into a two-dimensional coloured pattern. This effect is reinforced by the isolating of the building, shown without a background. Only in the arched recesses has the artist added some delicate shading, to suggest some depth in the architectural forms. G.H.R.T.

257 Inside the Main Entrance of the Purana Qila, Delhi

Robert Smith, 1823
Oil on canvas, 81.9 × 107.3 ($32\frac{1}{4} \times 42\frac{1}{4}$)
Yale Center for British Art, Paul Mellon Collection (B 1976.7.73)

In his versatility, Colonel Robert Smith (1787–1873) was typical of British engineers in India: he was an architect, archaeologist, and painter, as well as being an accomplished military engineer, laying the mine that breached the wall of Bharatpur fort in 1826. Early in his career, while serving as an ADC in Calcutta, he knew George Chinnery (see no.265). Subsequently he was a field engineer during the Nepal War and probably knew the Fraser brothers (see no.255). Poor health obliged him to take a post in Penang, which was considered to have a healthy climate; he was there from 1816 to 1819, and his views of the island were later published as aquatints by William Daniell.

After his return to India, he was appointed Garrison Engineer at Delhi, and in this role was responsible for the care of some of the city's ancient monuments. He restored the Qutb Minar and the Jami Masjid; and painted a number of oils of Mughal buildings. The fort known as the Purana Qila, though founded by Humayun, was substantially built by the usurper Sher Shah Sur, following his capture of Delhi in 1540 (see no.249). Smith's view shows the inner face of the fort's northern gate.

During this phase of his career, Smith lived on the walls of the Delhi fort with an Indian mistress. Though almost *de rigueur* in the previous century, by the 1820s such a lifestyle would have struck many Britons as outlandish; but Delhi still had relatively few European residents. Smith also produced designs for St James's Church in Delhi (built in 1836) for his friend Colonel James Skinner. After his return to Europe, Smith put his knowledge of Mughal architecture to good, if eccentric, use by designing Indian-style palaces for himself in Nice and Paignton. G.H.R.T.

LITERATURE: Archer 1972, p.87; Cormack 1985, p.208; Mahajan 1988, p.122.

EXHIBITION: New Haven, Yale Center for British Art, *The British View of India*, 1978.

258 The Fort at Allahabad

Robert Smith, 1833
Watercolour on paper, 19 × 34.3 ($7\frac{1}{2}$ × $13\frac{1}{2}$)
India Office Library and Records (WD 2087)

Captain Smith (1792–1882) of the 44th East Sussex Regiment – not to be confused with his older namesake (see no.257) – had a most energetic career, fighting campaigns in Sicily, Spain, America and elsewhere before arriving in India in 1828. Like many soldiers of his period he was an accomplished draughtsman and devoted much of his leisure to topographical sketching. From his time in India there survives a series of watercolours depicting sites that he visited, including some along the Ganges such as Benares, Chunar, Monghyr and Allahabad – places that had long been favourites among travelling artists. The fort at Allahabad, overlooking the important Hindu pilgrimage centre at the confluence of the Ganges and the Jumna, was built by the Mughal Emperor Akbar from 1583 onwards.

Smith passed through Allahabad in March 1829 and again in January 1833. As he recounted in his journal, he was struck not only by the 'picturesque object' of the fort, but also by a local tax on the pilgrims:

> The fort of Allahabad was built by Akbar to protect the Dooab, the tract of country lying between the two rivers, but probably also for enforcing the collection of the revenue derived from the bathers who pay a heavy toll for permission to do so in this place. The Brahmins first instituted this tax on the credulity of the people here . . . but on the Mahommedans becoming possessed of the country they deprived those priests of the greatest part of this revenue which they had contrived to increase to an enormous amount; the

258

259

English then becoming masters, thought this, we may suppose, too great a prize to be easily relinquished ... and now rival their Mahommedan predecessors in the emolument they derive from this idolatrous imposition (Smith MS, vol.2, p.692).

G.H.R.T.

LITERATURE: Archer 1969, p.322.

259 The Ghats at Mahableshwar

William Carpenter, *c.*1855
Watercolour on paper, 16.5 × 25.4 ($6\frac{1}{2}$ × 10)
India Office Library and Records (WD 3875)

Between 1850 and 1857, Carpenter (1818–99) travelled widely within the subcontinent, especially in western India and Kashmir, painting the countryside and members of princely courts. Though small in scale and variable in quality, his work has a greater immediacy than that of many other artists who worked in India. His landscapes are often highly coloured, indicating a frank response to the peculiarities of India, and particularly to its climate. A number of his Indian views were exhibited in South Kensington in 1881. The scene shown here is at Mahableshwar in the Western Ghats, the principal hill station in the Bombay Presidency. G.H.R.T.

260 The Palace at Amber

William Simpson, *c.*1861
Watercolour on paper, 47 × 48 ($18\frac{1}{2}$ × $18\frac{3}{5}$)
India Office Library and Records (WD3951)

Coming from a poor family in Glasgow, Simpson (1823–99) was self-taught as an artist and largely self-educated. Having made his name with his views of the Crimean War, he was sent to India by the lithographers Day & Son to depict scenes of the Mutiny of 1857. But from the start Simpson regarded this commission in a wider way: he prepared for his visit by studying the aquatints of Hodges and the Daniells in the India Office Library, to see what subject-matter was available and what work had been done. While in India, between 1859 and 1862, he travelled extensively, often in the party of the Governor-General, Lord Canning; but early in 1861 he struck out on his own to explore parts of central India and Rajasthan. The present picture was probably worked up later from sketches made on that tour.

The palace at Amber, built in stages from about 1600, was the fortified residence of the rulers of the Kachwaha Rajputs before the foundation of the city of Jaipur in 1727. It still appears today much as it does in Simpson's picture, for his work is often highly accurate, especially with regard to architectural detail. But the force of the Picturesque is also still apparent in the grouping of the foreground figures, which add interest and depth to the composition, and in the unusual light, which creates a rhythmic pattern across the palace walls.

Simpson's project to produce a great book of Indian views foundered with the liquidation of the publisher soon after his return to England, with the result that he did not acquire the reputation he deserved, and he is only now being rediscovered. Much of his work after the Indian tour was for the *Illustrated London News*, which sent him travelling throughout the world from America to China (and also again to India) in search of war and other newsworthy events. But he always remained an enthusiast of Indian civilization, and aspects of Indian art and iconography are among the varied subjects of his copious writings. G.H.R.T.

261 A View of Benares

Edward Lear, 1873
Watercolour on paper, 16.5 × 25.4 ($6\frac{1}{2}$ × 10)
India Office Library and Records (WD2330)

Lear (1812–88), like Simpson, travelled in many countries besides India. He spent much time in the Mediterranean region, his greatest love being for Greece. In dealing with European classical subjects he was always conscious of his European artistic heritage, and he was following a well-established tradition in deliberately combining truth to detail with a Picturesque treatment, to create what he called 'poetical topography'. During his comparatively brief sojourn in India, from November 1873 to January 1875, he applied this method to Indian subjects.

260

261

Within a month of his arrival in India he made for Benares, and so joined the long succession of British artists who were attracted there by the city's religious importance and antiquity – those who had preceded him included Hodges (no.246), the Daniells, Robert Smith, James Prinsep and Simpson. But Lear was not immediately captivated: his customary bad temper, the inconvenience of his hotel, and above all the strangeness of the city and of its inhabitants, all conspired against his attempts to draw, and he became enraged against the city. By the end of his stay, however, he had come to terms with it and declared himself 'truly glad to have seen this wonderful place'. In his journal he recorded how he spent his time sketching the *ghats*:

> Got a boat, a large one, for no one can have the least idea of this Indian city's splendour without this arrangement. Utterly wonderful is the rainbow-like edging of the water with thousands of bathers reflected in the river. Then the colour of the temples, the strangeness of the huge umbrellas and the inexpressibly multitudinous detail of architecture, costume, etc.... How well I remember the views of Benares by Daniell RA; pallid, gray, sad, solemn. I had always supposed this place a melancholy, or at least a staid and soberly-coloured spot, a gray record of bygone days. Instead I find it one of the most abundantly *bruyant*, and startlingly radiant of places full of bustle and movement. Constantinople or Naples are simply dull and quiet by comparison (Murphy [ed.] 1953, p.46). G.H.R.T.

LITERATURE: M. Archer 1969, p.620; W. Archer 1970, p.103.

262 The Chillum Smoker

Baltazard Solvyns, *c.*1795
Watercolour on paper, 36.8 × 25.4 ($14\frac{1}{2}$ × 10)
Giles Eyre Esq. & Charles Greig Esq.

The Belgian artist Baltazard Solvyns (1760–1824) arrived in Calcutta in 1791. Setting up as a portrait painter, he was not successful but managed to make a living through teaching amateurs and undertaking odd jobs such as cleaning and restoring pictures. This way of life was typical of many European artists in India at the time, for not all made their fortunes as Zoffany did. Less typical was his solution to the problem. He conceived the idea of producing a huge series of coloured etchings illustrating the manners and customs of the Hindus. He worked feverishly at this project, not only making hundreds of sketches, but doing the printing himself as well. Few artists at this time paid such attention to the lives of the more humble members of Indian society and to the villages – Arthur William Devis being the only other notable exception.

Solvyns issued his 250 prints between 1796 and 1799. Financially they were a failure. Their style was judged to be inadequately picturesque and the quality of the printing to be crude. Solvyns left India for France, where he published a second and larger edition of his work between 1808 and 1812. This too was unpopular. Particularly galling for Solvyns was to see the great success of an imitation of his book published in

262

England by Edward Orme in 1804–7. Orme had sixty of Solvyns's plates redrawn, with more idealized figures and prettier colours, and these appealed to the taste of the day more than the often lugubrious originals by Solvyns.

Solvyns's book includes several plates illustrating Indian methods of smoking. In the text accompanying the print made from this drawing, he explains the *chillum*:

> The Hindoos give this name to the part of the Hooka which contains the tobacco and the fire. Those who have not the means to procure a *Nariel* [pipe] must be satisfied with a *Chillum*, which they hold in one hand while they inhale the vapour through the hollow of either of their hands (Solvyns 1811). G.H.R.T.

PROVENANCE: Francis Edwards, 1920s.

LITERATURE: Solvyns 1799, ill. no. 189; Solvyns 1810, III, part 10, pl.6.

263 The Rajpootnee Bride

William Daniell, 1826
Oil on board, 30.5 × 22.9 (12 × 9)
Dr Maurice Shellim

The production of the aquatints of the volumes of *Oriental Scenery* occupied the Daniells for fourteen years after their return to England in 1794. When this great work was complete, Thomas Daniell continued to paint oils of Indian landscapes. William (1769–1837) diversified to other subject-matter including (most famously) the coastal towns of Great Britain. But he also maintained his interest in India and in printed media. He published aquatints of eastern topography after drawings by artist friends such as Samuel Davis and Robert Smith (see nos.247, 257), and in the last years of his life he collaborated with Rev. Hobart Caunter to produce the six volumes of the *Oriental Annual* (1834–9) in which Caunter's text is illustrated by engravings after William's pictures. One of the engravings is based on this small oil depicting a Rajput bride.

Though meticulous in its recording of Indian jewellery, this work is typical of many by William in portraying not an individual but an ideal of Indian womanhood – a treatment which the art historian Thomas Sutton saw as evidence of a 'romantic, chivalrous attitude'. The engraved version is accompanied by a story told by Caunter that shows the same romanticized vision of the Rajput people. Based loosely on an historical episode that had been related by James Tod in his great history of the Rajputs (published in 1829), the story is much embellished by Caunter; it is a tale of Rajput heroism and pride, of elopement and doomed love, ending with death in combat for the men and the inevitable *sati* for the unfortunate bride. G.H.R.T.

LITERATURE: *Oriental Annual* 1835, pl.13; Shellim 1988, p.32; Spink 1988.

263

264 Raja Heera Singh

L. Dickinson after Emily Eden, 1844
Plate 7 from *Portraits of the Princes and People of India,* 1844
Lithograph, 38.1 × 25.4 (15 × 10)
Charles Greig Esq.

Emily Eden (1797–1869) spent seven years in India from 1835 to 1842 while her brother, Lord Auckland, was Governor-General. In 1838 she and her sister accompanied him on a long diplomatic mission across northern India. The high point of this tour was the month spent at Lahore at the court of Maharaja Ranjit Singh, the Lion of the Punjab. Though still beguiling, the ageing warrior was by this stage a somewhat seedy figure, affecting gruff manners and shabby dress.

264

Eden was much more taken with the young Raja Heera Singh, the son of Ranjit's Prime Minister. She first noticed the youth during an audience in which her brother presented Ranjit Singh with a portrait that she had painted of the Queen. Heera Singh was the Maharaja's favourite and so was seated by him, 'loaded with emeralds and pearls'. At a later audience, Eden was seated close to Heera Singh and was delighted to find that he had 'learnt a little English, and has a good idea of making topics'. She persuaded him to visit her so that she could make a sketch – the basis of the present lithograph. Later, he was appointed her guide when she visited Ranjit Singh's *zenana*; the young nobleman had privileged access to the *zenana* 'in his capacity of favourite ... and I should think must endanger the peace of mind of some of the thirty-two Mrs Runjeets. He is very good looking' (Eden 1866, vol.1, p.283; vol.2, p.29).

Eden's sketches of members of the Sikh court anticipate similar studies of Indian royal courts, such as those made by William Carpenter in the 1850s. The present work is one of twenty-four lithographs made from her sketches and published in 1844. The letters which she wrote while on tour were published as *Up the Country* in 1866.

G.H.R.T.

265 Self-Portrait

George Chinnery, *c.*1840
Oil on canvas, 71.1 × 53.3 (28 × 21)
National Portrait Gallery, London (779)

Chinnery (1774–1852) was one of the most talented of British professional artists to work in India. He was resident in the country from 1802 to 1825, for most of that time working in Calcutta. This self-portrait – one of a large number that he painted during his career – was produced after he had moved on to Macau. It may be interpreted as a manifesto piece: Chinnery depicts himself as a landscape painter specializing in India and China. Before him on the easel is a Picturesque composition with a ruined Indian tomb and figures by a river, while hanging on the wall behind him is a view of the Praya Grande in Macau. In reality, Chinnery painted few oil landscapes on the scale of the canvases depicted here; the majority of his landscape work was executed in watercolour or pen and ink (see no.252), and much more of his time was spent painting portraits, from which he earned his living. But following the orthodoxy of his generation, Chinnery regarded landscape as a nobler genre; and in his self-portrait he has depicted himself as he wished to be regarded.

Apart from the subject-matter of the pictures included, there is nothing to locate this scene in the East. Chinnery's painting equipment, his dress and the furniture are all thoroughly European, as are the pictorial conventions of the portrait itself. Consequently, the work may stand not only as a personal manifesto for Chinnery, but as an image of the typical British artist abroad, carrying aspects of his homeland with him on his voyage of discovery in exotic realms.

G.H.R.T.

PROVENANCE: Given by Chinnery's friend John Dent on behalf of his uncle Lancelot Dent Esq. of Macao, 1888.

LITERATURE: Ormond 1968, p.160; Hutcheon 1975, p.111; Archer 1979, p.381.

EXHIBITION: London, Royal Academy of Arts, 1846.

265

The British Understanding of India

266 Sir William Jones (1746–94)

Arthur William Devis, *c.* 1793
Oil on canvas, 74.3 × 55.8 ($29\frac{1}{4}$ × 22)
India Office Library and Records (F840)

266

William Jones was the most accomplished European intellectual to go to India in the eighteenth century. He had learnt Arabic and Persian in England and had made a number of much admired translations of poetry in both languages. He earned himself a reputation as a linguistic polymath. He became a lawyer and was appointed a judge of the Calcutta Supreme Court in 1783.

In Calcutta he gave a strong impetus to the group of scholars already working under Hastings's patronage (see no.132). In 1784 Jones founded the Asiatic Society of Bengal. Papers were read on 'oriental' subjects, both cultural and scientific, which were then published in the Society's journal, *Asiatick Researches*. The most distinguished contributions to the journal's early issues were Jones's own essays. Through them he announced the progress of his studies from Arabic and Persian to Sanskrit. Here he readily acknowledged that he built on the achievement of Charles Wilkins, whose translation of the *Bhagavad Gita* had appeared in 1785. In 1786 Jones delivered a famous paper, 'On the Hindus', in which he pointed out the similarities between Sanskrit, Latin and Greek and established his claim to be the formative influence on the future study of comparative linguistics. The most famous of his translations from Sanskrit was the play *Sacontala, or the Fatal Ring*. His last major work was a version of the great legal text *Institutes of Hindu Law, or the Ordinances of Menu*.

Jones died in India in 1794. His scholarship was impressive but it was reinforced by an unrivalled capacity for presenting and publicizing his findings in a way that made them accessible, not only to literati in Britain but throughout continental Europe as well.

A.W. Devis was the son of the portrait painter Arthur Devis (1712–87). He was employed by the East India Company in 1782 as a draughtsman to accompany an expedition to China on board the *Antelope*, which was wrecked *en route*. Devis eventually settled in India in 1785 and did not return to England until 1795. During those years he divided his time between Calcutta and Madras with various excursions to towns in Bengal and Bihar. Apart from portraits he painted historical events (see no.169) and continued to paint Indian scenes after his return to England. Jones is shown with an image of the God Ganesha in his guise as patron of learning.

P.J.M./C.A.B./B.A.

PROVENANCE: Spencer collection, Althorp; sale, Christie's, 11 November 1983 (165); purchased by India Office Library.

LITERATURE: Marshall 1970; Garlick 1974–76, XLV, p.17, no.126; Archer 1979, p.251, pl.174; India Office Library *Newsletter*, no.31, April 1984, pp.3–4, ill.; Archer 1986, p.112, no.159, pl. XXXII.

EXHIBITION: London, British Library, *Bicentenary of the Asiatic Society of Bengal Exhibition*, 1984.

267 Henry Thomas Colebrooke (1765–1837)

Sir Francis Chantrey, 1820
Marble bust, height 69 (27)
Inscribed on back: *H.T. Colebrooke. Member of the Supreme Council of Bengal 1807 to 1812. Chantrey sc. 1820*
India Office Library and Records (F435)

Henry Thomas Colebrooke was described by Max Muller (1823–1900) as 'the greatest Oriental scholar that England has ever produced'. He had a depth of Sanskrit learning beyond that acquired either by Charles Wilkins or William Jones in an earlier generation (see no.266).

Colebrooke was the son of Sir George Colebrooke, former Chairman of the Company. He served in the Bengal civil service continuously from 1782 until 1814. He learned Sanskrit in order to complete a work begun by Jones, a code of Hindu law intended to replace the earlier one produced under Hastings (see no.269). Colebrooke completed the work as *A Digest of Hindu Law*, published in 1798 in four volumes. Colebrooke was much involved in the work of the Asiatic Society of Bengal, becoming its President. It was in the Society's *Asiatick Researches* for 1805 that he published his famous essay 'On the Vedas'. This was the first authoritative study of these ancient sacred writings of Hinduism to appear in any European language.

In 1819 Colebrooke gave his collection of Sanskrit manuscripts to the East India Company's library and it may have been this act of generosity that occasioned the Company to commission a marble bust of him in the same year.

Chantrey was paid 120 guineas by the Company for the bust. A preliminary drawing by Chantrey is in the National Portrait Gallery (316a [19]), the plaster model is in the Ashmolean Museum and replicas, executed by Henry Weekes, are in the Asiatic Society of Bengal in Calcutta and the Royal Asiatic Society of London. B.A./P.J.M.

267

PROVENANCE: Commissioned by the East India Company in 1819.

LITERATURE: 'Sir Francis Chantrey's Ledgers of Accounts' n.d., p.98; Colebrooke 1873 (engraved as frontispiece by Frank Holl); Foster 1924, p.84, no.435; Archer 1965, p.407; Walker 1985, p.118; Archer 1986, p.93, no.129.

268 The Malabar New Testament, Vepery, 1772

Bound book, 18.5 × 12 ($7\frac{3}{10} \times 4\frac{7}{10}$)
The British Library Board (Or. 72 b.11)

The Dutch in Ceylon pioneered the translation of Tamil and the first version of the New Testament was commenced in 1688. Fabricius's version appeared in 1715. Tamil type had been cut by the Portuguese as early as the sixteenth century. Biblical and literary works were being published in Tamil in some numbers by the end of the eighteenth century, especially from mission stations at Tranquebar and Vepery. C.A.B.

269 Halhed's Bengali Grammar

N.B. Halhed, 1778
Bound book, open 22.5 × 35 ($8\frac{4}{5} \times 13\frac{3}{5}$)
India Office Library and Records (T6863)

Nathaniel Brassey Halhed (1751–1830) joined the Bengal civil service at the age of 21, which meant that he was rather older than other recruits and, unlike them, had been to university (he spent three years at Oxford). He had literary interests which earned him the patronage of Warren Hastings (see no.132). As was not uncommon in the East India Company's service, he learnt Persian, the official language of Mughal India. Hastings then appointed him to put into English the Persian version of a compilation of Hindu law that had been prepared for the use of the Company's courts. Halhed's translation was published in Britain in 1776 as *A Code of Gentoo Laws*. A Preface by the translator was attached to it, which shows that Halhed was developing linguistic interests that went well beyond the study of Persian. He was trying to learn Sanskrit and, as was soon to be shown, was immersed in Bengali. In 1778 he produced his *Grammar of the Bengal Language*. This was published in India from type specially made by Charles Wilkins (*c.*1749–1836), one of the Company's servants and himself a notable scholar of Indian languages.

Halhed's *Grammar* was not in fact the first grammar of Bengali to be published by a European, nor perhaps was Wilkins's type the first piece of printing in the language, but both achievements were very significant. They show that the cultural impact of the British was not limited to making the great classical traditions of India accessible to Europeans, and indeed to Indians, but included a powerful stimulus to the development of regional languages and cultures.

Halhed's later life was an intriguing one. The study of Hinduism seems to have inclined him to mysticism and he became a convert to millenarian prophecies. P.J.M.

270

270 James Prinsep's Memorial, Calcutta

William Prinsep, *c.*1859
Oil on canvas, 62.2 × 106.7 ($24\frac{1}{2}$ × 42)
Spink & Son Ltd

This view in Calcutta shows the stately Ionic pavilion erected as a memorial to the Orientalist scholar James Prinsep (1799–1840). He was one of the eight sons of John Prinsep, a dealer in indigo in Calcutta in the 1770s and 1780s, and like most of his brothers he also worked in India. His first important post was as Assay Master of the Mint in Benares (1820–30), and living there encouraged his interest in antiquities. He made, for example, a detailed survey of the city's temples and repaired the minarets of Aurangzeb's mosque (see no. 246). He was also a specialist in numismatics and early Indian languages. In 1838 he deciphered the Brahmi script – the script used in the Asokan edicts – and so provided the key to important mysteries of early Indian history.

Like some of his brothers, James was a gifted amateur artist, though the most accomplished among them in this pursuit was William (see also no. 254; and 221, 237). William's oil shows his brother's memorial in its original setting: at Prinsep's Ghat on the banks of the River Hughly near Fort William. The environment has since changed considerably though the building still stands. G.H.R.T.

271 A Map of the North Part of Hindustan or a Geographical Survey of the Provinces of Bengal, Bahar, Awd, Ellahabad, Agra and Delhi

Major James Rennel, FRS, Engineer Surveyor-General to the East India Company, 1794
Coloured engraving on card, 70 × 107 ($27\frac{3}{10}$ × $41\frac{7}{10}$)
The Syndics of Cambridge University Library

James Rennell (1742–1830) was the first great cartographer of British India. Attached to the East India Station of the Royal Navy in 1760, he participated in a survey of the Philippine Islands and then, after 1764, in Governor Vansittart's survey of Bengal. He made numerous arduous expeditions in eastern India (in 1776, for instance, his party was attacked by armed *Sanyasi* raiders) and collected the route maps of other travellers, some of which were based on Mughal originals. In 1779 he published *The Bengal Atlas* and after he had retired to England, his house became a centre of geographical enquiry and a resort for travellers and navigators. Rennell's great work was done in a period when exploration and military security motivated cartography, but after 1800 trigonometrical methods were introduced as maps became more important for the assessment and collection of land-revenue. C.A.B.

LITERATURE: Phillimore 1945–54, I, II.

268

272

272 Colonel Colin Mackenzie (1754–1821) and his assistants

Thomas Hickey, 1816
Oil on canvas, 58.5 × 38 (23 × 15)
India Office Library and Records

Colin Mackenzie entered the Madras Engineers in 1782, pursuing a distinguished career with a corps that became increasingly important as British power penetrated the interior of the Presidency. But he was also a man of inexhaustible inquisitiveness. In the tradition of the great travellers and topographers he amassed histories, descriptions and oral traditions wherever he went. Here Indian knowledge and religious lore is shown tamed and ordered by European science. Mackenzie is shown with his three Indian servants: holding the telescope is Kistnaji, his peon; on the left is his old Jain *pandit* carrying a palm-leaf manuscript; and slightly to the rear is his Telugu Brahmin *pandit*. Behind is shown the huge tenth-century statue of the hero-king Bahubali which dominates Shravan Belagola, the holiest Jain pilgrimage place in south India; Mackenzie was probably the first European to measure and record it.

Mackenzie's collections, which are now housed in the India Office Library, London, and in Madras, are still regarded as among the most important sources for the study of south Indian history between the fifteenth and nineteenth centuries. Many of them record the otherwise unknown histories of the petty 'poligars', chieftains of the south who ruled the countryside before the Arcot and Hyderabad regimes attempted to establish centralized states. Here, too, are works on Hindu and Muslim holy men and descriptions of towns and villages.

In 1816 Mackenzie was appointed Surveyor-General of India and this portrait probably commemorates his advancement. One of Hickey's last and finest pieces, this painting of Mackenzie was produced when the artist was seventy-five years of age. B.A./C.A.B.

PROVENANCE: Henry Traill, first Treasurer of the Asiatic Society of Bengal; presented by him to East India Company, June 1822.

LITERATURE: Foster 1924, p.7, no.13; Foster 1931, pl.VI; Phillimore 1945–54, II, pl.22; Archer 1979, pp.232–3, pl.157; Archer 1986, pp.30–31, no.36, pl.VI.

EXHIBITIONS: London, Royal Academy, *The Art of India and Pakistan*, 1947–8 (899); London, Commonwealth Institute, *India and Britain*, 1982 (130).

273

273 William Carey (1761–1834) and his chief pundit, Mritunjaya

Robert Home, Calcutta, 1811
Oil on canvas, 126 × 100.8 ($49\frac{1}{2}$ × $39\frac{1}{2}$)
The Baptist Missionary Society

The East India Company was very suspicious of missionary activity in India, which it believed would unsettle the local population and make trading and political conditions more hazardous. The earliest British missionaries in Bengal were Baptists who operated from the Danish East India Company's settlement at Serampore. The first and most famous of them was William Carey (1761–1834), a cobbler by trade, who reached India in 1793 and spent the next three decades preaching and translating the scriptures and other Christian writings into Bengali. In his early life Carey had been attracted to radical politics, but later he turned to 'more important things', the propagation of the Gospel. Official British opinion gradually became less hostile. Wellesley and the teachers of his Fort William College, which was founded to train civil servants, approved of Carey's linguistic work. In Britain influential evangelicals such as William Wilberforce forced a gradual reappraisal of the importance of missionary work in India. This resulted in a more liberal attitude when the Company's charter was reviewed in 1813.

Carey and the Baptist Missionary College had their greatest influence among the Bengalis. They made relatively few converts to Christianity, but in translating the Christian scriptures into Bengali they prompted a rediscovery and re-evaluation of the Indian sacred texts themselves. Mritunjaya, Carey's chief *pandit*, was an orthodox Brahmin who made a distinguished contribution to scholarship on the Hindu sacred books (the Vedas). Hindu opinion, in fact, quickly learned to counter Christian arguments in its own terms and the dialogue laid the foundations for much of the new revived Hinduism of the present era.

This portrait of William Carey and Mritunjaya was painted in Calcutta in 1811. Home charged 1,200 rupees (£138) for it. B.A./C.A.B.

LITERATURE: Archer 1979, p.313, pl.216.

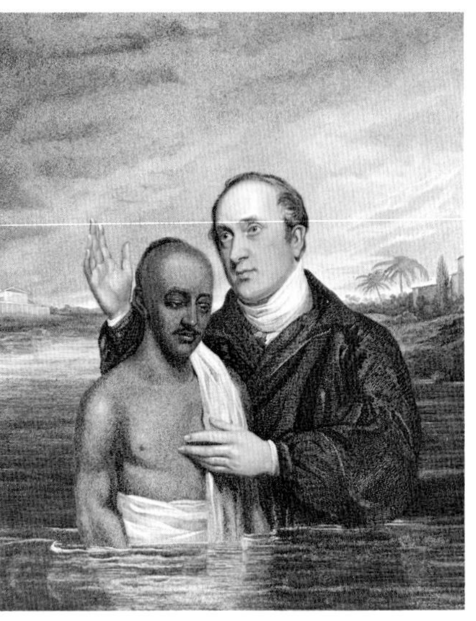

274

274 William Ward (1769–1823) baptizing a Hindu

Henry Meyer after John Jackson
Engraving, 46.3 × 55.9 (18 × 22)
Scottish National Portrait Gallery (EPL. 98/1)

Like Carey, William Ward (1769–1823) was another Baptist missionary who played a prominent part in the translation and circulation of Christian tracts in the Bengali language. Again, like Carey, he was of relatively humble origins having been born at Derby, the son of a carpenter, and apprenticed as a printer. Ward had been active in the Sunday School movement in Birmingham, but in 1799 he left for the mission station at Serampore. Ward worked hard for the dissemination of Christian and European knowledge amongst boys and girls in Bengal, relying on voluntary subscriptions raised in Britain and India. His attitude to Indian religion and culture was tolerant and respectful. He wrote that 'No reasonable person will deny to them [ancient Hindus] the praise of very extensive learning ... let the most learned and profound of the Hindoo writings be compared with the writings of any nation flourishing at the same period and the decision ... will be in favour of the Hindoos.' (Laird 1972, p.56). It is not surprising, perhaps, that his work contributed to the revival of classical learning in India, rather than the mass Christian conversion for which he so devoutly wished. C.A.B.

LITERATURE: Laird 1972.

275 Reginald Heber, Bishop of Calcutta (1783–1826)

Thomas Phillips, 1823
Oil on canvas, 141 × 109.2 ($55\frac{1}{2}$ × 43)
Signed and dated: *T.P.* [monogram] *1823*
The Warden and Fellows of All Souls College, Oxford

By 1810 the evangelical movement in Britain and the missionary activities of Nonconformists had finally spurred the Church of England to a more active mission in India, though one which was still marked by great caution. The first Bishop of Calcutta was ordained in 1813. Heber, who was offered the see in 1822, came from a High Church background and was educated at Oxford (he became a Fellow of All Souls in 1805). However, he had been drawn to the evangelical cause by what he had seen on his extensive travels in Europe; he also had a connection by marriage with Sir William Jones (see no.266). Heber spent much of the few remaining years of his life travelling through his extensive see, and the book of memoirs his widow published in 1828, *A Journey through India from Calcutta to Bombay*, is one of the best observed and most evocative accounts of India in the early nineteenth century. He seems to have enjoyed meeting the people and was much less censorious than many of his contemporaries.

275

Heber's appointment as Bishop of Calcutta probably prompted the commission for this portrait by Thomas Phillips since it was executed within months of his assignment. A distant view of Calcutta Cathedral can be seen through the opening to the left. Thomas Phillips (1770–1845) started out as an apprentice to a stained-glass worker and came to London with a recommendation to Benjamin West. He became a successful portrait painter and was appointed Professor of Painting at the Royal Academy Schools in 1824.

276

This work was engraved by S.W. Reynolds in 1824. C.A.B./B.A.

PROVENANCE: Presumably painted for All Souls' College, Oxford.

LITERATURE: Lane Poole 1925, II, p.197, no.58; Heber 1930; Hughes 1986; Archer 1986, no.51.

EXHIBITION: Oxford, *Exhibition of Historical Portraits*, 1906 (167).

276 Thomas Babington Macaulay, 1st Baron Macaulay (1800–59)

Edward Matthew Ward, 1853
Oil on canvas, 63.5 × 76.3 (25 × 30)
Inscribed (on the original frame) c.f.: *The Rt. Hon. T.B. Macaulay in his Study.* /*E.M. Ward, R.A.* and on either side, in a later inscription: *Borough of Stretford Purchased 1934*
National Portrait Gallery, London (4882)

The great historian Thomas Macaulay was the son of Zachary Macaulay (1768–1838), former Governor of Sierra Leone and stalwart of the anti-slavery lobby. The younger Macaulay was a passionate advocate of government reform, a cause which he propagated through the *Edinburgh Review*. His interest in the utilitarian philosophy of Jeremy Bentham and James Mill drew his attention to their ideas on Indian government. But when offered an appointment to the new Supreme Council, created by the India Act of 1833, the immediate reason for Macaulay's acceptance was the simple need for money. He did not relish a future as a 'publisher's hack'. During his five years in the subcontinent he undertook an extensive review of the judicial procedures of the Government of India which many felt to be antiquated and inefficient. The result of this labour was Macaulay's draft Indian Penal Code. Though the code was not enacted until many years after his departure, it remains a founding document of Indian law. He also played a vigorous part in the debate between those who considered that the language and style of education in the Company's territories should be English and those 'orientalists' who favoured the Indian classics – Macaulay was dismissive of the value of Indian learning and literature, unlike many of his predecessors. In 1839, he became Secretary at War in Lord Melbourne's Ministry. After he left office he became increasingly absorbed in writing his monumental *History of England*.

This is one of at least seven portraits of writers in their studies executed by E.M. Ward in the 1850s (the others are Thackeray, Bulwer Lytton, Stanhope, Dickens, Hall and Forster). They seem to have been conceived as a series which Ward may have hoped to exhibit together, perhaps with the intention of selling and engraving them as a group. Certainly portraits of literary figures were popular at the time. The setting for the portrait is evidently Macaulay's chambers in the Albany which G.R. Trevelyan described as 'comfortable, though not very brightly furnished'. Macaulay records sitting for his portrait in his 'Journal' for 18 May 1853: 'Ward came at eleven. I had a long sitting. I am tired to death of these sittings. He did not go till three, and would not have gone then if I had not sent him away'. A week later he remarked of Ward, 'He has made me uglier than a Daguerotype [*sic*]. However he is a clever fellow'.

B.A./C.A.B.

PROVENANCE: E.M. Ward, his sale, Christie's, 29 March 1879 (82), bt. Agnew; Richard Hurst, his sale, Christie's, 25 April 1899 (125), bt. Agnew; presented to Whitworth Art Gallery, Manchester, through R.D. Darbyshire, 1899; purchased from the Whitworth by the Borough of Stretford, 12 June 1934, and sold by them, Henry Spencer and Sons, Retford, 14 May 1971 (222); sale, Bonham's, 1 July 1971 (98), bt. Abbott and Holder; purchased from Patrick Corbett by National Portrait Gallery, 1972.

LITERATURE: Macaulay's 'Journal', n.d., VI, pp.73–4, 76; Scharf 'Sketchbooks', n.d., XCIX, 22, under 1879; Ormond 1973, I, pp.568–9, II, pl.570; Clive 1973.

EXHIBITIONS: London, South Kensington Museum, *Third Exhibition of National Portraits*, 1868 (538); Manchester, *Royal Jubilee Exhibition*, 1887 (788); London, New Gallery, *Victorian Exhibition*, 1891–2 (330).

277

277 Missionary Influence or How to Make Converts

Thomas Rowlandson, 1815
Handcoloured engraving, 14.6 × 23 ($5\frac{7}{10}$ × 9)
India Office Library and Records (P2688)

Missionary activity had its enemies, and not only amongst the Hindu and Muslim population. Some officials retained the eighteenth-century view that oriental religions were suited to their local context and provided stability and self-respect for their devotees. But this view was rapidly going out of fashion as assaults on Hinduism, such as those in James Mill's *History of India* (1818), became common. More substantial objections came from conservative Christians who felt that faith could only be reached through the exercise of reason, and that a massive educational and economic programme in India would have to precede outright evangelization. People of this opinion were particularly contemptuous of the 'uneducated', newer breed of missionary who, it was said, shouted the Christian message in English without any understanding of the language or prejudices of the people. This sort of evangelization was blamed for the mutiny in the Vellore garrison of the Madras army in 1806, which ostensibly occurred because the sepoys were forced to cut their beards and wear European dress and headgear. The most usual criticism, however, was simply that Indians were drawn to Christianity for the wrong reasons – for rice which the missionaries dispensed, or because they were attracted by the outward show, as this caricature by Rowlandson suggests.

C.A.B.

278 Sacrifice of an Hindoo Widow upon the Funeral Pile of her Husband

Johann Zoffany, *c.*1780
Oil on canvas, 101.6 × 127 (40 × 50)
Giles Eyre Esq. and Charles Greig Esq.

Sati, or the self-immolation of widows on their husbands' pyres, is an ancient tradition of sacrifice among many of the Hindu warrior communities such as the Rajputs. This Indian custom both fascinated and moved Western observers. In the Benthamite mood of the late 1820s, the horrified British banned it. But in an earlier period, British attitudes were often ambivalent, and some were inclined to see it (as presumably did those who encouraged and committed it) as a heroic gesture.

This recently rediscovered painting is of great significance for the light that it sheds, not only on the matter of *sati*, but also on the work of the artist Johann Zoffany (see nos.133,138,140).

His painting of a *sati* shows it quite unambiguously as a heroic act. The widow here is not a sentimental figure inviting pity, but a moral exemplar to be admired. This intention is strongly underlined by the composition. The figures are arranged in processions across the canvas, ranked in a series of flat planes rather than grouped in space. This type of composition, derived from classical bas-relief sculpture, was commonly used by late eighteenth-century neo-classical painters, such as Gavin Hamilton; and it was used particularly in the popular genre of scenes illustrating heroic virtue. Such scenes were often conceived in classical terms, with subjects from ancient history. Zoffany has followed these current mannerisms, while translating the genre from the antique to a contemporary, but exotic realm.

In this respect the work relates to Zoffany's famous painting of *The Death of Captain Cook* (National Maritime Museum, London). Here too, a planar composition is used to depict a heroic action; and the pursuit of the classical ideal is again combined with an attention to exotic details – in this case, the Hawaiian natives rather than the string of fakirs and ascetics seen in the foreground of the *sati* scene.

In some other respects, the composition is similar to another of Zoffany's Indian works, *The Embassy of Haidar Beg* (engraved by Earlom in 1800). Each is populated by a great multitude of figures, and though there is a central focus, this does not command everyone's attention: some of the figures are engaged in their own activities, seemingly oblivious of the central drama. Both pictures are evidence of a fascination with native Indian life

278

which, as Mildred Archer has argued, informs much of Zoffany's work.

That this fascination extended to *sati* is quite evident. Two of Zoffany's group portraits (those known as the Polier and Blair conversation pieces) include paintings of *satis* in their backgrounds. And the catalogue of the sale of Zoffany's effects following his death lists three pictures of this subject. It is likely that the present work is one of these three, executed in England after Zoffany's return home. G.H.R.T.

279 The Burning System

Thomas Rowlandson, 1815
Handcoloured engraving, 14.7 × 24 ($5\frac{7}{10}$ × $9\frac{2}{5}$)
India Office Library and Records (P2687)

The missionary assault on Hinduism in the early nineteenth century dramatized the practice of *sati* and made it a focal point for the denunciation both of the East India Company and of Hindu 'superstition'. Even before Lord William Bentinck had outlawed the practice in 1829, British officials had sometimes intervened in cases where they thought the sacrifice was not voluntary, as the Hindu scriptures specified it must be. But this only appeared to implicate the government in *sati* where it was carried out 'correctly'. Missionaries denounced all forms of *sati* and started up a pamphlet war in India and Britain which they hoped would see not only the legal suppression of *sati*, but the first stage of the collapse of Hinduism itself. Certainly, a vast amount was published, and British Parliamentary Papers have many volumes of evidence concerning the issue. C.A.B.

LITERATURE: Thompson 1928.

280 Sri Rani Sati

Ramachandra, *c.* 1985
Oleograph, 34.5 × 24.5 ($13\frac{1}{2}$ × $9\frac{1}{2}$)
Private Collection

This contemporary popular print depicts an idealized *sati* on the burning pyre of her deceased husband. Such prints, and the very occasional occurrence of a *sati*, are vehicles employed largely by today's Rajasthani Rajputs for asserting the strength of their faith and its power to conquer a fierce brute reality. For their many opponents in India, *satis* are proof of a resurgent patriarchy.

It is said that when a *sati* goes willingly and with joy to her death it is not necessary for any human to ignite the pyre: the gods, as shown in this oleograph, will send down a beam of heat from the sky. A true *sati* involves no coercion and, perhaps ironically, offers

280

women deification in return for this supreme act of negation.

All arguments, for or against, are engaging with *sati* as a product of colonial discourse – as a practice to be eradicated in the name of 'progress' or preserved in the name of 'tradition'. Britain and India, feminism and patriarchy and a complex set of gender symbolizations all combine to imbue the apparently simple question of *sati* with a great historical complexity. C.P.

279

281(i) Fakir's cage

Iron, height 58 ($22\frac{4}{5}$)
The Trustees of the British Museum (As.1956. A.4.17)

281(ii) Fakir's grid

Iron, length 45.5 ($17\frac{7}{8}$)
The Trustees of the British Museum (As.1956. A.4.18)

These were nineteenth-century artefacts used for the mortification of the body by Hindu ascetics. This was an aspect of Hindu religion which British Protestants brought up in a tradition hostile to 'Romish fasting' found most objectionable. C.P./C.A.B.

PROVENANCE: Acquired by present owners from Methodist Missionary Society, 1956.

282 A Hindu renouncer (*Sanyasi*)

G. Western, *c.*1865
Albumen print, 19.9 × 14.8 $(7\frac{13}{16} \times 5\frac{13}{16})$
Inscribed: *'a suniassie' by G. Western Esq. 750/4*
Cambridge University Museum of Archaeology and Anthropology

Sanyasis (sometimes *Bairagis*, *Atits* and *Gosains*) were those who had severed their links with the world. Technically 'dead', they had actually undergone Hindu death rites. But paradoxically, renouncers, organized into *mathas* or monasteries, were prominent in trade and even warfare in eighteenth- and nineteenth-century India. Western is chiefly for his collaboration with W.W. Hooper. C.A.B./C.P.

282

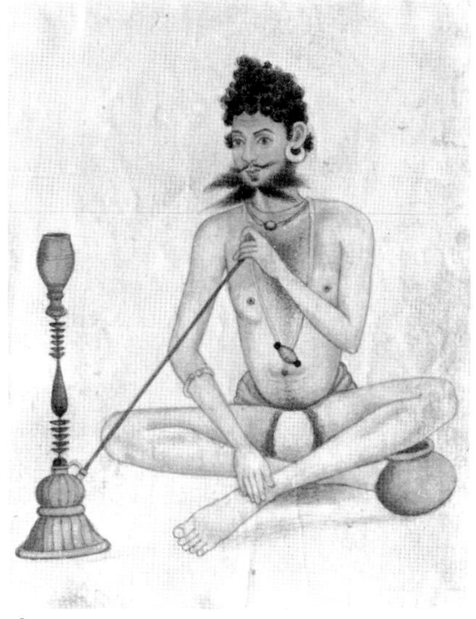

283

283 Hindu ascetic smoking a hookah

Company School, *c.*1820
Gouache, 17.8 × 15.2 (7 × 6)
Private Collection

284

284 Charakpuja, the hook-swinging festival

James Atkinson, 1831
Oil on canvas, 91.5 × 71 (36 × 28)
India Office Library and Records (F145)

In Hindu teachings Lord Shiva is the God of Destruction, a necessary counterpart to Brahma the Creator and Vishnu the Preserver. He performs acts of austerity to purge the cosmos so that the cycle of regeneration can begin again.

Hindus who had withdrawn from the world (*sanyasis*) and ordinary people who had made a vow, or wished to do penance, sometimes subjected themselves to austerities and suffering in the pursuit of their faith. In parts of Bihar and Bengal, Shiva was worshipped by devotees who attached themselves to a huge representation of his great wheel (*charka*), which represented the cycles of the cosmos. This was done by means of wires threaded between the shoulder-blades of the devotees, who then let themselves swing freely.

This type of austerity and 'self-torture' in worship fascinated European observers, but was particularly offensive to the Christian missionaries who entered India more freely after 1813. Hook-swinging became the object of attack and was discouraged, although the practice was officially banned only in the immediate vicinity of European houses.

It was while James Atkinson (1780–1852) was in Calcutta that he took painting lessons from George Chinnery (see no.215). The ceremony of the hook-swinging festival is described in the artist's poem, *The City of Palaces* (1824).

C.A.B./B.A.

PROVENANCE: Presented by the artist's son, the Rev. Canon Atkinson, 1910.

LITERATURE: *Asiatic Journal and Monthly Register*, xxxv, 1828, p.33; Foster 1924, p.44, no.145; Archer 1986, p.64, no.81, pl.xvi.

EXHIBITION: London, Victoria and Albert Museum, *India Observed*, 1982 (132).

285

285 Pilgrim with a snake-headed staff

Unknown Mughal artist, *c.*1570
Gouache, 50.8 × 63.5 (20 × 25)
The Trustees of the British Museum, Oriental Antiquities (1983.7–27.1)

Under both Mughal and British governments Hindu pilgrimage flourished. The relative peace of Mughal rule made journeys to the great sites on the sacred rivers such as Gaya, Allahabad and Benares much safer. Mughal officials realized that trade benefited from pilgrimage, and their administration also levied fees directly on pilgrims. The *Ain-i-Akbari* (no.6) contains much detail about the location of religious sites. In the eighteenth century, pilgrimage became an important political issue for the British, since they effectively controlled the three most important centres of Hindu pilgrimage after 1803. It was necessary for them to license Hindu rulers who passed into their territories, to levy pilgrim tax and to try to ensure that untoward incidents did not occur. In 1840 the British abolished the taxes as the Company felt vulnerable to the charge of patronizing 'heathen' worship. This swelled the numbers of pilgrims still further. The snake-headed staff in no.285 may indicate that this is a Shaivite devotee.

C.A.B.

PROVENANCE: Sale, Christie's, 13 June 1983 (44).

286 The Harihar Kshetra festival at Sonepur, near Patna (Bihar)

Sevak Ram, 1809
Watercolour on paper, 43.2 × 57.5 (17 × 23)
India Office Library and Records (Add. Or. 15)

Sonepur, located at the confluence of the sacred rivers Gandak and Ganges, was the site of the festival dedicated to Harihar Nath Mahadeva (Shiva and Vishnu conjoined). A ritual bath here was popularly believed to confer as much merit as the gift of a thousand cows. The holiest times for bathing were the days around the full moon in Kartik (October-November) when hundreds of thousands of people converged on Sonepur. Naturally, the festival was a great magnet for commerce, especially for the sale of horses, cattle and elephants, and it remains so to this day. In the late seventeenth century John Marshall, an English visitor, noted that people travelled here from the 'remotest parts of India' and from as far away as Tartary in Central Asia (cited Yang 1989, p.17). By tradition the 1857 rising in Bihar was also planned here by the aged guerrilla leader Kunwar Singh (no. 330). In the twentieth century the fair became a resort of political and religious preachers. In this picture, heavily influenced by the European conventions introduced to Patna by Charles D'Oyly, boatmen take ladies onto the river for their ritual bath while a horse waits on the bank. C.A.B.

PROVENANCE: 1st Earl of Minto, Governor General 1807–13; purchased by India Office Library, 14 June 1954.

LITERATURE: Yang 1989, pp.14–19; Archer 1972, no.68, iii.

287 Scene at a shrine, apparently dedicated to Shiva

Unknown artist, Murshidabad, *c.*1760
Gouache with gold, pale blue borders with floral decoration in gold, 25.3 × 33.3 (10 × 13¼)
India Office Library and Records (Add. Or. 483)

Sanyasis are seen here near a Shiva shrine. Devotees carry baskets containing Ganges water to pour over the idol or other offerings (*gangajalis* or *kavadis*) for the deity (see no.290). Shiva worship was common in the Bengal countryside, especially among Brahmins. It was often connected with the cults of Shiva's consort, either in her manifestation as Durga, or as the more fearsome goddess, Kali (no.400). However, the devotional cults of Lord Vishnu and his manifestations, Rama and Krishna, had become popular in the sixteenth and

286

287

seventeenth centuries. Vaishnavite devotional worship discouraged blood sacrifice; observers noted that where it was predominant, *sati* was virtually unknown. C.A.B.

PROVENANCE: Purchased January 1957.

LITERATURE: Welch 1963, no.84; Archer and Falk 1981, no.374, i.

288 The Holi festival at Lucknow

Unknown Lucknow artist, *c.*1800
Watercolour on paper, 35 × 44.6 (14 × 17½)
India Office Library and Records (Add. Or. 1966)

Holi, the Hindu fertility festival which marks the coming of summer, is cele-

288

brated with jollity, loud music and a ceremonial inversion of roles reminiscent of the ancient Roman Saturnalia. Here, at the gates of a great building in Lucknow, the crowd mimics and parodies the Indian symbols of royalty. A man, garlanded with shoes and stained with coloured water, is carried on an up-ended bed (*charpoy*) and 'fanned' with a broomstick. Drummers and a naked mendicant attend him. Even in the early nineteenth century the good humour of these celebrations sometimes turned to violence when Hindu crowds were thought to have violated the solemnity of Muslim ceremonies or places of worship. C.A.B./K.P.

PROVENANCE: Purchased 14 July 1962.

LITERATURE: Archer 1972, p.159, no.121, iii, pl.53; Fisher 1987.

289 A drummer at a *dargah*

Unknown artist, Patna, *c.*1840–70
Painting on mica, 12.7 × 7.6 (5 × 3)
Private Collection

This is a typical example of one of the sets of paintings on mica of castes, occupations and religious figures that were made in Patna in response to European demand and the patronage extended by the D'Oyly circle. On the left is the base

289

of the tomb-shrine of a Muslim 'saint' (*pir*). On the death day of such venerated figures an annual *urs* festival would be held at which popular devotional songs in the *kawwali* style would be sung into the night. The standing emblems are *panjas*, symbols of power represented by an open hand, which are commonly seen at celebrations of Mohurrum and other Muslim holy days. Bihar Sharif, near Patna, is the site of a particularly celebrated *dargah* or tomb-shrine, where Muslims venerate the example of the saint or seek his intercession, while Hindus, especially Hindu women, openly worship him. C.A.B.

290 Two figures with ceremonial offerings

Unknown artist, Patna, *c.*1840–70
Paintings on mica, 12.7 × 7.6 (5 × 3) each
Private Collection

No.290(ii) is difficult to place. He carries baskets of ceremonial offerings (*kavadis*) similar to those shown near the Shiva shrine in no.287. On the other hand, the cut of his beard and his green garments suggest that he may be Muslim. At *urs* ceremonies (see no.289), Muslims made

290(i)

290(ii)

offerings of rose-petals, sugar, cloth and sandalwood paste at the saints' tombs. These were then redistributed amongst the celebrants in sanctified form, a practice very reminiscent of the distribution of *prasad* at Hindu ceremonies. Such uncertainties are an object lesson in the close interpenetration of the themes and practices of popular Hinduism and Islam in India in the nineteenth century, and even today. C.A.B.

Thuggee: a Colonial Stereotype

The British considered that the suppression of Thuggee, the strangling and robbery of wayfarers, was one of the great beneficent acts of their rule, along with the outlawing of *sati*, the introduction of rail transport and the building of the Punjab canals; they were heavy weights to be cast on the imperial side in the balance of history. Sir William Sleeman, progenitor of the 'Thuggee and Dacoitee Department', is reputed to have suppressed a practice which took the lives of a million people in the early years of the nineteenth century through an executive programme which was the very embodiment of the rule of law and the 'Pax Britannica'.

Much of the evidence about Thuggee remains puzzling, however, and the British reaction to it riven with contradictions and inconsistencies. Some Indian historians now tend to argue that Thuggee was a 'colonial construct', a bundling together of a number of rather different phenomena which allowed the British to impose stronger controls on Native States and further legitimated their rapidly expanding rule.

What is not really in doubt is that the early years of the nineteenth century saw widespread disturbance and travel remained extremely hazardous, with many merchant and pilgrim bands subject to murderous attacks. As to whether Thuggee was an organized conspiracy, let alone one which was based exclusively on the worship of the ferocious goddess Kali, this was less clear.

From 1810 or so some reports of thug bands were received from various districts and some arrests were made. But it was after a series of spectacular trials in 1829 and 1830 that officials began to assert that Thuggee *was* an organized, all-India system, and one which only the Paramount Power could combat. The campaign against thugs was imbued with a sense of mission, and there was much publicity concerning the hanging of thugs at Saugor and Jabbalpur. Whereas earlier there had been a sense of mystery about the thugs, it was now claimed by Sleeman that the 'secrets' of thug lore had been unlocked. 'I am satisfied', wrote Sleeman, 'that there is no term, no rite, no ceremony, no omen or usage that they have intentionally concealed from me....' Nevertheless arrests were still made through the familiar channel of the 'approver', the member of a gang who turned 'king's evidence', and in the regular courts judges were often reluctant to convict a man if the only evidence was that of the approvers. Against this insistence on 'technicality', the supporters of the campaign argued that Thuggee was so different from ordinary crime that different criteria for conviction should be accepted. Sleeman presented thug genealogies to argue that the crime was hereditary over generations (see no. 295). Eventually, in 1836, an Act was passed making it possible to convict a man on a charge of being a member of a thug gang, though the term 'thug' or 'thuggee' was not explained in the law. It was easier to convict a suspected thug on this lesser charge than to prove a specific charge of murder against him. In addition, it was beginning to be felt that the hangings in the early 1830s had been too bloody. The thug approvers and their families congregated in little colonies at headquarter towns. At Jabbalpur, in central India, an 'industrial reformatory' was set up for the approvers and those thugs who had been sentenced to life imprisonment; there they occasionally demonstrated their skills for the first generations of photographers travelling in India (no.291).

There is no doubting the dramatic impact that the 'revelations' about Thuggee in the 1830s had on British and European perceptions of India. When Meadows Taylor published his highly successful picaresque novel *Confessions of a Thug* in 1839, Queen Victoria asked for each chapter to be sent to her as it was corrected by the author. But even before its publication, Indian artists were making models of the murderous practices of the thugs (no.294), apparently for sale to European collectors. The powerful image of the strangler and worshipper of Kali then passed into Hollywood lore (no.293) and has quite recently reappeared in camp form in Steven Spielberg's *Indiana Jones and the Temple of Doom*. R.S./C.A.B.

LITERATURE: Sleeman 1936; Freitag 1985.

291 Thugs demonstrating their techniques

Copyprint after photograph by Bourne & Shepherd in *Thug, or a Million Murders* by J. Sleeman, London, 1933, in the Cambridge University Library

292 Thug's handkerchief

1878

Cotton, with embroidered wool, 107 × 35 (45 × 14)

The Trustees of the British Museum (As. 1878.c.5.860)

A note accompanying this piece, which was given to the British Museum in 1878, quotes the donor's description – 'Assamese pocket-handkerchief (*roumal*) as used by the Thugs'. None of the three assertions made in this statement are likely to be true, but the piece demonstrates the continuing interest in the thugs throughout the nineteenth century.

Appearing as it did many decades after the Thuggee scare, this handkerchief is not simply a piece of nostalgia: it was part of a grand imperial system of documentation, one of whose functions was to maintain that image of India which Thuggee was made to represent, and to act as a point of comparison for future occurrences. In the RKO version of *Gunga Din* (see no. 293), it is only when Cary Grant notices the resemblance between weapons recently captured from local villains and those from the heyday of Thuggee on display in the Mess museum that the resurgence of Thuggee is discovered.

This handkerchief also illustrates the manner in which the whole episode of Thuggee was made to act as an example of the power that the British possessed to 'bring to light' problems to which remedies could then be successfully applied. The suppression of Thuggee was not merely a military or political exercise; it can also be seen as the triumph of a paradigm of knowledge of which the museum display was a part. The ambivalence of fear and the pleasure of display is apparent in Meadows Taylor's lament that, had he been allowed to remain in Hyderabad after 1829, 'I should have been the first to disclose the horrible crime of Thuggee to the world; but it fell to the good fortune of Major Sleeman to do so afterwards' (1882, p. 64). C.P.

PROVENANCE: Presented by Dr J.M. Foster to British Museum, 1 June 1878.

LITERATURE: Chevers 1870; Meadows Taylor 1882.

293

293 *Gunga Din*

Copyprints after film stills from *Gunga Din*, directed by George Stevens (1939) in the Kobal Collection (GUN 010AE, 010AB)

294(i) Thugs murdering their victims

Native artist, Madras, 1847
Wood, clay and cloth, 40 × 51 ($15\frac{3}{4}$ × 20)
The Trustees of the British Museum (6–30.5.As.3.23)

294(ii) Thugs murdering their victims

Native artist, Madras, 1847
Wood, clay and cloth, 40 × 51 ($15\frac{3}{4}$ × 20)
The Trustees of the British Museum (6–30.6.As.3.24)

A series of similar models illustrating 'some of the most obnoxious crimes committed by highway robbers or thugs' was made for T. Holbein Hendley's Jeypore Museum (now the Jaipur

294(i)

294(ii)

296

Central City Museum). Photography was also used to reconstruct the exact procedures supposedly used by thugs. A sequence of images was taken in the Jabbalpure Government School of Industry, where many thugs were rehabilitated, to illustrate the methods used to follow the victims and throttle them (India Office Library and Records MSS.Eur. D.951/32). C.P.

PROVENANCE: Given by Mrs B.W. Horne in 1847.

295 *Thug Genealogy*

Captain James Paton
Printed book, 19 × 31.5 ($7\frac{1}{2} \times 12\frac{3}{8}$)
The British Library Board (Add.MS.41.300)

Fanny Eden noted when she visited Lucknow, 'We met a Captain Patten who is a great Thug fancier – has a prison full of them and makes positive pets of some. He wanted us to go and see them and the gentlemen did go and see a regular Thug exhibition .... He had some horrible drawings and models of the whole process and Emily has sent some to Ld. F. Egerton'. She also observed that, 'all the Europeans who have had much to do with their examinations view them in an almost romantic light, and look upon those who are hanged almost as martyrs' (Dunbar 1988, pp.104, 119–20). R.S.

LITERATURE: Dunbar 1988.

296 Three paintings of thugs

Charles Wade Crump, *c.* 1850
Watercolour on paper, 54 × 39 ($21\frac{1}{4} \times 15\frac{2}{8}$) each
India Office Library and Records (WD 3089.f.36)

Reform and Religious Revitalization in India

297 Raja Ram Mohan Roy (1772?-1833)

Unknown artist
Watercolour on paper, 12.7 × 10 (5 × 4)
India Office Library and Records (WD 1288)

The great Hindu reformer was probably born near Hughly and his family had been in service to the Nawabs of Bengal. Ram Mohan is said to have studied Bengali in his village home, Persian and Arabic at Patna and Sanskrit at Benares. He worked in a number of subordinate administrative positions in the early 1800s, but he soon showed signs of a powerful, creative mind. Though he had been brought up an orthodox Vaishnavite Brahmin, he published in 1803–4 a book called *Tuhfat-ul-Muwahiddin*, in which he condemned image worship and preached strict monotheism. Later he published a number of important Upanishads (early devotional hymns) and he revived Vedic studies in India, considering that the Vedas were a 'purer' statement of an original monotheistic Hinduism. In 1818 he published his first Bengali book against *sati*, and in 1820 the *Precepts of Jesus*. Ram Mohan was influenced by Christianity, European Deism and Islamic monotheism, but he found none of these entirely satisfactory and instead founded in 1828 his own association, the Brahmo Samaj, to propagate a purified and monotheistic Hinduism. Brahmo Samajis were beyond the pale of orthodox Hindu society in Bengal, but they were usually of elite family origins and played a powerful part in the modern history of India. In a sense the Brahmo Samaj was the first Western-style voluntary association founded in India by Indians, and the fierce debates between Brahmos, British missionaries and orthodox Hindu *pandits* did more than anything else to create a public with social and political awareness in early nineteenth-century India. Journeying finally to England, he died in Bristol on 27 September 1833. C.A.B.

LITERATURE: Kopf 1984; Archer 1986.

298 *Ayat Allah ur-Kamilah*, Lahore, 1897

Shah Waliullah
Printed book, 27 × 18.5 ($10\frac{6}{10} \times 7\frac{1}{4}$)
The British Library Board (14104.ee.23)

Shah Waliullah (1703–62) and his son Shah Abdul Aziz (1756–1824) were among the most powerful and creative of the reforming Muslim theologians and jurists of the late eighteenth and early nineteenth centuries. Their school in Delhi pioneered a revival of Islamic learning throughout the whole of north India. When the British conquered Delhi and the north, Shah Abdul Aziz seemed to suggest that India remained *dar-ul-Islam*, that is to say that since the Christian foreigners apparently observed principles of religious toleration, Muslim worship could continue and there was therefore no question of armed resistance.

The work featured here is a translation of Shah Waliullah's major Arabic commentary on the Islamic faith, the *Hujjat-allah al-Baligha*, which asserted the rational basis of Islam and also argued that Muslim pilgrimage to Mecca differed fundamentally from Hindu pilgrimage to Haridwar. He sought therefore to distance Indian Muslims from the sort of doctrinal syncretism which had characterized the Emperor Akbar's *Din Illahi* (no.23). C.A.B.

LITERATURE: Rizvi 1980; Metcalf 1982, pp.277–95.

299 *Taqwiyat ul-Iman*, Lucknow, 1876

Muhammad Ismail of Delhi
Printed book, 25 × 16.5 ($9\frac{7}{8} \times 6\frac{1}{2}$)
The British Library Board (14104.F.15)

In the first half of the nineteenth century, several movements of religious revival and reform developed among the Muslims of India. In Malabar there were holy wars launched by the Mappilas, in northern India there was the Tariq-at-i Muhammadiyya movement associated with Sayyid Ahmad Barelvi (1786–1831). From 1818 Sayyid Ahmad preached his reforming message from Delhi to Calcutta. In 1826 he launched a holy war against the Sikhs, whom he regarded as interfering with Muslim religious life, and in 1831 he and 600 followers died in battle at Balakot on the Northwest Frontier. Followers of Barelvi, however, continued to be active in India for much of the nineteenth century. The *Taqwiyat ul-Iman*, or the 'Strengthening of the Faith', was one of the movement's major texts.

Muhammad Ismail was a grandson of the leading Muslim thinker of the eighteenth century, Shah Waliullah of Delhi (no. 298), and was himself regarded as one of the most learned men of his time. He joined Sayyid Ahmad's movement in 1818 and wrote down his teachings in two books, *Sirat ul-Mustaqim*, or the 'Straight Path', and *Taqwiyat ul-Iman*. Composed in the more widely-known Urdu rather than Persian, the latter attacks saint worship and the excesses of Muslim mystics (Sufis), in particular practices which compromised the unity of God or indicated the influence of Hindu customs. Contemporary British observers saw such attacks had been influenced by the Wahhabi movement of eighteenth-century Arabia. For much of the twentieth century Indian scholarship has insisted on their indigenous origin. Recent research, however, suggests that there is substance in the British view. F.C.R.R.

LITERATURE: Metcalf 1982; Gaborieau 1989.

300 *The Mahommedan Commentary on the Bible*

Sayyid Ahmad Khan, Ghazipur, 1862
Printed book, 27 × 21 ($10\frac{6}{10} \times 8\frac{1}{4}$)
The British Library Board (10104.d.10)

Sayyid (later Sir) Ahmad Khan (1817–1898) was a Muslim gentleman from Delhi who worked as a subordinate judge in the Company's service during the 1840s and 1850s. Even before the Rebellion of 1857 Sayyid Ahmad had become convinced of the need to revive the Muslim community through the disciplined introduction of Western ideas and teaching methods. His 'modernist' position was, however, reinforced by the ruin that overcame his community in 1857. After that date he became a tireless propagandist for modern education, urging Muslims to read the Western classics, including the Bible, and to reinterpret their own scriptures on the basis of rational enquiry. In 1875, on Queen Victoria's birthday, he founded what was to become the Mahommedan Anglo-Oriental College at Aligarh, which sought to revive and modernize Islamic learning in surroundings similar to an Oxbridge college (cricket became an essential part of the curriculum, for instance). In time Aligarh became a forcing-house for a new Muslim intelligentsia, but one that competed with, and merged with, the circles of the traditional Muslim jurists (*ulama*) rather than replacing them.

C.A.B.

LITERATURE: Lelyveld 1978; Hardy 1972, pp.101–7.

301 *The Indian Musalmans – Are they bound in conscience to rebel against the Queen?*, 1871

Sir William Wilson Hunter
Printed book, 23 × 30 (9 × 11⅞)
The British Library Board (8022.dd.20)

Hunter, who was a Bengal civil servant, epitomized the suspicion with which the British regarded the political aims of Indian Islam, and which was so powerfully reinforced by the events of 1857. Hunter, who had been asked to write on the subject by the Viceroy Lord Mayo, concluded that Muslims were predisposed both by their faith and by their gradual loss of political power to oppose the interests of the British empire. By a selective use of evidence he attempted to show that Muslims had been the leaders of the Rebellion and that the natural allies of the British were the new Hindu middle classes, though he did allow that Muslims might be weaned away from 'fanaticism' by modern education. Such assertions had brought a sharp riposte from Sayyid Ahmad Khan (no.300), who contributed in 1860 to *An Account of the Loyal Mohammedans of India*, arguing that large numbers of civil servants like himself had fought hard on the British side. The controversy between Hunter and Sayyid Ahmad Khan, along with the foundation of the College at Aligarh, set the scene for a rapprochement between Indian Muslims and the British in the later nineteenth century. Many Muslims, fearing the consequence of their minority status, held aloof from the rising tide of Indian nationalism. C.A.B.

LITERATURE: Robinson 1974; Hardy 1982, pp.87–103.

The Indian Mutiny and Rebellion of 1857–9

As one of the central events of the modern history of India, the Rebellion of 1857 has stirred fierce historical controversy. As early as the winter of 1857 civil officers of the North-Western Provinces were claiming that the outbreak was simply a mutiny brought about by the insensitivity of the military establishment to Hindu 'caste prejudices'. The military responded by claiming that the harsh land-revenue settlements of the civil authorities and the injudicious annexation of what remained of Awadh in 1856 were to blame. Indian writers and modern historians remain divided on the issue. Some see it as a popular rebellion betrayed by the landed 'ruling classes' (the *zamindars* and *taluqdars*), who ultimately laid down their arms and compromised with the diplomacy of 'Clemency' Canning (no.304). Others see it as a full-blown nationalist movement, uniting all classes; certainly, this is the official view propagated on television and radio in India and Pakistan today. In general, British historians no longer deny that the civil population widely rose in rebellion. But the consensus among them stresses that the motives of the rebels were often particular and local, that family betrayed family, caste fought against caste, and 'class' against 'class'.

All historians agree that the Rebellion had several causes. The Indian troops of the Bengal army, the sepoys, felt that their privileges and their special status as respected high-caste men were under threat from military reform. The incident of the 'greased cartridges', when soldiers were made to bite on bullets supposedly greased with the fat of the sacred cow and the unclean pig, was simply the last straw for men deeply concerned about their future. The soldiers, however, made common cause with the Indian princes and the nobility who had been pushed aside and stripped of their authority as a consequence of the 'doctrine of lapse' pursued by Lord Dalhousie (no.303). This modernizing Governor-General had annexed several Indian states. The Rebellion also had a popular character in the Ganges plains and in central India. Here small landholders and peasant farmers, oppressed by heavy or inequitable rates of land tax, as well as nomads and unsettled peoples from the 'fringes', joined in insurrection and looting, though this was as often directed against Indian rivals as against the fragile symbols of Company authority.

In the British mind, the suppression of the Indian 'Mutiny' and the sack of Delhi were just retribution for the deaths of British civilians which had occurred during the Rebellion's earlier stages. The betrayal and murder of these civilians, and the final triumph of the British were the themes most prominently portrayed in contemporary depictions of the 'Mutiny'. It is more difficult to represent the views and motives of the defeated and the rural poor. Little was recorded about them in either words or pictures. C.A.B.

LITERATURE: Stokes 1986; Mukherjee 1984.

302 Henry Hardinge, Viscount Hardinge of Lahore (1785–1856)

Francis Grant, after his portrait of 1849
Oil on canvas, 127.3 × 101.6 (50⅛ × 40)
National Portrait Gallery, London (437)

This picture is a replica of the portrait of 1849 in the collection of Viscount Hardinge. The idealized Indian landscape recalls Hardinge's campaigns. He is wearing the star of the Order of the Bath, and the sword which Napoleon wore at Waterloo, presented to him by the Duke of Wellington at the Great Review of the Allied Army in 1816.

Hardinge was born in Wrotham, Kent and saw early action at the Battle of Ligny in June 1815, shortly before Waterloo where he lost a hand. He later became M.P. for Durham and served as Secretary at War in both Wellington's and Peel's ministries (1828 and 1841–4 respectively). In 1844 he succeeded Ellenborough as Governor-General of India and his main achievement during his tenure was the successful prosecution of the Sikh war, which crushed the power of the Sikh army and laid the basis

302

303

for the full annexation of the Punjab. Hardinge's administration persisted with the retrenchment that had been a feature of the 1830s and had been prolonged by the poor state of the economy and the huge expenditures on the Afghan campaign. He slashed military manpower, a policy which was heavily criticized by his successors, and which some blamed for the poor state of readiness with which the army faced the Rebellion of 1857. But Hardinge had a more direct connection with forthcoming events. For it was he, as Master of the Ordnance and as Commander-in-Chief in Britain, who began to modernize the equipment of the British Army. One result of this was the introduction of the Lee Enfield Rifle (no.313) with its infamous cartridges, which was so disastrously implicated in the mutinies. C.A.B./B.A.

PROVENANCE: The artist, presented by him to the National Portrait Gallery, 1876.

LITERATURE: Ormond 1973, I, p.212, no.437, II, pl.399.

303 Sir James Broun Ramsay, 10th Earl and 1st Marquess of Dalhousie (1812–60)

Sir John Watson-Gordon, 1847
Oil on canvas, 242.5 × 151.1 (95$\frac{1}{2}$ × 59$\frac{1}{2}$)
Signed and dated b.l.: *J. Watson Gordon ARA Pinx 1847*
National Portrait Gallery, London (188)

This portrait was painted in 1847, the year before Dalhousie was made Governor-General of India, a post he held until 1856. During his term of office the pace of change quickened throughout India. The steamship, the electric telegraph and the first railway lines began to transform transport and communications. In the wake of the railway boom in Britain and Europe, larger quantities of British capital found their way to India. The Government of India began to act in a more confident, even aggressive manner. Territorial expansion began anew in Burma, while in India Dalhousie's 'modernizing' regime was now much less willing to treat the Indian princes with circumspection. Dalhousie implemented the 'doctrine of lapse', by which those Indian princely states in which the direct male line failed were absorbed into British India, with the result that the shrinking Indian aristocracy felt increasingly embattled. In many respects the Rebellion of 1857 was a legitimist movement, a belated attempt to halt and reverse changes which seemed on the point of overwhelming the old political order of the subcontinent; the rajas' and nawabs' real loss of power had long been masked by the preservation of ceremonial and the illusion of independence under Paramountcy. C.A.B./B.A.

PROVENANCE: Presented to the National Portrait Gallery by the artist's brother, H.G. Watson, 1865.

LITERATURE: Ormond 1973, I, p.128, no.188, II, pl.240; Howlett 1981.

EXHIBITION: London, Royal Academy, 1847 (63)

304 Charles John Canning, Earl Canning (1812–62)

Mayall, *c.* 1860
Carte-de-visite photograph, 10.5 × 6.3 ($4\frac{1}{8} \times 2\frac{1}{2}$)
National Portrait Gallery, London (x5619)

Though he became the first Viceroy of India, Canning was unfortunate in his Governor-Generalship. In 1856 he

304

inherited a deteriorating situation in Awadh where British intervention earlier that year had followed a long period of strained relations. There followed the Rebellion of 1857. But Canning's role in pacifying north India, and in re-establishing relationships with the north Indian aristocracy, was not appreciated in the British community in India or among sections of domestic opinion. His refusal to pursue more vigorous acts of revenge against the rebels, and his tendency to pardon the leaders if this promised stability in the countryside, earned him the derisory title of 'Clemency Canning'. C.A.B.

305 A Bloody War: Punch cartoons from 1857–9

(i) 'The Execution of "John Company"'

Copyprint after cartoon published in *Punch*, 15 August 1857

(ii) 'The British Lion and the Bengal Tiger'

Copyprint after cartoon published in *Punch*, 22 August, 1857

(iii) 'Justice'

Cartoon published in *Punch*, 12 September 1857, vol. 33, p.109
28 × 22.5 ($11 \times 8\frac{7}{8}$)
National Portrait Gallery, London

(iv) 'The Clemency of Canning'

Copyprint after cartoon published in *Punch*, 24 October 1857

(v) 'Too "Civil" by Half'

Copyprint after cartoon published in *Punch*, 7 November 1857

(vi) Title page of *Punch*

Cartoon published in *Punch*, 25 December 1858, vol.35
28 × 22.5 ($11 \times 8\frac{7}{8}$)
National Portrait Gallery, London

(vii) 'The New Year's Gift'

Copyprint after cartoon published in *Punch*, 12 January 1858

(viii) 'Havelock'

Copyprint after cartoon published in *Punch*, 16 January 1858

(ix) 'A Game of Foot-Ball'

Copyprint after cartoon published in *Punch*, 29 May 1858

(x) 'The accession of the Queen of India'

Cartoon published in *Punch*, 11 September 1858, vol. 35, p. 107
28 × 22.5 ($11 \times 8\frac{7}{8}$)
National Portrait Gallery, London

Since the British public had been led to believe that India was quiescent and gratefully receiving the benefits of

305(iii)

305(i)

THE CLEMENCY OF CANNING.

305(iv)

TOO "CIVIL" BY HALF.

305(v)

civilization, the events of the Rebellion came as a rude shock. Rumours of atrocities against British women and children began to filter back by the autumn of 1857, and the supposed role of Muslims and of hitherto loyal household servants of the European expatriates in fomenting violence was highlighted by the newspapers. Disraeli asked in Parliament whether the British were standing in the presence of a 'great national rising'. But most people in Britain were disposed to believe that it was the indolence of the military and of the East India Company which was largely to blame. Hence the abolition of the Company and the imposition of direct Crown government in India was welcomed. *Punch* celebrated the execution of 'John Company' by representing him being blown from a gun, the gruesome fate which awaited mutinous sepoys who had been captured or disarmed (no.305[i]). Queen Victoria became Queen of India and the residual authority of the Mughal emperor was done away with after the aged incumbent, Badadur Shah, had been tried in the Red Fort and banished to Rangoon (no.307). Hereafter, the role of the monarchy was enhanced in India. Regular royal durbars were held, royal honours were distributed and in 1876 the Queen became Empress of India.

As opinion in Britain was further inflamed by the stories of massacre and atrocities, the policy of Canning came under attack. He was accused of undue leniency in his treatment of rebellious rulers (no.305[iv], 305[v]). In fact, he realized that wholesale reprisals would only damage British authority by sweeping aside those 'natural leaders of the people', the princes and landholders of north India, who had to be pacified and accommodated if a few thousand foreigners were to continue to rule several hundred millions. Canning also opposed the calls for barbarous punishments for the rebels, and for the demolition of the Great Friday Mosque in Delhi, which were raised as news spread of the 'Cawnpore massacre'.

Previously only Tipu Sultan had stung British opinion to such hatred as the leaders of the Rebellion were now doing. This time, however, venom was directed at a whole people rather than an individual. Unpleasant racial stereotypes were reinforced – and the depiction of Indians in public print and books became harsher. Yet the picture is a complex one, for the new openness of India after the Rebellion also encouraged many British people to go there as teachers, doctors and technicians. C.A.B.

LITERATURE: Metcalf 1965, 1979.

306 The Sepoy Revolt at Meerut

Illustration from the *Illustrated Times*, 11 July 1857
39 × 27 ($15\frac{4}{10} \times 10\frac{6}{10}$)
India Office Library and Records (P2664)

While the events of 1857 were much more than a mutiny, popular rebellion spread rapidly because the Bengal army and the Company's police mutinied, or attempted to mutiny, at practically every station between the borders of Bengal and the gates of Lahore. Army discipline had become lax. A series of new regulations, brought in to modernize the Bengal army, seemed to the sepoys to threaten the privileges which they and their predecessors had accumulated over the century since the Battle of Buxar (1764). For instance, Lord Canning had promulgated an order that Bengal sepoys should be ready to serve overseas at any time, even though the crossing of the *kala pani* ('black waters') was held by the orthodox Hindus to violate caste. Again, the annexation of Awadh had deprived sepoys of certain privileges; it also put economic pressure on the high-caste rural communities from which they had traditionally been recruited. Since the Company itself had fostered the sense of caste exclusiveness and high status among these Bhumihar Brahmin and Rajput sepoys (see, for instance, no.191), it is not surprising that the men reacted bitterly when they saw their preserve invaded by the 'lower orders', or felt that their religion was in danger.

Thus the rumour that cartridges greased with pig and cow fat were to be used with the newly introduced Lee Enfield Rifle (no.313) acted like a spark in a tinder box. There was trouble at stations in Bengal proper during January and February 1857. But the critical outbreak took place at the great station of Meerut on 9 and 10 May, when men of the 3rd Light Cavalry and the 11th and 20th Bengal Native Infantry regiments mutinied, killed their European officers and set off on the road to Delhi, forty miles to the south-west.

306

Pursuit was deemed impossible because no-one knew in which direction the mutineers had gone. The 1,700 European effectives were retained in the station because a civil revolt amongst people in the city and on the edge of the cantonments had broken out almost immediately. European families were thought to be in danger. This vital breathing space allowed the mutineers to get to Delhi on the following day, there to throw the whole city into turmoil. C.A.B.

LITERATURE: Stokes 1986, pp. 17–47.

307 Bahadur Shah, King of Delhi (1775–1862)

P.H. Egerton, 1858
Photograph, 23 × 18 (9 × 7)
India Office Library and Records (Photo 831)

This learned and mild ruler, a fine Persian poet, proved to be the last of the Mughal emperors, dying miserably in Rangoon where he had been exiled as an old man.

For months after the occupation of Awadh by the British, Delhi had been disturbed by rumours of war and conflict. Some said that British power would fade exactly one hundred years after it had begun (at Plassey). Others prophesied a general war of the Muslim kings against the Christian powers, for the Persians and Afghans were already embattled by the Company. When the rebellious sepoys reached Delhi after the Meerut mutiny in May 1857, Bahadur Shah was put in an impossible situation. The sepoys had proclaimed the full restoration of the Mughal empire, so he had to put himself at the head of the revolt or forfeit all authority and risk general anarchy. Yet he does not appear to have entertained much hope of success against the British. During the war and the long siege of the capital he played a statesmanlike part, trying above all to prevent religious zealots on either side from endangering the cooperation between Hindu and Muslim. For instance, he banned the sacrifice of cattle at Muslim religious festivals to avoid offending Hindu sensibilities. But his reign ended tragically with the sack of the city in September 1857 and the arbitrary execution of his sons by William Hodson, commanding Hodson's Horse. His subsequent trial in the Red Fort on charges of treason and rebellion was published in British Parliamentary Papers. C.A.B.

308

308 Zinat Mahal, the King of Delhi's favourite wife

Unknown artist, *c.*1857
Engraving, 27 × 17.5 (10½ × 6⅘)
India Office Library and Records (P2380)

The Awadh Court on the Eve of Annexation and Revolt

These fascinating photographs from one of the earliest Indian studios in Lucknow were taken a few months before the Kingdom of Awadh was abruptly annexed by the Company. Awadh had lost its richest territories to Lord Wellesley in 1801–2, but the Company was happy to build up the power of its client, the Nawab, giving him the title of King and discreetly encouraging him to foster Shia orthodoxy within his state. This had the effect of distancing Awadh from the residual authority of the Sunni Mughal emperors in Delhi. Awadh found it difficult, however, to exist as a viable polity on the fringes of the awesome power of British India. Governors-General exerted pressure from the outside, while inside the kingdom the influence of the Residency and its financial and military connections fragmented authority and eroded resources. For instance, the Company had its own police force within Awadh to pursue fugitives and deserters from its army (no.312), but this scarcely helped confirm the authority of the local police.

Economic decline and disorder took hold in the 1830s, and there were more strident calls for the occupation of the country. William Sleeman of 'Thuggee' fame and Resident in the 1850s, fiercely denounced the 'misgovernment' of Awadh, but he argued that 'Annexation or confiscation are not compatible with our relations with this little dependent state'. Nevertheless, the Company went ahead in early 1856, Sir James Outram having taken over from Sleeman as Resident. The King and his entourage went to Calcutta to plead his case against annexation, but a large part of the Court remained at Lucknow where the royal ladies, and soldiers such as Mohib Ali Khan (no.309), played a leading role in the Rebellion. They were joined by a large section of the Awadh army (which had been cashiered by the Company), by landholders and peasants who had been savaged in the Company's summary settlements of the land-revenue, and by local Muslim leaders who resented the intrusion of what they saw as an 'infidel' government and its grasping agents into their homeland. C.A.B.

LITERATURE: Feaver 1969, Mukherjee 1984; Cole 1988; Fisher 1987.

309

312

309 Mohib Ali Khan, a Captain in the service of Wajid Ali Shah

Copyprint after a photograph by Ahmed Ali Khan (1855) in the India Office Library (269 1/2)

310 Hajee Saheeh, a court official

Copyprint after a photograph by Ahmed Ali Khan (1855) in the India Office Library (269 1/2)

311 Alixeen ood Doulah, favourite eunuch to the Begum

Copyprint after a photograph by Ahmed Ali Khan (1855) in the India Office Library (269 1/2)

312 Puran Chand, Chief of Police to the East India Company

Facsimile photo album after original album of photographs by Ahmed Ali Khan (1855) in the India Office Library (269/1)

Weapons captured by British forces during the Rebellion

The wide range of ages of these captured weapons indicates that north India remained a heavily-armed society over many generations.

313 Lee Enfield percussion rifle for Bengal Native Infantry

Lent by permission of the Director, National Army Museum, London SW3 4HT (7907–60)

This was the type of rifle which ostensibly brought about the 1857 Rebellion. Cartridges for this weapon were rumoured to be greased with the fat of pigs and cows. Biting the round to prepare it for loading would thus pollute both Hindu and Muslim. However, more general anxieties lay behind the Rebellion. C.A.B.

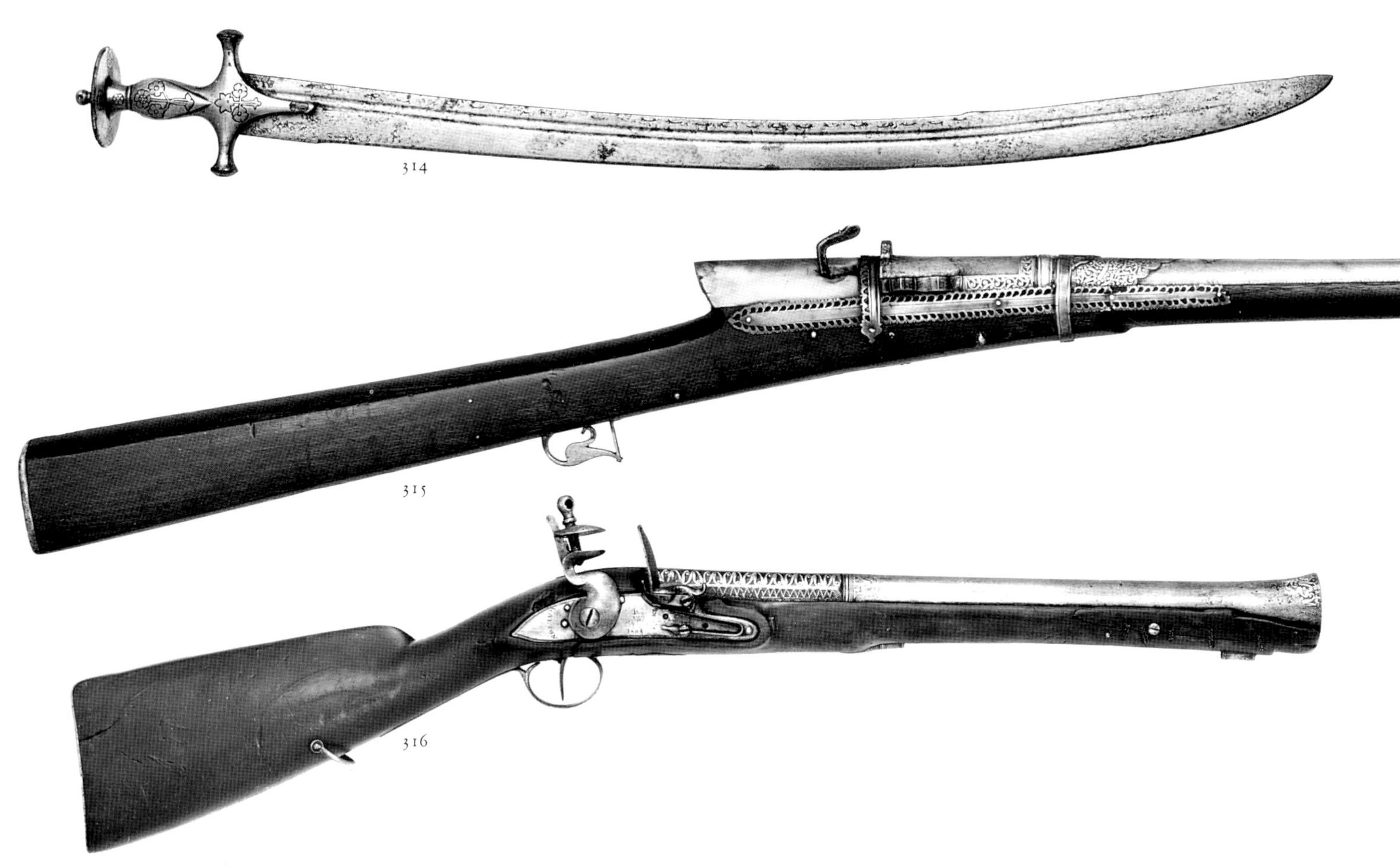

314 Sword (*talwar*)

German (?) blade, north Indian hilt, early 19th century
Length 88 ($34\frac{6}{10}$)
Royal Armouries, HM Tower of London (XXVI.92S)

This sword has a curved blade with two fullers and a quarter-length false edge, and a short ricasso. The hilt is covered in *koftgari* silver with simple gold flowers.

T.R.

PROVENANCE: Presented by the Indian Government to the Board of Ordnance in 1861, following the disarmament of 1859 after the Indian Rebellion.

LITERATURE: Hewitt 1865, Ad.no. 191, p.6; Dillon 1910, class XV, no. 654, p.4.

315 Matchlock musket (*toradar*)

Indian, early 19th century
Length 139 ($54\frac{6}{8}$)
Royal Armouries, HM Tower of London (XXVI.77.F)

The matchlock musket was introduced to India by the Mughals in the sixteenth century, and continued to be manufactured and used well into the nineteenth century. The mechanism was very simple; a long, sprung trigger was connected by a linkage inside the stock behind the breech with the serpentine. The glowing match was clamped in the jaws of the serpentine, and pressure on the trigger lowered it into the pan. Although the European flintlocks were imported into India and copied there, they were expensive and were largely confined to sporting guns.

T.R.

PROVENANCE: From Awadh; presented by the Indian Government to the Board of Ordnance in 1861, following the disarmament of 1859 after the Indian Rebellion.

LITERATURE: Hewitt 1865, Ad.no., 275, p.8 (1910 renumbered class XV, no. 738).

316 Carbine (*bokemar*)

Indian, early 19th century with English lock, dated 1804 and marked *GALTON*, over heart containing *VEIC*, crown over 2
Length 88 ($34\frac{6}{10}$)
Royal Armouries, HM Tower of London (XXVI.109F)

The carbine is supposed to have been used by officers of the camel corps. It is fitted with an East India Company military lock by Samuel Galton of Birmingham, and imitates English manufacture of the early nineteenth century.

T.R.

PROVENANCE: Presented by the Indian Government to the Board of Ordnance in 1861, following the disarmament of 1859 after the Indian Rebellion.

LITERATURE: Hewitt 1865, Ad.no. 280, p.11; Dillon 1910, class XV, no. 785, p. 26.

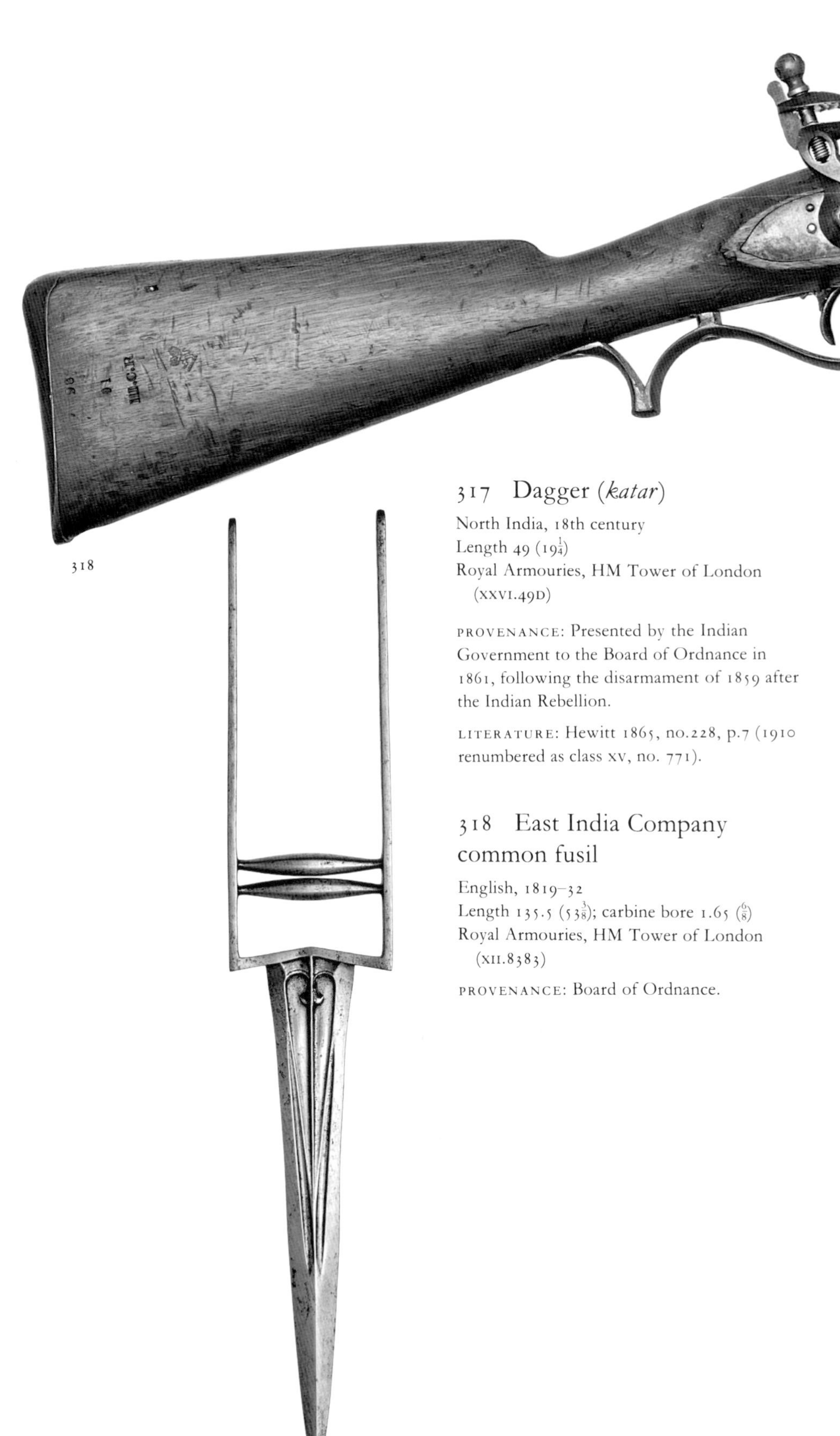

318

317

317 Dagger (*katar*)

North India, 18th century
Length 49 (19¼)
Royal Armouries, HM Tower of London (XXVI.49D)

PROVENANCE: Presented by the Indian Government to the Board of Ordnance in 1861, following the disarmament of 1859 after the Indian Rebellion.

LITERATURE: Hewitt 1865, no.228, p.7 (1910 renumbered as class XV, no. 771).

318 East India Company common fusil

English, 1819–32
Length 135.5 (53⅜); carbine bore 1.65 ($\frac{6}{8}$)
Royal Armouries, HM Tower of London (XII.8383)

PROVENANCE: Board of Ordnance.

The Siege of Delhi

The war of 1857 had three major centres, Delhi, Lucknow and Cawnpore (Kanpur). Of these Delhi was the most important because it was the symbolic centre of old India, and the residence of Bahadur Shah (no.307) who had been declared Emperor of all Hindustan by the incoming sepoys. A large part of the Hindu and the Muslim population of the city joined the revolt with alacrity. To the sepoys were soon added numbers of Muslim zealots (*ghazis*, warriors of the faith) who felt that Company rule had been revealed as a hostile, Christian one.

Though Delhi provided the Rebellion with a symbolic focus and a titular leader, it also proved its undoing; the rebels flooded into the city to do battle against the British relief force and thereby checked the rapid expansion of the rebellious zone. To the west of Delhi the British were already in a strong position in the Punjab, which they had recently conquered and whose people showed much less enthusiasm for revolt. Some Muslim Punjabis welcomed the end of Sikh rule; few had much sympathy for those very same sepoys who had recently abetted in their conquest. Administrators of the stamp of Sir John Lawrence, later Lord Lawrence and Sir Herbert Edwardes, were more accommodating and more tactful than revenue officers had been in the North-Western Provinces and Awadh.

On 8 June 1857 a few thousand British troops from Ambala and Meerut took up positions on the ridge above Delhi. But they were able to do little until Lawrence and his subordinates in the Punjab had sent a huge siege train to the Ridge. Bitter fighting took place around strong points such as Hindu Rao's house (no.321). On 14 September the Kashmir Gate of the city was blown in and after further days of street fighting, in which Sir John Nicholson was killed, the city fell to the British. From this point the Rebellion ceased to be a major threat to the British Raj. It is true that local warfare continued until 1859, and Lucknow was not yet relieved. But the armies of the rebels were now divided and without a central focus. It had been proved decisively that the old order in India was beyond restoration.

C.A.B.

LITERATURE: Stokes 1986.

319 The bridge of boats

Copyprint after a photograph by Robert and Harriet Tytler (1858) in the British Library (193[i])

320 The magazine and the cemetery inside the City

Copyprint after a photograph by Robert and Harriet Tytler (1858) in the British Library (193[ii])

321 Hindu Rao's house, Delhi

Felix Beato, *c.* 1857
Photograph, 22 × 31 ($8\frac{1}{2}$ × 12)
India Office Library and Records (25[36])

321

Allahabad, Cawnpore (Kanpur) and the Massacre (1857–8)

In Delhi and Lucknow it was the families of the Mughals and of their Vazir (the King of Awadh) who took up arms to restore the old order. Further south and east, however, the heirs to the authority of the Maratha Peshwas sought to benefit from the collapse of British power. The last Peshwa, Baji Rao II, had been exiled to the town of Bithur near Cawnpore in 1818, but his successor Nana Sahib was to take a leading part in the revolt. He, his servants and the Rani of Jhansi, another disenchanted Maratha leader, proclaimed the restoration of the authority of the Maratha states and called for the expulsion of the foreigner. Peasants and landlords from the central Gangetic plain who had suffered from raised land-revenues, or the loss of their titles to land, joined the rebellious princes and the sepoys in large numbers.

It was obvious to the British that their strategy should be to fight westward, along the rivers Ganges and Jumna and along the Grand Trunk Road, until they could join up with the forces from the Punjab which were besieging Delhi. But their desire to regain Cawnpore and wreak vengeance on the rebels was immeasurably strengthened by the news of the massacre of British civilians which had taken place in the city. The garrison of about 1,000 under Sir Hugh Wheeler had been forced to surrender on 27 June 1857. Nana Sahib, who by now commanded the rebels, is supposed to have offered them a safe passage to Allahabad by boat, but apart from a few who escaped by water the British captives were mown down by the rebels. Later, a further 200 or more British civilians, the vast majority women and children, were slaughtered in a palace called the Bibighar. Their bodies were thrown down a well. The British blamed the incident on Nana Sahib and his lieutenant Tantia Topi, but it seems likely that mob vengeance, a blind desire to efface everything and everyone associated with foreign rule, played its part. At any event the vengeance exacted by Colonel Neill's returning armies was no less savage.

Cawnpore had a larger than usual number of British residents in 1857 because it was a major up-country bulking point for the river trade along the Ganges. It received cotton and oil seed from central India, and many firms with interests in Awadh were also based here. It seems that Indian society had been more radically disrupted here than around older centres of population such as Benares or Agra. Rights to land in the district had fallen into the hands of 'new men', bankers and former Awadh courtiers; there was also a large population of day labourers and artisans subsisting on fluctuating wages. Cawnpore had long been called the 'Alsatia' of north India, a reference to its rootlessness, and this perhaps helps to explain the violence and savagery of the outbreak.

Marochetti's memorial to the dead of the massacre (no.323) reads simply that the monument is 'sacred to the perpetual memory of a great company of Christian people, chiefly women and children. These are they that have come out of great tribulation'. General Havelock's column reached the city just too late to prevent the murder of those civilians who had survived the earlier massacre on the river. C.A.B.

322

322 Cawnpore, the scene of the massacre with men of the Bengal European Regiment

E. Walker after Lieutenant W.G. Sankey, 1857
Chromolithograph, 35 × 48.3 (13 3/5 × 18 4/5)
Lent by permission of The Director, National Army Museum, London SW3 4HT (6312–196–10)

This is one of a pair of prints on the subject of the massacre at Cawnpore, published by Day & Son, 10 June 1858.

B.A.

PROVENANCE: Parker Gallery, 1963.

323

323 Memorial well, Cawnpore

Bourne & Shepherd, *c.*1864
Photograph from album, 24 × 45.72 (9 5/8 × 17 7/8)
Royal Commonwealth Society Library (Y3022D/36 1206)

324

324 Miss Wheeler defending herself against the sepoys at Cawnpore

Copyprint after illustration in *The Narrative of the Indian Revolt* from the National Army Museum, London

325 In Memoriam

Sir Joseph Noel Paton R.S.A., 1858
Oil on panel, 123 × 96.5 (48½ × 38)
Signed and dated with monogram: *JNP 18–58*
Private Collection

The letter-press on W.H. Simmons' engraving after this work, published in 1862, reveals that this picture was 'Designed to Commemorate the Christian Heroism of the British Ladies in India during the Mutiny of 1857, and their ultimate Deliverance by British Prowess'.

This picture was one of the most contentious works exhibited at the Royal Academy in the nineteenth century. The critic of the *Illustrated London News* thought the picture 'too revolting for further description ... which ought not to have been hung, and in justice to the hanging committee, we believe that it was not done so without considerable compunction and hesitation'.

Paton's composition, derived from Renaissance prototypes, recalled Christian martyrdom scenes with its figures turning eyes to heaven in prayer. Paton inscribed on the picture frame the words of the 23rd Psalm, 'Yea though I walk through the Valley of the Shadow of Death; Yet thou art with me'. This deliberately reverential air stirred mixed emotions in the reviewer for *The Critic*, who considered *In Memoriam* 'one of those sacred subjects before which we stand not to criticise, but to solemnly meditate. We feel it almost a profanation to hang this picture in a show-room, it should have a chapel to itself.'

The picture was felt to be offensive by so many viewers at the Academy in 1858 that Paton was persuaded to make changes. In the original version 'maddened Sepoys, hot after blood', as *The Times* put it, were bursting through the door. In their place Paton painted Highland soldiers entering the room to rescue the women and children. Clearly the imagery of white women in the clutches of black soldiers challenged long-established taboos and, as Joan Hichberger has recently put it, 'For the wider public Paton decided to sacrifice the martyrdom aspect so as not to disrupt the mythology of white women as inviolable and remote from the male world of war and insurrection' (1988). B.A.

325

PROVENANCE: Alexander Hill, 1858–67; Mrs Whitelaw, 1888; Alexander Whitelaw, 1911.

LITERATURE: *Art Journal*, 1 June 1858, p.169; *The Illustrated London News*, 15 May 1858, p.498; *The Times*, 1 May 1858, p.5; *The Critic*, 15 May 1958, p.235; Beck 1973, p.61, no.31 (engr. ill.); Wood 1976, p.234, pl.250 (engr. ill.); Hichberger 1988, pp.174–175.

EXHIBITIONS: London, Royal Academy of Arts, 1858 (471); Edinburgh, Royal Scottish Academy 1859 (146); Glasgow, International Exhibition, 1888 (313); Glasgow, Scottish National Exhibition, 1911 (243).

326 Sir Henry Havelock (1775–1857)

A.H. Ritchie, 1857, published in *The Albion*, New York, 1859
Engraving, 67.7 × 48 (26½ × 18¾)
Lent by permission of The Director, National Army Museum, London SW3 4HT (7403–41)

More than any other 'Mutiny' general, Havelock was responsible for holding the British position against the rebels,

326

and for the success of the eventual riposte against them. He was born in Sunderland, the son of a wealthy shipbuilder. After abortive legal studies he entered the army in the 95th Rifle Brigade, but in 1823 followed his brothers Charles and William to India, transferring to the 13th Light Infantry.

327

He saw service in the Burma War, in Afghanistan in 1841 and in the Sikh campaigns of the later 1840s. He was unusual for his mastery of oriental languages. Mobilized in 1856 for a war with Persia that never materialized, Havelock was diverted to command a column which was to fight through the heart of rebel territory, 'to quell disturbances in Allahabad, to support Lawrence in Lucknow and Wheeler at Cawnpore, to disperse and utterly destroy all mutineers and insurgents'. Lady Canning, the Governor-General's wife, recorded of this appointment, 'General Havelock is not in fashion, but all the same we believe he will do well. No doubt he is fussy and tiresome, but his little old stiff figure looks as active and fit for use as if it were made of steel'. He fought as far as Cawnpore, which he took, but was twice turned back from relieving Lucknow as his men were wasted by disease and guerrilla warfare. Reinforced by Outram's troops, he finally took the city on 25 September 1857, but died of dysentery and exhaustion on 24 November. He was posthumously honoured by Parliament and his statue stands in the Embankment Gardens, London. C.A.B.

PROVENANCE: Suckling & Co., 1974.

LITERATURE: Kaye 1867.

327 Havelock's column attacking the mutineers before Cawnpore

Illustration from Charles Ball, *History of the Indian Mutiny*, 2 vols., London, n.d.
Steel engraving, 18 × 26.9 (7 × 10½)
Lent by permission of The Director, National Army Museum, London SW3 4HT (6110–52)

PROVENANCE: Hubert French, 1961.

328 Eastward Ho! August 1857

Henry Nelson O'Neil, 1858
Oil on canvas, 135.9 × 108 (53½ × 42½)
Elton Hall Collection

As Rosemary Treble pointed out in an excellent entry on this picture in *Great Victorian Pictures*, the British public responded with patriotic fervour to O'Neil's scene of soldiers departing from their families. The picture was immediately successful as the artist exploited the emotions roused by the publication, in cheap pamphlets and prints, of lurid details of the massacres in India. O'Neil used a dockside farewell, familiar in emigration scenes, rather than an Indian setting like Paton's *In Memoriam* (no.325), also exhibited for the first time at the Royal Academy exhibition of 1858. The only specific reference to the Rebellion is in the picture's title.

Contemporary critics found much to admire. *The Athenaeum*'s critic concluded his comments by remarking, 'The grief is wonderfully varied, and is always concentrated, deep and without self-consciousness. The straining, longing eye of the poor wife and the entranced, heedless sorrow of the widow will live with us many a day'.

O'Neil's sequel, *Home Again 1858*, exhibited the following year, was not greeted with the same critical acclaim but the engraving after *Eastward Ho!* by William Turner Davey, published in September 1860, was hugely successful and by the time the picture was exhibited again in London at the *International Exhibition* in 1862 it was already one of the best known works of the century.

The author of a review of the 1862 exhibition described O'Neil's art as 'emphatically English ... because we in England are daily making ourselves a contemporary history. ... Britain is a land of action and of progress, trade, commerce, growing wealth, steadfast yet ever changeful liberty; a land and a people wherein a contemporary Art may grow and live, because in this actual present hour we act heroically, suffer manfully and do those deeds which by a picture and by poems, deserve to be recorded!' B.A.

PROVENANCE: Edward Aldam Leatham, MP by 1862; his sale, Christie's 18th May 1901 (134), bt. Lister for William Proby, 5th Earl of Carysfort; by descent to the present owner.

LITERATURE: *The Times*, 1 May 1858, p.5; *The Athenaeum*, 8 May 1858, p.596; *The Times*, 22 May 1858, p.9; *The Critic*, 29 May 1858, p.258; *The Art Journal*, 1 June 1858, p.168; *The Art Journal*, July 1862, p.151; *The Art Journal*, February 1864, p.40; *Gazette des Beaux-Arts*, 1 September 1867, pp.214–215; Chesnau 1885, pp.273–6; *A Catalogue of the Pictures at Elton Hall*, 1924, p.99; Reynolds 1953, p.86, fig.69; Reynolds 1966, p.29; Beck 1973, pp.36, 60; Wood 1976, pp.224–5.

EXHIBITIONS: London, Royal Academy, 1858 (384); London, *International Exhibition*, 1862 (607); Paris, *Exposition Universelle*, 1867 (88); London, Guildhall, 1895 (16); London, Royal Academy, *The First Hundred Years of the Royal Academy*, 1951–52 (356); London, Royal Academy, *Great Victorian Pictures – their paths to Fame*, 1978 (40), p.62–3.

329 Brigadier General James Neill (1810–57) in a frock coat

Copyprint after a calotype print from an album compiled by Surgeon John MacCosh from the National Army Museum, London (6204–3)

329

Neill was, and remains, the most controversial of the 'Mutiny' generals. Born in Ayr, he attended Glasgow University and entered the East India Company's service in 1827. From 1828 to 1852 he carried out local duties with the 1st Madras Europeans, but in 1852 he served with distinction in the Burma War and then in 1855 undertook the reform and discipline of the Turkish contingent which was raised for the Crimean War. In 1857 Neill reacted with remarkable speed to the news of the outbreak of the mutinies in north India. He marched his forces north from Calcutta and by 4 June 1857 had completely crushed all signs of revolt in the critical station of Benares, which hereafter became the forward base for the operations against Allahabad and Lucknow. He then moved to Allahabad (the 'most precious [fortress] in India at the moment', as Canning put it) and thrust against Cawnpore, completely destroying the rebels and taking severe reprisals against dissident villages on the way. At Cawnpore 'while the traces of the massacre were yet fresh, Neill inflicted the death penalty on all his prisoners with the most merciless rigour'. Neill went on openly to criticize his commanding officer, Havelock, for falling back in the relief of Lucknow. Nevertheless, he was given a brigade command and led the attack during the final assault on the city. He was killed by a bullet as the assault was driven home. C.A.B.

LITERATURE: Kaye 1867.

330 Defence of Arrah House against a large body of insurgents under Koer Singh

After W. Taylor, 1857
Colour lithograph, 34.3 × 50.7 ($13\frac{1}{2} \times 19\frac{3}{4}$)
Lent by permission of The Director, National Army Museum, London SW3 4HT (7102–33–40)

Koer, or Kunwar, Singh was one of the most important of the rebel leaders in Bihar and the Benares borderlands to the east of the main areas of revolt. On the 25 July 1857 the disarming of recalcitrant sepoys at Dinapur near Patna went disastrously wrong. The sepoys broke out and fled to the jungles around Arrah in the Shahabad district where they were rallied by Koer Singh, a Rajput, who is said to have concerted a plan for the rout of the British in Bihar at the Sonepur festival (no.286). The astute old warrior ambushed and decimated a large force of Sikhs and Europeans who were in pursuit of the mutineers. Despite the successful defence of Arrah House, in which the Europeans had taken shelter, this sent a shock wave down the Grand Trunk Road and seemed to threaten the British with revolt along the whole southern flank of their main lines of communication. For nearly two years the struggle continued in central India, where Koer Singh and other guerrilla leaders launched hit-and-run campaigns against the slowly gathering British strength. The fatal weakness of the rebels was that they were unable to move over to the defensive and break decisively the British line of communications up river and along the Grand Trunk Road. Their lack of artillery and officers condemned them to local fire-fighting and ambush.

C.A.B.

LITERATURE: Stokes 1986.

331 Durbar of Scindia, Maharaja of Gwalior

Copyprint after photograph (*c.*1857) in the National Portrait Gallery

331

The photograph shows Maharaja Jayaji Rao Scindia (Shinde) in his durbar. It is interesting to compare this with Mabon's sketch of the same court under Mahadji, Jayaji's illustrious forebear, who founded the state in the late eighteenth century (no.91). The revolt of most of the citizens and chiefs of Gwalior on 1 June 1858 was embarrassing for the British. Militarily, the great fortress of Gwalior was one of the most important in central India. Politically, Gwalior was thought to be a model state, for its *diwan*, Sir Dinkar Rao, had been introducing modern reforms there from 1852. But the social changes which such reforms unleashed may have added fuel to the fire of revolt which had been set alight by Nana Sahib's call to restore the Peshwaship and the Maratha states. One of Tantia Topi's agents recorded that 'Scindia being one with the English, does not regard the Peishwa. His Raj is great. Seeing his course, all the rajas, great and small are cowed, and side with the English. On account of him we have not been able to get any opportunity. Wherefore we must first gain his troops, and get him into our hands, when the Peishwa shall rule' (*Freedom Struggle*, iii, 445). Scindia fled to Gwalior as Tantia Topi and the Rani of Jhansi took the city, but he was later restored on 20 June by Sir Hugh Rose. He was handsomely rewarded by the Government, later becoming a Counsellor of the Queen-Empress and Commander of the Indian Empire. He died in 1886.

C.A.B.

PROVENANCE: Given by Professor Robert Frykenberg, 1990.

332 Nana Sahib, Indian hero of the revolt†

Contemporary oleograph, 50.8 × 38.1 (20 × 15) National Portrait Gallery, London

333

Nana Sahib, heir of Peshwa Baji Rao II, was properly called Dhondu Pant. Living in exile from his native Poona on his estate at Bithur, he seemed well disposed to the large European population of the nearby station of Cawnpore. He was educated and well connected with missionaries, so much so that a military man was heard to remark a few years later that 'we taught the Nana to read French novels and he still cut our throats'. For Nana Sahib deeply resented the loss not only of his ancestors' kingdom but also the *jagir* (revenue-free land rights), which the British Government had discontinued after the death of Baji Rao in 1853. When the Cawnpore sepoys revolted, Nana Sahib declared himself Peshwa. Large numbers of Marathas, including the Rani of Jhansi, accepted his leadership, while even Muslims such as the Nawab of Banda accepted his suzerainty. He attempted to forge alliances outside the region, sending ambassadors to Lucknow, the hill state of Jammu and even to Russia (which immediately rejected his advances). But despite Nana's extirpation of British influence and personnel in the Cawnpore region, the officer-less sepoys could never hold Havelock's thrust up the Grand Trunk Road, which was supported by gunboats on the river and rapidly developing logistical support. Nana fled before Cawnpore, escaping to the Terai and Nepal where he is thought to have died some years later. C.A.B.

LITERATURE: Rizvi and Bhargava 1959, iii, pp.529–30.

333 Tantia Topi awaiting execution

Copyprint after photograph in the Nehru Memorial Museum and Library, New Delhi

Tantia Topi ('Daddy' Topi was a family name) was the most resourceful of all the Nana Sahib's commanders and the one the British found most cunning and elusive. His real name was Ramchandra, son of Panda Rang. A Deshashta Brahmin from the Poona region, he had served as Superintendent of the Kitchens at Bithur. Called by the British 'the soul of the Nana's cause', he helped organize the rebel government at Cawnpore and made contact with the Rani of Jhansi. He was also implicated in the massacre of British civilians at Cawnpore. Following the loss of the city, he moved south and led the defence of Jhansi against Sir Hugh Rose (no.334) in April 1858. He administered Gwalior in the name of the Peshwa (Nana Sahib) and led its final defence along with the Rani of Jhansi (no.334). Tantia Topi 'fought like a Mahratta' (no.90), moving rapidly across the country and mounting guerrilla ambushes, but in April 1859 he was eventually captured and hanged by the British after a drumhead trial.

C.A.B.

LITERATURE: Rizvi and Bhargava 1959, iii, pp.565–82.

334(i)

334(ii)

334(i) Rani Lakshmi Bai of Jhansi

*c.*1930
Bazaar oleograph, 50.8 × 38.1 (20 × 15)
National Portrait Gallery, London

334(ii) Rani Lakshmi Bai of Jhansi

Unknown artist, Kalighat, *c.* 1890
Watercolour and silver on paper, 43.5 × 27.5 (17 × 10¾)
India Office Library and Records (Add. Or. 1896)

The Rani of Jhansi, India's 'Joan of Arc', became an embodiment of female resistance and sacrifice in the service of the nation. Jhansi was a Maratha state, set in the midst of a countryside controlled by Bundela Rajputs. In 1817 the Peshwa ceded all rights over the Bundelkhand area to the British Government, but the little state continued to exist until 1853 when the incumbent Raja died childless. Under Dalhousie's 'doctrine of lapse', the kingdom then escheated to the Company; but this was contested by his widow, the Rani, and by Indian custom which allowed the royal family to adopt an heir. The Rani appealed, in vain, to the Company and her plaints were given an edge by popular hostility to changes wrought by the increased British presence, particularly by the slaughter of sacred cattle. In the summer of 1857 mutinies broke out at both Jhansi and nearby Gwalior, one of the key fortresses of central India, and soon much of the country was up in arms. The Rani, fighting alongside Tantia Topi, valiantly defended both cities but was killed in action near the Phul Bagh cantonement at Gwalior in June 1858. The British Political Agent recorded that she was overtaken resting and drinking sherbet near the Phul Bagh batteries. All but fifteen of the rebels escaped but 'The Ranee's horse refused to leap the canal, when she received a shot in the side and then a sabre cut on the head, but rode off. She soon after fell dead and was burnt in a garden close by

... The rebels were deeply dispirited by the Rani's death' (cited Rizvi and Bhargava 1959, iii, pp.462–3).

As the Kalighat painting (no.334(ii); for Kalighat see no.401) shows, the Rani quickly became a cult heroine. She combined the female power of the active goddess (*shakti*) with the virtue of self-sacrifice associated with the medieval Rajput heroines who committed *sati* after defeat. Indian nationalists quickly took her up as a symbol of armed resistance to British rule, even though her own motives appear to have been patriotic defence of her dynasty's honour rather than any clear concept of Indian nationality. During the so-called extremist phase of Indian political activity from 1905 to 1910 her image was taken out on floats during the Ramlila festival to the irritation of the British police. C.A.B.

LITERATURE: Savarkar 1909.

War Correspondents and Artists

335(i) Under the Tope

335(ii) Sick and wounded in Doolies

335(iii) My Gharee

Copyprints after illustrations by Egron Lundgren from *My Diary in India in the Year 1858–9* by W.H. Russell in a private collection

In addition to the rash of memoirs and biographies of the British soldiers and civilians who were caught up in the Rebellion, newspapers played a more important part than ever in informing the public in Britain. After the Crimean War, the 'Mutiny' was the second major British conflict in which the war correspondent, the war artist and the photograph moulded public opinion. The results were more ambiguous than those which had been produced by amateur artists and history painters at the time of the conflicts with the Marathas and Tipu Sultan. W.H. Russell (1821–1907), *The Times* war correspondent who dominated the columns between 1850 and 1890, was often a harsh critic of military incompetence and brutality. He was born near Dublin and educated at Trinity College. His journalistic career effectively began when *The Times* used him to report O'Connell's political campaigns in Ireland. In 1849–50 he reported on the Danish war and thereafter he was present at practically every major conflict: the Crimea, the Indian Rebellion, the Franco-Prussian War of 1870, the Battle of Bull Run during the American Civil War, and Lord Wolseley's Egyptian campaign of 1882. He founded the *Army and Navy Gazette*.

In India he was attached to the Headquarters of Lord Clyde (Colin Campbell) and was present at the final capture of Lucknow and various battles in the western region of revolt. He was awarded the Rebellion war medal with the Lucknow clasp. Russell was less critical of military failings than he had been during the Crimean War, but his despatches carried the full horror of the war and its impact on British and Indian civilians quite impartially. Along with Disraeli, he argued from the beginning that the Rebellion was a mass rising against an unpopular foreign rule, rather than a simple military debacle. He was critical of the 'prize agents', who looted and tortured in Delhi in order to accumulate the largest possible provision of booty for the army which had captured the city.

This dispassionate and humane view of the war was shared by the Swedish artist Egron Lundgren (1815–75), whose sketches illustrated the published version of Russell's diary and despatches. A widely-travelled genre painter, Lundgren studied in Stockholm and Paris; in 1852 he came to England, where he was commissioned by Queen Victoria to make illustrations of court festivals. Lundgren visited India in 1858. He distanced himself from the sentimental, nationalistic and melodramatic types of art which characterized the war and chose instead to depict the victims of war, the wounded and the prisoners.

C.A.B.

336 The Relief of Lucknow, 1857

Thomas Jones Barker, 1859
Oil on canvas, 105.4 × 181.3 ($41\frac{1}{2} \times 71\frac{3}{8}$)
Signed and dated 1859
National Portrait Gallery, London (5851)

At Lucknow, Sir Henry Lawrence, who had become Chief Commissioner of Awadh, retired with all the European and Christian population into the heavily fortified British Residency, guarded by a small force of loyal sepoys. Lawrence himself was killed early in the siege and Brigadier Inglis took over command. Resourceful and gallant defence preserved the Residency until 25 September when Outram and Havelock (no.326) stormed their way through and reinforced the depleted garrison. Their small force had thrust up into Awadh, fighting sepoys who had returned to their villages and the heavily-armed *zamindars* and peasants along the whole route. Finally in mid-November, Colin Campbell, who had been sent from England to take over as Commander-in-Chief, conducted the exhausted garrison out of the city. It was not finally reoccupied until March 1858. The defence and relief of the Lucknow Residency became, understandably, a famous episode in British military annals. But the war in Awadh was something of a sideshow. The critical issue was control of the key routes from Calcutta to Delhi – the River Ganges and the Grand Trunk Road. The rebels failed because they were unable to sever the arteries of British power.

The Union Jack flew over the ruins of the Residency until midnight on the day of Indian Independence. It has since

336

been replaced by a plaque commemorating the thousands of Indians who died in the siege, trying to free their country from foreign rule.

This is one of two versions of the subject painted by Thomas Barker. The larger version (274.3 × 482.6) was originally in the Glasgow Museum and Art Gallery but was irreparably damaged during an air-raid in the Second World War. Both versions were based on sketches made by the Swedish artist Egron Lundgren (see no.335), the only European artist in India during the Rebellion. The dealers Agnews, in their capacity as print publishers, realized that it was impossible to despatch an artist to India and expect him to produce a painting quickly enough to exploit topical interest; so they purchased hundreds of Lundgren's sketches and made them available to Barker. The larger of the two versions was exhibited at Agnews' gallery in 1860, presumably to prompt sales of the engraving by C.G. Lewis.

The picture portrays the encounter between the three most popular heroes of the campaign, Colin Campbell, Sir James Outram and General Sir Henry Havelock. C.A.B./B.A.

PROVENANCE: Sir Ernest Davis; Lion Breweries Ltd; anon. sale, Sotheby's, 18 June 1975 (16); purchased by National Portrait Gallery.

LITERATURE: *Art Journal*, 1860, p.184; *National Portrait Gallery: Illustrated Report and List of Acquisitions 1985–6*, pp.18–19, ill. fig.9; Hichberger 1988, p.61–2.

337 The new Nussaree Battalion, a Gurkha battalion raised in 1830 and disbanded after the Mutiny

Copyprint after photograph in the National Army Museum, London (5909–109)

337

338

339

338 The 22nd Madras Native Infantry preparing to move from Vellore

Captain F. Bannerman-Philips, 1855
Watercolour, 46 × 69 (18 × 69⅕)
Lent by permission of The Director, National Army Museum, London SW3 4HT (Prints 5011–12)

Both nos. 337 and 338 illustrate the strength with which the British faced the Rebellion of 1857. The Madras army was tightly and efficiently controlled after the debacle of the Vellore Mutiny of 1806. It proved thoroughly reliable in 1857 and under Neill it played an important part in securing Benares as a forward post on the Ganges. The British could also count on the Sikh troops who had been recruited after the annexation of the Punjab with the promise of good conditions (see no.207). Troops recruited from outside the traditional areas of south Awadh and the Benares region, notably the Gurkhas, were also of vital importance. They had little sympathy with the old sepoy force. Finally, the British were lucky enough to be able to divert fresh European troops from an expeditionary force to China, and so reinforce their position in Bengal soon after the Rebellion broke out. C.A.B.

PROVENANCE: Miss E.I.A. Bannerman-Philips, 1950.

EXHIBITION: London, National Army Museum, *The Armies of India*, 1987.

339 Indian Mutiny medal awarded to Major Sir E.R. Wetherall

Lent by permission of the Director, National Army Museum, London SW3 4HT (7912–88–4)

340

340 The Battle March

*c.*1859
Sheet music, 35.5 × 30.5 (14 × 12)
Private Collection

The Rebellion and its suppression raised a patriotic wave in Great Britain unlike any that had been associated with India since the defeat of Tipu Sultan. Vast numbers of publications appeared and there were celebrations, awards and benefits for the returning military. This medley of popular airs starts with *The Clock Strikes on the Moghul's Palace* and proceeds through *The Mutineers are Disturbed by the Approach of British Cavalry* to *Hail, the Conquering Hero* and *The British Grenadiers*. C.A.B.

SECTION III

THE VICTORIAN RAJ AND THE RISE OF NATIONALISM

1858–1914

Colonial Anthropology in the 'Laboratory of Mankind'

CHRISTOPHER PINNEY

Fig. 27 An Ooria or Orissa Brahmin; from *The Costumes of Hindoostan. Elucidated by Sixty Coloured Engravings with the Descriptions in English and French, Taken in the Years 1798 and 1799* by Balt Solvyns, 1807

The Western spirit of enquiry known as anthropology can trace its curiosity towards India at least as far back as Megasthenes.[1] Two thousand years later one might see a visual anthropological impulse in the representations by those such as De Bry and Picart of India in the sixteenth, seventeenth and eighteenth centuries (Cohn, n.d). Likewise, the many sets of paintings in the Company School style of castes and occupations which travellers and residents collected from the mid-eighteenth century (see no.341), or compendia such as Balt Solvyns's *The Costumes of Hindoostan* (1807; Fig. 27) or *Les Hindous* (1811) may also be seen as early precursors of what, by the middle of the nineteenth century, had become a recognizably 'anthropological' concern. These all constitute early forms of anthropological collection and description.

By the mid-nineteenth century, however, anthropology, as it was brought to bear upon India, was distinguished from its earlier incarnations by two important factors: its organization and regulation within the framework of learned societies[2] and its increasing concern with the veracity and reliability of its observations and comparisons. This increasing systematization coincided with the general introduction of photography, whose history was significantly to parallel that of anthropology, and indeed one can see in the processes of this new technology a kind of metaphor for a new, more rigorous form of knowledge about distant peoples and objects. Anthropology found in life casts (no.344), photography and the 'impartial' measurements of what was known as 'anthropometry' apparently objective guarantees of truth on which it later modelled a whole theory of fieldwork.[3] Such representations, with their causal and material connections to the information they conveyed,[4] were to serve as transmitters of unimpeachable signs from the 'laboratory of mankind', as the Indian Empire soon became[5] (see Fig. 28).

Although some scholars have suggested that the history of anthropology in India may be divided into three stages (Vidyarthi 1977; Sinha 1968), for our purposes it is useful to make a crude distinction between an early form of anthropology chiefly concerned with establishing a framework of certainty within which all the peoples of India might be understood and assigned a position, and a more recognizably modern form which from about 1900 onwards focused increasingly on very detailed small-scale studies of social and cultural organization.

The colonial search for order

One powerful nineteenth-century impulse was the desire to establish order.

India, as it was viewed by the traveller, administrator and anthropologist, presented, paradoxically, both a confusion and a clarity of vision: a variety and a singularity, a kaleidoscope which eventually dissolved into meaningful order. Anthropology, particularly in its earlier 'physical' form (from which modern 'social' anthropology has consciously distanced itself) provided a means of comprehending this paradox, in which the initial bewilderment created by the variety of social groups in India gave way to a reassuring certainty that they were all identifiably distinct elements which could be arranged legibly and clearly in the 'living museum of mankind'.[6]

The paradox lay in the initial apprehension that India was composed of such variety that only confusion could result.[7] There is a hint of this in the painter and humorist Edward Lear's first reaction on landing in Bombay in 1873: 'Anything more overpoweringly amazing cannot be conceived. Colours and costumes and myriadism of impossible picturesqueness' (Lear 1953, p. 37). But within this variety and difference lay a certainty with which nineteenth-century anthropology was to become particularly concerned. This was also mirrored in popular texts such as John Oliver Hobbes's *Imperial India: Letters from the East* which described 'those brilliant moments when one unforgettable impression succeeded another ... (the light of the East makes every scene a permanent silhouette in one's mind – nothing here is elusive) – I saw for me, a whole continent revealed' (1903, p. 6). For the nineteenth-century anthropologist also, India was a place in which, after the initial confusion, nothing was elusive. Indeed, in the biological and racial theory of the time it was precisely in the confusing variety that certainty lay.

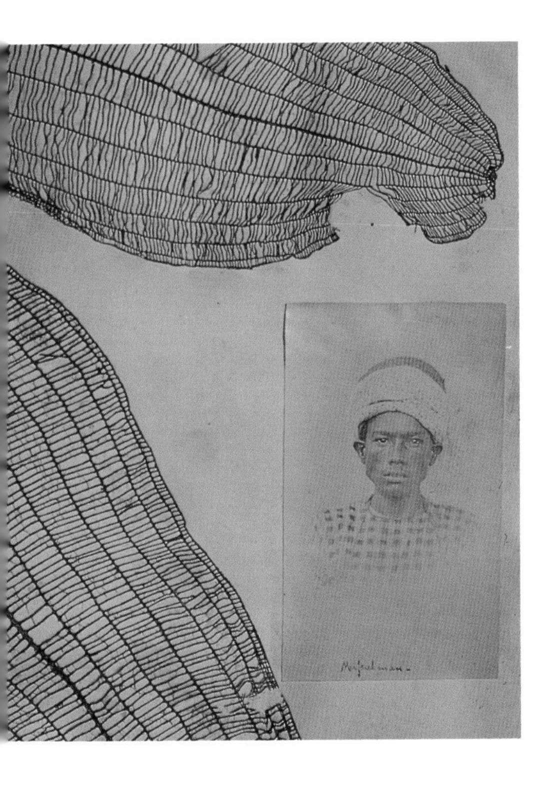

Fig. 28 Mufsalman (Muslim); carte-de-visite albumen print and dried skeletons of leaves from an album of 'types', *c.* 1870s (Museum of Mankind, London). The albumen print functions as a trace, or material vestige, like the leaf-skeletons.

For most Victorians, each person literally embodied his or her racial and cultural identity.[8] Within anthropology a central concern was to establish through the study of physical characteristics the connections between the 'great families of mankind' (Risley 1915, p. 6). The ultimate goal of anthropology at this time was the discovery of the origins and movements of peoples through history, a concern which in India assumed a particular resonance after Sir William Jones's discovery at the end of the eighteenth century of an Indo-European language affinity which encompassed both Britain and India.[9] One hundred years later this was to enable Max Müller to remind the Indian Civil Service candidate in 1882 that his heart should not sink when approaching the shores of India, for he was 'going to his "old home", full of memories, if only he can read them' (1919, p. 32).

For the anthropologist the route to establishing this genealogy lay in the study of actual physical characteristics: 'Physical characters are the best, in fact the only true tests of race, that is of real affinity; language, customs etc, may help or give indications, but they are often misleading' (William Flower, cited by Risley 1915, p. 6). India was to prove particularly attractive in this respect because the initial variety concealed groups of what appeared to be endogamous[10] castes in which physical characteristics marked cultural differences. The variety of what became known as 'types' was held, at least by the school which had by the end of the century become a virtual orthodoxy, to be the result of a pattern of strict marriage within castes. According to this theory, castes were 'races', separate populations within the population. This mapping of culture within physiology also perfectly suited the administrators' drive to erect a framework of categories which allowed him to understand India in terms of a hierarchy of castes which had discernible features and definable limits, and eventually a fully documented set of material objects, behaviour patterns and political loyalties:

> ... a caste was a 'thing', an entity, which was concrete and measurable, above all it had definable characteristics – endogamy, commensality rules, fixed occupation, common ritual practices. These were things which supposedly one could find out by sending assistants into the field with a questionaire and which could be quantified for reports and surveys; or one could learn about the castes of a particular district by sitting on one's horse or in the shade of the village banyan tree as an adjunct to one's official duty (Cohn 1968, p. 15).[11]

Fig. 29 Khan Mahomed, embroiderer (prize Medallist 1862), Mussulman, Sind; albumen print by Houghton and Tanner (Asiatic Society of Bombay; no.346[v])

The People of India

It is perhaps not too fanciful to see in representations of Tipu Sultan's death,[12] such as the paintings by Devis (no. 169) and Wilkie (Fig. 13) the establishment of a framework for the inspection of the bodies of Indians by an imperial power. Within its later 'academic', anthropological idiom, the surface of the body, rather than marking the end of political resistance (as in the case of Tipu's corpse) served as the object of a theoretical concern, for the bringing to bear of the force of knowledge upon Indians.

If the representation of Tipu's death did indeed establish the frame for the ensuing objectification of Indians, then one can perhaps see the huge photographic project *The People of India* as the second landmark in the development of this Western scientific – and aesthetic – discourse about the inhabitants of India. In 1856 Rev. Joseph Mullins had proposed to the Photographic Society of Bengal that photography should be used to capture 'all the minute varieties of Oriental life' (cited in Falconer n.d., p. 16) and in many ways *The People of India* is simply a technological incarnation of much earlier collections such as Solvyns, the 'para-ethnography'[13] of Company Style paintings of occupations and other popular representations. But *The People of India* also marks one stage in the transformation of such curiosity into a structured framework – the sort of 'grid' to be found in museums and exhibitions – in which the judgements and disciplines of scientific theory and the state were imposed.[14] *The People of India*, which was initiated by an informal request by the then Governor-General Canning, to civilians and army officers for souvenirs of India (Desmond 1982, p. 36; Thomas 1980, p. 48), was transformed by the Indian Rebellion of 1857 into an official project of the Political and Secret Department (who were to retain half of all the sets of eight volumes published between 1868 and 1875 [no.346] for official use). It used a mixture of photographs taken by amateurs and the early products of the army's recent policy of using the camera in survey work, for example Lieutenant Tanner and Captain Houghton's Sind photographs of 1861–2[15] (Fig. 29). The moral preoccupations of an earlier period are occasionally apparent, but in general it is hierarchical observation and normalizing judgement which predominates as castes and tribes are described in terms of their administrative complexities. One can trace here in its descriptions of 'marauding frontier tribes' and the 'lawlessness' of various caste groups an intensification in official thinking on the convergence of ethnic identity and the potential for disorder which was to reach its fruition in the Criminal Tribes Act of 1871.[16]

Three years before the first volume of *The People of India* appeared Dr Joseph Fayrer[17] had proposed that the Asiatic Society of Bengal should organize an ethnological exhibition 'with typical examples of the races of the old world'. He further suggested that the exhibits be classified according to races and tribes and 'should sit each in his own stall, should receive and converse with the Public, and submit to be photographed, painted, taken off in casts and otherwise reasonably dealt with in the interests of science' (*Proceedings of Asiatic Society of Bengal*, 1867, p. 90). Although such an exhibition was not held, Fayrer was expressing what was to become the dominant museological mode of looking at India. This stressed the discrete and describable nature of India as an aggregate of things which could be understood through strategies of 'typicality' (see no.376), 'miniaturization' (see no.365) and, above all, 'display' with its continual assumption of knowledge to be gained through visibility.[18] Information about people, caste, dress, ritual belief and material culture could all be arranged within grids which could be substituted one for another.

Occasionally all these grids and structures of knowledge can be seen operating very closely together. This is clear in the case of the Victoria and Albert Museum in Byculla, Bombay, now known as the Dr Bhau Daji Lad Museum. Founded by George Birdwood in 1858,[19] the museum sought to incite 'amongst the masses habits of observation and taste for rational pleasures' (Birdwood 1864, p. 14). It displayed examples of 'Indian and Eastern commercial products', representative samples of India's natural history, and

Fig. 30 Contemporary display of nineteenth-century models of headwear in the Dr Bhau Daji Lad Museum, Bombay; photograph by Christopher Pinney, 1989

Fig. 31 Craftsman preparing clay models for a mythological panorama in the Dr Bhau Daji Lad Museum, Bombay; photograph, *c.*1890 (Dr Bhau Daji Lad Museum)

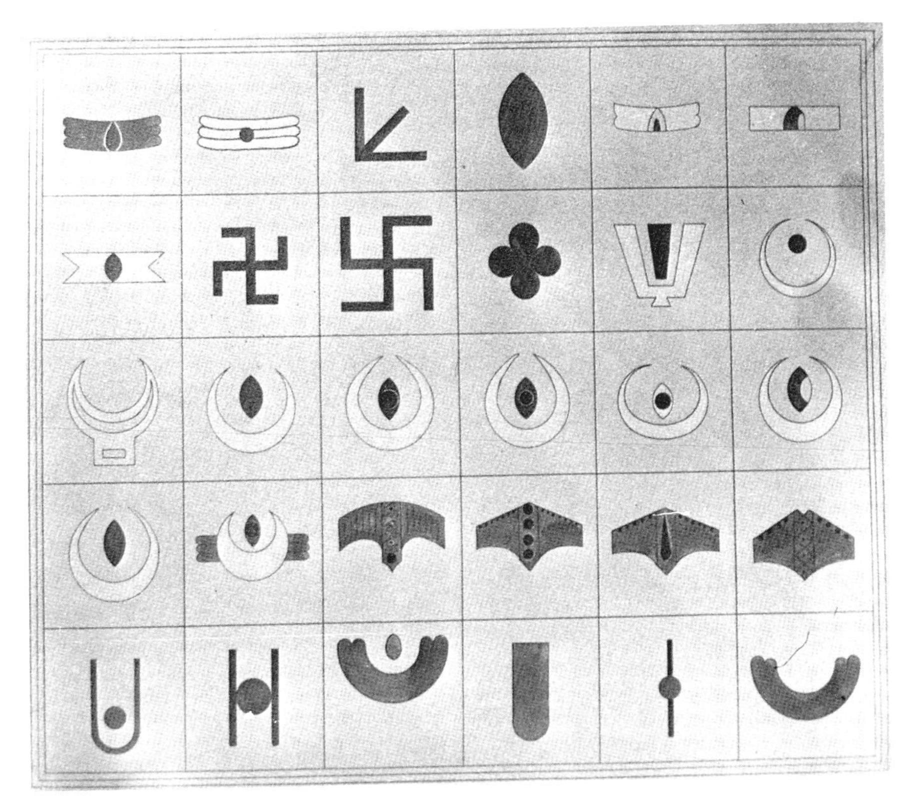

Fig. 32 Paintings of devotional and sectarian insignia; albumen print, *c.* 1880 (Dr Bhau Daji Lad Museum)

Fig. 33 Fisherman from Bandra (Salsette) and his wife in the Victoria Gardens, next to the Dr Bhau Daji Lad Museum; photograph collected by S. M. Edwardes for the 1911 census (Dr Bhau Daji Lad Museum)

exhibits relating to the human population of India. 'Types' were present in the form of small clay models, headwear was presented in ordered rows, and subjects ranging from 'caste' and sectarian insignia to the various postures of a yogi were subject to a similar inspection (Figs. 30, 31, 32). Next to the museum Birdwood planned a botanical garden in which representative samples of India's flora were similarly collected. Fifty years later this microcosm of Indian plant life was to provide the backdrop for a series of photographs of 'types' collected by S. M. Edwardes, Commissioner of the Bombay Police, in connection with the 1911 census[20] (Fig. 33).

Representations of caste 'types' pull in two apparently conflicting directions. One genre, the head and shoulders 'mugshot', can be seen to involve a denial of Indians' participation in productive activity. It has been pointed out that such a distancing of the 'other' from the material world was a recurrent feature of 'Orientalist' discourse and in the Indian context was part of a package which stressed the fundamentally religious nature of caste. However, parallel to this, Indians were represented as ontologically tied, or created through a series of material objects which specified their occupationally determined caste. This is apparent in the photographs used by Crooke (no.372) and that showing J. P. Wildeblood, a district engineer, with his wife and family servants grouped outside their home in Bareilly. The *dhobi* (laundryman) clutches his iron, the *mali* (gardener) holds a trowel, the *darzi* (tailor) sits behind his sewing machine and the cook holds a pot; in the inscription only the two dogs are named (Fig. 34).

It is tempting, though I suspect too simplistic, to see these two approaches as merely reflections of two different theoretical attitudes to caste during the nineteenth century (see below). This might see the mugshots as informed by Risley's genetic theory of caste, in which occupation was a mere incidental excrescence imposed on the more fundamental difference of blood, and those photographs which stress occupation and caste vocation as reflections of the theoretical approach developed by, for instance, Ibbetson, Nesfield and Crooke.

Administration and science

The work of Herbert Hope Risley, which constitutes the third moment in this brief narrative of colonial anthropology in India, makes explicit the conjunction of academia and the interests of the state and reveals most clearly the paradox, already alluded to, whereby diversity and difference guaranteed certainty in the analysis of the peoples of India. Risley was to dominate the anthropological study of India for twenty years from 1890 and held a number of important posts including Census Commissioner and Honorary Director of the Ethnological Survey of the Indian Empire (Crooke 1915, pp. xiii–xiv). He propounded a form of anthropology which was inseparable from administrative concerns, arguing that an ethnographic survey was as necessary as a cadastral (land registry) survey for the efficient administration of Bengal and that, because of the holistic and encompassing nature of 'Eastern society', it was impossible to define where administration ended and science began.[21]

Just as the rigid structure of authority within colonial India appealed to a class which was being displaced by the process of democratization in Britain

Fig. 34 J. P. Wildeblood and his household servants, Bareilly; albumen print, *c.* 1892 (Centre of South Asian Studies, University of Cambridge)

(Kiernan 1972, p. 37), so Risley's anthropology appeared to discover a comforting certainty grounded in difference which had all but disappeared in Europe. This was but one of several theories. Denzil Ibbetson, J. C. Nesfield and William Crooke, for instance, stressed the importance of occupation as 'the primary basis of caste' (Ibbetson, 1916, p. 3) and argued against the contention that 'caste is perpetual and immutable' (1916, p. 2).[22] However, it was Risley's 'biological' theory of caste, which stressed genetic difference, that held sway during the latter part of the nineteenth century and is preserved in the theoretical preambles to the Imperial Gazetteer and Indian Army Caste Handbooks.

According to Risley, where there was a 'national type' (as in the nation states of Europe), the genetic muddying of the population was such that constituent subtypes could no longer be discerned. India, by contrast, presented:

> ... a remarkable contrast to most other parts of the world, where anthropometry has to confess itself hindered, if not baffled, by the constant intermixture of types, obscuring the data ascertained by measurements. ... In India the process of fusion was long ago arrested ... There is consequently no national type, and no nation in the ordinary sense of the word (Risley 1909, p. 288).

The main conclusion to emerge from the vast array of statistics in Risley's *Tribes and Castes of Bengal* (1891) concerned the reliability of the 'nasal index' as a guide to the status of its owner. Whereas Ibbetson had stressed the fluidity of caste and other groupings in response to changing patterns of occupation and social mobility – he notes for instance that the 'ease with which' particular groups 'are manufactured is proverbial' (1916, p. 8) – Risley stresses the inscription of caste status in the permanent physical exteriors of Indians' bodies:

> If we take a series of castes ... and arrange them in order of the average nasal index, so that the caste with the finest nose shall be at the top, and that with the coarsest at the bottom of the list, it will be found that this order substantially corresponds with the accepted order of social procedure (Risley 1891, p. xxxiv).

This, if true, would have been of vital interest to the state since caste was not merely an index of status, but had (as *The People of India* argued) formed the basis of opposition to alien rule in 1857. To discover political allegiance so clearly mapped in the physiognomy of the citizen was an administrator's dream, a sociological form of fingerprinting – which itself had emerged several years earlier from Bengal (Herschel 1916). And each act of identification confirmed the apparently fragmented nature of Indian society and continued the displacement of the political resonances of Hindu social organization on to a 'biological' and 'ritual' notion of caste. This stress on 'multiple ethnicities' and the non-material aspects of Hindu society carried obvious benefits for the imperial society which produced this discourse, but it was also a set of ideas which was to some extent incorporated by Indians themselves in their own caste and ethnic representations and strategies (Washbrook 1982; O'Hanlon 1989, p. 102).[23]

Throughout the nineteenth century anthropological investigation relied on evidence which in semiotic terms is called 'indexical' – physical traces of the object under study, like the rings that cold glasses leave on tables (Krauss 1985, p. 31). This is evidenced in this exhibition in the Schlagintweit casts, photography and fingerprinting; and above all through anthropometry, which found in statistics transcribed from the outer physical forms of Indians an effacement of all subjectivity and unreliability. One school of anthropometry used a grid composed of silk threads hung on a wooden frame. This had been suggested by J. H. Lamprey of the Royal College of Surgeons in 1869 and would enable the peoples of the world to be compared with one another against this portable and reliable rule.[24] By 1890 Denzil Ibbetson, then President of the Anthropological Society of Bombay (and on this point at least, very much in agreement with Risley) was able to vouch for anthropology's indexical reliability in a talk on 'The Study of Anthropology in India'. He isolated physical measurements as the 'most valuable of all, because most trustworthy' and 'statements of undoubted fact':

> No one who has not made the attempt can well realise how difficult it is to secure a full and accurate statement of custom on any given point by verbal enquiry from Orientals and still more, from semi-savages. ... Cranial measurements, on the other hand, are probably almost absolutely free from the personal equation of the observer (1890, p. 121).

As the source of these diverse indexical traces, India became the testing ground of a Western science whose power lay in its ability to transform the wonder and dazzlement of travel accounts into the ordered, normalized and objective (Fig. 35).

Towards a 'social' anthropology

The early history of anthropology in India, as surveyed by this essay and the

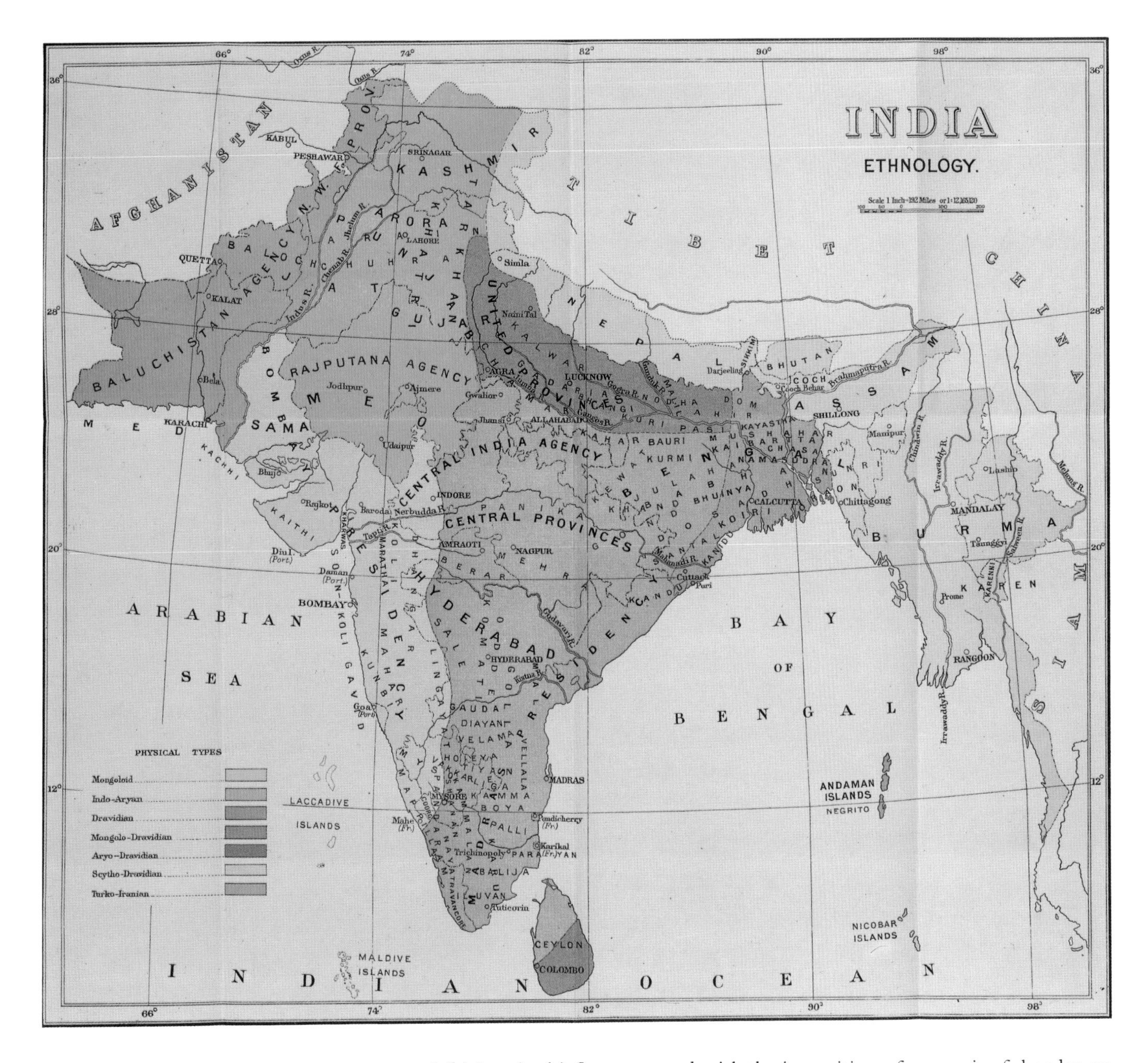

Fig. 35 Map illustrating Risley's classification of the peoples of India into seven 'types'; from *The People of India* by H. H. Risley, 1915

exhibition, is chiefly concerned with the imposition of a meaningful order on the apparent kaleidoscope of Indian society and with the determination of a hierarchy which would be of use to the administrators of the Raj. Within this alliance of anthropological and 'official' endeavour there was also room for the disinterested scholar, the Indophile, and figures such as Risley who had more direct contacts with the emerging anthropological 'establishment' in Britain (at one point he even temporarily persuaded Sir James Frazer to pay a brief visit to India[25]), but the intimacy of academic and administrative investigation is a recurrent feature of this period.

From the turn of the century this relationship certainly continues,[26] but the appearance of a professionalizing anthropology induces a shift in the focus of interest away from caste society and towards 'tribes'. This may have

Fig. 36 Christoph von Fürer-Haimendorf; bromide print, *c.* 1940 (Royal Anthropological Institute, Photographic Collection)

been in part a result of a desire of an emerging academic discipline to distance itself from studies of direct administrative utility, but the study of tribes rather than the amorphous and frequently enormous castes fitted better with the emerging stress on an anthropology defined through a period of fieldwork in a small-scale society. Fieldwork as the *sine qua non* of this new anthropology had emerged in Britain in the late 1890s with A. C. Haddon's second Torres Straits Expedition, and was to encounter its mythical apotheosis in Malinowski's enforced residence in the Trobriand Islands during World War One.[27]

In the South Asian context, the practice of fieldwork – a circumscribed period of interaction with another culture with the sole and express purpose of investigating its social and cultural construction – can be traced to W. H. R. Rivers's stay with the Todas in 1901–2, C. G. Seligman's work with the Veddas of Ceylon in 1907 and 1908, and A. R. Radcliffe-Brown's visit to the Andaman Islands from 1906 to 1908 (Stocking 1983, p. 83).[28] Both Rivers and Seligman were veterans of the 1898–9 Torres Straits Expedition and Radcliffe-Brown was to become Malinowski's chief rival in metropolitan anthropology during the inter-war years.[29]

The Todas, Veddas and Andaman Islanders now became the focus not of description and arrangement justified by an administrative rationale, but rather a test case for a different form of anthropology which was concerned to dispel old misunderstandings and distortions as it sought to demonstrate its intellectual and methodological rigour. This sea change towards a different form of anthropology made many of the earlier forms of 'physical anthropology' and anthropometry look like irrelevant statistical obsessions. Thus the Todas, about whom Harkness in 1832 had posed the question 'WHO CAN THEY BE?' and whom a work of popular anthropology had described as inhabitants of 'a sort of tropical Switzerland [where,] draped in a sort of toga ... they have quite the grand air' (Hutchinson *et al.* *c.* 1900, p. 188), are presented by Rivers as rational, mundane people motivated by 'the practical necessities of their daily life (1906, p. 26).

Radcliffe-Brown's fidelity to this new practice of 'relinquish[ing] his comfortable ... position on the verandah' (Malinowski 1926, p. 147; cited by Stocking 1983, p. 82) is rather more doubtful, but he himself certainly played an important role in the evolution of the contemporary anthropologist, in whom the Victorian division of labour between what Sir James Frazer described as 'men on the spot' (who provided ethnography) and the armchair-bound academic theorizer was reconciled in a single figure (Clifford 1983).

Within India, however, the developments of the first decade of the twentieth century were held in abeyance until after independence, when a new wave of American, Indian and European anthropologists made field studies which form the backbone of the contemporary anthropological understanding of India. The long history of the 'practical' utility of anthropological study within India seems to have deterred many British resident anthropologists from taking a special interest in it: they preferred the more fragile cultures of Melanesia and Polynesia.

The administrative and academic nexus of anthropology was maintained in the present century through figures such as T. C. Hodson and J. H. Hutton who, after ICS careers in Assam, both went on to become, respectively and

Fig. 37 Dr L. K. Ananthakrishna Iyer; bromide print, *c.* 1935 (Royal Anthropological Institute, Photographic Collection)

successively, Reader and Professor of Anthropology in the University of Cambridge. More importantly, however, the period from 1910 to independence saw the production of many highly detailed studies of tribal groups by individuals for whom Indian tribals were a lifelong commitment. Sarat Chandra Roy, who published several important monographs relating to Central and Eastern India and was to establish the journal *Man in India*, remains an important figure in the development of an anthropology of India practised by Indians themselves – who today constitute an anthropological tradition which speaks with equal authority to that of Western anthropologists. Verrier Elwin had a similar regional interest to that of Roy, and propounded a romanticizing commitment which in many ways sought to reverse Rivers's and Seligman's methodology of disenchantment. Christoph von Fürer-Haimendorf, with seventeen years of study in India and an unrivalled expertise on tribals, was to serve as Adviser for Tribes and Backward Classes to the Nizam of Hyderabad's government (1945–49), before linking the world of Elwin to that of metropolitan academia with his work at the School of Oriental and African Studies from 1949 to 1976 (Fig. 36).

This early twentieth-century scholarly and administrative concern with the tribal or 'aboriginal' population of India, and in particular the protection afforded by the Excluded Areas and Partially Excluded Areas regulations in the Government of India Act of 1935, were the object of much criticism from Indian nationalists, who saw it as a further attempt to divide and rule through the institutionalization of two Indias – one composed of 'castes' and the other composed of 'tribes'. There was general agreement among nationalists that the 'tribal problem' was of British making (Gadgill 1942, p. vii) and that legislation which sought to formalize differences between autochthonous[30] and non-autochthonous groups was merely, in the words of the Indian anthropologist G. S. Ghurye, 'a device to keep the power of the British Government' (1942, p. 154). Even Thakkar Bapa (Amritlal Thakkar), an enthusiastic supporter of tribal rights and confidant of Gandhi, claimed that the policy of isolation and protection advocated by administrators and many British anthropologists 'was like keeping them in [the] glass cases of a museum for the curiosity of purely academic persons' (Singh 1985, p. 187).

The organization of Hindu caste society, although the subject of occasional works such as *Behind Mud Walls in India* (1932) by the two American missionaries William and Charlotte Wiser, was largely unstudied during the early twentieth century. Three more caste and tribe compendia appeared – by Iyer (1908; Fig. 37),[31] Thurston (1909) and Russell and Hiralal (1916) – which continued the tradition and format established by Risley (1891) and Crooke (1896), together with a tranche of studies of Assamese groups. These can be seen as the tail end of that great attempt to codify the signs by which the British could decipher the nature of what Max Müller called their 'old home'.

The post-independence period has seen the appearance of many very detailed village ethnographies[32] and the strengthening of Indian voices in social anthropology. More recently a debate has emerged about the nature of Indian society and in particular the importance of caste within it, which sees the history and development of anthropological views of India as one important determinant of the current anthropology of India's chief concerns and preoccupations.[33]

NOTES

Studies into the nature of colonial anthropology in India have benefited immeasurably from Bernard Cohn's work on the wider historical and intellectual context and John Falconer's research into the anthropological uses of photography. This essay has benefited from the suggestions made by Chris Bayly and Roslyn Poignant and from the help and enthusiasm of Meenal Pananjpi and Manjiri Telang.

1. Megasthenes was Greek ambassador from 306 to 298 BC at the court of Chandragupta. He divided Indian society into seven classes: philosophers, husbandmen, shepherds, tradesmen or labourers, warriors, inspectors, and counsellors (Cohn 1968, p 4).
2. The Aborigines' Protection Society was established in 1837 and the Ethnological Society of London in 1843. The Anthropological Institute of Great Britain and Ireland (now the Royal Anthropological Institute) was founded in 1871. For a detailed history of the establishment of these societies and the issues which divided them see Stocking (1971).
3. 'Fieldwork' and 'participant observation', which have come to define social anthropology in the twentieth century, can be seen as metaphorically very similar to photography. The 'truth' of the anthropologist's account, like that of the photograph, depends on his having come into direct, unmediated contact with that which he represents, just as film is exposed to light.
4. In semiotic terms, life casts, photographs and fingerprints are 'indexes' inasmuch as they are *causally* connected to what they represent. In this respect they are different from paintings (which are *iconically* related to what they represent through 'resemblance') and language (which is arbitrary and *symbolic*). This threefold classification was first suggested by the American mathematician and philosopher, C. S. Peirce.
5. This contemporary phrase has been used by Cohn (1983) and McKenzie (1987).
6. The idea that India was a large museum or exhibition recurs continually in nineteenth- and early twentieth-century texts. Thus the Sanskritist Monier Williams comments during his journey to India in 1875 on the steamship *Venetia* that 'the whole company would well have illustrated a lecture on the ethnology of the world' (1879, p. 11). Likewise, the writer E. V. Lucas commented in 1921 that 'it is difficult for a stranger to India ... to lose the impression that he is at an exhibition – in a section of a World's Fair' (Lucas 1921, p. 5). See also Cohn, n.d.
7. The movement from confusion to certainty is also evident within academic anthropology. T. C. Hodson, then William Wyse Professor of Social Anthropology at Cambridge, wrote in 1937 that:

    It is a familiar experience that the ordinary untravelled European on first arriving in India, finds much difficulty in distinguishing one native of the country from another. . . . An observant man soon shakes off these illusions, and realises the extraordinary diversity of the types which are to be met with everywhere in India (1937, p. 9).

8. Partly as a result of the great influence of Johann Caspar Lavater's *Physiognomy* (1775–8), it was widely held that bodies and faces were legible and readable. Careful observation could reveal the man inside. On this see Shortland (1985) for a fascinating discussion.
9. See Schwab 1984, p. 41. Jones suggested in 1786 that Sanskrit, Greek and Latin all shared a common source.
10. Endogamy is the practice of marrying within a particular group. Although certain groups' marriage practices were recognized as 'hypergamous' (women moved from lower to higher groups), the endogamous characteristics of many castes and subcastes were greatly stressed by Western observers and were to form the basis of theories such as Risley's. His view was later stated very starkly by J. D. Anderson: 'Caste has undoubtedly tended ... to perpetuate such differences between classes of men as we readily-recognise between different breeds of horses or cattle' (1913, p. 5).
11. Commensality rules specified the categories of persons with whom food could be shared. The lack of time and official support for anthropological investigation, despite its obvious administrative uses, was a common complaint of many writers. Crooke's investigations for *The Tribes and Castes of the North-Western Provinces and Oudh* (1896), for example, were made under the auspices of the area's local government. However, his ethnological interests were conducted mostly in his spare time and his survey relied heavily on the reports of Indian deputy collectors and non-official enquirers who had devoted their 'scanty leisure' to this pastime (Crooke 1896, I, p. v).
12. All the paintings, significantly, depict the discovery of his body, rather than the moment of death. It is the certification of the event by the British, rather than the event in itself, which appears to be important.
13. This is a term used by James Clifford (1983). Its practice can be traced from Solvyns, through Emily Eden's *Portraits of the Princes and Peoples of India* (1844) and early twentieth-century postcards of caste 'types', to today's *National Geographic* accounts.
14. This is what the French historian and philosopher Michel Foucault termed 'normalization': the process which 'compares, differentiates, hierarchizes, homogenizes, excludes' (1979, p. 183).
15. They had been ordered by the Commissioner of Sind to take the 'likenesses' of the regional tribes (Thomas 1980, p. 48), following a directive from the Foreign Department of the Government of India to collect suitable images for the 1862 London International Exhibition. Many of the Sind images also appear in *The People of India*. The only known copy of Houghton and Tanner's work is in the Asiatic Society of Bombay's Library.
16. The Criminal Tribes Act was revised in 1897, 1911 and 1923 and was not applied to South India until 1911. As Arnold notes, the original legislation arose from specific problems of policing in the North-Western Provinces and Punjab. The characterization of whole communities as 'inherently' lawless can be seen as the reverse side of a system of classification that categorized other groups as 'martial races', and allowed the 'continuation of the earlier campaign against thugi and dacoity' (Arnold 1986, p. 138).
17. Fayrer is perhaps better known as the inhabitant of the house in Lucknow in which Sir Henry Lawrence died in 1857 (Curzon 1923, p. 162).
18. On these exhibitional strategies see Stewart (1984) and Breckenridge (1989).
19. The Victoria and Albert Museum was declared open in May 1872. Its name was changed to the Dr Bhau Daji Lad Museum in November 1975 in memory of its Indian co-founder (Barve 1975, pp. 32–5).
20. A set of these photographs in the Dr Bhau Daji Lad Museum has no documentation (Pict/Alb/13; 2241). The set in the Royal Anthropological Institute is accompanied by a letter from Edwardes.
21. This has a long pedigree. As early as 1769, for instance, the Governor of Bengal had 'stressed the necessity for the collection of information on the history of ... leading families and their customs as these affected their positions in relation to landholding' (Cohn 1987, p. 231).
22. The difference of position between Crooke and Risley is apparent in Crooke's introduction to the second edition of Risley's *The People of India*, which he had undertaken to edit following Risley's death in 1911 (1915, pp. xvi–xvii).
23. It can, for instance, be argued that 'the University of Oxford could be said to bear prime responsibility for modern casteism in South India for a large number of early caste activists were its graduates' (Washbrook 1982, p. 158).

24. Lamprey hoped his grid would provide a means whereby 'the anatomical structure of a good academy figure or model of six feet can be compared with a Malay of four feet eight in height' (1869, p. 85).
25. See *Journal of the Anthropological Society of Bombay* 1890, p. 254. Risley was instrumental in the foundation of a Standing Committee of the British Association in 1889, which included E. B. Tylor among others. Risley reported that Frazer had 'undertaken to visit India next cold weather for the purpose of prosecuting inquiries on the spot, and there seems to be every prospect that a great stimulus will be given to the study of Indian Ethnology' (ibid.).
26. The Ethnographic Survey first proposed in 1882 finally received Government funding in 1901 and the major publications in G. A. Grierson's vast linguistic Survey of India did not appear until 1902–28.
27. Bronislaw Malinowski, who later became Professor of Social Anthropology at the London School of Economics, came to symbolize a 'modern' social anthropology based on extended fieldwork and linguistic competence.
28. However, there were important examples of detailed ethnography which predated this such as Grierson's *Bihar Peasant Life* (1885) and E. H. Man's many papers on the Andaman and Nicobar Islands.
29. See Kuper (1983) for a general discussion of the importance of these figures in twentieth-century anthropology.
30. 'Indigenous' or 'son of the soil'.
31. Iyer's early work formed part of Risley's Ethnographic Survey initiative. He later became the Head of the Anthropology Department in Calcutta University. See Bala-Ratnam (1963) for a useful summary.
32. Among the most impressive have been the full-length ethnographies by Mayer (1960), Beteille (1965), Parry (1979) and Raheja (1988).
33. The historically-based critique has originated largely from the United States. Bernard Cohn has been a consistent and inspirational source of ideas (see his collected essays, 1987).

Photography in Nineteenth-Century India

JOHN FALCONER

> As there is now scarcely a nook or corner, a glen, a valley, or mountain, much less a country, on the face of the globe which the penetrating eye of the camera has not searched, or where the perfumes of poor Archer's collodion has not risen through the hot or freezing atmosphere, photography in India is, least of all, a new thing. From the earliest days of the calotype, the curious tripod, with its mysterious chamber and mouth of brass, taught the natives of this country that their conquerors were the inventors of other instruments beside the formidable guns of their artillery, which, though as suspicious perhaps in appearance, attained their object with less noise and smoke.[1]

Samuel Bourne (1834–1912), the author of these words, perhaps more than any other photographer in nineteenth-century India, can be seen as the heir of those artistic seekers after the picturesque and the exotic who interpreted the splendours and barbarities of the Indian scene for European consumption. But the work of artists like the Daniells, although produced in engraved form in some quantity, could never attain the circulation of photographic prints which, by the 1860s, had achieved a level of technical sophistication allied to cheapness of manufacture in bulk that allowed the medium to reach a far greater audience than any previously produced work. Bourne's forthright and revealing use of military metaphor highlights something of his own attitude to the nature of the British presence in India, indicating both his vision of the power of photography as a weapon in the colonial arsenal, and of the photographer's interpretative role. The passage quoted above was written as an introduction to a long series of articles published in *The British Journal of Photography* between 1863 and 1870, in which Bourne supplied a detailed narrative of his time in India, and in particular of three major photographic expeditions through Kashmir, into the Himalayas, and to the source of the Ganges. Acutely aware of photography's links with the graphic media, with which for a period it co-existed, and ultimately superseded, Bourne in his work and writings was always concerned with theories of artistic composition, theories largely outmoded in the larger artistic world but still forming an integral part of the vocabulary of the innately conservative photographic world of the period. A constant preoccupation with the components of the picturesque is present throughout his writings, as the recalcitrant magnificence of the Himalayan landscape either obstinately refused to arrange itself according to his formulaic compositional precepts, or was

Fig. 38 The staff of Bourne & Shepherd, official photographers at the Delhi Durbar; platinum print by Bourne & Shepherd, 1903 (India Office Library and Records)

reduced to insignificance on the impartial ground glass of the camera. India, in fact, is seen through the eyes of England, and though the subcontinent must somewhat grudgingly be acknowledged as the possessor of wonders and beauties, it is generally sadly deficient in the gentler attractions of the English countryside – India is too often indecently massive and 'altogether too gigantic and stupendous to be brought within the limits imposed on photography'.[2]

By the time of Bourne's arrival in India in 1863, photography was well-established on both amateur and professional levels. Bourne himself was surprised to witness the support commanded by the Bengal Photographic Society at its meetings, and he noted that while 'lovers of the picturesque will find very little *materiel* . . . the professional photographers in Calcutta appear to be doing a good stroke of business: the *carte de visite* is as popular as in England'.[3] Bourne was himself to found the most famous and enduring photographic business in India, and one which, after various permutations of name and ownership, still exists today in Calcutta as Bourne & Shepherd (Figs 38, 39). Patronized by succeeding viceroys and by the elite of European and Indian society, with studios in Calcutta, Simla and later Bombay, winner

Fig. 39 Hunting party at Srinagar; albumen print by Samuel Bourne, *c.* 1864 (Royal Commonwealth Society)

with almost tedious predictability of exhibition gold medals throughout the subcontinent, the firm of Bourne & Shepherd flourished to such an extent that by the late 1860s it was able to issue a catalogue of some 77 pages of photographs whose subject matter encompasses the whole British vision of India. From its pages the visitor or resident could select a comprehensive range of views, from the architectural splendours of Georgian Calcutta to the more homely and suburban attractions of hill stations like Simla, Mussoorie or Ootacamund. Portraits of viceroys and groups of the most notable regiments supply the human face of the British presence, while studies of Indian types and architecture offer a glimpse of the splendid and exotic East. While such views remained available in later catalogues issued by the firm, as the decades went by photography's reflection of changing circumstance can be seen in the greater emphasis on the documentation of economic progress and development: side by side with reminders of the Indian Rebellion of 1857, in pictures of the ruined Residency and cemetery at Lucknow, come sections devoted to the industrial processes of coal, iron and steel production. Bourne & Shepherd, whilst being the most prominent, and arguably the most technically accomplished photographic company in the subcontinent (in the person of Samuel Bourne at least), was only one of a host of firms anxious to capitalize on a market which, by the late 1860s, was rapidly expanding. In later years firms such as Baker & Burke and Johnston & Hoffmann were to issue catalogues of similar size, scope and pretension, and other notable business such as Nicholas & Curths in Madras, Albert Thomas Watson Penn in Ootacamund, the Sachés in Naini Tal and Frederick Bremner in Quetta expanded this documentation. And while each firm tended to offer its own particular speciality – Baker & Burke, for instance, being strong on subjects relating to the North-West Frontier – all in their way reflected and reinforced the cultural interests, privileged viewpoint and social prejudices of the imperial ruling class for whom they were, by and large, produced.

This role was not restricted to the productions of commercial operators, although these perhaps most fully presented and preserved an interpretation of India that gave consumers an acceptable image of their status in that world; war photographers such as Felice Beato in the aftermath of the Rebellion or John Burke (*c.*1843–1900) in the second Afghan War recorded the inevitable triumph of British arms; while government-inspired and sponsored photographers were fully aware that photographic data had a function in administrative control. Amateurs were encouraged to use the medium to record the archaeological heritage and ethnological diversity of the subcontinent, and John Forbes Watson in 1874 explicitly noted the camera's value in the recording of tribes whose distinctive characteristics were disappearing under the 'extension of a regular government'.[4]

The year 1839 saw the public announcement of the photographic processes of both William Henry Fox Talbot and Louis Jacques Mandé Daguerre. Whilst it was Talbot's process of negative-positive photography on paper which was ultimately to form the basis of photography as practised up to the present day, it was Daguerre's invention which was dominant during the early years of photography. The daguerreotype produced a unique, minutely detailed (but laterally reversed) image on a metal plate; despite the astonishing accuracy of its silvered surface, it can be argued that in concept the daguerreotype had not fully broken free of its artistic predecessors, and herein lay the seeds of its redundancy: not possessing those attributes most commonly associated with the photograph – speed and ease of operation, cheapness and the facility of duplication – its life was inevitably limited. For a few years, however, and for a variety of reasons (not least among them Talbot's restrictive patents on his own calotype process) the daguerreotype was to reign supreme, and its spread worldwide was rapid.

Daguerre had made the first public announcement of his process in August 1839, and by December the *Bombay Times* was able to publish a translation of his pamphlet on the daguerreotype which gave sufficient information to 'allow those who may wish to test its accuracy by experiment' to do so.[5] How far such information was acted upon is difficult to assess, since little work from the first years of photography in the subcontinent has survived. Interested amateurs such as Dr (later Sir) William O'Shaughnessy (1809–1889), Professor of Chemistry at Calcutta Medical School, certainly took up the new art, and it is reported that he was demonstrating his 'photographic drawings, [made] by means of the sun's light, of which the principle wholly differs from that of Europe' to members of the Bengal Asiatic Society in October 1839.[6] No further results of these experiments have come to light. Newspaper advertisements offering chemicals and equipment attest to early interest, and a lithograph of the Sans Souci Theatre in Park Street, Calcutta, copied from a daguerreotype of 1840, also indicates successful early results. It seems likely, though, that initial enthusiasm waned in the face of uncertain chemical supplies, lack of experienced tuition, and the specific difficulties of the Indian climate.

The first recorded commercial operator whose name at least survives is one F. M. Montairo, who in 1844 announced his willingness 'to take likenesses

Fig. 40 European house with Indian servants, Calcutta; hand-coloured salt print from calotype negative by Frederick Fiebig, *c.* 1851 (India Office Library and Records)

by the daguerreotype process' in Calcutta. Five years later F. Schranzhofer was working with the calotype process ('takes likenesses on paper') from Kyd Street, Calcutta. Others, no doubt, have slipped through the net of the commercial directories and newspaper advertisement columns, but the paucity of references up to the early 1850s, and the lack of any large body of surviving work indicates the precarious economic footing of photography outside the metropolitan centres of Europe and North America. For some the limited nature of available markets enforced a peripatetic existence until a centre of sufficient size could be located and tapped. J. W. Newland, for example, had photographed in South America and the Pacific before opening studios in Sydney in 1848 and Hobart, Tasmania in 1848–9.[7] In Calcutta in the early 1850s he finally found a city with sufficient population to sustain a photographic business whose results were by now both more predictable and more acceptable to the general public. For the remainder of the decade Newland's Daguerrean and Photographic Gallery in Loudon's Buildings was one of the most successful professional firms in the city.

Many of the early photographers had previously worked as portrait painters, and the uncertain outlook of their new profession was shown by a tendency not to commit themselves fully to photography but to continue to offer their services as artists. In a few cases this continued until the late 1860s. One interesting and significant example of this cross-fertilization can be seen in the work of Frederick Fiebig (Fig. 40). This obstinately mysterious figure was originally an artist and lithographer; in 1846 in Singapore he was preparing drawings for a so far untraced panoramic view of the settlement which he proposed to lithograph and market.[8] In the following year he produced a lithographed *Panorama of Calcutta in six parts*. From this time nothing is known of him until 1856, when he approached the Directors of

Fig. 41 The Church at Cawnpore; salt print from calotype negative by Robert and Harriet Tytler, 1859 (India Office Library and Records)

the East India Company with a proposal to sell to them a series of photographic views of Calcutta, Madras, Ceylon, Mauritius and the Cape.[9] The Company purchased some 437 of these hand-coloured calotypes, which form one of the most important early photographic documentations of the topography of Calcutta, Madras and the Coromandel coast. Nothing further is known of Fiebig's movements or activities.

From the mid-1850s photographic work survives in quantities sufficient to demonstrate the secure foothold the medium had secured in the subcontinent. Some of the reasons for this reside in technical advances. Although a few obstinate studios continued to advertise themselves as 'Daguerrean artists' until the late 1860s, the daguerreotype had been effectively superseded by the mid-1850s by the calotype, or by Frederick Scott Archer's wet collodion process. This latter photographic method was introduced in 1851 and produced a negative on glass from which prints could be taken. Despite the difficulties of the process, and the weight of equipment required by the operator, the results were such that wet collodion came to dominate photography for the next thirty years. Some workers, particularly in India, remained loyal to the calotype and other paper processes which held specific advantages for the travelling photographer in terms of portability and ease of manipulation: talented amateurs such as Dr John Murray (1809–1898) used large paper negatives to record the scenery and architecture around Agra, as did Robert (1817–1872) and Harriet (1827–1907) Tytler, who had been taught photography by Felice Beato, and who produced a large series of views of places connected with the Rebellion (Fig. 41). But in general the public responded most favourably to the sharply defined, richly toned and glossy albumen prints made from collodion negatives. While the 1860s–80s were to be the golden age of the commercial photographer in India, producing

Fig. 42 The Persian Consul at Bombay; albumen print by William Johnson and William Henderson, 1856 (Royal Commonwealth Society)

thousands of images for hugely increased numbers of visitors and residents, the foundations were laid in the 1850s not only by professionals but by the enthusiasm of amateurs: it was the contribution made by a succession of military men, civil servants, doctors and others from the 1850s–70s which marked out work in India both in quality and quantity from that produced in Britain's other colonial possessions. This was in part due to a long tradition of research into the history and culture of the subcontinent, an area of study for which the camera was particularly well-suited: when, for example, Robert and Harriet Tytler showed their large-format (22 × 18 in.) prints of the Upper Provinces to an admiring audience at the Bengal Asiatic Society in 1859, they stressed that their purpose in showing them was 'chiefly with the object of encouraging photography in a scientific point of view; such illustrations were of great value in elucidating the researches of the Society'.[10]

In 1854 a photographic society was founded in Bombay, and in 1856 the Bengal and Madras Presidencies followed suit. Acting as a forum for the exchange of technical information, for meetings and for exhibitions, the Bombay society was also able to give its patronage to the production of a monthly publication containing three mounted prints with descriptive letterpress. The *Indian amateurs photographic album* ran for 24 issues between December 1856 and October 1858, with portraits of Indian types (supplied by William Johnson and William Henderson), landscapes and architectural studies (photographed by among others Henry Hinton, Dr George Ballingall and William Henry Standish Crawford). Both Johnson and Henderson were professional photographers, as were a number of other contributors to the series, and Johnson used a number of his studies in a further publication designed to promote the study of ethnology through photography, *The oriental races and tribes: residents and visitors of Bombay* (2 vols, London, 1863–6; Fig. 42). In Calcutta the enthusiasm of the Bengal society's members resulted in an impressive exhibition in March 1857 of some 460 items. Contributions were solicited from all over India, and included portrait studies, landscapes and architectural views both from within the subcontinent and from abroad. Perhaps the most intriguing exhibits were the series of daguerreotypes by Josiah Rowe, Professor of Drawing and Surveying at the Presidency College, who is described in the society's journal as 'the oldest photographer in Calcutta'. Little of his work survives, and apparently none of the daguerreotypes shown, which included a five-part panoramic view of Calcutta taken from the Ochterlony Monument.

The photographic societies brought together a cross-section of Europeans with wide cultural interests, and thus the Rev. Joseph Mullins, in a talk 'On the applications of photography in India',[11] was able to advocate the advantages of the 'stern fidelity of photography' in a programme of activity that would include its use in such fields as astronomy, medicine, public works and police investigations. A series of studies of Indian life and customs would be of value not only in its own right, but might serve 'higher interests, in the political and commercial world'. Such sentiments echo the words of Dr John McCosh who, in recommending to his colleagues 'this fascinating study of photography,' emphasized the benefits to posterity of 'such collections that would be a welcome contribution to any museum'.[12]

Government also, recognizing practical and economic advantages, played its part in the encouragement of the art, and from 1855 tuition in photography was available to cadets at the East India Company's seminary at Addiscombe, supplied by the drawing master Aaron Penley. In the field of public works Colonel Faber, Chief Engineer in Madras in 1855, was in no doubt as to the value of the camera, even in inexpert hands, considering that it would soon supersede the 'tedious and highly paid labors of the professional draughtsman'. In time, he considered that knowledge of the medium would form part of the duties of all engineers.[13] Aside from the great mass of surviving material detailing railway construction and official building works, the use of the camera in documenting projects of this nature can be seen in published form in *The Ganges Canal* (Roorkee 1867) by Thomas George Glover (1826–1881), a photographic record of one of the great engineering feats of the nineteenth century.

Notions of economy also formed an important aspect of the official use of photography in the documentation of India's archaeological heritage. In the Bombay Presidency, for example, an artist named Fallon had been employed, originally for one year from 1851, to copy the sculptures in the caves at Elephanta. Four years later he was still at his labours with no end in sight, a drain on the Company's resources which provoked a testy despatch from London pointing out how much more quickly photography could complete the task.[14] This duty fell to Captain Thomas Biggs of the Royal Artillery, who produced some very fine work before being called back to his regiment. Many of his photographs appear in three large folio volumes published with architectural notes by James Fergusson in 1866: *Architecture at Ahmedabad, Architecture at Beejapoor,* and *Architecture in Dharwar and Mysore.* Biggs's successor in the post, Dr William Henry Pigou (1818–1858) of the Indian Medical Service, took a number of the photographs in the last named volume. Photographers working for the Archaeological Survey, in fact, produced some of the best photographic work in India during the nineteenth century, among them J. D. Beglar, assistant to the Director of Archaeology General Alexander Cunningham; William Henry Cornish (d.1925) of the Bengal Police; Major Henry Hardy Cole RE, Curator of Ancient Monuments; and Major Robert Gill (d.1875), who dedicated years of his life to painting and photographing the Ajanta frescoes, and many of whose photographs were mounted in James Fergusson's *The rock-cut temples of India* (London, 1864).

Government sponsorship in the field of archaeology resulted, in Madras at least, in some remarkable photography. Linnaeus Tripe (1822–1902) of the Madras Army, who in 1855 had produced a large portfolio of Burmese views while attached as photographer to the mission to Ava, was in October 1856 appointed Presidency Photographer. Tripe spent most of the year photographing antiquities, returning to the Madras School of Arts to teach photography during the monsoon season. In the three years that he held the post, Tripe achieved a body of photographic work which stands comparison with any in the nineteenth century, and six slim volumes of his softly toned studies of south Indian architecture appeared in 1858.[15] Just as photography's cheapness had been one of its most attractive features, so official parsimony cut short Tripe's appointment, which was abolished by the Governor of Madras Sir Charles Trevelyan in 1860, the reason given being 'the present state of finances of the Presidency.'

A fresh initiative in Madras a few years later led to the appointment of the professional photographer Edmund David Lyon (d.1891) to record the ancient monuments of the Presidency. Lyon, formerly a captain in the 68th Foot, practised as a photographer in Ootacamund from *c.*1865–70, and some 300 of his photographs were retained by the Archaeological Survey of India. The exceptional quality of his prints, and their present state of perfect preservation after some 130 years, are a vivid testimony to his skill (Figs. 43, 44). His work was shown at the London Photographic Society Exhibition of

Fig. 43 The judge's residence at Madura; albumen print by Edmund David Lyon, *c.* 1868 (India Office Library and Records)

1869, where it was highly praised for its 'tenderness and delicacy.' Lyon was ingenious in solving the technical problems posed by architectural photography in India, as in the way in which he stationed Indian employees out of sight but holding reflectors, in order to light the long corridors found in some southern Indian temples. In the two very different styles of their work, Tripe and Lyon achieved some of the most impressive photographic records of nineteenth-century India. By 1900 the India Office was able to issue a catalogue of archaeological views containing several thousand negatives by Survey employees, amateurs, and specially commissioned professionals. This compilation comprises perhaps the single most important visual record of the architectural heritage of India, a fact acknowledged by James Fergusson in his statement that 'there are now very few buildings in India – of any importance at least – which have not been photographed with more or less completeness; and for purposes of comparison such collections of photographs as are now available are simply invaluable'.[16]

Writing in 1874 *On the measures required for the efficient working of the India Museum and Library*, John Forbes Watson had stressed the necessity of

Fig. 44 Massive arcade in the Palace at Madura; albumen print by Edmund David Lyon, *c.* 1868 (India Office Library and Records)

'securing the traces of many tribes now fast disappearing or losing their distinctive characteristics,' and he considered that such investigations could well be modelled on the work of the Archaeological Survey. Indeed, these two aspects of Indian culture had been paired twenty years earlier in the instructions to Linnaeus Tripe, who had been charged with photographing the people of Madras Presidency as well as its architecture. The growing interest in ethnology in the second half of the nineteenth century, coupled with the known antiquity of Indian culture, inevitably focussed attention on the subcontinent, to the extent that even on an amateur level George Campbell, author of *The ethnology of India* (1872), could state:

> I soon expect to find that, instead of collecting postage stamps, young ladies of an intellectual turn will collect nice little cabinets of crania for the inspection of their friends ...[17]

John McCosh (1805–1885), a pioneer of photography in the subcontinent, had made several ethnographical portraits, and this use of the camera was continued in both amateur and professional hands. In the latter case such

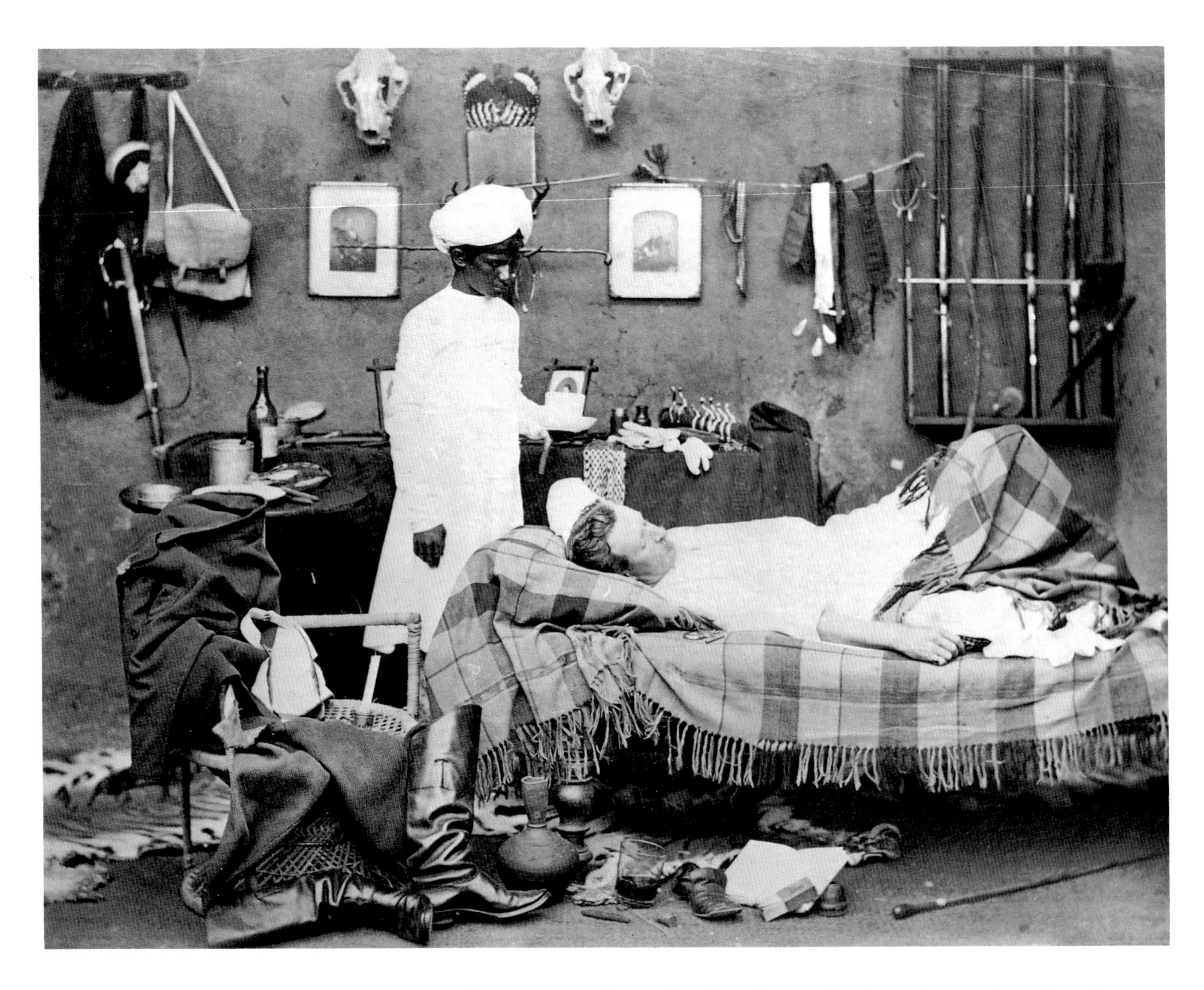

Fig. 45 English officer attended by his servant; albumen print by Willoughby Wallace Hooper and George Western, 1870s (India Office Library and Records)

work was generally confined to the production of portraits of exotic types, often posed in somewhat unconvincing tableaux to demonstrate workplace practices, religious observances and other cultural phenomena. On a more scientific level, it was acknowledged by 1865 that 'the appearance, which can be so well preserved and conveyed by photographs' was, along with language, social customs and osteology, one of the 'four main divisions of enquiry' in ethnological research.[18] The interest of amateur photographers, in the persons of those soldiers, doctors and civil servants who came in closest contact with remote aboriginal tribes, led to the publication of perhaps the most famous large-scale ethnographical work to be illustrated with photographs. Produced in eight volumes between 1868 and 1875, *The People of India* contains nearly 500 mounted prints by some of the best-known photographers of nineteenth-century India. Some work by commercial firms such as Shepherd & Robertson was included, but the majority of contributors were amateurs in government service such as Willoughby Wallace Hooper (1837–1912; Fig. 45), Henry Charles Baskerville Tanner (1835–1898) and James Waterhouse (1842–1922). These volumes owed their appearance to the photographic enthusiasms of

Lord and Lady Canning, who wished to build up a collection of photographs to remind them of India in later life. When the collection exceeded the bounds of private interest, however, its importance was considered sufficient to warrant official sanction, and the publication appeared under the imprint of the India Museum.

Implicit in the use of photography to study the races of India was the assumption that the gathering of such data would serve a pragmatic function in the administration of the congeries of racial and religious groupings that came under British rule – at this period more than ever, as roads and railways opened up to regular government areas hitherto largely unadministered (see 'Colonial Anthropology in the "Laboratory of Mankind"', pp. 252–63). These ethnological investigations gave added impetus to photography. One solid result was the publication of Edward Tuite Dalton's *Descriptive ethnology of Bengal* (Calcutta, 1872), illustrated with lithographs very faithfully reproduced from photographs mainly by Dr (later Sir) Benjamin Simpson (1831–1923). Simpson had exhibited a series of 80 portraits of north Indian types at the London International Exhibition of 1862, for which he was awarded a Gold Medal. Some of his earlier work was used by Dalton, but he was also given leave of absence to travel to Assam to complete the series. The calibre of Simpson's sympathetic and striking portraits stands comparison with the best of such work in this field produced in India or elsewhere.

While a host of amateurs contributed photographs of this nature, some brief mention should be made of the most comprehensive photographic record made of any one racial group. Carried out on behalf of the British Museum, and backed up by detailed notes and anthropometric measurements, the photographic documentation of the Andaman Islanders by Maurice Vidal Portman (1861–1935) was a remarkably ambitious project, undertaken in the knowledge that the race was rapidly dying out. Impressive as Portman's work may be, to the modern eye these clamped figures form a distressing contrast to more humanely executed earlier photography.[19]

On his arrival in India in 1863 one of the first things Samuel Bourne noted about the Calcutta photographic scene was that 'it is no uncommon thing to see native portrait establishments.' He also found an impressive quality of work among the Indian students learning photography at the Madras School of Arts, which he felt compared favourably with the productions of some professional establishments in London. By the time of Bourne's arrival the connection of Indians with photography was well-established, at least among that well-born and educated section of the population that moved with ease in European social and intellectual circles. In the early years of the Bombay Photographic Society, for instance, a number of well known Indian photographers took an active part in the society's affairs, both serving on its council and contributing photographs at its meetings. Ardaseer Cursetjee (1808–1877), in charge of the great shipyard at Mazagon, was the author of *Diary of an overland journey from Bombay to England* (London, 1840). His obituary in the Proceedings of the Institute of Civil Engineers also credits him, perhaps over-fulsomely, as 'foremost in introducing photography . . . into Bombay,' and as well as serving on the Photographic Society's council he made numerous contributions to its exhibitions. Two brothers, both doctors, also played a prominent part in the early days of the society. Doctors Bhau (1821–1874)

Fig. 46 Parsi family at Bombay; albumen print by Hurrichund Chintamon, *c.* 1867 (India Office Library and Records)

and Narayan Dajee were enthusiastic in their support and both served on the council. Of the two Dr Narayan Dajee appears to have been the most prolific, and indeed practised as a commercial photographer from premises on Rampart Row between 1858 and 1868. Not only did he exhibit some 200 photographs at Bombay in 1856, but also contributed over 40 landscapes and portraits to the Photographic Society of Bengal's exhibition in the following year. Also in Bombay, the firm of Hurrichund Chintamon & Co., professionally active from the late 1850s, produced an impressive body of work, including a number of studies of the castes and tribes of India which were shown at the Paris International Exhibition of 1867 (Fig. 46).

Indians were also active in the affairs of the Photographic Society of Bengal, with Preonath Sett serving as secretary and also offering tuition in photography to other Indians. The unstable position of Indians in European society, however, is seen in the case of Rajendra Lal Mitra (1824–1891). One of the most notable scholars and intellects of nineteenth-century India, and the first Indian to be elected President of the Asiatic Society of Bengal (1885), he became Treasurer of the Photographic Society of Bengal in 1856. An intemperate speech condemning the oppressive behaviour of the indigo planters of Bengal led to his expulsion from the society, and despite European support from some quarters, he did not gain readmittance until 1868. Also in the mid-1850s Ahmud Ali Khan was producing a series of portraits of the residents of Lucknow, two volumes of which are now preserved in the India Office Library. While the quality of these small salt prints is very variable, the tragic events which overtook many of the sitters make this a poignant and historically important record.

Among the princely classes photography was also taken up as a pastime. Although Samuel Bourne was surprised to find photography figuring among the interests of the Raja of Chumba, it transpired that his delight lay more in showing off his camera, lenses and darkroom equipment than in actually using them. Others displayed real talent. Val Prinsep was photographed by Bulwant Rao, natural son of the Maharaja of Gwalior, and found the results 'pretty successful,' while both Prinsep and Louis Rousselet considered Sir Ram Singh Bahadur, Maharaja of Jaipur, to be a photographer of real skill.[20] He had presumably learnt the craft from the Englishman Colin Murray, who was attached to his court as photographer in the late 1860s, and who later became a partner in the firm of Bourne & Shepherd.

No Indian photographer, however, approached the commercial success of Lala Din Diyal (1844–1910), who took up photography in the 1870s after training as a draughtsman at the Thomason College in Roorkee. He recorded the Prince of Wales' visit to Indore in 1875–6, and after attracting the patronage of a number of senior British administrators, was appointed court photographer to the Nizam of Hyderabad. His photographic business, Raja Din Diyal & Sons, formed in the mid-1870s, was probably the only native Indian business to compete successfully and on equal terms with European-owned studios. In 1892 he opened a Bombay branch, and made a comprehensive record of the Indian visit of the Prince and Princess of Wales in 1905–6. Much of his finest work, however, was in the recording of Indian architecture, and many of his negatives were acquired for the records of the Archaeological Survey of India. Perhaps his best work in this field appears in the autotype reproductions of his photographs in Sir Lepel Griffin's *Famous monuments of Central India* (London, 1886). In 1877 John Blees had published a guide to photography in India with his *Photography in Hindostan; or, reminiscences of a travelling photographer*, but it was not until 1895 that a systematic manual in the form of George Ewing's *A handbook of photography for amateurs in India* appeared. The publication in 1899 of H. M. Ibrahim's Urdu work *Rahno-ma-il-photography-ya-usil-i-musawery* (A guide to photography or the rules for taking photographs) signals the full absorption of the medium into the mainstream of Indian life and culture.

The appearance of such works reflected the growth of a new generation of amateur photographers in the closing years of the nineteenth century: simplified equipment placed the medium within the reach of all, with a consequent falling-off in demand for the products of the professional. Some businesses failed to adapt to the change and ceased to trade; others diverted their energies to catering for this new market by selling equipment, film and processing facilities. Some of the larger firms continued to sell photographic prints of scenic views for many years, but demand was by now far greater for cheaply produced postcards, and by the end of the First World War the era of the carefully composed, minutely detailed and richly toned prints of the nineteenth century was irrevocably gone. More than forty years earlier Samuel Bourne had prophetically seen the coming struggle between those dedicated to aiming, at whatever cost, 'at the highest achievements of the art,' and those who were willing to sacrifice quality for the convenience of more compact equipment, producing 'small scraps fit only for the scrapbook'.[21] By 1918 that battle was over. By the 1930s and 1940s international photographers of the calibre of Margaret Bourke-White, Henri Cartier-Bresson and Cecil Beaton were visiting the subcontinent. While attracted by the unique qualities of India and her people, these visits signal the start of another chapter of Indian history: while forming a part of the story of Indian photography, they indicate more importantly India's arrival as a significant factor on the international scene.

NOTES

1. Bourne 1863, p. 51.
2. Bourne 1864, p. 51.
3. Bourne 1863, p. 269.
4. Watson 1874, p. 26.
5. The *Bombay Times*, 14, 18, 21 December 1839.
6. The *Asiatic Journal*, vol. 31 (n.s.), January–April 1840, p. 15.
7. For Newland's activities in Australia, see Davies and Stanbury 1985, pp. 10–13.
8. The *Singapore Free Press,* 2 April 1846.
9. IOR miscellaneous letters received, vol. 193, 1856.
10. *Proceedings of the Asiatic Society of Bengal*, May 1859, p. 182.
11. *Journal of the Photographic Society of Bengal*, no. 2, 21 January 1857.
12. McCosh 1856, p. 7.
13. Quoted in IOR/E/4/842 ff. 134–5.
14. Bombay public despatches, 14 June 1854 (no.23), f.1420 (IOR/E/4/1100).
15. *Photographic views of Madura; ... of Poodoocottah; ... of Ryakotta and other places in the Salem district; ... of Seringham; ... in Tanjore and Trivady; ... of Trichinopoly.*
16. Fergusson 1876, preface.
17. *Proceedings of the Asiatic Society of Bengal*, August 1865, pp. 142–3.
18. Ibid, p.148.
19. A reasonably detailed account of the progress of Portman's photographic work, and its relationship to his other duties, can be found in the *Report on the administration of the Andaman and Nicobar Islands and the penal settlements of Port Blair and the Nicobars* for the period 1890–1900.
20. Rousselet 1882, p. 239.
21. Bourne 1871, p. 425.

Anthropology and the Colonial Image

341

341 Talc paintings of Indian occupations and ascetics

Early 19th century
3 sets of paintings (12, 12 and 11) in green leather slip-cases
The Trustees of the British Museum (3706, 3704, 3703)

Talc paintings were produced by Indian artists chiefly in Patna, Benares and Tanjore (Birdwood 1878, p.86).

One of these sets depicts a remarkable range of 'Fakirs and snake charmers', including examples of members of the huge ascetic/renouncer movements which exerted considerable power in India until the late eighteenth century. This Western fascination with the 'other-worldly' asceticism of some aspects of Indian culture was a recurrent theme in missionary, and some sociological and anthropological representations of the country. The delineation of occupations, illustrated here by the example of the *bania* trader, probably became the most popular means of understanding India in terms of a hierarchy of trades. These talc paintings find their direct lineal successors in early twentieth-century postcards of 'occupational types'. C.P.

LITERATURE: Birdwood 1878.

342 *A Description of a Singular Aboriginal Race Inhabiting the Summit of the Neilgherry Hills, or Blue Mountains of Coimbatoor in the Southern Peninsula of India,* London, 1832

Captain Henry Harkness
Printed book, 175 pp., 25 × 33 ($9\frac{7}{8}$ × 13)
The Syndics of Cambridge University Library (8460.c.145)

Harkness's work is one of the first book-length studies of an Indian group which is recognizably 'anthropological' in its concerns. It is also noteworthy for its striking frontispiece of 'a Tuda [i.e. Toda] Family' in 'a manner suggestive of a Jewish patriarchal family' (Rooksby 1971, p.113). Images such as these, with their obvious Europeanization and romanticization, were to be adduced later by enthusiasts of photography as evidence of pre-technological 'distortions' (Falconer n.d. [1984], p.26).

There was much speculation from the start of the nineteenth century concerning the origins of the Todas, a pastoral tribal group in the Nilgiri Hills, with theories advanced of 'God's ancient people' and marooned Roman colonies. Harkness is equally intrigued, but gets no further towards an answer in his publication than the capitalized enunciation 'WHO CAN THEY BE?' (p.171). Indeed, although certain aspects of Toda origins were shrouded in mystery, it was their very strangeness and individuality which appealed to Harkness. It was precisely this 'singularity', in the words of the time, which produced 'the power of discriminating with certainty between the various tribes and classes of which the native population of India is composed' (*op. cit.,* Preface). According to Harkness, the Todas contrasted markedly with their neighbours: they had 'open and expressive countenances', 'a large, full and speaking eye' and their 'expression of cheerfulness and good humour, are natural marks, prominently distinguishing them from all other natives of India' (pp.6–7). C.P.

LITERATURE: Rooksby 1971, p.113; Falconer n.d. (1984), ill. p.32.

343 An 'Indian Type'

Copyprint after calotype by John McCosh (1852–3) contained in album of 310 calotypes in the National Army Museum, London

The very early calotype was taken in Burma by John McCosh (1805–85), a surgeon with the East India Company who was often described as 'the first war photographer'. The photograph illustrates the categorization of non-European photographic subjects as 'types' rather than individuals. It has been noted that the images in McCosh's album

> fall into two very clearly defined subgroups. British officers and their wives are represented very much as individuals, with the sitter's name and rank or title indicated in almost every case. By contrast the non-British subjects are identified throughout by a more generalized reference to their nationality or racial background – 'Burmese Beauty', 'Madras Man' (McKenzie 1987, pp.113–14).

This approach set the tone for the next

hundred years, during which time Britain regarded individual Indians as representatives of a particular class or norm. McCosh reinforced his view in his *Advice to Officers* (1856) with remarks concerning the physiognomy and physical forms of 'Asiatic types'. In more general terms this can perhaps be seen as the beginning of a means of apprehending India which involved a powerful system of knowledge which could speak decisively about its colonial subjects, rather as Flaubert was able to speak about the Egyptian courtesan Kuchuk Hanem – '*He* spoke for and represented her ... and [told] his readers in what way she was "typically Oriental"' (Said 1985, p.6). C.P.

LITERATURE: Falconer n.d. (1984), ill. p.17; Said 1985; Mackenzie 1987, vol. II, no.2, pp.109–18.

344 Lagári Gõd (*Gond*) life mask taken in Amarkántak, central India

Schlagintweit brothers, *c.*1856–8
Metal cast in wooden frame, 45.9 × 25.5 (18 × 10)
Inscribed: *Lagari, Gõd, Amarkantak, Central India. Schlagintweit Collection of Ethnographical heads, 1854–1858*
The Trustees of the British Museum (Q.72.As.1661)

Like photographs, life casts were considered valuable because of their immediate connection with their subject. Indeed, Emil Schlagintweit argued that casts 'offer a wider field of enquiry than mere photographs' (cited by Falconer n.d. [1984], p.27).

The four Schlagintweit brothers were commissioned by the East India Company in 1853 to survey the Himalayan region and travelled extensively throughout India between 1854 and 1858. Subsequent voluminous publications reported on their investigations into trigonometry, hydrology, zoology and ethnography. Volumes of panoramas and maps were also published, together with a series of metallic casts of 'Ethnographical Heads from India and High Asia' which were advertised thus at the end of their 1861–6 multi-volume work:

> This splendid collection, dedicated by permission to Her Majesty the Queen of England, consists of 275 facial casts and 37 casts of hands and feet, which have been taken from living people.

This was but one of the Schlagintweit brothers' 'plastic publications' (others included a galvanized model of the Zugspitze) and was sold by the publisher J.A. Barth of Leipzig for the huge price of £350 for the series.

This Gõd (*Gond*) cast was prepared by Robert Schlagintweit, whose 'journeys led him through the mountain systems of Central India – unhealthy centres inhabited by the wild aboriginal tribes of the Gõds, Bhils and Kols' (Schlagintweit 1861, vol. I, p.21). The Schlagintweits' account goes on to describe Amarkantak as being 'for the physical geographer and ethnographer, a most interesting country' (p.22).

Plaster casts of live subjects had been made in large numbers by Dumoutier during the cruise of the Astrolabe through Melanesia and Polynesia in 1837–40 (Falconer n.d. [1984], p.26). In India, as elsewhere, casts were commonly made of archaeological and architectural features. Between 1868 and 1871 the Government of India financed at least three expeditions to procure plaster casts of sculptures in Bombay and Orissa (*The Indian Antiquary,* March 1873, p.84). Several examples of 'Trans-Himalayan Tribes', probably from the Schlagintweit series of casts, are currently on display in the Dr Bhau Daji Lad Museum, Bombay. C.P.

LITERATURE: Schlagintweit 1861–6; Schlagintweit 1867, pp.127–32; Falconer n.d. (1984), pp.26–8.

345 Canarese Brahmins

William Johnson and W. Henderson, 1857
Albumen print, 25.5 × 19.5 (10 × 7¾)
Royal Commonwealth Society Library (Y3022A)

This image originally appeared in *The Indian Amateurs Photographic Album* which was issued in 24 parts between December 1856 and October 1858. In this early form it was described as 'Brahmin Students of English', and was

345

part of a series of 'Costumes and Characters of Western India'. Many of these studies later appeared against montage landscapes in *The Oriental Races and Tribes, Residents and Visitors of Bombay: A Series of Photographs with Letterpress Descriptions* (2 vols., 1863 and 1866).

The preface to the first volume observed that Bombay 'contains numerous representatives of almost all the races and tribes of the Indian Continent and Islands' (vol. 1, p.9), and that 'the INDIANS, composed, then, as they really are, of different tribes, have great differences in their physiognomy, by which it is not difficult for near observers to recognise them' (vol. 1, p.12). A brief guide is then given on how best to recognize Hindus, Parsis, Muslims, Christians, Bene Israelis, Chinese, Malays, Arabs and so on. The plates and letterpress in the first volume cover Gujerat, Kutch and Kathiawar; the second covers 'the Mahratta country'. A planned third volume, a 'miscellaneous Collection', never appeared.

Frith, a professional photographer, became famous for three photographic expeditions to Egypt and the Holy Land in 1856, 1857 and 1858 which produced a celebrated corpus of images. Published as *Frith's India* series in the 1870, this print was reproduced in vol. 1, p.141. He never visited India but collected images from various sources for use in selections of world-views produced by his company. C.P.

LITERATURE: Hershkowitz 1980, ill., p.51; Falconer n.d. (1984), pp.20–1.

346 Photographs from *The People of India: A Series of Photographic Illustrations, with Descriptive Letterpress, of the Races and Tribes of Hindustan,* London, 1868–75

Copyprints after albumen prints by J. Forbes Watson and J. W. Kaye in the India Office Library:

(i) *zamindar,* Goojar landholder, Saharunpoor
(ii) *Brinjara* and wife, itinerant grain merchants, Saharunpoor
(iii) *Bunnea*, Hindoo tradesman, Delhi
(iv) Carpenters and Hindus, Lahore
(v) Khan Mahomed, embroiderer. Sind. (Illustrated Fig. 29)

The People of India was initiated by an informal request from Governor-General Canning to civilians and army officers for pictorial souvenirs of their time in India; it was transformed by the revolt of 1857 into an official project of the Political and Secret Department (Desmond 1982, p.119). Half of the 200 copies produced after 1868 were reserved for official use.

The work consisted of 468 photographs with letterpress produced by Houghton and Tanner (see Fig. 29), Simpson (see no. 349), the studio of Shepherd and Robinson, and W.W. Hooper, among many others. Forbes Watson noted in his preface to the first volume that the 'great convulsion' of 1857–8 had 'imparted a new interest to the ... people who had been the actors in these remarkable events', and a concern with the administrative complications and dubious political loyalties of various groups is apparent throughout the work. *Goojurs* (Gujars), for instance, are 'given to indiscriminate plunder in times of disturbance' (pl. 157). *Brinjaras* (Bunjaras), on the other hand, had been of great use in the Mahratta War and 'beneficial' in the Sikh campaign and had a 'reputation for perfect honesty' – 'no matter how long, or how arduous the march, or how great the value of the goods they carry, they deliver them according to promise' (pl. 161). (They were later classified, ironically, as a 'criminal tribe'.) The *Bunnea* (Bania) was a rather more complex case, being dishonest and unpopular, but useful:

> if he has cheating propensities and indulges them to the utmost of his power, the Bunnea is a useful person, and contributes very largely to the furtherance of the general trade of India ... He little thinks perhaps that his bags of oil seed will go to Marseilles, or his madder, cotton, and sugar to Liverpool; but they have yielded him a good profit, and he passes them on to others, who will make more than he has, in their progress to their ultimate destination ... (pl. 184).

The People of India, which was organized on an idiosyncratic basis of caste, tribe, sect and occupation, also provoked Sayyid Ahmad Khan, a subordinate judge in the North-Western Provinces, to comment in 1869:

> The young Englishmen who ... come to the India Office preparatory to starting for India, and, desirous of knowing something of the land to which they are going, also look over this work. What can they think, after perusing this book and looking at its pictures, of the power or the honour of the natives of India? (Lelyveld 1978, p.3; cited in Cohn n.d.). C.P.

LITERATURE: Lelyveld 1978; Desmond 1982; Cohn 1988; Pinney 1990.

347 Large hookah (*hukka*)

5 pieces
Wood, coconut and silver, longest piece 60.5 (23¾)
The Trustees of the British Museum (As.1866.c.1.4004)

The West has always seen the hookah (*hukka*) as an important object within Indian society, whether as a symbol of pleasure, decadence, reconciliation, or the focus of rules concerning caste purity which tolerated or forbade the sharing of mouthpieces. The letterpress to pl. 157 in *The People of India*, which depicts a *Gujar*, comments on the hookah he holds and notes that 'Gujars are much addicted to smoking, particularly ganja ... this has a peculiarly exciting and intoxicating quality.' Hookahs were keenly collected for museum displays – there was a fine one in the University Museum, Cambridge; an interesting selection remains in the Pitt Rivers Museum, Oxford. However, these were not silent material objects or occasional props in the photographic depiction of caste; rather, they were seen as weapons in the service of a subjugated disorder which threatened colonial power.

In many accounts, 'bhang' served as a metaphor for what was seen as a quixotic fanaticism. In W.H. Fitchett's *The Tale of the Great Mutiny* of 1901 the sepoy Mungal Pandey is described as 'half-drunk with bhang, and wholly drunk with religious fanaticism' (1901, p.1) and the material substance is credited with the power to evoke a communion of hysteria which threatened society: 'The man, in fact, is in that condition of mingled bhang and "nerves" which makes a Malay run amok; and every shout from his lips runs like a wave of sudden flame through the brains and along the nerves of the listening crowd of fellow-sepoys' (Fitchett 1901, p.2).

C.P.

PROVENANCE: 'From Kew' to Museum of Mankind, date unknown.

LITERATURE: Fitchett 1901.

348 *Five Hundred Questions on the ... Social Condition of the Natives of Bengal,* Calcutta, 1862

Rev. J. Long
Printed pamphlet, 41pp., 21 × 30.5 ($8\frac{1}{8}$ × 12)
The British Library Board (8022.b.90 [10])

There were a number of early manuals designed to systematize the study of India. In 1827 the Royal Asiatic Society issued 'Desiderata and Inquiries connected with the Presidency of Madras and Bombay ... on points relating to the language, literature, ancient history of families, antiquities, coins, people, architecture, landed tenures, arts and manufactures, of India' (Long 1862, p.1). There were also more general manuals produced by the British Admiralty, and in 1854 the British Association for the Advancement of Science issued a *Manual for Ethnological Enquiry.* Long's 1862 work (first read as a paper to the Royal Asiatic Society), however, was the first detailed list of Indian topics for 'the proper study of mankind' and took the form of a long list of questions. Various European expeditions to the South Seas had resulted in attempts to formalize the procedure of scientific enquiry, such as Degerando's *Observation of Savage Peoples* at the end of the eighteenth century. Long's work represents the development of a similar attempt within an Indian context, although with more overtly humanitarian aims. The anonymous author of the introduction to a later edition proposed a division of labour between Bengali and European inhabitants of Bengal: 'The natives are able and willing to supply the data and facts, – while the European can classify and arrange them on the plan laid down by Statistical and Sociological Societies' (Long 1852, p.2).

Long, a missionary, hoped through the spirit of enquiry shown in this publication to soften 'the asperities arising from antagonism of race' (p.2). His questions include a consideration of the influence of snake-charmers' music over snakes; the proportion of beggars motivated by choice, necessity or religion; 'the profits and numbers of those who *burn* the *dead*'; 'Parrots, how trained to repeat *Radha Krishna*?'; whether there are nowadays fewer obscene words uttered in the Holi festivities; the degree of literacy of *nautch* (dancing) girls; and whether 'a variety of *soils* [has] any influence on the character of the people, as low and marshy coasts are said to furnish a sordid, degraded race?'

C.P.

LITERATURE: Long 1861; Long 1865; Long 1898; Degerando 1969.

349 *Descriptive Ethnology of Bengal,* Calcutta, 1872

Edward Tuite Dalton, with lithographs after photographs by Benjamin Simpson and Tosco Peppe
Printed book, 327 pp. plus plates
School of Oriental and African Studies, University of London (S IV. L. 26195)

Dalton's book originally started as a descriptive catalogue to accompany Joseph Fayrer's proposed exhibition in Calcutta (see 'Colonial Anthropology in the "Laboratory of Mankind"', p.255), a work which he felt 'might prove a useful guide to the ethnological exhibition' (1872, p.ii). The exhibition was cancelled because of fears about the health of the live specimens which were to be exhibited in booths. It was suggested that it would be difficult to induce 'those strange shy creatures', 'the wild tribes of India', to attend an event whose purpose they would have been unable to comprehend, and the Commissioner of Assam 'stated his conviction that twenty typical specimens of the hill tribes of his province could not be conveyed to Calcutta and back at any time of the year without casualties that the greatest enthusiast for anthropological research would shrink from encountering' (1872, p.i). Dalton's book concentrates on tribal groups in Assam and Chota Nagpur, reflecting his experience in those two regions. The Government of Bengal made a grant of 10,000 rupees towards the cost of producing the volume.

349

Denied the opportunity of writing about the world represented through the exhibition, Dalton had to turn to the 'real' thing – 'an account of the tribes in Bengal' (1872, p.ii), but since there would be no place where the reader could go and see all the types described in a single convenient space it was decided that 'any descriptive work of the kind proposed should be abundantly illustrated' (p.ii). Most of the plates in his book are lithographs taken from a series of exceptionally beautiful photographs by Benjamin Simpson. A few are by a Dr Brown, the Political Agent at Manipur, and those of Chota Nagpur (including that illustrated here, 'Juang Girls') are by Tosco Peppe. Peppe had at Dalton's request 'proceeded into wild parts of Singbhum and Keonjhur, and brought his camera to bear on some of the most primitive human beings, the Juangs, never previously subjected to the process' (p.iii). The caption to pl. XXXIII notes that 'Mr Peppe had immense difficulty in inducing these wild timid creatures to pose before him, and it was not without many a tear, that they resigned themselves to the ordeal.' C.P.

LITERATURE: Risley 1915, ill. pl. XX.

350 Anthropometric study of Bengal sailor using the Lamprey grid

Unknown photographer, *c.*1880
Albumen print on board, 17.2 × 13.8 ($6\frac{3}{4} \times 5\frac{2}{5}$)
Inscribed: *Bengal Sailor*
Royal Anthropological Institute, London, Photographic Collection (1955)

The concern of early anthropology with the external characteristics of peoples' bodies (anthropometry) led to competition between different methods of recording this information. This photograph illustrates the particularly influential system devised by J.H. Lamprey of the Royal College of Surgeons and the Royal Geographical Society. In a short paper to the Ethnological Society of London in 1868–9, Lamprey had noted that 'collectors of photographs illustrative of the races of man, have experienced the greatest difficulty in questions of comparison of measurement of individuals by some common

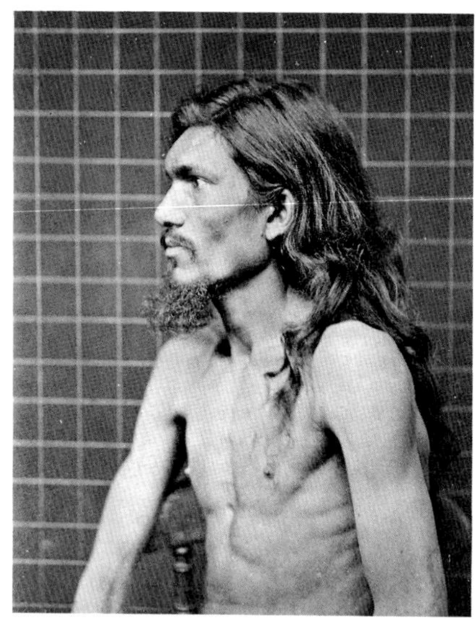

350

standard' (p.84). Lamprey's solution was to photograph models against a background grid formed by hanging silk thread on a large wooden frame so as to form 2-inch squares, and 'by means of such photographs the anatomical structure of a good academy figure or model of six feet can be compared with a Malay of four feet eight in height; and the study of all those peculiarities of contour which are so distinctly observable in each group, are greatly helped by this system of perpendicular lines ...' (pp.84–5).

Shortly after this the International Statistical Institute was established (1887), and copies of the Anthropological Institute's *Notes and Queries* and the Royal Geographical Society's *Hints to Travellers* were printed with gold-blocked 6-inch rulers along their front covers. In India, H.H. Risley formulated a standard data entry to make the recording of anthropometric survey information as efficient as possible. The cabinet of curiosities was by now a huge and well-organized museum in which all the objects on display could be compared one with another. C.P.

PROVENANCE: Presented to present owner by C.E. Peek.

LITERATURE: Lamprey 1868–9, pp.84–5; Foucault 1979, pp.177–94; Pinney 1988, pp.144–62.

351 Photograph of a 'Rong' from an album of Nepalese 'types'

Johnston & Hoffman, *c.*1880
Albumen print, 14.5 × 10.7 ($5\frac{3}{16} \times 5\frac{11}{16}$), in album, 28.7 × 22.5 ($11 \times 8\frac{7}{8}$)
Caption: *I (a), Rong – the 'Lepcha' of the Nepalese and Indians and aborigines of Sikhim. Sept, Tharthing (='chief's' clan). (wearing a Chinese coat, not the usual plaid of striped nettle-fibre home-made cloth.) see No. 13*
Royal Anthropological Institute, London, Photographic Collection (194)

This album of fifty-nine photographs of 'Types of Natives of Nepal, Sikhim, and Tibet' was made by the Calcutta firm of Johnston & Hoffman, probably in a Darjeeling studio, for L.A. Waddell, who subsequently presented the album to the Anthropological Institute.

The Rong are more usually known by their Nepali designation as 'Lepcha', and Waddell stresses the role the environment has played in shaping their character:

> living in a country which yields to him without husbandry, a profusion of wild fruits and edible roots and other jungle products, the Lepcha is naturally indolent and easy-going. His close companionship with nature has made him a naturalist, a tender of flowers, and something of a philosopher (1899, p.93).

A quarter-length profile of this subject

351

is embossed on the spine of Waddell's *Among the Himalayas*, but the text on the Lepcha is illustrated with an image of another Rong wearing the 'authentic' 'plaid of blue and white striped cloth of home-spun nettle-fibre' (1899, p.94).

Waddell spent a large part of his career in medicine and public health before becoming Professor of Tibetan at University College, London. He was a Professor of Chemistry and Pathology at the Medical College in Calcutta and a Deputy Sanitary Commissioner, which somehow gave him the opportunity to explore ancient Buddhist sites. In 1903–4 he was a member of the Tibet Mission to Lhasa. C.P.

LITERATURE: Waddell 1899; Poignant 1980, p.11.

352 E.H. Man with Andamanese friends

Unknown photographer, *c.*1878
Albumen print, 14.2 × 10.5 ($5 5\frac{9}{10} \times 4 1\frac{3}{10}$)
Pitt Rivers Museum, University of Oxford (B30.5e)

E.H. Man's father had annexed the Andamans, part of a chain of islands in the Bay of Bengal, for the British administration in India in 1858, with the intention of using it as a penal colony for mutineers from the 1857 Rebellion. In 1869, after his father had secured the intervention of the Viceroy, Lord Mayo, E.H. Man arrived in Port Blair to take up an assistant superintendentship in the Andamans where he was to continue working until his retirement as Deputy Superintendent in 1901. During his professional career Man served as District Magistrate, escorted Indian convicts to and from the Andamans and was in charge of the Andamanese 'Homes' inhabited by those who had been dispossessed of their land and livelihood during the building of the huge circular prison at Port Blair. This prison continued to be used for political and 'terrorist' prisoners into the twentieth century and was the scene of a series of celebrated hunger strikes during the late 1930s (Sinha 1988). Man quickly became interested in the Andamanese people, their language and customs. He was also appointed officer in charge of the Nicobars, a group of islands to the south of the Andamans which had come under British control in 1869; he developed a great interest in this area

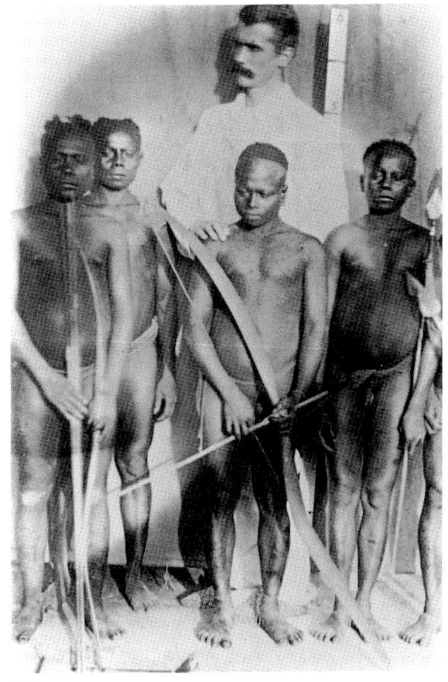

352

too, spending some six and a half years in residence here during his working life. On one occasion he brought with him the five Andamanese friends in this photograph. Man had a paternalistic devotion to the inhabitants of both groups of islands: 'he treated the Nicobarese as backward but well-meaning younger brethren; the Andamanese as wayward but attractive younger children'; 'his consideration for both indigenous peoples made him a humane and sympathetic governor' (Prain n.d. [1932], p.21).

In 1876, after receiving a copy of the first edition of the British Association's *Notes and Queries on Anthropology*, Man followed the advice given there and began to organize his data – including his very fine photographs. He published several papers in anthropological journals, a Nicobar Dictionary, and significant posthumous publications on the Andamans and Nicobars. He was also an avid collector of material culture, so much so that when threatened with further objects to display in the new Pitt Rivers Museum in Oxford, one university professor complained that Man was 'the sort of man who might send four or five entire Nicobar villages with all the inhabitants besides' (Edwards 1989, pp.75–6). C.P.

LITERATURE: Prain n.d. (1932); Poignant 1980, pp.12–13; Sinha 1988; Edwards 1989, pp.71–8, ill. pl. 37.

EXHIBITION: London, Photographers Gallery/Royal Anthropological Institute (and tour), *Observers of Man* 1980 (27024).

353 Two photographs of Andamanese in Port Blair

G.E. Dobson, May 1872
i) Chief and wife
Albumen print, 21.9 × 19 ($8\frac{2}{3} \times 7\frac{1}{2}$)
Inscribed on rev.: *No. 1. Chief of a Tribe of Andamanese living in the vicinity of Port Blair, and his wife*
Royal Anthropological Institute, London, Photographic Collection (5758)
ii) Female Andamanese
Albumen print, 21.6 × 19.4 ($8\frac{1}{2} \times 7\frac{2}{3}$)
Inscribed on rev.: *No.II. Group of five young Andamanese Women*
Royal Anthropological Institute, London, Photographic Collection (5759)

Dobson was a zoologist with the Indian Museum, Calcutta, and visited the Andamans to collect specimens in April and May 1872. The chief and his wife were photographed by Dobson on 4 May outside a Government 'Home' a few miles north of Port Blair.

Port Blair, which became the capital of the Andamans, was first occupied by the East India Company in 1789 and was then reoccupied in 1858. On both occasions there was resistance by the Andamanese, regarded by the Company as 'cupidity':

> Steps were taken, therefore, to teach the natives their aggressors' ideas of the laws of property, and when they had learned to appreciate the laws of other nations,

353(i)

353(ii)

> further efforts were made to establish Homes near the harbour for such survivors of the outlawed tribes as might be in need of food and lodging (Prain n.d., p.9).

The chief, controlled in his Government 'Home', was photographically emasculated in the *Journal of the Anthropological Institute* in which this image was used to illustrate Dobson's account. Here the chief's genitalia were obscured by a protective thicket of vegetation produced by scratching the negative. E.B. Tylor, who reproduced the image in his influential *Anthropology* (1881, p.88), dispensed with the whole of the bottom half of the couple.

The photograph of female Andamanese depicts a group who were perhaps even more incorporated within colonial society. Dobson notes that

> the central figure ... is that of a girl brought up from infancy at the Andamanese Orphan School, in Ross Island. This girl I had seen almost every day sitting in front of the school-house, and on Sunday at church, neatly dressed in white (1875, p.464).

Whereas propriety had demanded that the chief be covered up and deprived of any signs of potency, the scientific quest for authenticity demanded that the girl be revealed, stripped bare in all her 'primitive' reality, 'destitute of clothes, shaved, and greased with a mixture of olive-coloured mud and fat' (1875, p.464). C.P.

LITERATURE: Dobson 1875, pp. 457–67, ill. fpp. 456, 467; Praine n.d. (1932), pp.1–24; Poignant 1980, ill. p.9; Theye 1985, ill. p.66; Edwards 1989, pp. 71–8, ill. fp. 44.

354 *Henta-Koi*

Nicobar Islands, *c.*1880
Areca spathe, 169 × 129 (66½ × 44)
The Trustees of the British Museum
(As. 11[13].A)

This is a particularly beautiful example of a Nicobarese *henta-koi*, a shield to ward off malign spirits which was installed by a shaman (*Menluana*) in Nicobarese houses affected by sickness (Man n.d., p.76). It includes depictions of Nicobarese huts, animals (pigs, elephants, snakes), a long line of alternating dancing males and females, and at the bottom an extraordinarily precise array of aquatic life-forms (fish, crocodiles and a male mermaid, and below this a selection of squid, clams and crabs). The shield also includes more obvious signs of the Nicobarese contact with the outside world such as huge sailing ships, ships' compasses, pocket-watches, umbrellas and telescopes. Other such shields depict envelopes, guns and mirrors.

354

The Nicobar Islands, which were ceded to the Indian Government in 1869, had, since 1711 at least, experienced contact with Jesuit missionaries, Danes and the British, and for some time prior to this had been visited by Burmese, Malay and Ceylonese traders. It is accordingly difficult to identify precisely the iconography of these shields – many appear to combine costume elements of several of these contact areas in their central naval figures, a transformation of the figure Deuse. This example, however, which was probably collected by E.H. Man, almost certainly represents the British presence in the Nicobars and contains a fascinating transformation of a 'traditional' form described by De Röepstorff: he comments on a shield in which 'to the right are the various weapons used by hunters' (Man n.d., p.76). At the top right of this shield there is also an array of weapons, but here they appear to be arranged in a museum-like display guarded by a European. The possibility that this is a comment on European collecting activity is made more likely by its position at the top of the shield opposite a vignette showing captive chickens being tended, and a precisely delineated European dining-table on which are placed a decanter and glasses. Further down the panel, sailing ships of various origin are depicted (other shields show more clearly men-of-war, dhows and junks).

Signs of the exotic – in this case foreign power embodied in watches, mirrors, guns and writing – appear to be invoked as a source of strength to preserve the Nicobarese. The history of shields is very uncertain; Boden Closs suggests that 'the figures, pictures, and charms of many localities may be to some extent merely a degraded survival of the religious paraphernalia of the Jesuit missionaries' (1903, p.234). C.P.

LITERATURE: Man n.d., illus. fp.135; Ball 1875, pp.341–2; Man 1882, pl. XXV, p.293; Temple 1901; Boden Closs 1903, ill. fp.234.

355 Nicobarese drawing of E.H. Man photographing Nicobarese children

Unknown artist, accompanying slip dated 24 October 1885
Pencil on paper, 21 × 11 ($8\frac{1}{4} \times 4\frac{1}{4}$)
Royal Anthropological Institute, London, Photographic Collection (35612)

This drawing, evidently by a Nicobarese, transfers onto paper the style of the *henta-koi* with its layered frames, incorporating a scene of E.H. Man at work with his camera. An accompanying handwritten slip by Man describes the uppermost scene as 'E.H.M. taking a photo of some Nicobarese [children]. A Police orderly and a servant holding an umbrella are in attendance.' The slip also gives Nicobarese words for the various aquatic creatures depicted in the centre, including a crocodile, a porpoise, a turtle and a ray-fish. The lower panel 'represents the station St. Nancowry at anchor with Malacca village, Spiteful Bay and Leda Pt. in the background.'

355

Man's photographic activities were later invoked by Boden Closs in the Nicobars:

> Now and then we made rather unwarranted use of his reputation – did we want [*sic*] the portrait of a native who was rather nervous at the sight of the camera. 'here, come along, and don't be afraid, Mr Man does this,' and it was all right (1903, f.n. p.75). C.P.

PROVENANCE: Tipped into one of two photographic albums given by Man to Royal Anthropological Institute.

356 Observations on external characters of Andamanese

M.V. Portman, 1894
Printed schedule, 33 × 19.5 ($13 \times 7\frac{1}{2}$)
The Trustees of the British Museum

Portman's vast survey of the physical characteristics of the Andamanese, made with the help of W. Molesworth, a surgeon-captain in the Indian Medical Service in 1893–4, was probably the most elaborate such operation in the history of the British empire. The total (incomplete) survey consists of eleven large volumes and four smaller volumes of physiological data and photographs (see no.357). The latter consist of printed schedules detailing fifty-four items of information under the heading *Observations on External Characters*, to which tracings of the subject's hands and feet were appended. The final blank page of the form left room for more detailed observations, including in some cases an assessment of the subject's tempera-

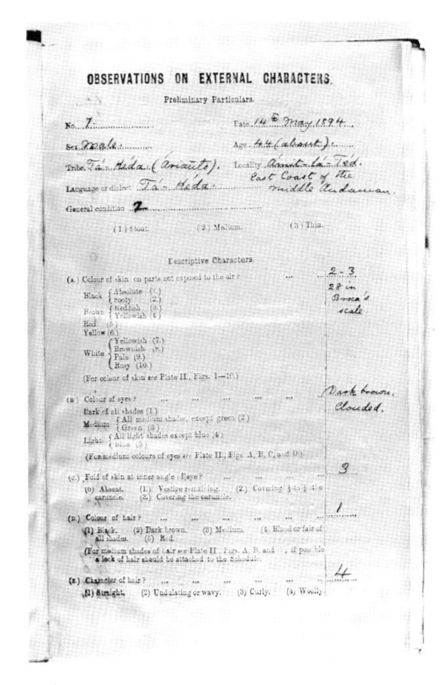

OBSERVATIONS ON EXTERNAL CHARACTERS.

Preliminary Particulars.

No. 7. Date 14th May 1894.
Sex Male. Age 44 (about).
Tribe Tá-Heda (Ariauto). Locality Ámit-la-Ted. East Coast of the middle Andaman.
Language or dialect Tá-Heda.
General condition 2
(1) Stout. (2) Medium. (3) Thin.

Descriptive Characters.

(A.) Colour of skin on parts not exposed to the air? ... 2-3 28 in Broca's scale
Black { Absolute (1.) Sooty (2.) }
Brown { Reddish (3.) Yellowish (4.) }
Red (5.)
Yellow (6.)
White { Yellowish (7.) Brownish (8.) Pale (9.) Rosy (10.) }
(For colour of skin see Plate II., Figs. 1—10.)

(B.) Colour of eyes? ... Dark brown. Clouded.
Dark of all shades (1.)
Medium { All medium shades, except green (2.) Green (3.) }
Light { All light shades except blue (4.) blue (5.) }
(For medium colours of eyes see Plate II., Figs. A, B, C, and D.)

(C.) Fold of skin at inner angle of eye? ... 3
(0) Absent. (1.) Vestige remaining. (2.) Covering ½ to ½ the caruncle. (3.) Covering the caruncle.

(D.) Colour of hair? ... 1
(1) Black. (2) Dark brown. (3) Medium. (4) Blond or fair of all shades. (5) Red.
(For medium shades of hair see Plate II., Figs. A, B, and C; if possible a lock of hair should be attached to the Schedule.

(E.) Character of hair? ... 4
(1) Straight. (2) Undulating or wavy. (3) Curly. (4) Woolly.

356

ment. Portman and Molesworth generated statistical norms from this mass of evidence, and their Preface gives average figures for height, pulse beats per minute, rates of abdominal and upper abdominal breathing, rates of respiration, temperature and weight of males of the North Andamans. Portman, the Officer in Charge of the Andamanese, noted that 'they are not the vindictive savages some people think,' but that 'their tractability and usefulness, becomes less ... after they pass forty years of age' (1894, Preface). C.P.

LITERATURE: Portman 1899; Desmond 1982, p.36; Falconer n.d. (1984), pp.37–9.

357 Anthropometric study of Andamanese woman

M.V. Portman, *c.*1893
Platinotype
The Trustees of the British Museum

This study is from Portman's huge photographic and statistical survey of the Andamans, copies of which were sent to the British Museum and the Government of India. In 1893 Portman rephotographed some of his earlier

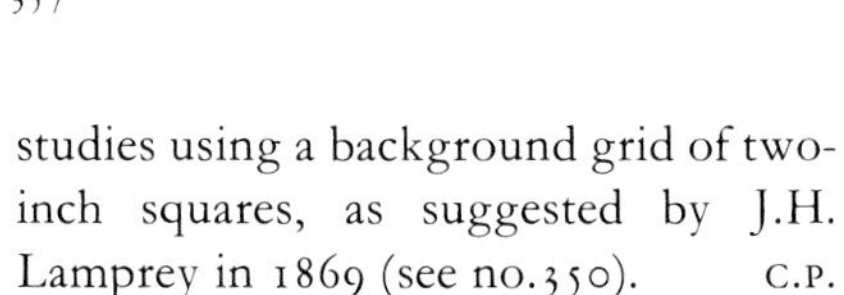

357

358(i)

358(ii)

studies using a background grid of two-inch squares, as suggested by J.H. Lamprey in 1869 (see no.350). C.P.

LITERATURE: Desmond 1982, ill. (from same series) pl. 43; Falconer n.d. (1984), ill. (from same series) fig. 34.

358 (i) Photograph showing stage of manufacture of an Andaman adze

M.V. Portman, 1893
Platinotype print, 34.1 × 27 ($13\frac{3}{8} \times 10\frac{2}{3}$)
Royal Anthropological Institute, London Photographic Collection (830)

358 (ii) Photograph illustrating the manufacture of the South Andaman bow

M.V. Portman, 1893
Platinotype print, 32.9 × 25.2 (13 × 10)
Royal Anthropological Institute, London, Photographic Collection (824)

Portman had first offered to make a series of photographs for the British Museum in 1889. These would show:

> every step in the making of a weapon, etc., so clearly, that with the assistance of the finished articles now in the British Museum, it would be possible for a European workman to imitate the mode of work (quoted by Falconer n.d., p.37).

Portman had also pledged to explain in the letterpress 'any notable peculiarity which cannot be expressed photographically'. This image, which comes about half-way through the sequence on adze manufacture, bears the following letterpress:

> A long wedge of wood is then taken, pushed in between the slips of 'Chaara' bark, which were placed there to prevent the wedge touching either the blade or the cane fastening, and pushing them out of position, is hammered home and then cut off short.

Portman's letterpress notes of no.358(ii):

> The most remarkable feature of this bow, in which it differs from the 'Jarawa' bows in the Andamans, and, I believe, any other bowes [*sic*] elsewhere in the world is its shape; the lower half of the bow being straight and the upper half curved. It is therefore necessary for this bow to select a tree or branch, similar to that in the photograph ... C.P.

LITERATURE: Falconer n.d. (1984), pp.16–46.

359 Adze from the Andaman Islands, *c.*1886

Wood, cane and iron, length 1.36 ($53\frac{1}{2}$)
Inscribed top of head: *M.V. Portman 1886 49*
The Trustees of the British Museum (86.11–29.49B)

An adze similar to that shown in no. 358(i). M.V. Portman collected several dozen such adzes for British museums. C.P.

360 Andaman Island bow

Wood, length 1.80 ($70\frac{7}{8}$)
The Trustees of the British Museum (86–11–291a)

This bow from the South and Middle Andamans was collected by M.V. Portman in 1886 for the British Museum. See no.358. C.P.

361 *The Andaman Islanders: A Study in Social Anthropology*, Cambridge, 1922

A.R. Brown (Radcliffe-Brown)
Printed book, 504pp., 22.5 × 33 ($8\frac{7}{8} \times 13$)
The British Library Board (010007.ee.25)

Radcliffe-Brown's book, based on fieldwork between 1906 and 1908, was, as other exhibits shown here demonstrate, just one in a long line of studies of the Andamans. However, whereas many of these earlier works, such as M.V. Portman's, were concerned with individuals as illustrative of a larger class or norm, professional anthropologists, among whom Radcliffe-Brown became a leading figure, saw these groups as instances of variation within the much broader classification of Mankind. Radcliffe-Brown, who was Rivers's first pupil in social anthropology at Cambridge, was known as 'Anarchy Brown' during the period that he conducted fieldwork. (His name was Alfred Reginald Brown until 1926, when he changed his name by deedpoll.) A Cambridge contemporary, E.L. Grant Watson, later wrote that Brown 'had lived as a primitive autocrat, exercising a beneficent but completely authoritarian sway over the simple Andamanese, who had not been in a position to criticise his grand gestures' (Kuper 1973, p.55).

The subtitle to his book (whose publication was greatly delayed by World War One) is significant, indicating a decisive shift away from the physical and quantitative concerns of earlier investigators, and it is noteworthy that although he deposited his large collection of skulls and skeletons in the Cambridge University Museum of Anthropology, he did not publish any results of his work on physical anthropology. Radcliffe-Brown represented a new breed of professional anthropologists who were able to claim, on the basis of relatively short study, a greater knowledge of a people than other investigators who lacked access to the validating professional structures and textual strategies of social anthropology. He is, for instance, dismissive of the contributions of earlier writers such as E.H. Man and M.V. Portman, although he relied heavily upon some of their data. The days of the amateur ethnographer, the administrator/anthropologist and the missionary recorder of local custom were numbered.

This modern 'social anthropology' saw the displacement of the desire for certainty on the part of the investigator from tangible outward physical features in favour of a system of knowledge whose reliability was vouchsafed by the writer's familiarity through direct contact with his subject. Whereas earlier work stressed the objectivity of measurements, photographs and other evidence, twentieth-century anthropologists proved their expertise by their own experience – by 'being there', living in a locality and learning a language which allowed of 'direct speech'. The criticism levelled against Radcliffe-Brown since this book was published shows how decisively the paradigm had shifted by the time his study emerged: it is pointed out that after a period struggling to learn the vernacular he came to rely on an English-speaking member of the Akar-Bale (p.viii) and that his general method of data collection was inadequate (Kuper 1973, p.59). C.P.

LITERATURE: Kuper 1973, pp.51–88; Thomas 1990, pp.20–4.

362 Caste handbooks for the Indian Army

i) *Rajputs*, Simla, 1898
Captain A.H. Bingley
Printed book, 181 pp., plus appendices and map, spine height 24.5 ($9\frac{3}{4}$)
School of Oriental and African Studies, University of London (JA.305.8)

ii) *Marathas and Dekhani Musalmans*, Calcutta, 1908
Major R.M. Betham
Printed book, 145 pp., plus appendices and map, spine height 24.5 ($9\frac{3}{4}$)
School of Oriental and African Studies, University of London (S.IV.3.270)

These two handbooks, 'intended primarily for the instruction of young officers' (Betham, preface) were part of a series that included studies of Pathans, 'Hindustani' and 'Panjabi' Muslims, Gurkhas, Brahmins, Mappillas or Moplah, Jats, Gujars and Ahirs, and Dogras. Like other 'applied' manuals (such as those produced by the Tea District Labour Association), much use was made of anthropological works – Bingley acknowledges the use of Crooke and Ibbetson, providing proof perhaps of Risley's claim that it was impossible in India to say where science began and administration ended.

The military value of the Rajput – the Kshatriya, or traditional warrior group – is firmly located in descent and genetics. A table of 'recruiting grounds showing clans in each district and the value of districts' (Bingley, Appendix C) warns against recruiting from certain districts, such as those in Rohilkhund, because 'a large number of the Rajputs are spurious'. In Etawah District in Agra Division, by contrast, they are 'good, especially along the banks of the Chambal'.

The manual contains much practical advice for both the recruiter and the commanding officer, relating to matters such as the appropriate period of leave to be granted to attend funeral ceremonies, and information on the Hindu ritual year, together with a military enumeration of the chief characteristics of the Hindu tradition. C.P.

LITERATURE: *Handbook of Castes and Tribes* 1924; Fox 1985.

363 Model of a bullock cart

Wood and cane, 75 × 42 ($29\frac{1}{2}$ × $16\frac{1}{2}$)
Attached label: *Model of a Bullock cart with a tilt of plaitted cane*
The Trustees of the British Museum (1901.6–5.80)

This model of a cart from Raipur in central India was almost certainly exhibited at the 1900 Paris Exposition, together with the Toda temple (no.392).

363

Such carts (minus the tilt) remain the chief means of haulage in rural areas and a symbol of an 'authentic' village India. An elaborate description of a (slightly different) Bihar bullock cart is given in Grierson (1926, pp.28–32). C.P.

LITERATURE: Grierson 1926.

364 Model of a Brahmin

Clay and wood, height 12.7 (5)
Attached label: *Bt. from India by the late Prof. Cowell*
Cambridge University Museum of Archaeology and Anthropology (1907.E.498Asia Box 4.B.12. Size 2)

From Warren Hastings onwards the British regarded the Brahmin more than any other grouping within India as the repository of the authentic and textually pure voice of Hinduism. While Hinduism and Indian social organization were seen to be carrying out some grand ancient scheme the Brahmins – literate mediators between the ordinary Hindu and the codified religious laws embodying divine injunctions – were seen as closest to the ideal plan.

Anthropologists were no less eager to purvey these 'privileged' Brahminical views, especially concerning 'caste' and 'dharma', or duty. Many anthropologists believed (some still do) that the Brahmins gave voice to ideals which every segment of Hindu society strove to copy, however imperfectly, through processes of 'Sanskritization'. More recent analyses, however, suggest that many anthropologists fell into the same trap as Warren Hastings and mistook a partial, idealistic view of Hindu society for a realistic, sociological consensus covering all groups within that society. In this view, even mid- and late-twentieth-century anthropological theories of caste perpetuate the error. The most influential exponent of this learned Brahminic perspective has been the French scholar Louis Dumont:

> In the relatively isolated, traditional, mountain village in which I did my initial Indian field research, I recounted to low caste people an explanation of caste almost identical to that which Dumont has since conveyed in his 1966 work *Homo Hierarchicus* (for it is a common one). They laughed, and one of them said, 'You have been talking with Brahmins.' And so I had. And so it seems, has Professor Dumont (Berreman 1971, p.23).

Professor E.B. Cowell, who purchased this model, is best known for his translations from Pāli of the Buddhist Jātaka stories in 1905. C.P.

PROVENANCE: Purchased by E.B. Cowell; donated to present owners by R. Bendall, 1907.

LITERATURE: Cowell 1905; Berreman 1971, vol. 5, pp.16–23; Raheja 1988, vol. 17, pp.497–522.

365 Figures of caste 'types' including a sadhu, musician, government employee, Muslims, pandits and a coolie

Clay and wood, various sizes
Cambridge University Museum of Archaeology and Anthropology (2.21092 [A–M] Box 4.B.11)

These miniature models of Indian 'types' (known variously as 'Lucknow' and 'Krishnanagar' models) were ostensibly designed to reveal to the museum visitor the different dress and stature of particular caste, occupational and religious groupings. They can also be seen as part of a more general strategy which attempted to understand and contain (and indeed maintain) the diversity of Indian peoples. Such models, together with other representations, produced a parallel miniature world to the one which the British were struggling to control. On the one hand, such models acted as a form of reassurance, rather in the same way that the contemporary West's interest in hand-made models of

364

365

cars, ships and aircraft manages to transform a bewildering mass-product of technology into the product of one's own hand (Stewart 1984, p.58). But on the other hand they also sever the possibility of what is represented answering back, and displace a sense of India's history onto a static space in a strategy whose colonial and anthropological practices have been described by Said and Fabian. As Susan Stewart notes in a discussion of the history of the miniature in Western society, there is a tendency towards the 'tableau' rather than towards 'narrative' – 'the observer is offered a transcendent and simultaneous view of the miniature, yet is trapped outside the possibility of a lived reality of the miniature. Hence the nostalgic desire to present the lower classes, peasant life, or the cultural other within a timeless and uncontaminatable miniature form' (Stewart 1984, p.66).

These miniature models also exemplify a colonial concern with what has been called 'the philosophy of the thing' in which '"things" seemed more and more to be built, arranged, handled or consumed as "signs of" something further' (Mitchell 1988, p.172), a process to which this exhibit and catalogue entry further contributes. Within India, as in many other colonies, this is apparent in the development of 'museums and zoological gardens, in Orientalist congresses and libraries, in statistics and legal codes ...' (Mitchell 1988, p.172).

Fine examples of similar, largely nineteenth-century models, many in elaborate tableaux, can be seen in the Albert Hall (City) Museum, Jaipur (thugs and headwear), the Dr Bhau Daji Lad Museum, Bombay (headwear, 'types' and occupations), and the Indian Museum, Calcutta (rural occupations, indigo plantations and factory scenes, including a tableau, 'searching workers leaving the factory'). C.P.

LITERATURE: Said 1978; Fabian 1983; Stewart 1984; Mitchell 1988.

366

366 'Caste marks'

*c.*1910
Iron, assorted designs
One with attached label: *a seal wherewith the pious man or woman of some Vania caste made his or her caste mark with red or white paste each morning. Baroda*
Cambridge University Museum of Archaeology and Anthropology (1912.208; 27.893; 1912.206–20 [Box 40.A.1])

Patterns and insignia, made usually on the forehead with a variety of coloured pastes, were among the many signs which early visitors to India gratefully took as a means of identifying the diverse groups they encountered. The Abbé DuBois noted that 'there are several castes ... which may be distinguished by certain marks painted on the forehead or other parts of the body' (1906, p.24), and in 1800 Fra Paolino da San Bartomoleo in *A Voyage to the East Indies* identified sixteen 'hieroglyphical marks of distinction' (Sherriffs 1916, p.2). In fact, these marks denoted sectarian allegiance rather than 'caste'. They were one set of signs, together with occupation, *varna, jati,* physique and costume, through which British observers sought to order India into a fully legible hierarchy. C.P.

LITERATURE: DuBois 1906; Sherriffs 1916, pp.1–10.

367 Bengal Police measurement roll card

From Colonel H.M. Ramsay, *Anthropometry in Bengal, Or, Identification of Criminals by Anthropometric Measurement and Thumb Impressions,* London, 1895, Appendix VIII
Printed book, 42 pp., spine height 24 (9½)
The Trustees of the British Museum

Prior to the acceptance of fingerprinting as a sole and reliable means of ascertaining identity, various anthropometric methods were used by the Indian Police for identification and by early criminologists who produced theories which made 'criminality' discernible in physiology and physiognomy. In India the Bertillon system was adopted. In 1894 the British Home Secretary, following the lead of the Bengal Police, issued orders for the adoption in England of

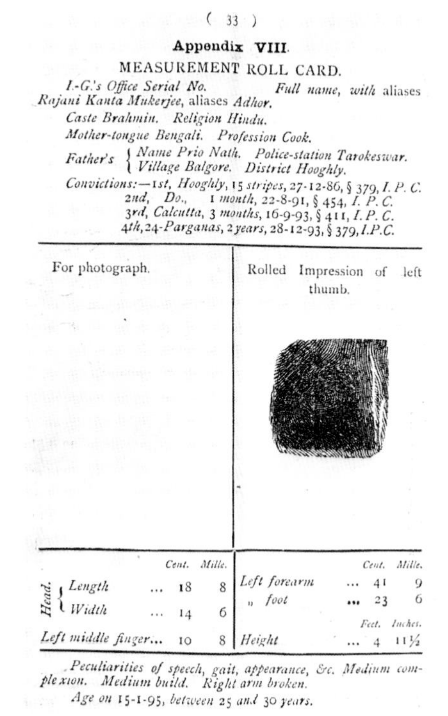

(33)

Appendix VIII.

MEASUREMENT ROLL CARD.

I.-G.'s Office Serial No. *Full name, with* aliases *Rajani Kanta Mukerjee,* aliases *Adhor.*

Caste Brahmin. Religion Hindu.

Mother-tongue Bengali. Profession Cook.

Father's { *Name Prio Nath. Police-station Tarokeswar.* / *Village Balgore. District Hooghly.* }

Convictions:—1st, Hooghly, 15 *stripes,* 27-12-86, § 379, *I. P. C.*
2nd, Do., 1 *month,* 22-8-91, § 454, *I. P. C.*
3rd, Calcutta, 3 *months,* 16-9-93, § 411, *I. P. C.*
4th, 24-Parganas, 2 *years,* 28-12-93, § 379, *I.P.C.*

For photograph.	Rolled Impression of left thumb.

		Cent.	*Mille.*		*Cent.*	*Mille.*
Head.	*Length* ...	18	8	*Left forearm* ...	41	9
	Width ...	14	6	" *foot* ...	23	6
					Feet.	*Inches.*
Left middle finger...		10	8	*Height* ...	4	11½

Peculiarities of speech, gait, appearance, &c. Medium complexion. Medium build. Right arm broken.

Age on 15-1-95, *between* 25 *and* 30 *years.*

367

the Bertillon system and also Galton's system of classifying fingerprints which was a development of Herschel's earlier work in Bengal.

The system advocated by Bertillon, which involved eleven measurements and seven classifications of the colour of the eyes, in a sense merely named what was already taking place in India. An anonymous civil surgeon in Berar, writing to the *Times of India* in 1890, claimed to have been operating his own identical system in local jails since 1887, and tables of caste measurements were offered in journals as contributions to 'police detective anthropometry' from the early 1890s onwards (see *Journal of the Anthropological Society of Bombay*, vol. II, 1890, p.367). The work of Cesare Lombroso in particular encouraged amateur ethnographers to compile data which promised to be useful in the administration of India. In 1890 Dr J. Gerson Da Cunha was able to tell the Anthropological Society of Bombay that the 'local criminal annals' supplied 'an immense amount of materials to fill up the canvas with full-size figures, illustrative of this branch of anthropology' (p.361).

In more general terms, Ramsay's exposition of the Bengal system of anthropometry and fingerprinting, with its elaborate filing and cross-checking system, can be seen as a median stage in the development of a belief that an imperial form of truth and scientific prowess could ensure the efficient administration of British rule in India. An early stage of this could be seen in 1856, in the belief of Dr Norman Chevers (Secretary to the Medical Board at Fort William) that photography was so powerful that when confronted with photographic records of the scenes of their ghastly deeds murderers would confess. A later stage appeared a few years after Ramsay's work, advocating the combined use of anthropometry and fingerprinting, when in 1899 E.R. Henry, Inspector General of the Bengal Police, proposed the sole use of fingerprints because '*being absolute impressions* taken from the body under conditions which *eliminate error in transcribing or recording*, the "Personal Equation" error is reduced to a minimum'. C.P.

LITERATURE: Chevers 1856; Gerson Da Cunha 1890, pp.354–67; Henry 1899; Herschel 1916.

368 Sir Herbert Hope Risley, KCIE, CSI

Lafayette, *c.*1910

Vintage print with signature, 20.2 × 14.2 ($7\frac{9}{10} \times 5\frac{1}{2}$)

Royal Anthropological Institute, London (Presidents' Portraits Collection; 1143)

Following the publication of *The Tribes and Castes of Bengal* in 1891, Risley rose to become the leading figure within Indian anthropology, as well as an important figure in the administration of India. From 1890 onwards he served on a commission with the Indian police, worked for the Bengal and Imperial Government Secretariats, became honorary Director of the Ethnological Survey of the Indian Empire (with the encouragement of Curzon), and in 1899 he was appointed Census Commissioner for the 1901 decennial Census of the Empire. He later became Home Secretary under Curzon and then a temporary member of the Council of the Governor-General. He was actively involved in a number of scholarly fields, being a President of the Asiatic Society of Bengal, a Trustee of the Indian Museum, Secretary of the Queen Victoria Memorial Committee, and for the last two years of his life, President of the Royal Anthropological Institute.

Risley's reputation declined almost as quickly as it rose. Although he had a

368

few enthusiastic supporters and followers (see, for example, Anderson 1913), within British anthropology the tide turned very quickly against both anthropometry and Risley's particular version of it. Risley rates no mention at all in Haddon's 1910 *History of Anthropology,* and in his introduction to the posthumous second edition of Risley's *The People of India,* William Crooke itemises recent criticisms of Risley's approach, concentrating in particular on the need to stress environmental factors and the mutability and contingent nature of caste in future studies. C.P.

LITERATURE: Risley 1891, vol. xx; Haddon 1910; Anderson 1913; Risley 1915, frontispiece; Rothermund 1968, pp.131–58; Cohn 1987.

369 *The Tribes and Castes of Bengal,* Calcutta, 1891

H.H. Risley
Printed book, 2 vols., 429 pp., 443 pp., spine height 25.5 (10)
School of Oriental and African Studies, London University (IV.3.104.5.35426 a/b, iv.3.104 a/b)

Two volumes of this work financed by the Bengal Government consist of anthropometric data (measurements of 6,000 types of heads representing 89 different sections of the population) collected by Dr James Wise and Risley using the latest instruments developed by Topinard. It was from this data that Risley came to his famous conclusion concerning the importance of the 'nasal index' as a guide to caste status, and a general theory concerning the 'biological' basis of caste which was to be hotly contested by Crooke and others. The other two volumes comprise the ethnographic glossary produced through a system of correspondence with 190 'coadjutors'. This involved 'a series of leading questions to be answered by the district officers, missionaries, native scholars, and such other private correspondents and local agents as he could enlist in the work' (*The Times*, 24 August 1891), a system which he later systematized in his *Manual of Ethnography* (see no.370).

Risley stresses the administrative utility of his work: 'He shows how such a survey will be a help to a good government; that, instead of being a mere scientific luxury, as it might be in Europe, it was almost an administrative necessity in a country like Bengal' (*The Times*).

Risley's work developed a useful ideology which allowed the British to establish themselves within a historically sanctioned niche in Indian society. The argument Risley develops around an image printed on the cover of his work makes a contribution towards this.

Like many imperial publications, Risley's work was a masterpiece of the bookbinder's art. Even in its 'Official edition, circulated for criticism' it was carefully bound in mock vellum and imprinted in red with a scene from one of the carvings at Sanchi of a Buddhist *jātaka* story. Three women kneel in prayer in front of an altar. To the right of this a procession of monkeys brings offerings, while in the background four figures of 'tall stature, regular features . . . look on with folded hands and apparent approval at this remarkable act of worship.' For Risley this is the 'sculptured expression of the race sentiment of the Aryans towards the Dravidians, which runs through the whole course of Indian tradition and survives in scarcely abated strength at the present day. . . . It shows us the higher race on friendly terms with the lower, but keenly conscious of the essential difference of type' (1891, vol.I, p.i). This conclusion, which ran counter to the accepted truths of Indology, illustrated an important element in Risley's theory of caste as being originally caused by the marital strategies of invader societies; but there is also here a covert and significant suggestion that Britain was to India as the Aryans were to Dravidians. As a member of the Indian Civil Service, Risley must have enjoyed his position as an 'English Brahmin', but his argument here suggests that he believed that this was more than just whimsically the case.

C.P.

LITERATURE: *Journal of the Anthropological Institute* 1892, pp.335–41; Klass 1980, pp.42–58.

370 *Manual of Ethnography for India – General Instructions, Definitions and Ethnographic Questions,* Calcutta, 1907

H.H. Risley
Printed pamphlet, 27 pp., 25 × 18 ($9\frac{7}{8}$ × 7)
India Office Library and Records (P/V 124 Sir H.H. Risley)

Although the Government of India responded warmly to Sir William Plowden's suggestion in 1882 that a comprehensive ethnographic survey be undertaken throughout India, it was not until 1901 that, at the behest of Curzon, any money was forthcoming to make this possible. It was then decided that there should be an Ethnographic Survey involving 'the systematic description of the history, structure, traditions, religions, and social usages of the various races, tribes, and castes in India,' and in addition an Anthropometric Survey concerned with the determination through measurement of the physical characteristics of the groups under study. The Ethnographic Survey was largely devolved to regional Superintendents of Ethnography and was to result in works such as Iyer's *Tribes and Castes of Cochin* (1909–12) and Russell and Hiralal's *Tribes and Castes of the Central Provinces* (1916). For the purposes of anthropometry India was divided into two – Edgar Thurston took charge of the south while Risley covered the rest of India (Risley 1911, p.16). As Director of Ethnography Risley was also in overall control of the large ethnographic investigation and sought to set out basic guidelines in this manual, much of which was written in 1902. Risley's preface, which discusses his earlier experience in Bengal, gives an interesting insight into his method of data collection:

> Each correspondent was supplied with a list of castes to be enquired into and with a copy of the *thana* statistics in which all obscure names were marked . . . send for any persons who have a local reputation for extensive acquaintance with castes, and go through the caste statistics with them noting down the explanation they give of the entries underlined in red in the copy of the statistics forwarded to you by me (1907, pp. 2, 4).

In a final lecture as President to the Anthropological Institute, shortly before his death, Risley turned to the relationship of such survey work to the emerging brand of anthropology based on intensive 'fieldwork' in one locality (he mentions Spencer and Gillen's work in central Australia and Rivers's work on the Todas). 'The Indian operations,' he wrote, 'fell far short of the high standard of research attained by these observers.' But he claims that his were merely 'surveys' intended to 'demarcate the field of vision ... leaving it to others to fill in details as time and opportunity may serve' (1911, p.19). C.P.

LITERATURE: Risley 1911, XLI, pp.8–19.

371 *The Tribes and Castes of the North-Western Provinces and Oudh*, Calcutta, 1896

William Crooke
Printed book, vols. 2, 3 and 4, 499 pp., 500 pp., 516 pp., each 25.3 × 16 (10 × 6¼)
India Office Library and Records (v6311)

The 200-page introduction to Crooke's huge work contains a robust critique of Risley's earlier work on Bengal, but the bulk of the four volumes is made up of an immensely detailed, alphabetically arranged ethnographic glossary which further refines the form initiated by Sherring (1872).

Crooke (1848–1923) spent all his official life as a magistrate and collector in the United Provinces of Agra and Awadh (Oudh). It was during his last posting at Mirzapur that he completed his *Tribes and Castes*. Crooke was a prolific author and editor, producing many other influential texts, editing the journal *Panjab Notes and Queries* and helping to re-popularize several important historical texts relating to India. However, 'he could not win the promotion to which his unusual acquirements entitled him' (Temple 1926, p.576), being an outspoken critic of the Secretariats and incurring official disapproval.

It is difficult to say what part his relations with Risley played in this neglect, but it is certain that throughout Risley's life the major challenge to his genetic and static view of caste (see no.369) came from Crooke, and it is ironic that after Risley's death Crooke should have offered to edit the second edition of Risley's *The People of India* (see India Office Library and Records, Risley Collection, Mss.Eur.E.295/27, sheaf 51).

In his 1896 work Crooke revived arguments which had been made earlier by such people as J.C. Nesfield and D. Ibbetson, that caste was the result of a 'community of function or occupation' (p.cxxxix) rather than the isolation of completely separate genetic, 'racial' groups over many thousands of years, as Risley had argued. Crooke followed Nesfield in arguing that 'a "stranger walking through the classrooms of the Sanskrit College at Benares would never dream of supposing that the students seated before him were distinct in race and blood from the scavengers who swept the roads"' (p.cxxv).

Crooke produced copious anthropometric data collected by Surgeon-Captain H.E. Drake-Brockman to refute Risley's arguments, concluding that 'no evidence could be more convincing, if anthropometry has any meaning' (p.cxxxvii) and he supported the suggestion made by C.J. O'Donnell in the 1891 Bengal Census Report that even Risley's own anthropometric data contradicts his argument. C.P.

LITERATURE: Sherring 1872; Crooke 1896; Keane 1898, pp.158–62; Temple 1926, pp.576–9.

372 Caste 'types' from Mirzapur

Sergeant Wallace, R.E., *c.* 1895
Albumen prints:
i) Bhangi, 19.3 × 14.3 (7½ × 5⅗)
ii) Brahmin Pandit, 19.3 × 13.8 (7½ × 5⅖)
iii) Chamars, 19.6 × 14.4 (7¾ × 5⅔)
iv) Mallah, 19.5 × 14.6 (7⅗ × 5¾)
Royal Anthropological Institute, London, Photographic Collection (2723, 2729, 2722, 2726)

Two of these images, those of the Chamars and the Mallah, appear as plates in Crooke's *Tribes and Castes of the North-Western Provinces* (no.371) where they are credited to 'Sergeant Wallace, R.E., of the Rurki College'. Wallace may well have learnt his skills at Chatham where, from 1856 onwards, photographic instruction formed part of the Royal Engineers' military training (Desmond 1985, p.53).

372(i)

All four photographs were taken at Mirzapur, near Benares, and illustrate caste groupings described in Crooke's glossary. The written entries draw upon the work of official and non-official enquiries, including 'a large body of native gentlemen' who are thanked for their 'generosity in devoting some of their scanty leisure to this investigation' (Crooke 1896, p.v).

The figures of the Brahmin and the Bhangi represent the two poles of the caste system as commonly understood. The Brahmin priest mediates between men and the gods and guards his purity from all those groups lower in the hierarchy, whereas the Bhangi, traditionally a sweeper and remover of night-soil, will accept food from nearly all those above him. The Bhangi photographed by Wallace was, judging by his dress, employed in an urban and probably British context, thus demonstrating the apparent paradox that for this caste at least growing urbanization from the nineteenth century onwards involved a return from village labour to their 'traditional' occupations within towns,

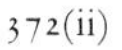

372(ii)

372(iii)

372(iv)

often as relatively highly paid municipal employees (see Searle-Chatterjee 1981). Chamars, like the Bhangis, are an Untouchable group, their 'traditional' occupation being the curing of skins and leatherworking. Social change, however, had further diminished their involvement in such work, with Crooke noting that increasing numbers were taking to field labour and other unskilled work (see Cohn 1955). The Mallah (boatman) is a further, more dramatic example of the impact of social and economic change, for his livelihood was being dramatically reduced by the growth of the railway system which was reducing river traffic (vol. III, p.467). The Chamars and the Mallah lent very strong support to Crooke's argument against Risley's contention that 'caste is a permanent institution, transmitted unchanged from the dawn of Hindu history and myth' (1896, p.xvi). C.P.

LITERATURE: Crooke 1896; Cohn 1955; Searle-Chatterjee 1981; Desmond 1985, pp.48–61.

373(i)

373(ii)

373 Photographs of 'Tamil Dancing Girl'

Unknown photographer, *c.* 1870
(i) Albumen print, 23.5 × 15.2 ($9\frac{3}{5} \times 6$)
(ii) Albumen print, 23.5 × 16 ($9\frac{3}{5} \times 6\frac{3}{5}$)
Cambridge University Museum of Archaeology and Anthropology

These three-quarter-length full face and profile studies of this striking subject suggest that although the photographic process was able to impart certainty, it was often difficult to establish precisely what this certainty was. A caption at the bottom of the image reads: *Indian/? Tamil/Dancing Girl/Kallar,* indicating that it was first thought that she was a representative of the Kallars, a group of predatory cattle-keepers (Bayly 1989, p.22). Having dispensed with this, a wider south Indian identity as a Tamil is also questioned. This doubt persists in a further note on the mount – *the jacket worn is called 'navakkai' in Tamil. These women are probably of Northern India (Hindus).* C.P.

LITERATURE: S. Bayly 1989.

374 Ethnographic Survey of India. Punjab and North-West Frontier Province. Notes and Queries

H.A. Rose, 1903
Cyclostyled typescript, 32 × 19 ($12\frac{1}{2} \times 7\frac{1}{2}$)
School of Oriental and African Studies, University of London (IV.3.L.99 35.151)

This is one of a large series of 'Notes and Queries' forms issued by H.A. Rose, the Superintendent of Ethnography for Punjab and the North-West Frontier Province, as part of the Ethnographic Survey of India. In a memo circulated in 1902, Rose explained that:

> It is not intended that the collection of material for the Survey should be made by highly-paid officers of the Government. Accounts of shrines, local beliefs, customs and practices, and even of tribes, can well be written by subordinate officials, or non-officials who are willing to undertake such work (memo on Ethnographic Survey, 23 August 1902, Simla).

Each circulated form requested specific points of information on particular groups – the first fifty include 'Eunuchs in Panipat', 'Head Compression among the Pathans', 'Tattooing in Nahan' and 'Superstitions and Beliefs connected with Mourning in Bahawalpur'. The form on 'the Telis' (illustrated here) requests information as to whether all Telis in the district are Muslim, whether they have *panchayats* and 'Who was Babu Hassan?' A reward of 50 rupees was offered for the best account, providing the following conditions were met:

> 1. Each account must be certified to be substantially correct by an officer of, or above, the rank of a Tahsildar.
> 2. Each account must, if written in English, be written on one side of the page only, or, if written in Urdu, accompanied by a correct translation in English which must be written on one side of the page only.
> 3. The decision of the Superintendent of Ethnography as to the award or awards of the reward is to be absolutely final.

Prizewinning entries were subsequently printed in Lahore or Simla and further circulated. These notes were printed on the right-hand side of the page only, 'in order that additions, corrections or comments may be inserted in the blank margin with as little trouble to correspondents as possible' (Rose, memo).

This system of data collection through questionnaires had first been suggested by Ibbetson in 1882, and was later perfected by Risley (1907). C.P.

LITERATURE: Ibbetson 1882; Risley 1907.

375 Ethnographic circular concerning astrology sent by E.A. Gait

Inscribed: *Circular No. 2 from E.A. Gait Esq. C.S., Superintendent of Ethnography, Bengal. To all District Officers and Local Correspondents on Ethnography. Simla 1903*
India Office Library and Records (Risley Mss. Eur. E.295/11)

Sir Edward Albert Gait (1863–1950) joined the Indian Civil Service in 1882. He was twice Census Commissioner for India – in 1903 and again in 1909 – and also served as a magistrate and collector in Bengal, Commissioner for Chota Nagpur (see no.386) and Lieutenant Governor of Bihar and Orissa. This circular reprints an extract from a letter received by Gait from J.F. Hewitt, the former Commissioner of Chota Nagpur, concerning various calendrical systems operating in India, and appeals for information 'regarding the rules by which astrologers ... prepare their calendars and fix the dates for caste festivals.' Indian calendrical systems were of interest to astronomers, Indologists and those who sought to understand the relationship between the conceptual division of time and ritual activity. In many cases these investigations were put to practical, administrative and commercial uses. A manual compiled for the Tea Districts' Labour Association suggested that:

> The sahib who can speak to the labourer in his own language without the aid of an interpreter, who understands that leave is essential at certain festivals and knows what these festivals mean and imply; who is aware that three or four days off each year are necessary to perform 'sradh' ceremonies for deceased parents and relatives, and does not jeer and laugh when an application is made year after year beginning with the formula 'my father is dead' ... is an epitome of the attractiveness of an Estate where it is possible to live and work in comfort and without peril to the soul (p.5). C.P.

LITERATURE: Tea Districts' Labour Association 1924.

376 *Typical Pictures of Indian Natives in Colours*, 7th edn, Bombay, 1902

F.M. Coleman
Printed book, 50 pp., 24 plates, spine height 25 ($9\frac{7}{8}$)
Private Collection

Coleman's popular guide to some of the inhabitants of India was first published in 1897 and went through seven editions in the next five years. The idiosyncratic selection of characters includes representatives of castes (the Brahmin), regions (Marwari, Bengali and Cabuli), occupations (postman, Bombay servants), religions and sects (Parsis, Mohammedan, Jew), several of them blurring many of these categories.

In the preface to the first edition Coleman, a Managing Partner of the *Times of India*, observed that 'the "Gorgeous East" if robbed of the vivid colouring which is its greatest charm, would cease to please the only one of the senses to which it ever appeals,' echoing an argument made thirty years

376

earlier by J.W. Kaye, who had invoked 'form and colour, appealing to the fleshly eye' in pursuit of 'truthful impressions' of the country. 'Plain photographs,' Coleman writes, are unable to convey 'the real picture' of the East, and to this end the plates in the book are made from coloured photographs 'to enable travellers to present to their friends at home a true rendering of the varied and picturesque costumes worn by Natives of India in general, and of Bombay in particular.' Coleman's text, which is generally ironic and jaundiced in tone, reflects both prevailing generalizations and stereotypes about certain groups, and an affection for particular individuals. Thus the Bengali 'belongs to a class who are as little distinguished for courage as any race in the world' (p.32), whereas the Brahmin depicted in the first plate, who fell a victim to the 1896 Bombay plague, was 'a pattern of industry, honesty and truth, respected by every one with whom he came into contact, he leaves a blank which it will be difficult to fill' (p.9). C.P.

LITERATURE: Kaye 1867.

377 Postcards of Indian caste and occupational 'types'

(i) *dhobi*
(ii) milk woman
(iii) *bhistee*
(iv) table servant
Clifton and Co., Bombay, Moorli Dhur & Sons, Ambala, and others *c.*1903–8
Printed colour postcards, each 13.5 × 8.7 ($5\frac{7}{16} \times 3\frac{7}{16}$)
Private Collection

Phototype postcards first appeared in 1899 and were immediately hugely popular. In India many dozens of companies produced images, many of which, like these, depicted caste and occupational types. In addition to those illustrated here, the firms of Macropolo (Calcutta), Bourne & Shepherd (Calcutta) and Higginbotham (Madras and Bangalore) were famous for their postcards as well as general photographic work.

Most cards depicted occupational groups identified through a set of appropriate material objects often represented in a relationship of dependency to British colonial society – the table servant bears afternoon tea and the Bhistee waters imperial flowerpots. C.P.

378 Publications for Captain C.E. Luard's *Ethnographical Survey of the Central India Agency*, Lucknow, 1909

i) *The Modhs of Malwa*
Keshav Lal Ojha
Printed book, 11pp., spine height 26.5 ($10\frac{1}{2}$)
School of Oriental and African Studies, University of London (S.IV.L.54801)

ii) *The Jungle Tribes of Malwa*
C.E. Luard
Printed book, 101pp., spine height 26.5 ($10\frac{1}{2}$)
School of Oriental and African Studies, University of London (IV.3.133.2)

iii) *Bundelkhand Castes*
C.E. Luard
Printed book, 18pp., spine height 26.5 ($10\frac{1}{2}$)
School of Oriental and African Studies, University of London (IV.3.133.2)

Captain Luard was Superintendent of Ethnography in central India and published a number of significant general gazetteers. In his 'General note on the Survey' he observes that

> Ethnography does not appeal to the administrations of native states, and the small district staff which is ordinarily employed, not as a rule highly educated, is unable to render much assistance. The Central India Survey, therefore, must not

377(ii)

377(i)

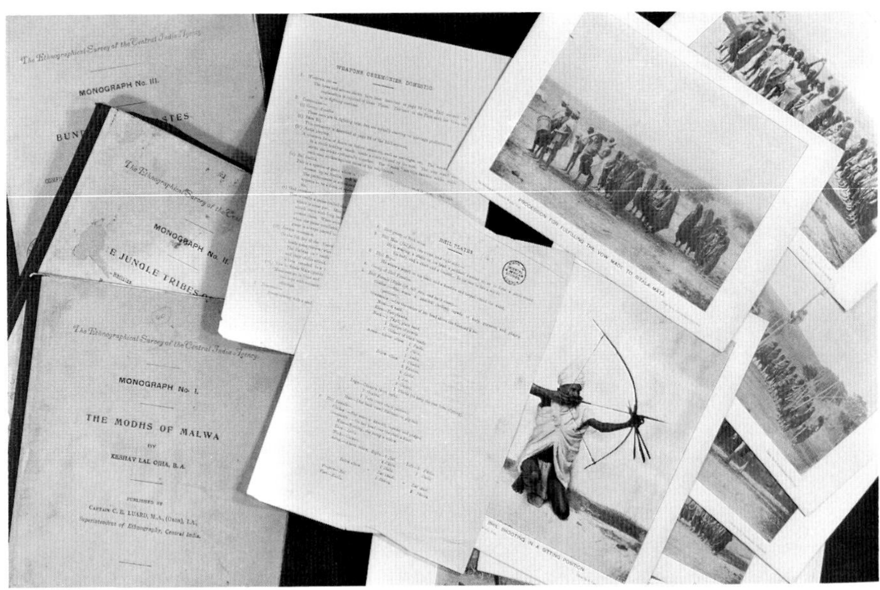

378

> be compared with work done in British India, or in states where a special officer has been deputed to do the work.

Pandit Keshav Lal Ojha's contribution to the monograph series provides a refreshing contrast to the dead weight of Risley's statistics, noting at one point that evidence from the area 'lends support to the idea which is advanced by some that in remote times the peninsular of Kāthiāwār was an island and that Shri Krishna, the hero of the Mahābhārat, fled here from his favourite city of Mathura on the banks of the Jamna' (p.1). Luard, in a prominently placed note, declares that 'This paper has been written by Mr Keshav Lal Ojha, and I am ... in no way [responsible] for its subject matter'. The second monograph in the series also includes various interesting photographic plates made by S. Vasudeorao of Indore. In addition to museologically inspired displays of bows and arrows, there are a number of studies of village ritual (for example, a 'Jawāra procession' and 'vow to Sitâla Mātā') which until this period are almost wholly absent from the photographic record of India.

Luard also published an exhaustive bibliography of sources for the study of central India, which recommended that interested residents of the region subscribe to the Library of the Asiatic Society of Bombay which would despatch them parcels of books. C.P.

LITERATURE: Luard 1908.

379 *Castes and Tribes of Southern India,* Madras, 1909

Edgar Thurston, with the assistance of K. Rangachari
Printed book, 7 vols., spine height 22 ($8\frac{7}{10}$)
The British Library Board (0100 58.h.21)

This was the largest single product of the Ethnographic Survey of India. Thurston (1855–1935) collected much of his data in accordance with the guidelines laid down in *Notes and Queries on Anthropology* (1st edn, 1874) and Risley's manual of ethnography, and his presentation of anthropometric material is limited to a short introduction to the series.

Following the Government's decision to fund the Ethnographic Survey in 1901, Thurston was detailed to 'record the "manners and customs" and physical characters of more than 300 castes and tribes, representing more than 40,000,000 individuals, and spread over an area exceeding 150,000 square miles' (1909, p.xiii). He encountered difficulties from a number of sources – he was able to devote only three months in a year to this work because of the pressure of other official duties, and he was hampered by the suspicion of the local population:

> In carrying out the anthropometric portion of the survey, it was unfortunately impossible to disguise the fact that I am a Government official, and very considerable difficulties were encountered owing to the wickedness of the people, and their timidity and fear of increased taxation, plague innoculation, and transportation (1909, p.xvi).

On one occasion a Paniyan woman believed that Thurston was going to 'have the finest specimens among them stuffed for the Madras Museum' (p.xvi); in Mysore he was mistaken for a recruiting sergeant looking for replacements for those who had been killed in the Boer War; and in one temple town so many coolies had fled in advance of his arrival that there were insufficient to pull the temple car in a procession, 'so I had perforce to move on, and leave the Brahman heads unmeasured' (p.xvii). Although Thurston presents these reactions in a humorous tone as a foil to his 'superior' rationalist science, they tell us a great deal about the human beings that are recorded in the tables of cephalic indexes. C.P.

380 'Anthropology of Living Indians'

Edgar Thurston (?), *c.*1900
Manuscript sheets (2), 29 × 42 ($11\frac{1}{2} \times 16\frac{1}{2}$)
Royal Anthropological Institute, London, Photographic Collection (Box 165)

This table of data on the physical characteristics of various south Indian groups was probably drawn up by Edgar Thurston, later Superintendent of Ethnography for southern India. The classification of skin, eye and hair colour may well have been made with the assistance of Broca's system which was published in the form of a folding coloured lithograph in the British As-

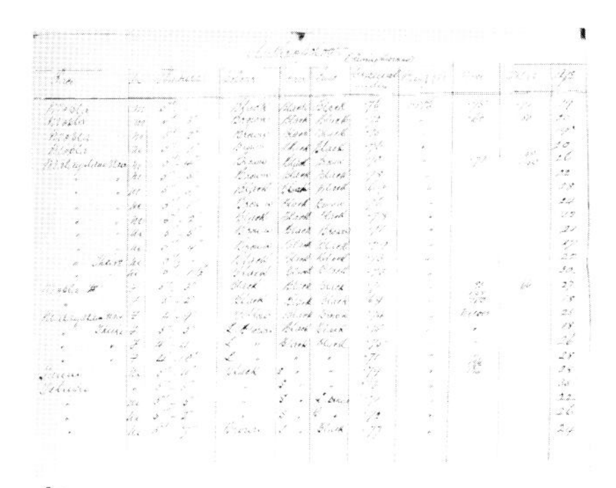

380

sociation's *Notes and Queries* (1874). Alternatively, the compiler of the table may have used a bizarre booklet produced by the Anthropometric Committee of the Anthropological Institute in 1878. This consisted of ten coloured patterns, each 12.7 × 7.6 cm (5 × 3 in), 'carefully matched with typical specimens of hair kindly furnished by Mr Douglas, hair-cutter, of Bond Street' (*Journal of the Anthropological Institute,* 1878, p.392). The cranial index (more properly the cephalic index, since the subjects were alive) gave the proportion of breadth to length of the head:

> Heads with a breadth of 80 per cent and over are classed as broad or brachycephalic; those with an index of under 80, but not under 75, are called medium heads (meso- or mesoti-cephalic); long or dolicho-cephalic heads are those in which the ratio of breadth to length is below 75 per cent (Risley 1915, p.26). C.P.

LITERATURE: Risley 1915.

381 Photographs of fire-making procedures

Edgar Thurston, *c.* 1900
Vintage prints pasted on board:
i) Nayadis making fire by friction, 6.7 × 7.2 ($2\frac{1}{2} \times 2\frac{3}{4}$)
ii) Paniyans making fire (horizontal method), 5 × 7.3 ($2 \times 2\frac{3}{4}$)
iii) Yanadis making fire by friction, 5 × 7.5 (2 × 3)
Royal Anthropological Institute, London, Photographic Collection (6161, 6194, 6206)

The subject of early anthropology was defined, to a large extent, in terms of

381(i)

what was about to disappear: its prime purpose was to 'salvage' ancient customs as they vanished in the face of 'progress'. The apparent vitality of caste-society was perhaps one of the reasons why it attracted comparatively little non-administrative interest from anthropologists; Indian 'tribes', on the other hand, seemed eminently frail and suitable:

> it behoves our museums to waste no time in completing their anthropological collections. Tribes which, only a few years ago, were living in a wild state, clad in a cool and simple garb of forest leaves, buried away in the depths of the jungle, and living, like pigs and bears, on roots, honey, and other forest produce, have now come under the domesticating, and sometimes detrimental influence of contact with Europeans (Thurston 1909, pp.xiv–xv).

Thurston may well have been motivated to make these comparative studies of fire-making by tribal groups by *Notes and Queries on Anthropology*, which advocated the recording of such threatened procedures. C.P.

LITERATURE: Thurston 1909, vol. V, ill. fp. 280; vol. VI, ill. fp. 70; vol. VII, ill. fp. 418.

382 Rajputana (Bhil) twin fire sticks, drill action

Four pieces of carved wood, 45 ($18\frac{3}{4}$), 25 ($9\frac{4}{5}$)
Cambridge University Museum of Archaeology and Anthropology (1894.30a/b Box 15.A.Z.)

These Rajasthani tribal fire-making sticks were collected by a Captain Lovett. C.P.

PROVENANCE: Donated by Captain Lovett's brother, Edward Lovett, to present owner, 1894.

382

N. KUNJAN PILLAI, Esq., M. A., B. Sc., Ph. D.
Census Commissioner,
TRAVANCORE.
Telegraphic Address:
"CENSUS", Trivandrum.
GOVERNMENT OF TRAVANCORE
No. 461
Trivandrum,
13th Novr: 1931.

My dear Sir,
In acknowledging receipt of your D. O.
No.18-Rept., dated the 3rd October, I beg to thank you
sincerely for your very valuable suggestions on my
notes on the primitive tribes of Travancore. I always
welcome your criticisms and would request you to make
them as severe as possible so that ... may be free
from incorrect statements and un...
defects you have pointed out wi...
objectionable portions will be...
which appear to be incorrect...
corrected. I have already...
the Kanikar's method of m...
process was demonstrated...
in the slot, wood dust...
in the slot and igni...
of the word 'fluff'... Some
dust that is formed...
remains in the slot and the heat
ignites it.

-3-
...ining industries and on
...es.
...e primitive tribes, copies of
...time ago, were shown to a
...on none of them would print
...on fresh photographs and am
...er a copy each of these.
...good as to advise me as to
...age, be used for my report
...e photographs need not be

I am,
Yours sincerely,
N. Kunjan Pillai

383

383 Letter from N. Kunjan Pillai to J.H. Hutton, Census Commissioner for India

Trivandrum, 13 November 1931
Typed letter, 4 leaves, 25.5 × 20 (10 × 7¾), 2 photographs, 10.2 × 8 (4 × 3⅛)
Cambridge University Museum of Archaeology and Anthropology (Haddon Collection)

Pillai's letter gives a good idea of the esoteric and detailed length to which enquiry in India went in search of what Risley had earlier referred to as 'really primitive institutions'. Commenting on the Kanikar's method of fire-making by friction, Pillai notes that 'no tinder is used. The use of the word "fluff" is incorrect. Some dust flies off, but some also remains in the slot and the heat generated by friction ignites it'. Pillai proceeds to comment on various topics such as the nature of projectiles in pellet-bows, the mode of burial of the Vishavan and the sex ratio among the Uralis. Among the photographs included with his communication are studies of a 'Kanikaran making fire by friction' and 'Kanikaran making fire by flint and steel method'. C.P.

384 *The Mūndās and Their Country*, Calcutta, 1912

Sarat Chandra Roy
Printed book, 546 pp. plus appendices, spine height 18 (7⅛)
School of Oriental and African Studies, University of London (S.IV.3.266)

385 *The Orāons of Chōtā Nāgpur: Their History, Economic Life, and Social Organisation*, Ranchi, 1915

Sarat Chandra Roy
Printed book, 488 pp., spine height 18 (7⅛)
School of Oriental and African Studies, University of London (IV.3.131)

Although later in his career Sarat Chandra Roy became a great proponent of 'functionalism', a style of analysis which stresses the cohesive and enduring elements of social organization, his important early work is marked by a great interest in history, conflict and what he saw as the deteriorating position of tribal populations within India. However, although his first work is more a work of history than of simple 'ethnography', he was too great an enthusiast for 'a most sympathetic [British] Government . . . ever solicitous for [tribals'] welfare' (Roy 1915, p.49) to form any critical conclusions about colonialism and missionary activity. While Roy cites with approval Haddon's comments on the similarity which 'backward jungle folk' have to 'persistent

THE ORĀONS
OF CHŌTĀ NĀGPUR:
Their History, Economic Life, and Social Organization.

BY
Sarat Chandra Roy, M.A.
Local Correspondent of the Royal Anthropological Institute of Great Britain and Ireland; Anthropological Secretary of the Bihar and Orissa Research Society, Author of 'The Mundas and their Country.'

With numerous illustrations and a Map, and
AN
Introduction
BY
A. C. Haddon, M.A., Sc.D., F.R.S., M.R.I.A.
Ex-President of the Royal Anthropological Institute of Great Britain and Ireland; Reader in Ethnology in the University of Cambridge; Associate of the Anthropological Society of Paris, Corresponding Member of the Anthropological Societies of Berlin, Florence, Rome, & Stockholm; Author of 'The Study of Man' and other works.

RANCHI
1915

385

types dating from geological antiquity in various groups of animals that rejoice the heart of the Zoologist' (1915, p.iv), his commitment to and concern for those he studied are strong features of his work:

> Ill-housed, ill-clad, and underfed, generally over-taxed by the landlord, frequently oppressed by the money-lender, and occasionally duped by the labour-recruiter or fleeced by the law-tout, the Orāon of Chōtā-Nāgpur has indeed had an exceptionally hard lot in life (1915, p.207).

For Roy the villain in all this was the Hindu moneylender, against whom the Government and missions sought to protect the Oraons.

Both the Mundas and Oraons, as well as many other neighbouring groups, were convulsed by messianic resistance movements before and during the time that Roy was writing. Both Birsa Munda (active 1895–1900) and Jatra Oraon (active 1915–22) led political and social movements in support of the re-establishment of their groups' 'kingdoms'. Both these messianic movements combined Sanskritizing Hindu elements with aspects of Christian missionary teaching and ended in violent confrontation (Singh 1985, p.21; Roy 1912, pp.325–43). In addition to extensive further fieldwork with the Birhors and Kharias, among Roy's other activities were his Secretaryship of the Bihar and Orissa Research Society, editorship of *Man in India* from 1921 onwards and membership of the Legislative Council of Bihar and Orissa, the provincial committee of the Simon Commission and the Indian Franchise Commission. As a member of the last two bodies, Roy urged the creation of Chota-Nagpur as a separate political entity in which the interests of tribal populations could be best preserved. Like Elwin, Roy saw caste-Hindu society as the chief threat to India's tribal population, although Roy differed markedly in his favourable assessment of the impact of the missions. Like Elwin, he was seen by some nationalists as continuing a British game of divide and rule by raising the possibility of a conflict of interests between groups in an independent India. C.P.

LITERATURE: Singh 1985.

386 Oraon objects collected by E.A. Gait

i) Hunting knife
c. 1916
Length 32 (12¾)
Attached label: *knife used in hunting. Chota-Nagpur, India, Hon. Mr E.A. Gait. C.S.I. 1916*
Cambridge University Museum of Archaeology and Anthropology (1916.190.39)

ii) Brass anklets
c. 1916
Diameter 15 (6)
Attached label: *Brass anklets (Andu [Mundari] Pairan [Oraon]) worn by Oraons at marriages and at the Karam festival. Chota – Nagpur, India. Hon. Mr E.A. Gait. CSI*
Cambridge University of Archaeology and Anthropology (1916.190.29.A/B)

iii) Flute
c. 1916
Length 24.1 (9½)
Attached label: *Flute (Marli [Oraon]) played by Oraon boys, Chota-Nagpur. India. The Hon. Mr E.A. Gait 1916*
Cambridge University Museum of Archaeology and Anthropology (1916.E.190.45)

iv) Axe
c. 1916
Length 62 (25)
Attached label: *Axe (Muding Make [Mundari] Sanni Tonge [Oraon]) made by Lohars for cutting wood. Chota Nagpur India, the Hon*ble *Mr E.A. Gait. CSI 1916*
Cambridge University Museum of Archaeology and Anthropology (1916.148.33)

E.A. Gait (1863–1950), Commissioner of Chota Nagpur, wrote the introduction to Roy's first book, *The Mūndās and Their Country* (1912). He first met Roy when he was supervising the settlement of the Munda country and Roy had appeared as 'the sturdy champion of the Mundas' in almost all the cases involving Mundas and caste-Hindu landlords and moneylenders (Roy 1912, p.i).

Similar objects to these, together with about fifty other Oraon objects, were photographed in a display and reproduced as a plate in Roy's *The Oraons of Chota Nagpur* (1915). The knife may not be a hunting knife but a *Koha kanto*, a large kitchen knife for the preparation of meat and vegetables – Roy makes no mention of knives being used for hunting. The bamboo flute was occasionally worn by young men in a girdle made of twisted cotton-thread, together with bunches of keys, a cotton-purse, lime-case and pair of small pincers for extracting thorns (Roy 1915, p.93). The anklets, Roy stresses, were worn by Oraon brides at their weddings only (p.98), though the label on this item (presumably information supplied by

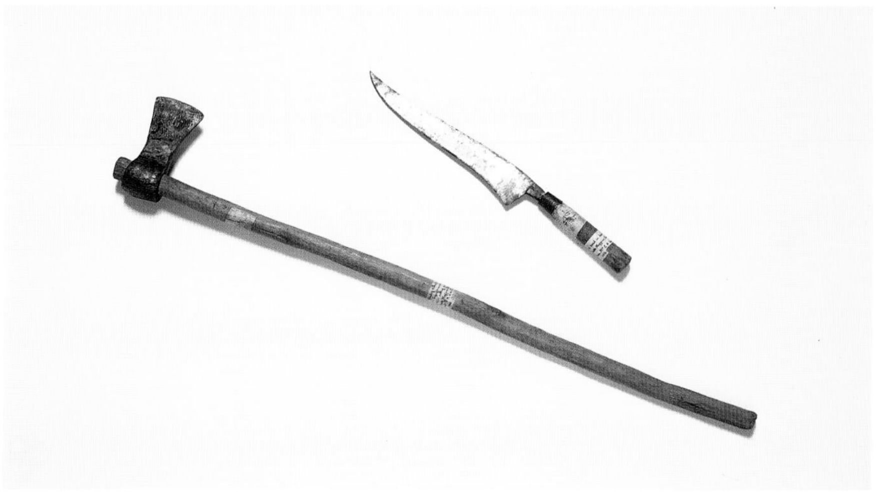

386

386(ii)

Gait) suggests that they were also worn for the Karam 'festival'. This is a series of dances, described by Roy, in which young Oraons dance in lines, singing in unison:

> The drummers move backwards and forwards, but more backwards than forwards. The boys who dance slowly move in a circle so as to make a circuit of the ākhṛā [public dancing ground] in due time; but now and again they quickly advance and recede, waving their 'chawars' and 'sailōs' [fans made of wild date-palm] in the air now upwards and downwards and again forwards and backwards and at times fanning the earth as if coaxing her to bear abundantly (Roy 1915, p.295).

C.P.

PROVENANCE: Donated to present owners by E.A. Gait, 1916.

LITERATURE: Roy 1912 (see also Gait, introduction to above, pp. i–x); Roy 1915, ill. fpp. 177, 216.

387 Photographs of Mundas and Oraons collected (and taken?) by Sarat Chandra Roy

Vintage prints, *c.*1910:

i) Inscribed: *Munda dance*, 14 × 19.5 ($5\frac{1}{2} \times 7\frac{6}{10}$)

ii) Inscribed: *Munda women drawing water from a* dari *(spring) from a photo by Mr A.J. Dutt*, 12 × 16.5 ($4\frac{3}{4} \times 6\frac{1}{2}$)

iii) Inscribed: *Household utensils, ornaments, musical instruments of the Oraons*, 14 × 9 ($5\frac{1}{2} \times 3\frac{1}{2}$)

iv) Inscribed: *Oraon women going on a journey*, 7.5 × 11 ($3 \times 4\frac{1}{4}$)

v) Inscribed: *Oraons driving cattle-disease-spirit from a village (a point of fact, while doing this they strip themselves quite naked; for decency's sake, however, they were made to put on clothes when the photo was taken)*, 14 × 8.5 ($5\frac{1}{2} \times 3\frac{1}{2}$)

vi) Inscribed: *Oraon boy planting splinters of bamboo (...) with bird-lime to catch birds*, 14 × 8.5 ($5\frac{1}{2} \times 3\frac{1}{2}$)

387

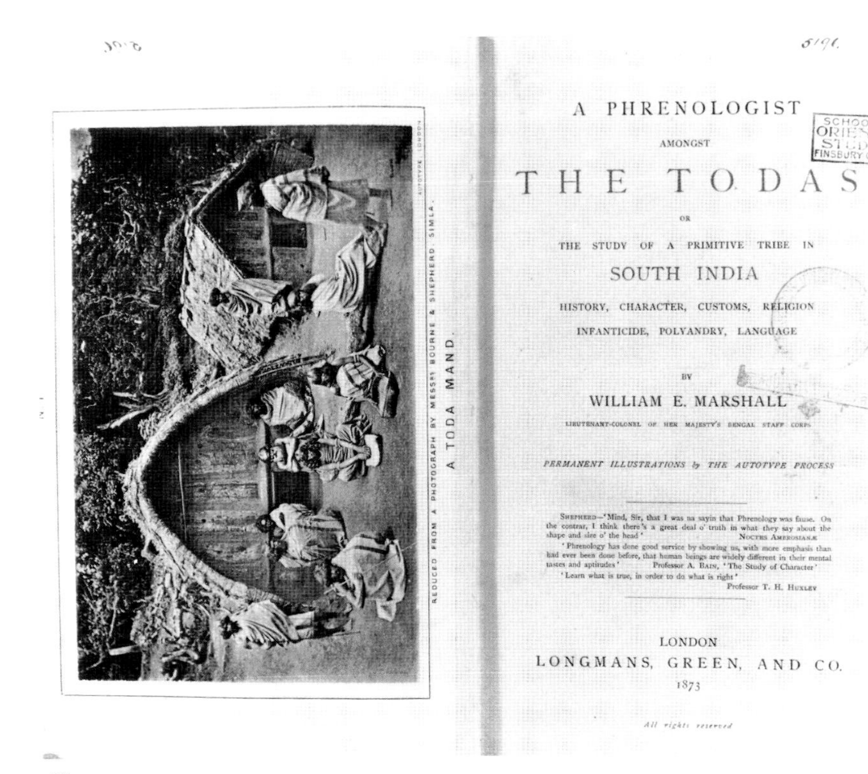

A PHRENOLOGIST

AMONGST

THE TODAS

OR

THE STUDY OF A PRIMITIVE TRIBE IN

SOUTH INDIA

HISTORY, CHARACTER, CUSTOMS, RELIGION

INFANTICIDE, POLYANDRY, LANGUAGE

BY

WILLIAM E. MARSHALL

LIEUTENANT-COLONEL OF HER MAJESTY'S BENGAL STAFF CORPS

PERMANENT ILLUSTRATIONS by THE AUTOTYPE PROCESS

SHEPHERD—'Mind, Sir, that I was na sayin that Phrenology was fause. On the contrar, I think there's a great deal o' truth in what they say about the shape and size o' the head' NOCTES AMBROSIANÆ

'Phrenology has done good service by showing us, with more emphasis than had ever been done before, that human beings are widely different in their mental tastes and aptitudes' Professor A. BAIN, 'The Study of Character'

'Learn what is true, in order to do what is right' Professor T. H. HUXLEY

LONDON

LONGMANS, GREEN, AND CO.

1873

388

PLATE I.

FRONTISPIECE.

THE FIVE HILL TRIBES.

AN ACCOUNT

OF THE

PRIMITIVE TRIBES AND MONUMENTS

OF THE

NĪLAGIRIS.

BY THE LATE

JAMES WILKINSON BREEKS,

OF THE MADRAS CIVIL SERVICE, COMMISSIONER OF THE NĪLAGIRIS;

EDITED BY

HIS WIDOW.

LONDON:

INDIA MUSEUM.

1873.

W^M H. ALLEN AND CO., 13, WATERLOO PLACE, S.W.

Publishers to the India Office.

389

Cambridge University Museum of Archaeology and Anthropology

Roy collected many photographs of Mundas and Oraons and both of his publications make extensive use of these illustrations. In his 1912 work Roy credits 'three Reverend gentlemen as also to some Indian friends for most of the illustrations of the book'. C.P.

PROVENANCE: Given to A.C. Haddon by S.C. Roy, *c.* 1916; thence to Cambridge University Museum of Archaeology and Anthropology.

LITERATURE: Roy 1912, ill. pp.5, 31; Roy 1915, ill. fp.127, fp.177, fp.254.

388 *A Phrenologist amongst the Todas or the Study of a Primitive Tribe in South India; History, Character, Customs, Religion, Infanticide, Polyandry, Language*, London, 1873

W.E. Marshall
Printed book, 269 pp., spine height 22 (8½)
School of Oriental and African Studies, University of London (s.IV.1.1560.5196)

389 *An Account of the Primitive Tribes and Monuments of the Nīlagiris*, London, 1873

J.W. Breeks
Printed book, 219pp., spine height 33 (10)
School of Oriental and African Studies, University of London (s.IV.L.54356)

Nos.388 and 389, published in the same year, are evidence of a continuing interest in the Todas throughout the nineteenth century. Marshall (a Lieutenant-Colonel in the Bengal Staff Corps) presented the results of investigations made with the Rev. Friedrich Metz of the Basel Missionary Society, illustrating 'what it must have been [like] in the prehistoric era long ere "Adam delved and Eve spun", *before man had much developed in manly qualities*' (p.vii). One chapter of Marshall's work is devoted to 'phrenology' of which he was a keen advocate, and he admits to 'difficulty in obtaining satisfactory results in investigations amongst very thick tangled hair' (p.29). However, he is still able to conclude that Toda 'idleness' is confirmed by a preponderance of dolicho-cephalic (narrow, long-headed) types.

Breeks's work, which was published posthumously, was the Madras Government's response to a request from the Trustees of the Indian Museum, Calcutta, in 1871 for collections to be made in order to illustrate 'the state of the arts among the aboriginal and other jungle races in India and its Dependencies' and 'objects found in ancient burial places'. Breeks, the Commisioner of the Nilgiris, proposed that if allowed 1000 rupees to cover costs and at least a year to investigate the Todas, Kurumbas, Kotas and Irulas, he would be able:

> I. – To make a collection of their dresses, weapons, implements, musical instruments, ornaments, utensils, and manufactures.
> II. – To obtain photographs or drawings of each of the tribes and of their houses.
> III. – To record all the facts I can collect with regard to their language, their present habits, ceremonies, and modes of life.
> IV. – To inquire if they have any traditions or legends illustrative of their history.
> V. – To collect objects that I may find in cairns, cromlechs, barrows, and stone circles still existing.
> VI. – To obtain drawings of all ancient sculptures to be found on the hills. (p.v.)

Marshall's work is illustrated with autotype reproductions of photographs by Bourne & Shepherd and Nicholas & Curths, some of which use the Lamprey grid (see no.350). There are a large number of albumen prints pasted into Breeks's volume, the product, according to his widow, of 'a photographer from the School of Arts at Madras, whose performances were by no means satisfactory' (p.iii). W.H.R. Rivers was to make use of illustrations from both these books in his important monograph of 1906 (see no.390). C.P.

LITERATURE: Falconer n.d. (1984).

390 *The Todas*, London, 1906

W.H.R. Rivers
Printed book, 755 pp. plus fold-out genealogies, 22.5 × 33 ($8\frac{3}{4}$ × 13)
The British Library Board (010058.h.25)

Some of the earlier studies of the Todas (e.g. Harkness 1832, Breeks 1873 and Marshall 1873) are represented in this exhibition. W.H.R. Rivers's important study stands apart from these as one of the first products of an emerging professional discipline of anthropology. Although Rivers's work appears unsystematic and deficient from the later perspective of the kind of very thorough fieldwork undertaken by Bronislaw Malinowski (and is from this position of hindsight categorized as part of an 'intermediate generation'), at the time his methods represented an important development of new and more reliable methods. Indeed, during the first and second decades of this century he played much the same messianic role among fellow academics as was subsequently assumed by Malinowski, being hailed as 'the apostle of the new approach to fieldwork, and as the greatest ethnographer who had ever lived' (Langham 1981, p.50).

Rivers studied the Todas for a period of five months between 1901 and 1902, and, having no command over the local vernacular, relied upon two local Christian interpreters, one of whom was employed by the Church of England Zenana Mission (Rooksby 1971, p.114). It had been suggested to Rivers that so much had already been written concerning the Todas that 'we had all the information we could expect to get' (Rivers 1906, p.1), but for Rivers this apparent plenitude provided an appropriate framework in which to demonstrate the superior power of his particular brand of investigation. He notes in his introduction that his book is concerned not merely with the customs and beliefs of a people, but also with a demonstration of 'anthropological method':

> The great need of anthropology at the present time is for more exact method, not only in collecting material, but also in recording it, so that readers may be able to assign its proper value to each fact, and may be provided with definite evidence which will enable them to estimate the probable veraciousness and thoroughness of the record (p.v).

Rivers's chief tool was his 'genealogical method' which he had developed during the Torres Straits expedition of 1899. In rather the same way that earlier physical anthropologists had relied on anthropometric measurements as something fixed in a sea of uncertainty, so Rivers believed that his genealogical method, which involved the collection of kinship terms and family trees, 'enables one to study abstract problems, on which the ideas of the savage are vague, by means of concrete facts of which he is the master' (Rivers 1900, p.74). The 72 genealogies provided as appendices to *The Todas* account for all but 69 of the 700 Todas recorded by the census (Rooksby 1971, p.113) and were later to be condemned by Malinowski as 'algebra'. Rivers, who was assisted in his Indian work by Edgar Thurston, the Superintendent of the Madras Government Museum (see no.379), was later to change his regional interests to Melanesia where research was a matter of urgency 'before primitive communities break down, whereas India, with its high and stable culture, can safely be left till later' (cited by Rooksby 1971, p.118). Rivers was a man of many talents. He played an important part in the clinical recognition of shell-shock during World War One and was closely associated with the war poets Siegfried Sassoon and Robert Graves. C.P.

LITERATURE: Rivers 1906, vol. xxx; Rooksby 1971, pp.109–22; Slobodin 1979; Langham 1981.

391 A Toda man

Wiele and Klein, 1901–2
Vintage print on board, 14.4 × 9.4 ($5\frac{3}{4} \times 3\frac{3}{4}$)
Royal Anthropological Institute, London, Photographic Collection (6518)

This image, which appeared as a plate in Rivers's *The Todas,* was taken by the studio of Wiele and Klein under Rivers's direction. Rivers argued strongly against earlier romanticizations of the Todas, but this is only partly sustained in his photographic illustrations, many of which reinforce the view outlined in popular anthropology texts that their countenances were 'such as we are accustomed to associate with the ancient Roman', and that, 'draped in a sort of toga, with one arm and thigh uncovered, they have quite the grand air' (Hutchinson *et al.*, *c.* 1900, p.188). Rivers noted that the Todas 'are grave and dignified' and 'are not in the slightest degree servile, and about many matters still believe that their ways are superior to ours, and, in spite of their natural politeness, could sometimes not refrain from showing their contempt for conduct which we are accustomed to look upon as an indication of a high level of morality' (Rivers 1906, p.23).

C.P.

LITERATURE: Rivers 1906, ill. p.19.

391

392 Model of a Toda temple

c. 1900
Cane, wood and straw, height 70 ($27\frac{1}{2}$)
Attached label: *No. 46. Paris Exhibition. Toda Temple. The Nilgiris. British India. Name: Toda Temple. Native name: Ehodiwar Kovil. Place of production: Madras (Nilgiris). Exhibitor: Forest Dept. Ref. No. 2880*
The Trustees of the British Museum (1901.3–18.80)

This was probably exhibited in the 1900 Paris Exposition. The three Paris Expositions Universelles of 1878, 1889 and 1900 were of a greater size than any British exhibitions during this period, although there had been a large British Indian Section in the 1878 exhibition consisting of economic products and handcrafts given to the Prince of Wales on a recent tour (Birdwood 1878, p.55). British exhibitions at this time stressed their educational value and frowned on the idea of 'entertainment'. The Paris tradition, by contrast, with its reconstructions, working displays and live-in groups of colonial subjects in carefully recreated villages, deliberately strove to produce a pleasurable effect among visitors. This small model of a Toda temple provided by the Forest Department (which had also exhibited at the 1878 Exposition – Birdwood 1878, p.159) may well have been something of a disappointment to the Parisian crowds in search of 'the real thing' (Greenhalgh 1989, pp.89–93).

In Britain, India featured prominently in international exhibitions. In the 1851 exhibition India had pride of place at the intersection of the Crystal Palace's two huge transepts (Breckenridge 1989, p.202); it provided many of the exhibits in the Indian and Colonial Exhibition at South Kensington in 1886; and was also celebrated in 1895 in *India, A Grand Historical Spectacle* at Earls Court, Olympia and *Empire of India* at the Crystal Palace, and again in the following year in the *India, Ceylon, Burma and Borneo Show* at Olympia (Greenhalgh 1989, p. 77).

This 'temple' is actually a conical type of Toda dairy. Referred to variously as a *boa* or *boath*, there were four in existence, with one in ruins in 1873 (Breeks 1873, p.15) and three in 1901–2 (Rivers 1906, p.43). These sacred dairies (there were also others which looked like ordinary houses) served as clan centres and played a crucially important role in the organization of Toda society.

C.P.

LITERATURE: Breeks 1873, pp.14–15; Marshall 1873, pp.163–9; Birdwood 1878, p.55; Rivers 1906, ill. pp.44, 46, 63; Breckenridge 1989, pp. 195–216; Greenhalgh 1989.

EXHIBITION: Paris, *Exposition Universelle*, 1900 (2880).

393 Photographs of 'Racial Types' supplied by the Ministry of Information to J.H. Hutton

Unknown photographer ('British Official Photographs'), 1943
Vintage prints, 20.5 × 15.2 ($8\frac{1}{4} \times 6$) each

i) Pasted typed slip on rev: *British Official Photograph. HAR.730. (Crown Copyright Reserved) Company Havildar-Sergeant of the Punjab Regiment. This man of the hills has vivid blue eyes. He comes from a race of people who are tall and strong and fine marksmen. They come from the Khybor Pass [sic] area, are Pathans and first class soldiers.*

ii) Pasted typed slip on rev.: *British Official Photograph. JAR.721. Crown Copyright Reserved. Naik-Corporal of the Royal Garhwal Rifles. The Gerhalis are men of the foothills of Nepal and Darjeeling and are used to a very hot climate, and therefore suited to desert warfare. They are cruited [sic] from families of high rank with long Army associations.*

iii) Pasted typed slip on rev.: *British Official Photograph. JAR.742. (Crown Copyright Reserved) Naik-Corporal with the Motor Transport Section of the Royal Army Section Corps. He comes from Rawalpindi, one of India's important garrison towns. He is a Punjabi Mussulman. As motor drivers these men are good. They are fearless, have fine eyesight.*

iv) Pasted typed slip on rev.: *British Official Photograph. JAR.734. Crown Copyright*

Reserved. Types of Indian Soldiers Photographed at a Reinforcement Camp. Sepoy-Private of the Mahratta Light Infantry. He is a Hindu: comes from Belgium, [sic = Belgaum] *district of British India in the Southern Division of Bombay. Discipline of Indian Regiments is perfect. Inheritance rather than training makes them the finest soldier in the world.*

(v) Accompanying letter from Professor Harlow's secretary to Hutton dated 31 August 1943 concerning Hutton's request for photographs for an 'Indian Racial Types' pamphlet

Cambridge University Museum of Archaeology and Anthropology (Haddon Collection)

J.H. Hutton was the William Wyse Professor of Social Anthropology at the University of Cambridge from 1937 until 1950, having succeeded his old Assam friend T.C. Hodson. Hutton was in the Indian Civil Service for twenty-seven years and published monographs on the Angami Nagas (1921) and the Sema Nagas (1921), and directed the 1931 Census. C.P.

LITERATURE: Ebin and Swallow 1984, p.31; Leach 1984, vol. 9, pp.1–12.

394(i)

MINISTRY OF INFORMATION,
MALET STREET,
LONDON, W.C.1

GP.491/9

31st August, 1943.

Dear Sir,

I enclose herewith copies of the twenty photographs which you chose when you were in the Ministry on August 20th, in connection with the "Indian Racial Types" pamphlet which you are preparing.

Yours faithfully,

N.W. Stewart

Secretary to Prof. Harlow.

Professor J.H.Hutton,
St.Catharines College,
Cambridge.

393

394(i) Head of Naga man

*c.*1890
Watercolour
Centre of South Asian Studies, University of Cambridge

394(ii) Head of Naga woman

*c.*1890
Watercolour
Centre of South Asian Studies, University of Cambridge

395 Sir Henry James Sumner Maine (1822–88)

Lowes Dickinson, 1888
Oil on canvas, 125 × 100 ($49\frac{1}{4}$ × $39\frac{1}{4}$)
The Master, Fellows and Scholars of Trinity Hall, Cambridge

Maine could be considered the chief ideological influence on the later British Raj. A comparative jurist and historian, he studied at Pembroke College, Cambridge, and later became a Tutor at Trinity Hall. His major work, *Ancient Law* (1861), studied the emergence of Roman forms of family law and rights of property, but considered India as part of the greater Indo-European background. Hindu society was of interest to Maine as it seemed to him that many early developments along 'European lines' had been aborted in India by the power of the Brahmins. In 1862 Maine became Law Member of the Indian Government (no.410), a position which he held until 1869. Maine dealt with questions of land law in the Punjab, civil marriage and the legal status of Indian converts to Christianity. Compared with the utilitarians and other 'social engineers' of the early part of the century, Maine was a conservative, seeking to preserve Indian institutions which he thought were on the point of a dangerous dissolution as commerce and the new communications eroded them. This paternalist cast of mind commended itself to the Indian civil servants of the later Victorian era, who had been trained in the law and classics. C.A.B.

LITERATURE: Feaver 1969.

The Victorian Raj and the Rise of Nationalism: New Ideas and New Techniques

396

396 The *Times of India,* machine room no. 1

Copyprint after photograph (1898) in the India Office Library (Eos Co. 643 [18v]; B18853)

Newspapers transformed political life in India. The *Indian Daily Mirror* (1860) was the first daily newspaper in English edited by Indians. In 1882 the number of journals of all kinds stood at 373, an aggregate circulation per issue of about 300,000. By 1900 there were about 600 newspapers alone. The expatriate European community was served by newspapers such as the *Times of India* (founded in Bombay, 1861), the *Pioneer* (Allahabad, 1869) and the *Civil and Military Gazette* (Lahore, 1872), for which Rudyard Kipling wrote (no.456). But English and vernacular newspapers in the Indian interest also burgeoned. These were carefully controlled through Indian government legislation, and regular reports on the contents of the vernacular press were compiled by each province. C.A.B.

LITERATURE: Natarajan 1962.

397

397 Swami Dayananda Saraswati (1824–83)

Copyprint after photograph in the Nehru Memorial Museum and Library, New Delhi

Dayananda was one of the most important figures of the Hindu revivalist movements of the nineteenth century. Son of a landlord and moneylender in the Morvi state of Kathiawar, western India, the first forty years of his life were passed as a typical holy man of the Shaivite sect (devotees of Lord Shiva). He learned the Hindu holy scriptures from a village Brahmin and spent many years as a wandering mendicant, frequenting the great pilgrimage sites across India. From his youth, however, he appears to have harboured some scepticism about the spiritual value of idol worship, religious offerings and the priestly role of Brahmins, a scepticism which was reinforced by his bruising encounters with Christian missionaries in Ajmer. From about 1865 he began to preach a new, reformed brand of Hinduism, which took as its foundation the Vedas, the most ancient sacred books of the Hindus, rejecting much of medieval and modern Brahminical Hinduism as worthless innovation. He held Sanskrit debates with traditional *pandits*, and he often accused the priesthood, especially those at pilgrimage centres, of ignorance and fraud. In 1875 he founded the first Arya Samaj, or Aryan Society, in Bombay. Through self-help, congregational worship and contempt for elaborate divisions of caste, Dayananda hoped that the Arya Samaj would return pristine purity to Hinduism, and national pride to India. In this retouched photograph Swami Dayananda appears as a traditional holy man, but in other photographs he appears in Western morning dress.

C.A.B.

LITERATURE: Sarda 1946; Jones 1976.

398(i) The *Satyarth Prakash* (Light of Truth), Bombay, 1875

Swami Dayananda Saraswati
Printed book, 25 × 17 ($9\frac{3}{4} \times 6\frac{3}{5}$)
India Office Library and Records (VT1073INDR2)

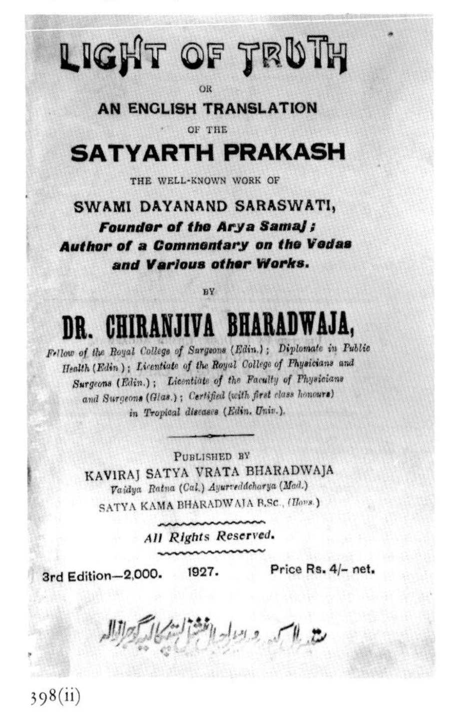

LIGHT OF TRUTH

OR

AN ENGLISH TRANSLATION

OF THE

SATYARTH PRAKASH

THE WELL-KNOWN WORK OF

SWAMI DAYANAND SARASWATI,

Founder of the Arya Samaj;
Author of a Commentary on the Vedas
and Various other Works.

BY

DR. CHIRANJIVA BHARADWAJA,

Fellow of the Royal College of Surgeons (Edin.); Diplomate in Public Health (Edin.); Licentiate of the Royal College of Physicians and Surgeons (Edin.); Licentiate of the Faculty of Physicians and Surgeons (Glas.); Certified (with first class honours) in Tropical diseases (Edin. Univ.).

PUBLISHED BY
KAVIRAJ SATYA VRATA BHARADWAJA
Vaidya Ratna (Cal.) Ayurveddcharya (Mad.)
SATYA KAMA BHARADWAJA B.Sc., (Hons.)

All Rights Reserved.

3rd Edition—2,000. 1927. Price Rs. 4/- net.

398(ii)

398(ii) English edition of the *Satyarth Prakash*, Bombay, 1927

Swami Dayananda Saraswati, translated by Dr Chiranjiva Bharadwaja
Printed book, 24.7 × 16 ($9\frac{6}{8} \times 6\frac{2}{8}$)
Private Collection

Dayananda made skilful use of modern communications, travelling by railway, unleashing pamphlet warfare on his Brahmin, Muslim and Christian opponents and lecturing in Hindi rather than the priestly Sanskrit language. This 'Hindu Luther' also produced the Arya Samaj 'bible', the *Satyarth Prakash*, which interpreted Vedic texts to provide a coherent commentary on Hindu attitudes to all major religious and social issues. Of course, the very act of gathering together and interpreting scriptural reference itself created a new and monolithic version of Hinduism. Another innovation was Dayananda's fierce criticism of other religions, reflecting perhaps Christian missionaries' assaults on Hindu belief and worship. On the page shown in 398(ii), he tries to refute Christian doctrine by raising inconsistencies within the New Testament. Besides English, the *Satyarth Prakash* was translated into a dozen or more Indian vernaculars. But though Arya Samaj branches were set up throughout India, the movement achieved particular success in the Punjab, where its rationalism and ideology of self-help attracted the younger generation of English-educated urban people. Many of the modern educational, social and political institutions of the Hindu Punjab were generated by members of the Arya Samaj, or those whom they had influenced. C.A.B.

LITERATURE: Jones 1976; Jordens 1976.

399 The Islamic Madrasah (College) at Deoband

Copyprints of photographs in the collection of Professor Ira M. Lapidus

Following the Rebellion Indian Muslim reformers redoubled their efforts to rebuild a community that now seemed in terminal decline. One approach was the modernism espoused by Sir Sayyid Ahmad Khan, who drew closer to the British and grafted Western methods of education onto an Islamic core in his Aligarh Anglo-Muhammadan college. But more orthodox reformers working in the tradition inherited from Shah Waliullah (no.298) distanced themselves from the Government and continued to teach the old Islamic syllabus. The Deoband College, founded in 1867, was probably the most important of this type of institution. Its graduates were active as teachers and leaders of prayers throughout north India. In the 1940s, however, Deoband was split on the question of the partition of the subcontinent; some felt that the minority of Muslims left in India would be exposed by the foundation of a separate state of Pakistan. Here the entrance to the College and the inner court with its alcoves for private study and discussion are shown. C.A.B.

LITERATURE: Metcalf 1982.

400 Kali

Calcutta, *c.*1870–80
Woodcut, with colouring, 45 × 27.7 ($17\frac{1}{2} \times 10\frac{4}{5}$)
The Visitors of the Ashmolean Museum, Oxford (1966–64)

While modern intellectuals tried to find accommodations between Hinduism and Western rationalism, older Hindu cults manifested themselves anew, drawing on wider support. Bengal was home to an ancient dialogue between the devotees of two of the great gods of the Hindu universe, Lord Shiva, the 'Destroyer and Regenerator', and Lord Vishnu, the 'Preserver'. Vaishnavite devotionalism was popular in the countryside, where it had been spread by preaching saints in the sixteenth century. In the towns, however, many Bengalis, some of them Western-educated and members of the clerical class, found comfort and pride in the worship of Kali, the consort of Shiva in his destructive mode. The fearsome Kali represents the power of divine female energy to cleanse the world of sin before the new beginning. Increasingly this cult came to occupy a more and more central position in Calcutta, where popular and middle-class worship focussed on the river bathing place at Kalighat. The worship of Kali often involved the sacrifice of goats and other animals; associated gymnasia for martial arts attracted the restless young intelligentsia of the city. This was a form of Hindu worship which European missionaries and officials found most difficult to understand, but it proved a powerful symbol of identity for some Bengalis. This was especially so because one of the more benign 'sister' manifestations of Kali was Bengal's patron goddess, Mother Durga. When Lord Curzon partitioned Bengal in 1905, many saw this as a deadly

400

insult to Durga, and the radical and terrorist movements which gathered pace in the next few years often turned to the fearsome Kali as protector and emblem of their struggle. C.A.B.

PROVENANCE: Presented by the Church Missionary Society, 1966.

401 The Tarakeshwar Murder, 1873

i) The *mahant* sees Elokshi, the errant wife, who presents him with sweets
Unknown artist, Kalighat, *c.* 1875
Watercolour and silver on paper, 54.6 × 33.6 ($21\frac{3}{10} \times 13$)
India Office Library and Records (Add. Or. 3346)
ii) The *mahant* fans Elokshi
Unknown artist, Kalighat, *c.* 1875
Watercolour and silver on paper, 45.8 × 28.6 ($17\frac{4}{5} \times 11$)
India Office Library and Records (Add. Or. 3347)

The Kalighat temple, which was built in 1809, stood two or three miles from the city's centre in an area that was sacred to Kali (no.400). The temple was close to the site of earlier structures which had been built by rich *banians* of the city, the Indian agents who had been raised to prosperity by the growth of British commerce. Members of the new professional and commercial classes venerated Kali as enthusiastically as the ordinary people, who had once been her major devotees. Kali's more benign form, Mother Durga, became the virtual deity of

401(i)

Bengal. Durga Puja, the great festival in her honour, attracted vast throngs of pilgrims to Kalighat. Artists who gathered here modified the *patua* style of religious painting, which was common in the Bengal villages, to the demands of the mass pilgrim market. They borrowed some of the free brush techniques of Western watercolour painting to create a vivid style.

Mythological scenes dominated the output of the Kalighat painters, but equally popular were depictions of the life around the temple, of the prostitutes and their clients, of exotic Europeans and scenes of business. Some paintings have a hard edge and lampoon the semi-Westernized *babu* (clerk in government office) and the corruption of religious authorities. These two paintings represent a local *cause célèbre* of 1873, when the Hindu *mahant* (abbot) of a monastic foundation was prosecuted for adultery with a clerk's wife who was later murdered by her jealous husband. The heady mixture of religion, sex and corruption gave the Kalighat painters a field day. But this was a period when many Hindu and Parsi religious institutions were torn by financial and sexual scandal. For both orthodox and 'modern' reformers responded to missionary attacks on Hinduism by exposing corruption through the pages of the burgeoning vernacular and English press, and by dragging traditional figures of authority into the British courts. C.A.B.

LITERATURE: Archer 1977, pp.139–43, 151.

402 'Mahatma' Jyotirao Govindrao Phule (1827–90)

Copyprint after photograph (*c.*1890) in the Nehru Memorial Museum and Library, New Delhi

Many of the nineteenth-century Indian reformers denounced the injustice of the caste system and scorned its rules of purity and pollution. Most, however, were themselves from the highest castes. This was not the case with Phule whose family, though very respectable, was of the Mali or Gardener caste. His father and brothers provided garlands and flowers for elite Maratha families, including those of the former Peshwas; the family name 'Phule' means 'flower'. Phule went to a Scottish missionary school in Poona where he was influenced by the works of Tom Paine and other English and European radicals. He became convinced that the caste system was iniquitous and that Brahmin domination should be overthrown through education and social uplift. In 1873 he founded the Satyashodhak Samaj (Truth Seekers Society) which was devoted to securing human rights and social justice for low-caste people.

402

Phule's attitude to the emerging nationalist politics of the elite was ambivalent. He considered that British rule in general was a liberating rather than a destructive force, and argued that the Indian National Congress could not be truly 'national' until it showed a more active interest in the welfare of the low castes. Some Indians regretted this stance at the time, and many still do so today. Certainly, British officials in western and southern India often gave tacit support to the growing non-Brahmin movements, for many of their early nationalist critics were Brahmins.

This print has been retouched to enhance its iconic significance and shows Phule with a work entitled *Satya Shod*, possibly a reference to the rule book of the Samaj, published in 1887.

C.A.B.

LITERATURE: O'Hanlon 1985.

403

403 *Dadashastri* (The Parasite Priest), 1927

Mukundrao Patil
Printed book, 15.2 × 10.8 (6 × 4⅕)
Dr R. O'Hanlon

After Phule's death the non-Brahmin movement developed a popular base in western India and made considerable progress in the Tamil- and Telugu-speaking areas of the south. This is a typical piece of early twentieth-century propaganda produced by the editor of *Din Mitra*, the main non-Brahmin newspaper. Its theme is how older Brahmins continue to insist on orthodox behaviour from others while their own younger generation is busy Westernizing and enjoying the benefits. The cover shows this well: an old-style priest is in the left-hand corner, a young Brahmin student in his smart trousers and jacket drinks tea, while the young Brahmin woman behind them, on a bicycle, has her *padar* slung daringly rather than decently over her shoulder, as is the custom for a respectable Maratha woman.

R.O'H./C.A.B.

404 Swami Vivekananda (1863–1902)

Chintamani Kar
Oleograph, 50.1 × 34.9 (19½ × 13⅗)
Private Collection

A critical figure in Indian religious history, Vivekananda (whose family name was Narendranath Datta) typified a movement of 'turning back' to Hindu devotional worship which attracted many young men and women in Bengal in the later nineteenth century. Vivekananda was educated in the Western style, and was influenced both by British idealist thought and by the religious accommodation between East and West that was pioneered by the Brahmo Samaj (see no. 297). Ultimately, though, Vivekananda found no solace in rationalism and searched long for a man who had 'seen God'. In 1882 he became the pupil of Sri Ramakrishna, a seer and teacher in the traditional Bengali Vaishnavite mould, and in 1886 Vivekananda stated that he had realized the Absolute Truth under his guidance. Over the next decade he built up a network of organizations (later called Ramakrishna missions) which bound young men to a life of penury, social service and religious

404

devotion. Vivekananda's influence spread beyond India to the West which had become eager for the wisdom of the East. In 1893 he travelled to Chicago to attend the World Parliament of Religions where he spoke on the antiquity and beauty of ancient Indian civilization. An intellectual nationalist rather than an activist, Vivekananda pleaded 'Let your country be the only God for the coming fifty years.' He celebrated a union of national pride, social service and traditional religious beliefs which anticipated in many respects the philosophy of Mahatma Gandhi. C.A.B.

LITERATURE: Gambhirananda 1957.

405

405 Playing cricket at Lawrence School, Mount Abu

Copyprint after photograph by Herzog and Higgins (*c.*1895) in the India Office Library (photo/m/430/48; 37)

With the exception of a few English-speaking schools in the major towns and an experiment in primary education in the North-Western Provinces, the British Government had provided little education for Indians before 1860. Thereafter the growth of English-language courts and the expansion of the administrative machinery necessitated the creation of a pool of manpower that was educated, especially in English. The Government was also increasingly sensitive to the charges of critics at home, and now in India, that it had failed in its vaunted civilizing mission in India. At the very least the British had to respond to the activities of the Indian reformers who were laying the foundations of a national identity through the system of private schools. Consequently there was an expansion of school and university education after 1860. However, even in 1947 only about 10 per cent of the Indian population was literate. The training and expectations of these few scholars were to have a dramatic effect on the social and political life of India for the next generation. From the English-educated professional people, highly trained but frustrated by the exclusive nature of British administration, were to come the leaders of the Indian National Congress. The Lawrence School at the hill station of Abu was an example of those schools originally founded to provide for the education of Indian aristocrats and princes. C.A.B.

LITERATURE: Seal 1968.

406

406 Pupils attending Maharani's Girls' College, Mysore

Copyprint after photograph (*c.* 1895) in the India Office Library (photo/430/41 915; B9854)

Though missionaries and Indian reformers in Bengal, Bombay and Madras had taken up the cause of female

407

education as early as the 1830s, little headway was made until the 1880s, and then it was generally among Hindus rather than Muslims. Most families still considered that exposing their womenfolk to view outside the family would bring discredit on them. The more successful ventures in education were those supported by patrons, in this case the Maharani. C.A.B.

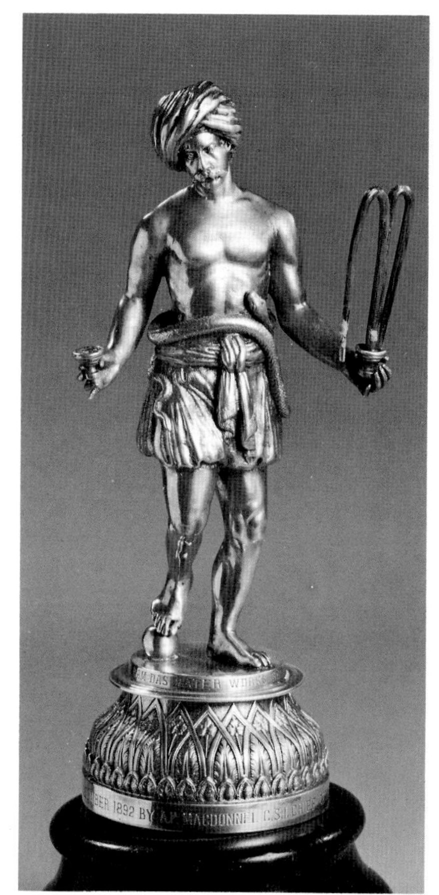

408

407 Medical staff and students at the Motlabai Wadia Obstetrics Hospital

Copyprint after photograph (*c.* 1905) in the India Office Library (photo 311/12 [8v] Dimmock; B10517)

Provincial governments funded some vaccination initiatives in the towns during the disease-ridden years of the 1830s, but outside the European community Western medicine was largely inaccessible until after 1860. In the later half of the nineteenth century Indian and Anglo-Indian charitable hospitals were established in some major cities and eventually the Indian Government established a medical department which began funding hospitals in the 1880s. Scientific knowledge and research were, however, generally neglected, a situation that became strikingly apparent during the 1890s when Bombay was visited by plague (see nos. 492–4). Although better-off Indians sampled Western medicines, traditional schemes of healing such as *ayurveda* (herbal remedies deriving from the Sanskrit tradition) and *unani* medicine (Greco-Muslim medical learning) remained more popular. C.A.B.

408 A water carrier, celebrating the opening of the Balram Das Waterworks at Raipur, Central Provinces

Unknown artist, *c.* 1893
Silver, height (including stand) 29.5 ($11\frac{1}{2}$)
Inscribed on base: *BALRAM DAS WATERWORKS, RAIPOR. OPENED DECEMBER 1892 BY A.P. MACDONNEL* (*sic*), *C.S.I. CHIEF COMMISSIONER*
The Visitors of the Ashmolean Museum, Oxford (1954.27)

Public health became a major concern after 1857. The need to provide cleaner water for the larger European military stations contributed as much as the new Victorian enthusiasm for 'improvement'. Indian notables were encouraged to direct their wealth towards civic improvement rather than religious patronage. Raipur, a town in the Central Provinces, was fed with water from the Kharun river by these waterworks which were largely funded by a local notable, Raja Balram Das of Raj-Nandgaon. Interestingly, even a modern venture such as this was celebrated with a traditional image, a model of a *Bhistee* or water-carrier. C.A.B.

LITERATURE: Imperial Gazetteer of India 1908.

409

The Steel Frame of Empire

409 Early start; Governor General's camp

William Simpson, 1860
Watercolour, 34.2 × 49.5 ($13\frac{1}{2} \times 19\frac{1}{2}$)
The Trustees of the Bowood Collection

The Rebellion of 1857, Parliamentary scrutiny and technological change galvanized the Indian Government into new activity. In his remaining years of office Canning devoted much time to travelling in those parts of north India where the Rebellion had taken place, meeting landholders and confirming their privileges as 'natural leaders of the people' whom the British would slight at their peril. Simpson (no.260) travelled with him on one of these journeys.

C.A.B.

LITERATURE: Archer 1986.

410

410 Lord Lawrence and the Supreme Indian Council, Simla

Bourne & Shepherd, 1864
Photograph, 14.5 × 21.5 ($5\frac{3}{5} \times 8\frac{2}{5}$)
National Portrait Gallery, London (P426)

One of the few early photographs of the Indian Government 'at work', this shows Lawrence with his powerful, and often recalcitrant, council. Notable are Sir Charles Trevelyan (sitting second from left), Finance Member and protagonist of administrative modernization; Sir Hugh Rose, Commander-in-Chief (at end of table on left); Robert Napier, 1st Baron Napier of Magdala (sitting next to Lawrence on right); Sir Henry Maine (no.395), Law Member (sitting at end of table on left); Sir Richard Strachey, Engineer, appointed Public Works Secretary to the Supreme Council in 1862 (behind Maine to the right); Sir Steuart Bayley, Home Secretary (sitting on far right). These men proved difficult for Lawrence to handle, but they were more constrained than their precursors before the Rebellion. Viceregal authority was held in check by the Secretary of State for India and his Council in London. Moreover, for legislative purposes only, the Council was augmented by non-official members, including representatives of European and Indian opinion. C.A.B.

LITERATURE: Gopal 1965; Bence Jones 1982, pp.52–3.

411 John Laird Mair Lawrence, 1st Baron Lawrence (1811–79)

G.F. Watts, 1862
Oil on panel, 62.2 × 50.5 ($24\frac{1}{2} \times 19\frac{7}{8}$)
National Portrait Gallery, London (1005)

Lawrence, a pious Protestant of Co. Antrim stock, straddled the India of the Company and the Crown. With his brother Henry, who died during the Rebellion, he had been a founding father

411

of the strong paternalist government of the Punjab, a province which helped the British to win the war of 1857–8 and later became a nursery for the British Indian Army. Lawrence was one of the few Indian civil servants to be appointed Governor-General or Viceroy (most were aristocrats or British politicians). But 'plain John' Lawrence was more at home in the saddle on the Northwest Frontier than at the Viceroy's ball. In terms of his real contribution to the welfare of the people of India, however, he was one of the greatest of viceroys. He was midwife to measures which protected the tenantry in Bengal and north India, and oversaw rapid development in railway building, and irrigation and sanitation works. C.A.B.

LITERATURE: Gopal 1965; Bence-Jones 1982.

412 Calcutta paddle steamer

Beecheheram Das, Kalighat, 1857
Lithograph, 38.2 × 24.1 ($14\frac{4}{5} \times 9\frac{2}{5}$)
India Office Library and Records (Add. Or. 3803)

This is another of the lively paintings produced for pilgrims who went to the famous Kalighat shrine in Calcutta. Europeans are represented aboard a gaudily coloured river boat like those which regularly plied the waters between the commercial districts of the city and the European suburban enclaves. Since the mid-1840s the steamboats had revolutionized transport up the rivers Ganges and Jumna. The up-river journey to Benares now took about a week, whereas before the introduction of steam it had taken at least six weeks. During the 1850s and '60s, large quantities of raw cotton from central India had been taken down the Ganges from the cotton mart at Mirzapur, near Benares, by steamboats which towed barges. British manufactured goods and military and civil supplies had gone in the other direction. During the 1857 Rebellion armed steamboats had moved at will up and down the rivers, harrying rebel positions. But the steamships' heyday was short. By 1859 the railway had reached Cawnpore and both freight and passenger traffic rapidly switched to rail. The introduction of the electric telegraph further improved the communications network, which was largely responsible for the greater effectiveness of the Indian Government after 1857.

C.A.B.

LITERATURE: Archer 1971, p.146.

413 Air-compressing engine, Khojak Tunnel

Copyprint after photograph (*c.*1888) in the India Office Library (photo 481/4 [40])

As early as 1867–8 the trains in India carried nearly 14 million passengers a

412

413

414

year, of whom nearly 95 per cent travelled third class. By 1907 there were 29,893 miles of rail in the Indian network, making it by far the greatest in Asia. The social effects were quite dramatic, bringing once-isolated regions into contact with each other and breaking down social distinctions. The economic effects were also considerable, though outlying areas rather than already productive areas benefited most. Equipment and even skilled labour (the men in the photograph are Welsh miners) were brought from Britain, and interest on funds raised for railway loans was remitted there, so that the developmental impact on the Indian economy was limited in significant ways. This photograph and no.414 show the construction of the Khojak Tunnel in the Quetta District of Baluchistan on the Northwest Frontier. Constructed between 1888 and 1891, partly for strategic reasons, it was 2½ miles long and cost 7 million rupees. C.A.B.

LITERATURE: Imperial Gazetteer of India 1908; Derbyshire 1987.

414 Pathan workmen, 1888–91

Copyprint after photograph (*c.*1888) in the India Office Library (photo 481/4 [49])

415 Great Indian Peninsular Railway Terminus (Victoria Terminus), Bombay

A.M. Haig, *c.*1880
Watercolour, 88.5 × 143 (34½ × 56¾)
India Office Library and Records (WD2443)

The railways inspired some of the greatest pieces of Anglo-Indian architecture. In Bombay, gothic forms began to replace the classical after about 1845, and large numbers of massive structures were built on the proceeds of the cotton boom of the early 1860s. The Victoria Terminus, as it was later known, was built to the plans of F.W. Stevens between 1878 and 1887. C.A.B.

415

416

416 Address casket in the form of an Indian country boat

Calcutta (?), 1923
Silver on ebony stand, supported by silver-gilt half lions, 38.7 × 63.5 × 30.4 ($15\frac{1}{2} \times 24\frac{7}{8} \times 12$)
Lord Cobbold

Boats such as this were the main form of inland transport on the Ganges and Jumna rivers before the railway and steamboat revolution. They remained common in Bengal, with its numerous backwater channels. The exchange of scrolls and addresses in elaborate caskets remained an aspect of official etiquette until 1947. Like the durbars, this was a conscious continuation of Mughal tradition. C.A.B.

India's Age of Capital

417 i) View of Government House, Calcutta

Copyprint after photograph by Bourne & Shepherd (*c.*1863) in the Royal Commonwealth Society Library (Y3022AA/3 [1717])

417 ii) View of the Esplanade, Calcutta, from the Ochterloney Monument

Copyprint after photograph by Bourne & Shepherd (*c.*1863) in the Royal Commonwealth Society Library (Y3022BB/10 [1720])

In these, some of the best cityscapes photographed by the famous studio of Bourne & Shepherd, the 'second city of the British Empire' is captured at a moment when its economic fortunes were beginning to turn down and its political life was becoming ever more active. In 1839 Calcutta's population was about 229,000; in 1901 it stood at 941,000. After the Crimean War the jute trade from inland Bengal had boomed, and Calcutta still acted as the great entrepôt for the whole of northern and eastern India. Its port rivalled the Port of London, while Hughly, across the river, had become the headquarters for many of the larger jute firms. The city centre still comprised the Esplanade, Fort William and the Calcutta Racecourse, but a huge Indian city had developed both north and south of the European centre. By the 1860s stresses and strains in Calcutta's society were becoming more evident. By the 1850s the Tagores and other indigenous entrepreneurs were being squeezed out by Scotsmen and Marwaris from north India. By the 1890s its pool of educated youth was becoming frustrated at the lack of opportunities for employment and advancement. C.A.B.

LITERATURE: Imperial Gazetteer of India 1908; Seal 1968; Losty 1990.

418 Jute factory in Bengal

*c.*1900
Photograph, 15.5 × 24.6 ($6 \times 9\frac{1}{2}$)
India Office Library and Records (photo 25[15])

Jute is a tough vegetable fibre, indigenous to Bengal. The East India Company had made rope from it at their factories in Cuttack as early as 1746. As the demand for commercial packaging increased in the early nineteenth century, the Dundee firm of Urquhart, Lindsay and Co. developed machinery for softening, batching and weaving the material to produce a hardy alternative to cotton and flax. In 1854 mechanical jute manufacture was introduced to India and by 1900 substantial amounts of British and Indian capital had been invested in the industry. The peasant farmers of east and north Bengal were able to supplement their meagre earnings by growing the crop, but the prices paid to them represented only a small part of the value of the commodity.
C.A.B.

LITERATURE: Chaudhuri 1964.

418

419

419 Photographs of the Lawrence jute mill, near Calcutta

G. Hebendon, *c.*1927
10 vintage prints, various sizes
Royal Anthropological Institute, Photographic Collection
(32973; 32976; 32998; 33013; 33034; 33042; 33060; 33063; 33071; 33078)

These photographs were taken by the manager of this jute mill owned by Bird and Co. The images depict jute crop harvesting, the main gate of the mill, the railway line from the mill towards Calcutta (there was no road), jute being unloaded onto a barge, interior views of the mill, groups in the labour quarters (the 'lines'), bale-handling coolies with a European 'finishing assistant' and evidence of Hindu and Muslim celebrations within the grounds of the mill. These last two show the completed statue of the Goddess Durga prepared for the autumnal festival of the Nine Nights of Durga. Muslims are shown celebrating Mohurrum.

LITERATURE: Chakrabarty 1989.

PROVENANCE: From Sir Edward Benthall to Paul Benthall, thence to the Royal Anthropological Institute.

420 A British merchant steamship

Chinese School, *c.*1880
Oil on canvas, 56 × 75 (22 × 29½)
National Maritime Museum, London (BHC1243)

With the invention of the steamship and the electric telegraph, British shipping companies increased their dominance in India's external trade. Indian raw materials and, later, textile manufactures were despatched to China and Southeast Asia, and also to Europe. The opening of further Chinese 'treaty ports' and of the Suez Canal in the 1860s provided new outlets for India's goods. C.A.B.

421 Embroidered muslin from Madras

The Textile Fabrics of India, 1868, vol.VII, second series by James Forbes Watson
The Trustees of the Victoria & Albert Museum (Forbes Watson Collection)

From the 1830s onwards British manufactured textiles tightened their grip on Indian markets. First Lancashire manufactured twist and yarn, then piece goods; first high quality goods were imported, then cheaper garments

420

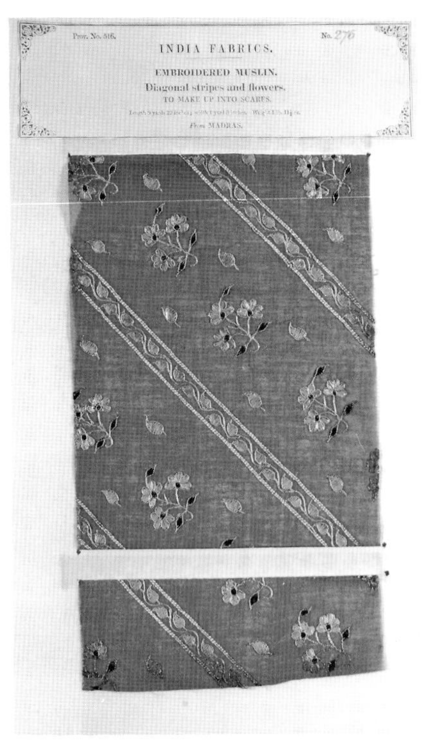

421

flooded in. The indigenous weaving industry declined further and Indian industrialized manufacturers, newly established in Bombay and Ahmedabad, found it difficult to compete. The British authorities were ardent free-traders and refused to concede the infant industry any significant protection by raising tariffs against imports. On the other hand British manufacturers began to target their Indian markets more precisely. The huge Forbes Watson collection of indigenous textiles, built up originally for the East India Company, was intended as a data base for commercial information. They illustrate the main varieties of dress from different provinces. The collection was formed on the assumption that 'few countries in the world are more conservative regarding their garments than the various races and castes of India' (Watts 1908, p.618).

C.A.B.

LITERATURE: Forbes Watson 1868; Watt 1908.

422 Weavers, eastern Bengal

Unknown photographer, *c.*1870
Photograph, 18 × 21.5 (7 × 8$\frac{4}{5}$)
India Office Library and Records (photo 124 [53])

Weavers suffered both from the competition of imported European manufactured textiles and from the expansion of the Indian textile industry, but the actual number of weavers as opposed to the diversity of their products appears not to have declined greatly. The population was growing and Indians still preferred everyday items (bags, sheets, bedspreads etc.) to be made from coarse local fabrics. Indeed, by the end of the century the *Swadeshi* (home industry) movement, designed to regenerate India's artisan industries, had begun to promote the virtues of home-made cloth.

C.A.B.

LITERATURE: *CEHI*, ii, 1983.

422

423 Jamsetji Tata

Frontispiece from *Jamsetji Nusserwanji Tata: A Chronicle of His Life*, London, 1925
Book, 23 × 15 (9 × 5$\frac{4}{5}$)
India Office Library and Records (T36738)

Indian industry developed against all odds in the later nineteenth century. This was a period when British opinion was convinced of the virtues of free trade and hostile to tariffs which might have protected India's nascent cotton cloth industry. Indian enterprises found themselves with little protection against the flood of Lancashire, and later Japanese, imports which entered the country having paid very small duties. Some Indian businessmen were canny and determined enough to carve out a niche for themselves in India's large domestic market. They specialized in lower quality products for the middle classes and the poor and set up factories mainly in the western cities of Bombay and Ahmedabad. One such entrepreneur, the founder of one of India's greatest industrial dynasties, was Sir Jamsetji Tata (1839–1904), a member of the Parsi community, known for its ability to adapt to the conditions of trade under British rule. Tata made (and lost) money in raw cotton speculation during the period of the American Civil War. He also made a considerable profit as contractor to the British expedition to Abyssinia in 1867–8. But his boldest move came in 1877 when he established the Empress cotton mills in the rather unpropitious surroundings of the inland city of Nagpur. His cotton manufacturing business, based in Bombay, Nagpur and Ahmedabad, rapidly expanded over the next two decades. Tata made a determined bid to keep up with the most modern mill technology. He was also a great patron of Parsi cultural institutions and of scientific education and research. One of his most lasting monuments, though, is the original Taj Mahal Hotel on Bombay's waterfront, which he established. C.A.B.

LITERATURE: Harris 1925.

424 The Birla Family Album

Five copyrights after photographs from the album in the Birla Museum, Rajasthan

While some of India's modern entrepreneurs, particularly the Parsis, eagerly took up Western lifestyles from an early date, this was not generally true of the tough Marwari traders of central India and Rajasthan, who had taken a commanding lead among indigenous industrialists by the turn of the century. Marwari merchant people were often pious Hindus and maintained a simple way of life even after they had amassed astounding fortunes. One of the most celebrated of these families were the Birlas. Gyansham Das Birla (1894–1983) had only the traditional shopkeeper's education in the Rajasthan village of Pilani and entered the family business at the age of sixteen. But by the First World War the family had extensive textile, steel and chemical industries all over India. Unlike many of the leaders of the modern industrial sector who had close connections with British business, Birla was a convinced nationalist, attracted to Gandhi's side as much by his piety and austerity as by the promise of the Indian National Congress to foster and develop India's industrial base. Birla and his relatives were great supporters of the Congress, and helped in the upkeep of Gandhi's *ashram* (retreat) at Sevagram as well as establishing temples all over India. C.A.B.

425

425 Bazaar, Bangalore

Copyprint after photograph (*c.*1880) in the India Office Library (photo 447/3 [31b])

While Western-style retail trading sprang up in Calcutta, Bombay and a few other cities, the Indian bazaar remained the heart of the commercial system. Bazaars in towns and large villages were specialized by commodity. C.A.B.

426 Group of bankers

Copyprint after photograph (*c.*1860) in the India Office Library (26/2 [35b] B.8865)

As communications improved after 1860 the purchasing agents of British firms and European-style banking houses began to grow in numbers in the major

426

stations. But much of inland private finance remained in the hands of families drawn from the traditional banking and trading castes, which had adapted their practice to the demands of the colonial economy. In the north enterprising merchant people from Marwar in Rajasthan entrenched themselves in the economy of Bengal and the Ganges valley. In the south Natukottai Chettiars from Ramnad District controlled much credit and trade, expanding their networks to take in Burma and Southeast Asia. C.A.B.

Rural Industries and Crafts

Heavy industry expanded in the later nineteenth century, though not as fast as nationalist economic spokesmen, such as Dadabhai Naoroji, wished. While the government's attitude to investment in the economy remained laissez-faire, there were some attempts to encourage rural and handicraft industry such as the Government Institute of Dyeing and Calico Printing at Shahdara, near Lahore, in the Punjab (no.427). In some parts of the subcontinent, such as the Punjab and Baluchistan where the provision of irrigation was a precondition for agricultural expansion, government money was put into canal schemes or into loans and grants for farmers who wished to bore deep wells (nos.428, 429). Peasant farmers became richer

427

428

429

where they were able to grow valuable crops such as sugar cane (no.430), cotton or jute and sell their produce on the market without the intermediary agency of a local merchant or moneylender. But the improvements in agriculture and transport mainly benefited the small landowners and more prosperous peasants. Rural artisans (no.431), wage labourers and poor tenant farmers fared less well, particularly now that the population was growing perceptibly faster.

LITERATURE: *CEHI*, ii, 1983. C.A.B.

430

427 Dye jigger in the factory, Government Institute of Dyeing and Calico Printing, Shahdara, near Lahore

*c.*1880
Photograph, 15.2 × 20 ($6 \times 7\frac{4}{5}$)
India Office Library and Records (photo. 83 [6])

428 Well-boring at Gulistan, Baluchistan

Copyprint after photograph (*c.*1887) in the India Office Library (481/2 [20])

429 Well rig with worker on top, Baluchistan

Copyprint after photograph (*c.*1887) in the India Office Library (481/2 [20] B21485)

430 Harvesting sugar-cane

Copyprint after photograph (*c.*1880) in the India Office Library (83 [1] B12634)

431

431 Potters (*kumhars*) in Gwalior, central India

Copyprint after photograph by R.L. Desai (*c.*1910) in the India Office Library (41/2 [54] Ward B10565)

Civil Servants, Princes and Landlords

The later nineteenth century was the heyday of the Indian Civil Service. It now drew into its ranks members of the new university-educated middle class, who were selected by competition and underwent a period of training in Indian languages and history before being sent into the field. The basic duties of the District Collectors and Assistant Collectors remained the same as in the early nineteenth century: the collection of the land-revenue and the maintenance of the rule of law at local level. The Indian Government had also decided that its policy towards the princes in the years which led up to the Rebellion of 1857 had been mistaken. Its aim was now to work as far as possible through princely authority, rather than to snub it. The princes were encouraged to give their sons an English education in 'chiefs'' schools and colleges. *Diwans*, or prime ministers, in the princely states were urged to press on with measures of administrative reform and viceroys treated their 'dear friends' among the princes with scrupulous respect, a far cry from the days of Dalhousie's 'Doctrine of Lapse'. C.A.B.

433(i)

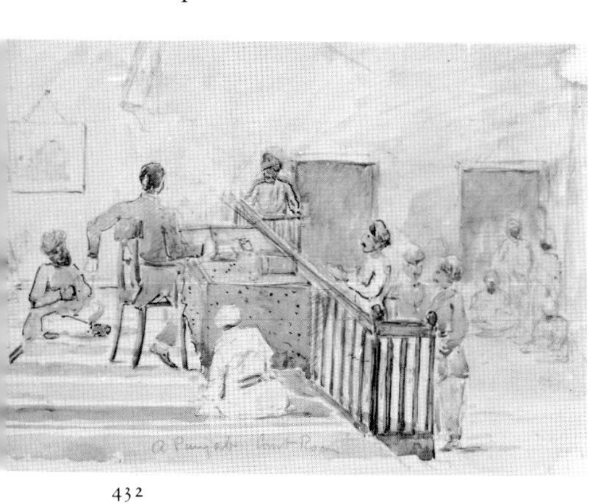

432

433(ii)

432 A court in the Punjab

Alfred Frederick Pollock Harcourt, *c.*1890
Watercolour and pencil on paper, 21 × 33 (8 × 12⅘)
India Office Library and Records (WD2479. f. 84)

433 *Curry and Rice on Forty Plates or the Ingredients of Social Life at our station in India*, London, 1859

Copyprints after illustrations in printed book by G. F. Atkinson in the India Office Library
i) Our Magistrate
ii) Our Judge

434 *Illustrated Historical Album of the Rajas and Taluqdars of Oudh*, Allahabad, 1880

Abbas Ali
Printed book, 25 x 17 ($9\frac{7}{8} \times 6\frac{6}{8}$)
India Office Library and Records (v6646)

In the 1830s and 1840s the civil officers of the North-Western Provinces had tilted towards the peasantry and against the landlords, characterizing the latter as 'drones of the soil'. They were influenced by contemporary British ideas of 'political economy' and the economic doctrines of David Ricardo and John Stuart Mill. When Awadh (Oudh) was annexed by the Company in 1856, land-revenue arrangements were made with important people in the villages and many territorial magnates were pensioned off, forfeiting their power and profits. This was one of the grievances which drove the great magnates of Awadh, the Taluqdars, to revolt in 1857 (see no.309). But, to their horror, the British found that many ordinary peasants, including the very types of people they had hoped to encourage by the arrangements of 1856, followed the Taluqdars into revolt against them. The British concluded that the territorial magnates were in fact 'natural leaders of the people'. In 1858 the Rajas and Taluqdars were confirmed in their holdings by charters from the Governor-General. Thereafter, the British devised many ways of cajoling and supporting the great magnates, who were seen to be critical to their rule. Glorious genealogies and histories were put together for men who were often only descendants of eighteenth-century farmers of revenue. Chiefs' colleges were established to educate them to become improving landlords rather than simple rentiers. The Court of Wards looked after their estates in cases of minority or incapacity among the great estate holders. The tactic worked well enough until the agricultural depression of the 1930s, but it did little to assuage the grievances of the ordinary peasantry of north India. C.A.B.

LITERATURE: Metcalf 1979.

435

435 The Raja of Kolhapur

Copyprint of photograph (1890s) in the India Office Library (photo 209 [16])

The Maratha princely state of Kolhapur, near Poona, became a centre of the non-Brahmin movement in the 1890s. The British authorities found this development to their taste as they preferred members of the old Maratha aristocracy to the 'Poona Brahmins', who were descendants of the families which had ruled the Maratha states under the Peshwas, and had become involved in political activities since the 1870s.

C.A.B.

436

436 Begum of Bhopal

Copyprint after photograph (1891) in the Bowood Collection

The Begum was descended from a Pathan family from north India, which had created a state in the Deccan in the later eighteenth century. A shrewd ruler and consummate politician, the Begum raised the status of her kingdom in British eyes. As a strict Muslim in full *purdah*, she was an unmistakeable figure at durbars and other official occasions.

C.A.B.

437

437 Maharaja of Jodphur (1898–1918)

Unknown photographer, 1915
Bromide print, 37.1 × 29 ($14\frac{6}{10} \times 11\frac{4}{10}$)
National Portrait Gallery, London (x34577)

438

438 A Prince of Hyderabad (1886–1967)

Unknown photographer, 1931
Bromide print, 24.3 × 19 (9½ × 7½)
National Portrait Gallery, London (x3591)

439

439 Ali Khan, Nawab of Rampur (1875–1930)

Unknown photographer, 1891
Bromide print, 37.2 × 29
National Portrait Gallery, London (x34582)

Police and Criminals in India

After 1857 the provincial governments devoted substantially more money to policing. The police force, based on the local police station or *thana*, was the most obvious manifestation of the power of the state and the only aspect with which most ordinary Indians had any contact. During the Rebellion discontented and poorly paid police had sometimes joined the rebels. As a consequence discipline and training were improved and attempts were made to wipe out corrupt practices and the periodic torture of suspects. The British District Superintendent of Police became a key figure in a local triumvirate of power along with the Collector and the District Judge.

Much police work centred on the extirpation of dacoity (no.443), defined as armed robbery committed by six or more people. The activities of such robber gangs increased according to the vagaries of the agricultural season. The imperial authorities, however, continued to believe that much criminality was hereditary within certain social or racial groups. The Criminal Tribes Act of 1871 in the United Provinces made it possible to proclaim a social group a 'criminal tribe'. The obverse of this notion was (slightly illogically) the idea that such groups could be reclaimed by honest toil. From the 1850s, therefore, regular regimes of work were introduced into most prisons (no.444).

The Indian branch of the police force never became the efficient and independent body that officials wished; too often it operated within the confines of local politics, especially as its members were usually drawn from dominant local groups with semi-martial traditions (Rajputs and Muslims in the north, Maravas and Kallars in the south, for instance). Nevertheless it served the British well until 1946, when serious disaffection surfaced again within its ranks.

C.A.B.

LITERATURE: Griffiths 1971; Arnold 1986.

440 Police officers and men, Gujranwala, Punjab

Copyprint after photograph (1869) in the India Office Library (photo 211/1 [675] B15945)

440

441

441 Group of Punjab police officers, Lahore, 1869

Copyprint after photograph (1860s) in the India Office Library (photo 211/1 [91] B15971)

442 *Lathi*, as used by Bihar police

c.1920

Length 165 (64⅞)

The Trustees of the British Museum (1924.11–11.62)

The *lathi*, or iron-shod staff, was the Indian police's main instrument of crowd control. C.P.

443 Three dacoit swords

Cambridge University Museum of Archaeology and Anthropology (30.1596 [x 2]; 30.1595)

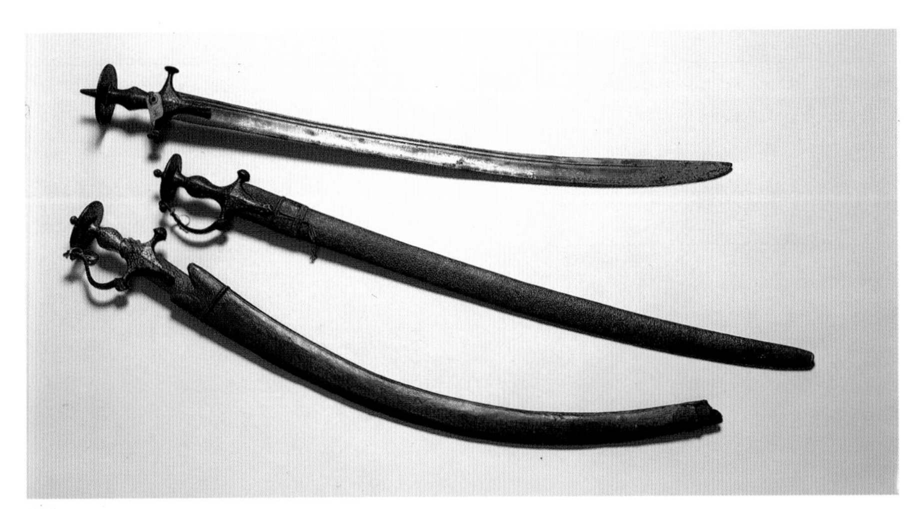

443

444

444 Convicts on the treadmill

Copyprint after photograph (*c*.1900) in the India Office Library (430/14 [63] B12579)

The Indian Army and its Enemies

The Rebellion brought about a major change in the organization and recruitment practices of the Indian Army. The ratio of British to Indian troops in the subcontinent was fixed so that Indians could not, theoretically at least, outnumber Europeans by more than two to one. The British troops were billeted in large and often newly constructed cantonments in or near the major cities, and could be rushed at short notice by road or rail to be employed against border rebels or to aid the civil power during disturbances. Following its near disastrous failure to foresee the Rebellion of 1857, the Army discontinued recruitment from the Awadh and Benares areas. Thereafter, and as late as 1942, it was the Punjab which was to supply the greatest number of recruits. These recruits were formed into regiments conforming with basic caste, religious or tribal divisions. The British felt they had paid insufficient attention to 'caste prejudice' and saw this as one cause of the Rebellion; at the same time they had elaborated a theory of 'martial races'. Punjabis and men of the Northwest Frontier were men of such 'martial races'; Bengalis or Tamils from their warm and enervating climes were not. The Indian Army was also forced to adapt its style to the guerilla warfare it encountered on the Northwest Frontier. As the Russian empire consolidated its position in Central Asia, the British were alarmed by signs of restiveness amongst the fiercely independent Pathan tribes, such as the Afridis (no.447), whose lands ran across their borders with Afghanistan. In 1878 a diplomatic crisis arose between Britain and Tsarist Russia, and in this context unfriendly moves by the Afghan ruler sparked off a full-scale war between the two countries. To begin with the British war effort seemed to be as ill-fated as it had been in 1841. The officials and garrison of the British Residency in Kabul, the Afghan capital, were overwhelmed and massacred. But under the dogged leadership of Frederick Sleigh Roberts (no.445), the empire struck back, defeating the Afghans at the Battle of Kandahar in 1880. One thing that tipped the balance in favour of the British was the deployment of the Gatling gun (no.448). But close control of Afghanistan was not possible given the guerilla tactics of the Afghan tribesmen armed with long *jazails*, or flintlock sharpshooting rifles.

Outside the subcontinent the Army was used on many occasions as a kind of 'imperial fire brigade'. It was sent to East Africa and Egypt, it fought the Boxer rebels in China, and during the South African War (1899–1902) Roberts led substantial contingents against the Boers. C.A.B.

LITERATURE: Mason 1974.

445

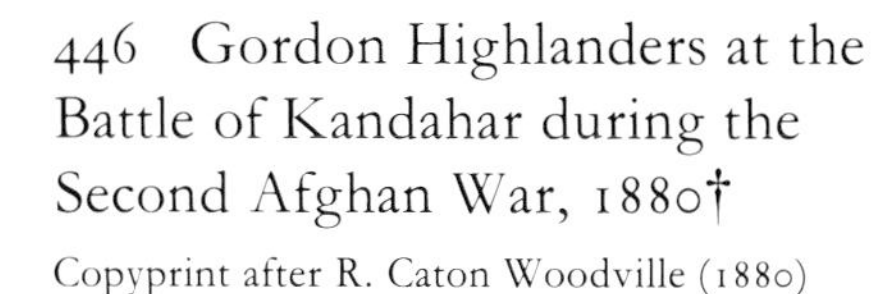

446 Gordon Highlanders at the Battle of Kandahar during the Second Afghan War, 1880†

Copyprint after R. Caton Woodville (1880)

446

445 Frederick Sleigh Roberts (1832–1914)

Inglis Sheldon-Williams, 1900
Watercolour and pencil, 29.5 × 24.1 ($11\frac{5}{8} \times 9\frac{1}{2}$)
National Portrait Gallery, London (1744)

Roberts ('old Bob' as he was known to his troops) was born in Cawnpore. He conducted himself with great valour during the Indian Rebellion and was awarded the Victoria Cross. Later he organized the movements of the Viceroy's camp in north India from 1861 to 1863 (no.409). His finest hour came during the Afghan campaigns of 1878 and 1880 where his rapid movement and attack won the Battle of Kandahar. He later served in Burma and South Africa.

LITERATURE: Roberts 1897. C.A.B.

447

447 Group of Afreedees from the Khyber Pass

Copyprint after photograph by Bourne & Shepherd (*c*.1864) in the Royal Commonwealth Society Library (photo Y3022D/50 [1387])

448

449

448 Second Afghan War, 1880: the Kurram Valley expedition with Gatling guns

Copyprint after photograph by Bourne & Shepherd (1880) in the National Army Museum (5504–42–28)

Indians Overseas

Indians played an important part in the expansion of the British empire. Some went abroad as soldiers, traders or as clerks, others as indentured labourers. There was an ancient population of Indian Tamils settled in the northern part of Ceylon (Sri Lanka). After 1795, when the British took the island from the Dutch, new merchant families arrived to take advantage of the increased trade between India and Ceylon. It was at this time that the Hindu temple in Colombo (no. 449) was greatly enlarged. Then, after 1840, large numbers of Tamils migrated to the central highlands of Ceylon to work on the tea estates there. By the end of British rule on the island, relations between the Singhalese and Tamil populations had begun to deteriorate as the host population believed themselves to be losing out in education and government jobs. Indians had also established themselves in East Africa, which was linked by ancient trade routes to the Indian subcontinent. Here members of the Muslim business communities of Bombay and the west coast, Khojas, Bohras and Memons, were prominent (see no. 451), but later, Hindu Pattidars from Gujarat began to play an important part in local commerce. In Malaya too, Indians found new areas of activity. South Indian Tamil Muslims (Lebbais and Marakayyars) accompanied British ships to the trading towns of Malacca and in 1829, Singapore (no. 452). The demand for labour on sugar estates in Fiji (no. 450) and South Africa took large numbers of Indians overseas in the second half of the nineteenth century. It was among Indian labourers in South Africa that Gandhi began his career of social and political reform. C.A.B.

449 Hindu temple, Colombo

Unknown photographer, late 19th century
Photograph, 26.4 × 34.9 ($10\frac{3}{8} \times 13\frac{3}{4}$)
Private Collection

450

450 Indian labourers in Fiji

Walker
Photograph
Royal Anthropological Institute, Walker Collection (35416)

451

451 Sewa Haji, an Indian contractor in East Africa

Copyprint from *A History of Medical Services in Tanganyika* by D.F. Clyde, with foreword by Julius K. Nyerere, Dar-es-Salaam, 1962

452 A *dargah* (shrine and meeting hall) Telok Ayyar Street, Singapore

*c.*1890
Photograph, 20.3 × 27.3 (8 × 10¾)
Private Collection

This shrine was a replica of one of the greatest south Indian Sufi *dargahs*, that of Shahul Hamid Sahib of Nagore on the Madras coast. This tomb shrine, long venerated by the coast's Muslim seafarers and merchants, rose to prominence in the eighteenth century when the four characteristic towers on the corners of the original structure were built. Exact replicas of the Nagore building were constructed on a smaller scale first at Penang and then at Singapore, which was founded by Sir Stamford Raffles in 1819 and later became a centre for south Indian Muslim traders. The *dargahs* were the heart of the religious and social life of the Tamil communities in these cities, and complemented the activities of the mosques. C.A.B.

LITERATURE: Bayly 1989.

453 A Hindoo 'Bishop' from *A Souvenir of Trinidad*, Trinidad, *c.*1900

Printed pamphlet, 15.3 × 10.1 (6 × 4)
Private Collection

452

Art, Literature and Architecture in Queen Victoria's India

454 Bombay Occupations

Lockwood Kipling, *c.* 1872
i) The banker
Pencil and wash, 35 × 24.5 (13¾ × 9½)
India Office Library and Records (WD1742)
ii) The *dhobi* (washerman) (Illustrated Fig. 56)
Pencil and wash, 35 × 24.5 (13¾ × 9½)
India Office Library and Records (WD1744)
iii) The *hajan* (barber)
Pencil and wash, 25 × 35 (9½ × 13¾)
India Office Library and Records (WD1745)
iv) The blacksmith (Illustrated Fig. 57)
Pencil and wash, 35 × 24.5 (13¾ × 9½)
India Office Library and Records (WD1747)

Lockwood Kipling (1837–1911) was the municipal architect in Bombay and later became curator of the Lahore Museum (1875–93). Trained as an artist in London, he was closely associated with

455

456

English artistic circles; his sister-in-law was married to the painter Edward Burne-Jones and he himself was instrumental in bringing mid-Victorian artistic sensibilities to India. In his work he stressed the importance of craftsmanship and heritage and deplored the uniformity and commercialism of the modern art world. In Bombay he set about revivifying the craft of the Indian stonemason. Kipling and his students were as interested in the depiction of Indian types and occupations as the Picturesque and Company School painters had been, but extended the media used to wood and stone. In these pictures of village servants in the Bombay Presidency, as in the sculptured decorations of the Crawfurd Market and other buildings in Bombay (no. 455), the older 'castes and occupations' style of representation was infused with a new naturalism. There is also a touch of sentimentality, for by the latter half of the nineteenth century it was clear that traditional India, like 'rural' and 'feudal' England, was rapidly disappearing in the face of modernity. C.A.B.

455 Stone figure on the first floor verandah arch of the Sir Jamsetji Jijhibhai School of Art, Bombay

Foy Nissen
Photograph, 24 × 16.2 ($9\frac{1}{2} \times 6\frac{3}{8}$)
Foy Nissen

456 Rudyard Kipling (1864–1938)

Sir Philip Burne-Jones, 1899
Oil on canvas, 74.9 × 62.2 ($29\frac{1}{2} \times 24\frac{1}{2}$)
National Portrait Gallery, London (1863)

Rudyard Kipling was born in Bombay while his father Lockwood was working there. He was educated, rather unhappily, at the United Services College, Westward Ho, Devon, but returned to India at the age of seventeen to become sub-editor of the *Civil and Military Gazette*, the famous Anglo-Indian daily paper of the Punjab. In 1886 he published *Departmental Ditties* (no.458), satirical verses on Anglo-Indian life, and in 1887 *Plain Tales from the Hills*, a collection of short stories which deal with Indian officialdom, social life and relations between the British and the Indians. Between 1887 and 1890, in a great burst of creative writing, he published *Soldiers Three*, *In Black and White*, *Under the Deodars*, *The Phantom Rickshaw*, *The Story of the Gadsbys* and *Wee Willie Winkie*. All of these were published by Wheelers Railway Library, Allahabad, for one rupee a piece. Kipling's Anglo-Indian masterpieces, *The Jungle Book* (1894) and *Kim* (1901), were published later, following extensive travels in Asia and the United States. He returned to Britain and was awarded the Nobel Prize for Literature in 1907. An unrivalled observer of Indian people and places, much of Kipling's work is a continuation in words of the Picturesque tradition. C.A.B.

LITERATURE: Rutherford 1964; Stokes 1974.

457 *In Black and White*, Allahabad, 1888

Rudyard Kipling
Bound volume, 13.1 × 21.2 ($5\frac{1}{10} \times 8\frac{4}{10}$)
National Trust for Places of Historic Interest or Natural Beauty

458 *Departmental Ditties* and other verse

Rudyard Kipling, *c.*1887
Autograph manuscripts, various sizes
National Trust for Places of Historic Interest or Natural Beauty

459 Rabindranath Tagore (1861–1941)

A. Bose, *c.*1920
Chalk on paper, 60 × 48 ($23\frac{4}{10} \times 18\frac{3}{4}$)
India Office Library and Records (Add. Or. 3906) (Illustrated Fig. 59)

Probably the most famous thinker and

457

458

man of letters to arise in nineteenth-century India, Tagore was born to one of the most wealthy and successful of the Calcutta families. He was the fourteenth son of Debendranath, businessman and prominent member of the Brahmo Samaj (see no.297). Rabindranath's formal English education at St Xavier's school was not a success, but he soon revealed his gifts in Bengali song and poetry, skilfully adapting traditional classical and popular forms to modern themes. He made his first public appearance at the age of fourteen, reciting a patriotic song he had composed himself. In 1878 he went to England where he studied English literature under Henry Morley at University College, London. On his return to India in 1880 he began a career in creative writing in Bengali and English which was to last into his seventies. In 1913 he was awarded the Nobel Prize for Literature for his Bengali poems, *Gitanjali*. A severe critic of British rule, Tagore nevertheless distanced himself from the more inward-looking forms of Bengali and Indian nationalism, later viewing Gandhi's campaigns with some scepticism. He developed and enriched the philosophy of accommodating the West while retaining the integrity of Indian culture which had been enunciated by Raja Ram Mohan Roy and nurtured by his grandfather, Dwarkanath.

Atul Bose pioneered the introduction of European-style portraiture into Bengal. He painted many of the most important political and literary figures of the National Movement. C.A.B.

460 Rabindranath Tagore with Albert Einstein

Copyprint after photograph in the Nehru Memorial Museum and Library, New Delhi

461 *Gitanjali. Song Offerings*, 1st edn, 1913

Rabindranath Tagore, introduction by W. B. Yeats
Book, 22.5 × 15 ($8\frac{3}{4} \times 5\frac{4}{5}$)
The British Library Board (14129 cc.29)

460

462 Premchand (1880–1936)

Copyprint after photograph in the collection of Cambridge University Press

After 1860 Hindu leaders in north India began to press the British Government to allow the Hindi language to be used in official business on the same terms as Urdu, which had replaced Persian as the Government's main indigenous language in 1837. The two languages had much in common, but Hindi was written in the Devanagri script (derived from Sanskrit) and Urdu in the Persian. Hindus who mainly, but not exclusively, used Hindi felt themselves disadvantaged in the race for official

462

appointments. But the new confidence of the Hindu merchant and clerical classes was bringing about its own revival of Hindi language and literature. Many Hindu newspapers were founded and writers began to switch from the flowery Urdu to a sober and realistic style of Hindi writing. One such was Premchand (his real name was Dhanpatrai), who came from a Benares clerical family of the sort which had traditionally learned Persian and Urdu in order to compete for government office. Premchand made a distinguished contribution to Urdu writing, but he was increasingly drawn to writing in Hindi on social and political problems. His most famous work, *Godan* ('The Gift of a Cow'), 1936, attempted to alert urban India to the existence and problems of the countryside. His literary work paralleled the rural campaigns of Indian nationalism after 1920. C.A.B.

463 Portrait of a woman

Ravi Varma
Oil on canvas, 53.8 × 36 ($21\frac{1}{8} \times 14\frac{1}{8}$)
The Trustees of the Victoria & Albert Museum (IS-59-1978) (Illustrated Fig. 58)

Ravi Varma (1848–1906) was born near Trivandrum in Kerala into a princely family connected to the Raja of Travancore. His oil paintings of romantic visions of India, Indian women and scenes from the Indian epics, presented in a Westernized style, won him many medals at exhibitions in Madras, Vienna and elsewhere from the 1870s onwards. Such was the demand for his work, particularly his mythological scenes, that he was encouraged to have them mass-produced as coloured oleographs and lithographs. Produced first by European presses, and later, in the 1890s, by his own Ravi Varma Press based near Bombay, these were the forerunners of the cheaply produced and brilliantly coloured devotional prints of gods and goddesses which are to be found all over urban and rural India today. C.P.

LITERATURE: Joshi 1911; Archer 1959; Vitsaxis 1977; Chaitanya 1984.

464 An Astrologer

Lala Din Diyal (Dayal)
Photograph, 27 × 22 ($10\frac{5}{8} \times 8\frac{5}{8}$)
Private Collection

The popularity of photography as a means of recording the affairs of Indian states was in large part due to the influence and example of 'Raja' Lala Din Diyal, who from 1884 to his death in 1910 was court photographer to the Nizam of Hyderabad. Although there were several hundred Indian photographic businesses operating from as early as the 1850s, Din Diyal's output was of an unrivalled standard and quantity.

464

Diyal, a Jain, was born near Meerut and established his reputation in Indore, central India, after 1874 with the encouragement of Sir Henry Daly and subsequently Sir Lepel Griffin. For the last twenty-five years of his life Din Diyal recorded all the important state events in Hyderabad (several hundred large albums are preserved in the Salar Jung Museum, Andhra Pradesh) and continued to run commercial studios in Secunderabad (near Hyderabad), Indore, and after 1896 in Bombay. As well as his intimate portraits and official groups, Diyal also excelled at urban and rural landscapes. Din Diyal's Secunderabad business was continued by his grandson Amichand and is now part of the firm Fotocrafts, run by his great-grandson Prabas Chand. C.P.

LITERATURE: Mitchell 1908; Worswick 1980, ill. p.132; Gutman 1982; Mitter 1982, pp.2–4; Desmond 1985, p.59.

465 E.M. (Edward Morgan) Forster (1879–1970)

Dora Carrington, 1920
Oil on canvas, 50.8 × 40.6 (20 × 16)
National Portrait Gallery, London (4698)

Kipling's novels and stories sometimes conveyed a sense of the alien nature of India for Europeans, but his was still an optimistic era. By the time E.M.Forster made his second visit to India in 1921 relations between the races had perceptibly deteriorated, and the mutual incomprehension of conqueror and conquered was the theme of his most famous work *A Passage to India* (1924). Forster's view of Anglo-Indian life was not favourable. He wrote of the playing of the National Anthem in the Chandrapore Club: 'It was the Anthem of the Army of Occupation. It reminded every member of the Club that he or she was British and in exile.... The meagre tune, the curt series of demands on Jehovah,

465

466

fused into a prayer unknown in England, and though they perceived neither Royalty nor Deity they did perceive something, they were strengthened to resist another day.' Ironically, though, Forster's interest in the subcontinent was itself a consequence of his close friendship with Ross Masood, who was the grandson of Sir Sayyid Ahmad Khan (no.300), the Muslim reformer. Forster first encountered Masood when he was engaged to tutor him in Latin by Theodore Morison, a former principal of Aligarh College. C.A.B.

LITERATURE: Furbank 1977.

467

466 A visit to caves near Bangalore

Copyprint after photograph (*c.*1880) in the India Office Library (photo 447/3; B18301)

This picture strikingly anticipates one of the central events in Forster's novel *A Passage to India*, the visit to the Marabar Caves where the British visitors are overcome by the awesome strangeness of India. C.A.B.

467 Design for a High School, Kolhapur

Copyprint after drawing by Charles Mant (*c.*1880) in the British Architectural Library Drawings Collection/RIBA (Z1/68)

Major Charles Mant of the Bengal Engineers was, with R.F. Chisholm, one of the leading advocates of Indo-Saracenic architecture (see also no. 468). His first work in this style was Mayo College in Ajmer, designed in 1875. Following the success of that project he was commissioned to build numerous palaces and other buildings by the maharajas of princely states, including Darbhanga, Baroda and Kolhapur. In Kolhapur he designed a town hall, a hospital and the school shown here, in addition to the maharaja's palace.

In the last quarter of the nineteenth century the Indo-Saracenic style became particularly fashionable among maharajas; it offered them, perhaps, a means of retaining an Indian identity through their buildings whilst at the same time promoting architecture that had the approval of the imperial government. This design is typical of Mant's work in drawing together motifs derived from Mughal and Rajput architectural traditions. G.H.R.T.

468 Elevation, Napier Museum, Trivandrum

R.F. Chisholm, 1872
Ink and watercolour on paper, 58 × 93 (23 × 36)
British Architectural Library Drawings Collection/RIBA (W11/2[2])

This drawing by the architect Robert Fellowes Chisholm shows his final design for the museum that was commissioned by the Maharaja of Travancore, at the southern tip of India. The building's name honours Lord Napier, then Governor of Madras.

Chisholm had been appointed Consulting Architect to the Madras Presidency in 1865, and he was one of the leading exponents of the movement in architecture that came to be known as 'Indo-Saracenic'. His intention was to base his designs on traditional local styles of architecture. Some of his work is highly eclectic, but the steeply pitched roofs and gables and the towers seen in this design are derived from traditional houses in Trivandrum itself.

The Indo-Saracenic movement had arisen from a debate over the relative suitability of various architectural styles to modern building in India, and a quest for a style that would be expressive of the character of the British Raj. Some favoured the uncompromising adoption of Western styles as a forceful expression of British values. But Chisholm was prominent among those who felt that the use of Indian styles would reflect the paternalistic qualities and Eastern location of the Raj.

Chisholm received vocal support for his efforts from Lord Napier, who saw the movement as a benevolent gesture promoting 'a revival in native art'. Others were more sceptical. The art historian E.B. Havell noted that Indian craftsmen were not involved in such designs except as labourers, and he criticized buildings like this as offering nothing more than 'the application of Indian archaeology to the constructive methods of the West'. G.H.R.T.

LITERATURE: Metcalf 1989, p.64, fig.6.

469

468

469 Victoria Memorial, Calcutta

Bedford Lemere & Co., c.1910
Photograph of architectural drawing, printed in sepia, 40.6 × 61 (16 x24)
Mr Vivian V. Esch

The Victoria Memorial was not only a monument to the great Queen. It became the personal project of Lord Curzon who conceived of it as the final embellishment of his term as Viceroy. It stands as the finest example of British

Indian classical architecture and one of the greatest monuments of the Raj. The celebrated architect Vincent Esch (1869–1950) arrived in India in 1898. He became architect to the President of the Railway Board on the construction of the Bengal-Nagpur Railway. In 1902 he was recommended to the Viceroy to become Superintending Architect in charge of the All-India Victoria Memorial, which opened in 1921. He also designed numerous commercial public and domestic buildings throughout India. C.A.B.

PROVENANCE: Vincent J. Esch, C.V.O., F.R.I.B.A., Superintending Architect to the Trustees of the All-India Victoria Memorial; thence to his son, Vivian V. Esch.

LITERATURE: *The British Builder* 1921; *The Builder* 2 December 1921.

Imperial Glory and Indian Dissent

470 Queen Victoria (1819–1901)

Sir George Hayter, 1863 (after his portrait of 1838)
Oil on canvas, 285.8 × 179 (112½ × 70½)
Signed and dated b.l.: *Hayter, Eques, & K.S.L./London 1863*
National Portrait Gallery, London (1250)

470

With the trial, deposition and exile of the Mughal Emperor, Queen Victoria became the fount of all legitimate authority in India. Immediately after the Rebellion a royal proclamation announced the British policy of religious toleration; Indians' concerns for their religious traditions had been one cause of the Rebellion. In 1877, however, Disraeli had Victoria proclaimed Queen-Empress of India by Lord Lytton, the Viceroy (no.475), at a magnificent durbar in Delhi in an attempt to impress nationalist opinion at home as well as the Tsarist empire. This was to be the prototype for the even grander durbars of 1903 and 1911.

This is a replica of the life-size, full-length portrait in the Royal Collection at Holyrood House, and both works were purchased by Queen Victoria from Hayter's executors in 1871. The original version, according to Hayter's son, was returned so that copies could be made for presentation. The setting appears to be imaginary; the Queen is shown wearing the same costume in Hayter's group picture of the coronation in the Royal Collection. B.A./C.A.B.

PROVENANCE: Purchased from the artist's executors by H.M. Queen Victoria, 1871, and presented by her to National Portrait Gallery in 1900.

LITERATURE: Documents in the Royal Archives, Windsor, relating to its purchasers (PPVIC 8580, 8701 and 12400) and to its presentation (PPVIC 3643); Ormond 1973, I, pp.474–5, no.1250, II, pls.941, 942 and frontispiece.

471

472

473

471 Queen Victoria (1819–1901)

Sir Francis Chantrey, 1841
Marble bust, height 70.5 ($27\frac{1}{2}$)
National Portrait Gallery, London (1716)

472 British and Indian officers of the Viceroy's bodyguard

Copyprint after photograph (*c.*1870) in the National Army Museum, London (5903–100)

473 The Prince of Wales in his private tent in Delhi

William Simpson, 1876
Pencil on paper, 21.1 × 33.9 ($8\frac{1}{5} \times 13\frac{1}{5}$)
Inscribed in black ink b.r.: *Wm. Simpson. 14th Jan.1876*
Inscribed in black ink b.l.: *Private Tent of H.R.H. The Prince of Wales, Camp, Delhi*
Her Majesty The Queen (RL 2113)

After 1858 the status of the Crown in

India was unambiguous, and royal tours became a means of reaffirming the legitimacy of British rule when honours could be conferred on favoured Indian subjects. C.A.B.

PROVENANCE: By 1877 in collection of Prince of Wales.

LITERATURE: *Illustrated London News*, 19 February 1876; Marlborough House and Sandringham Catalogue 1877, N.1213.

474 John Laird Mair Lawrence, 1st Baron Lawrence (1811–79)

Thomas Woolner, 1879
Bronze bust, height 63.5 (25)
Inscribed on front: *Lord Lawrence*
India Office Library and Records (F641)

Woolner executed two busts of Lord Lawrence in 1871. In the first Lawrence is treated in the classical manner,

474

without drapery, and it is this version that was the basis for the bronze copy commissioned by Lawrence's son-in-law for his wife (see Provenance).

The second bust shows him wearing a cloak decorated with the Star of India, and this became the basis for the marble monument of 1881 by Woolner in Westminster Abbey (Read 1982, ill. pl.103). B.A.

PROVENANCE: Commissioned by Frances William Buxton (son-in-law of Lawrence); Col. R.V. Buxton, bequeathed by him to Foreign and Commonwealth Relations Office, December 1953.

LITERATURE: Woolner 1917; Trevelyan 1978, pp.200–205; Archer 1986, p.107, no.155.

475 Edward Bulwer-Lytton, 1st Earl of Lytton (1831–91)

George Frederick Watts, 1884
Oil on canvas, 64.8 × 52.1 ($25\frac{1}{2}$ × $20\frac{1}{2}$)
National Portrait Gallery, London (1007)

Lytton was unique among Governors-General and Viceroys in being a prominent literary man. He was educated at Harrow and joined the Diplomatic Service as an attaché in 1850, receiving postings throughout Europe over the next decade. He married Edith, daughter of Edward Villiers, who was brother of the 4th Duke of Clarendon, and succeeded to the peerage and the Knebworth Estate in Hertfordshire in 1873. In 1875 he was appointed by Disraeli to the Viceroyalty at what was regarded as a critical juncture, for the Amir of Afghanistan had come directly under the influence of imperial Russia. Lytton pursued a vigorous policy on the Northwest Frontier which led to the occupation of Kabul in 1880. But, with the fall of the Conservative government, he resigned office before he could carry out the absorption of Afghanistan into the British empire, a policy which was reversed by the new Liberal government. Lytton was as definite in his domestic Indian policies. In his Vernacular Press Act he clamped down hard on what he regarded as sedition and made few concessions to Indian opinion, which became increasingly restive during his rule. It was under this 'Tory' Viceroy that Queen Victoria became Empress of India in 1877. C.A.B./B.A.

475

PROVENANCE: Presented by the artist to National Portrait Gallery, 1884.

LITERATURE: Yung 1981, ill. p.360.

476 George Frederick Samuel Robinson, 1st Marquess of Ripon (1827–1909)

C.F.Sternberg, after H. Herkomer
Mezzotint, 39.5 × 32.2 ($15\frac{1}{2}$ × $12\frac{1}{2}$)
India Office Library and Records (P548)

Born into a prominent Whig political family, Ripon began his career as an attaché in the British mission in Brussels. His first major political appointment was as Lord President of the Council in Gladstone's government (1868). In 1874 he became a convert to Roman Catholicism. When Gladstone's government took office again Ripon was sent to India as Viceroy. He attempted to pacify Indian political opinion, which had been alienated by Lytton's Vernacular Press Act and the strong line he had taken on Afghanistan. He inaugurated an Education Commission to take evidence on the development of schooling in the subcontinent and repealed Lytton's harsher measures against the Indian press. However, in the Ilbert Bill (1883) Ripon brought on himself the wrath of the Anglo-Indian community. This bill was intended to allow Indian magistrates jurisdiction over Europeans in some small cases, and led to violent racial agitation. Ripon left India with the decline of Gladstone's government in 1884. The British press in India was almost universally hostile, but Indians feted him. The lesson of aggressive lobbying by the expatriates against the Ilbert Bill was not lost on Indians. It was one of the catalysts which brought about the foundation of the Indian National Congress in 1885 (no.489). C.A.B.

LITERATURE: Gopal 1965; Rohatgi 1982.

477

477 Viceregal Lodge, Simla

Copyprint after photograph by F. Bremmer (1922) in the India Office Library (B6534)

During the hot summer months the hill retreat of Simla became the capital of India. The first European house was built there in 1819 and it was first visited by a Governor-General in 1829. Simla's reputation as a sanatorium led to a rapid growth in the permanent population from about 5,000 in 1880 to about 13,000 in 1901. But during the summer months the population was three times as great. Apart from being the seasonal capital of the Indian Government (from 1864), it was also the summer headquarters of the Punjab Government, of several military commands and of the imperial forestry services. Missionary, educational and private establishments followed. Simla also developed the distinction of being the social centre of Anglo-Indian life, a place where young men and women came to seek partners amidst the balls and under the deodar trees. This world was immortalized in Kipling's short stories. C.A.B.

478

478 Simla: general view

Bourne & Shepherd, *c.*1863
Photograph, 23.5 × 29.2 ($9\frac{1}{4} \times 11\frac{5}{8}$)
Royal Commonwealth Society Library (Y3022B/145 [1793])

479 A picnic given by the Viceroy: Lord Lansdowne's staff at Simla

Copyprint after photograph (1891) in the India Office Library (photo 175, p.66.13. B2012)

480 George Nathaniel, Lord Curzon, at his desk at Government House, Calcutta

G.P. Jacomb-Hood, February 1903
Watercolour, 43 × 45.25 ($16\frac{3}{4} \times 17\frac{3}{5}$) (framed)
The Viscount Scarsdale and the Trustees of the Kedleston Estate Trusts

Curzon's rule (1898–1906) was the Indian summer of the British Raj. Curzon had been born in 1859 and was educated at Eton and Balliol. An able scholar, he was a Fellow of All Souls before entering public life as Assistant Private Secretary to Lord Salisbury in 1883. He later served in Conservative governments as Under Secretary of State for India and for Foreign Affairs, gaining much experience of the Near East through travels in Persia and Afghanistan, about which he later wrote. Appointed Viceroy in 1898, Curzon's aim was to strengthen British power throughout Asia against what was perceived as a threat from Tsarist Russia. To this end he visited the Persian Gulf in 1903 and supported a military intervention in Tibet in 1904. But external power needed internal discipline and efficiency. Curzon wished to help the Congress to an early demise, but he also made himself unpopular amongst expatriates by vigorously punishing incidents of racial violence perpetrated by the army and by European planters.

Ironically, however, it was his drive for efficiency which was to prove his undoing. He cut back on the powers of Indian representatives in the Calcutta Corporation and in the universities. But in 1905 Bengal was stirred to fury by his plan to partition the province. This was ostensibly for administrative reasons, but there was little doubt that British administrators expected to benefit politically from creating two smaller provinces, one of which would be dominated by Muslims who regarded the Indian National Congress with some suspicion. Years of demonstrations, boycotts and terrorism were to follow until 1911, when the partition was annulled at the Imperial Durbar of that year.

479

481(i)

In this portrait, Jacomb-Hood catches an important feature of Curzon's character, his capacity for tireless administrative work which never declined, despite the acute discomfort caused him by the metal brace which he wore to support his defective spine. C.A.B.

PROVENANCE: Lord Curzon, then by descent to Kedleston Trustees.

LITERATURE: Gopal 1965; Dilks 1969–70.

481(i) Lord and Lady Curzon on a tiger hunt

Copyprint after photograph (*c.*1902) in the India Office Library

481(ii)

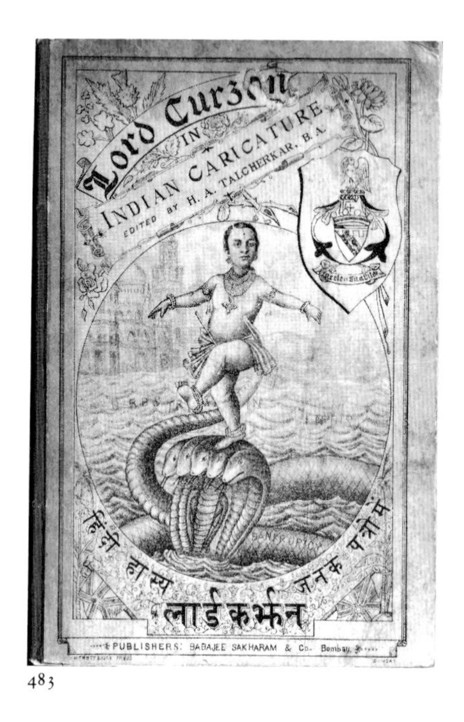

483

481(ii) Lord Curzon's autumn tour, Karachi

Copyprint after photograph (1900) in the India Office Library (photo 430/19 [2]; B10932)

482 Illustrated address to Lord Curzon, Viceroy of India

Unknown artist, January 1903
Ink and watercolour, 107.5 × 74 (42 × 29) framed
The Viscount Scarsdale and the Trustees of the Kedleston Estate Trusts

PROVENANCE: Presented to Lord Curzon by Mirza Abdool Latif Beg Mogul of the Ratnagiri Municipal Corporation, Bombay, on the occasion of the Delhi durbar, 1 January 1901; thence by descent to Kedleston Trustees.

LITERATURE: King 1984.

EXHIBITION: London, Barbican Art Gallery, *The Edwardian Era*, 1987–8.

483 *Lord Curzon in Indian Caricature*, Bombay, 1902

Ed. H.A.Talcherkar
Book, 24.8 × 16.5 ($9\frac{3}{4} \times 6\frac{1}{2}$)
Dr Gordon Johnson

In his first two years Curzon was quite a popular Viceroy owing to his stand against European racism and determination to reform the Indian police. An increasingly sophisticated Indian press gently chided his tendency to self-dramatization. But later relations rapidly deteriorated.

This work is of particular interest as it shows the Indian artist's unselfconscious use of the symbols of Indian tradition and religion in caricaturing a foreigner. Here Curzon is seen as the elephant-headed god Ganesh and as the young Krishna, dancing upon Shesha, the eternal serpent. Ironically, Ganesh was soon to become a symbol of the struggle of people in western India against the very imperial values which Curzon embodied so well. C.A.B.

16 *Lord Curzon in Indian Caricature.*

Hindi Punch] [Sept. 1899.

PROPITIATING SHRI GANESHA.

The arc of the heavens, and black is its shade
O'er thick-peopled village, o'er wild jungle glade."

And —

"Stark, gloomy with death
Roams the spirit of pestilence breathing that breath
That blasts all it touches." *

* "Rhyming Legends of Ind."—H. Kirkwood Gracey, B. A., C. S.

483

484

484 Indian troops praying for King Edward VII's recovery, Fulham Palace, London, 24 June 1902

Georges Bertin Scott, 1902
Wash heightened with white, 31 × 41 ($12\frac{1}{4}$ × 16)
Signed b.l. in black watercolour: *Georges Scott, London*
Her Majesty The Queen (RL 21048)

Muslim Indian cavalry officers, some in regimental mufti, are shown in the grounds of Fulham Palace praying for the King's recovery from illness. Georges Bertin Scott (b.1873) was a distinguished painter of French military dress who worked as a war artist during the First World War. B.A.

PROVENANCE: From 1902, Royal Library, Windsor Castle (Souvenir Album, XI, 44 [8], RL 2475/3).

LITERATURE: Haswell Miller and Dawn 1966, II, p.246.

485 King George V and Queen Mary on the balcony of the Red Fort, New Delhi

Copyprint after photograph by Bourne & Shepherd (1911) in the Queen Mary Collection, Commonwealth Trust (1911–12, microfiche 20 [170]) (Illustrated Fig. 47)

King George himself suggested that he should be the first British monarch to visit his Indian territories soon after his coronation. The idea appealed to the Liberal government and its Secretary of State for India, Viscount Morley (no.504), who was happy to use the royal presence as a further element in his policy of assuaging Indian public opinion. On 2 December 1911 the royal ship dropped anchor in Bombay. The royal party proceeded to Delhi, whose population had increased by nearly one million people since the beginning of the year. Here, the greatest of all imperial assemblages was held on 12 December 1911. The Indian princes and more than 70,000 invited guests and 20,000 massed troops paid homage to the King and Queen who were seated on thrones under a huge canopy. The editor of *The Times* was later to record that the durbar was 'probably the most magnificent and dazzling spectacle of its kind that the eye of mortal has ever beheld'. Indeed, it was a ritual to mark the passing of an age. In his speech the King announced the reversal of Curzon's partition of Bengal and the removal of the capital of British India from Calcutta to Delhi. Later the King and Queen greeted their people from the walls of the Red Fort in a gesture intended, as was so much else during the visit, to remind the Indian populace of the ritual of the previous Mughal rulers. In no.486, for instance, parade mace bearers reminiscent of the *chobdars* and *mihrdars* of the Mughals (no.11) attend the royal couple. C.A.B.

LITERATURE: Fortescue 1912; Irving 1981, pp.1–15.

486 Mace bearers with Royal Insignia

Copyprint after photograph by Bourne & Shepherd (1911) in the Queen Mary Collection, Commonwealth Trust (1911–12, microfiche 19–10 [121]) (Illustrated Fig. 48)

Political Dissidence and Social Conflict

487 Allan Octavian Hume (1829–1912), 'Father of the Indian National Congress'

Copyprint of photograph published in *The Times*

It is often forgotten that British radicals and reformers were closely involved with the Indian National Congress in its foundation and early years. Hume, who was educated at Haileybury and University College Hospital (where he studied medicine and surgery), inherited the radical bent of his father, Joseph Hume, and an abiding interest in botany and ornithology. In India he was a nonconformist Civil Officer, attracting opprobium from his fellows in the Indian Civil Service for 'excessive leniency' to Indians during the period of the 1857 Rebellion. After his retirement from the Civil Service in 1882, Hume moved from verbal criticism of the bureaucracy to direct action. In 1883 he founded the Indian National Union, which in 1885, at its first Bombay session, was renamed the Indian National Congress. Hume tried to organize Congress pamphlet campaigns and public meetings in all parts of India and his model here seems to have been radical movements such as Chartism and the Anti-Corn Law League. But by 1887 he realized that the Congress had to have direct access to British public opinion at home and to Parliament. In 1889 he helped set up a Congress Agency in London, and the later years of his life were devoted to spreading the nationalist message in Britain.

During all this time Hume retained an enduring interest in Indian religion and culture (for a time he was a theosophist), and also in Indian wild life. His unrivalled collection of Indian birds was donated to the British Museum of Natural History at South Kensington.

C.A.B.

LITERATURE: Wedderburn 1913.

488 The Famine in Bengal

(i) 'Arrival of Relief at a Distressed Village'
From the *Illustrated London News*
Engraving, 22.5 × 30 ($8\frac{3}{4} \times 11\frac{3}{4}$)
India Office Library and Records (P1373)
(ii) 'Sketches in Affected Districts' by a member of Famine Relief
From the *Illustrated London News*
Engraving, 30 × 22.5 ($11\frac{3}{4} \times 8\frac{3}{4}$)
India Office Library and Records (P1386)

The Indian national movement gained strength because educated Indians were excluded from government office and political power, and because traders and merchants felt threatened by the flood of British imports and the lack of tariff protection. Intellectuals, such as the Bombay leader and Parsi writer Dadhabhai Naoroji, argued that British rule had actually impoverished India, draining her wealth away and laying a huge weight of rural taxation on her people. But though there was little political activity in the countryside, the early nationalists were deeply concerned about the series of appalling famines which struck India after 1860, at a time when the British were supposedly modernizing and developing the economy. At least 15 million people perished of hunger and associated disease throughout the subcontinent in the last forty years of the nineteenth century. Critics of British rule argued that the opening of the country to the West via the railways and the steamship had simply encouraged peasants to switch from food crops to lucrative cash crops, so dangerously exposing the population when the rains failed, as they inevitably did once or twice every decade. Naoroji famously expounded this theme in his *Poverty and Un-British Rule in India*, 1901.

By the end of the nineteenth century the British authorities had finally perfected their techniques of famine prevention, though horrific mortality was to occur again during the Bengal famine of 1943, which was brought about by poor transport.

C.A.B.

LITERATURE: Bhatia 1963; MacAlpin 1977.

489 *Report of the Fourth Indian National Congress*, Allahabad, December 1888

Calcutta, 1889
Printed book, 33 × 47 ($13 \times 18\frac{3}{10}$)
The British Library Board (8022i)

When the Indian National Congress was founded in Bombay in 1885, the most common charge brought against it by the Anglo-Indian bureaucracy was that it was representative of only a 'microscopic minority' of the Indian people, that is to say, the educated middle class of the great cities. Congress in its early days fought hard against this stereotype, trying to show that its membership was in fact drawn from all classes and castes. This was one reason for the elaborate lists of delegates, with their castes and occupations, which occupied the later pages of the annual report. Congress made a genuine attempt to prove that it was above caste and religious concerns, a truly 'secular' force. In 1888 it carried a resolution to the effect that issues to which objections were raised by more than two-thirds of any religious community would not be discussed. Congress delegates were also elected, as the list shows, by a wide variety of public meetings and associations for social, religious or caste improvement.

In its early years the Indian National Congress had a rather loose institutional structure and generally came alive only at its annual winter meetings which were held at different cities and provided an occasion for widespread public meetings and pamphleteering.

C.A.B.

LITERATURE: Seal 1968.

490 Gopal Krishna Gokhale (1866–1915)

Copyprint after photograph in the Nehru Memorial Museum and Library, New Delhi

One of the leading Congress politicians of the early years of this century, Gokhale came from a similar Poona Brahmin background as his contemporary Tilak (see no.497), but they

490

differed radically in their views about India's political future. Gokhale was a professor of English literature and mathematics, but in the 1890s he became heavily involved in educational and charitable works through the Poona Sarvajanik Society. Gokhale was a critic of British rule, but he considered that the best way to improve the Government's record was through constructive criticism within those institutions created by the British to canalize Indian opinion. He was a member of both the Bombay Legislative Council and of the Imperial Legislative Council, besides being President of the Poona Municipality. As a political 'moderate' he opposed the attempts of Tilak, Bepin Chandra Pal and others to take the Congress in a radical direction, and he was prepared to see the Congress split on the issue in 1907. One of his most enduring legacies to the country was the Servants of India Society which he founded in 1905. This was a political and philanthropic organization which trained young men to go into the towns and countryside and alert the population to the need for national regeneration. In some ways Gokhale's methods anticipated those of Gandhi, and it was to Gokhale, now ailing, that Gandhi turned on his return to India in 1915. C.A.B.

LITERATURE: Johnson 1973; Nanda 1977.

The Plague in India: Government Action and Popular Reaction, 1895–1902

The bubonic plague which swept India in the last decade of the nineteenth and the first decade of the twentieth century may have killed more than ten million people. It was therefore comparable in mortality with the great famines of the nineteenth century, but much more terrible because it conjured up in the mind of Government and educated Indian society alike, memories of the great plagues of medieval and early modern Europe. The plague was most devastating in the Punjab and Bombay, but politically it was the outbreak in India's foremost port which was most significant because it threatened a highly articulate body of British and Indian residents and also raised the spectre of international interdicts against Indian trade to avoid the spread of the disease. The outbreak spurred the imperial and local governments to an unusual degree of intervention, cleansing what was seen as the breeding ground of disease – Bombay's squalid working-class quarters. Although many of the world's leading bacteriologists were present in India at one point or another, official medical knowledge still regarded plague as a contagious disease which spread in foetid slums and tenements rather than a flea-borne disease, spread above all along trade routes. The authorities therefore established stringent quarantine regulations, apprehended people supposed to be suffering from the disease, and invaded private quarters to dig up floors, demolish walls and soak whole quarters in disinfectant. Ironically, the population's flight from such measures probably spread the panic faster, but official stringency also provoked a vehement political reaction. Newspapers and meetings denounced official 'over-reaction' and in Poona, a plague official was assassinated. The radical nationalist leader Tilak (no.495) was imprisoned because the British insisted that his newspaper had incited the murder. When the disease became endemic and had established itself as a malady of the poor, or of the countryside, official action declined in intensity. C.A.B./R.S.C.

LITERATURE: Chandavarkar 1991.

491

491 Plague inspection, Sion Station, Bombay

Copyprint after photograph (1896–7) in the India Office Library (311/1 [15a] B10740)

492

492 Plague search party in the Muslim quarter, Bombay

Copyprint after photograph (1896–7) in the India Office Library (photo Dimmock B10716 311/1 [10 v.c.])

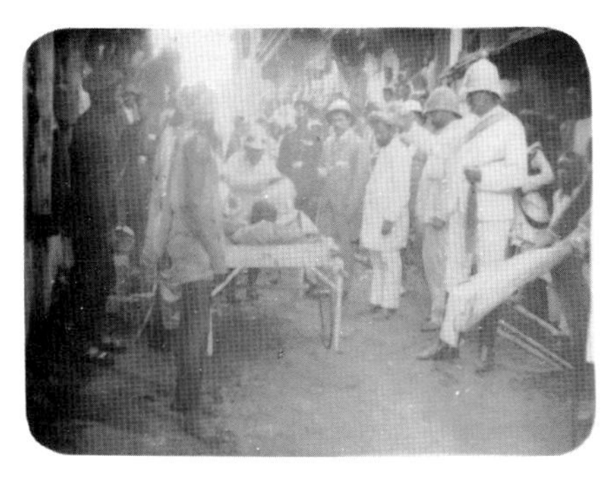

493

493 House-to-house search in Bombay: removal of plague case

Copyprint after photograph (1896–7) in the India Office Library (311/1 [9 v.e.] B10706)

494

494 The plague in Bombay: temperature-taking

Copyprint after photograph (1896–7) in the India Office Library (311/1 [14d], Dimmock B10733)

The Partition of Bengal, 1905

Until the end of the nineteenth century, the Indian National Movement had remained constitutionalist and socially narrow. Its critics amongst the younger generation of embittered, educated youth sometimes described it as a 'mendicant' organization, that is to say, it went cap in hand to the government begging for favours. Lord Curzon himself thought that he should be helping the Congress to 'an early demise'. Ironically, however, it was in part his own policies which speeded up the pace of political change and produced a new generation of radical leaders. Curzon was suspect amongst the educated Indian elite for his attempts to curtail the powers of the Calcutta Municipal Corporation, one political base where Bengali leaders had achieved considerable influence. His attempt to restore educational institutions to the control of the Indian Civil Service also aroused wrath. But his greatest error was to propose the partition of the large province of Bengal, ostensibly for administrative reasons. This measure, pushed through in 1905, threatened to cut off many Calcutta service families from their rural roots in the east and give Muslims a majority in the new province of east Bengal. Worse, it outraged the Bengali sense of regional patriotism expressed through veneration of the goddess Durga and celebrated in the great corpus of Bengali poems, plays and songs which had received new enrichment since the 1840s. Bengal erupted in huge demonstrations; British cloth was burned and boycotted as a sanction during the height of the so-called *Swadeshi* (home industry) Movement. C.A.B.

LITERATURE: Sarkar 1973.

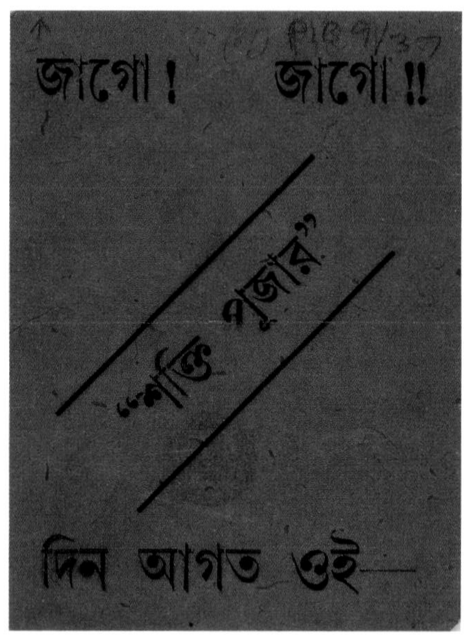

495

495 *Awake, awake*, a Bengali political pamphlet banned by the British, *c.* 1908

Handbill, 13 × 10 (5 × 4)
India Office Library and Records (P1.B9/37)

Large-scale peaceable demonstrations against the partition of Bengal and British policy generally were followed by boycotts of British cloth. Leaders in Calcutta and the District towns organized the *Swadeshi* Movement which urged Indians, by means of public meetings and the distribution of pamphlets and handbills, to buy only locally manufactured cloth. Some of these pamphlets hinted at the need for revolutionary and terrorist violence to overthrow the British Raj. In his last few months Curzon moved forcefully against 'seditious' publications. Under his successor Lord Minto, the Indian Special Branch, a lineal descendant of the Department of Thuggee and Dacoitee (no. 294), became more active in combatting the revolutionary terrorist cells which had been spawned among the embittered youth of Bengal. In time this policy resulted in the creation of a new category of banned Indian publication within the India Office Records in London. C.A.B.

LITERATURE: Das 1964; Barrier 1969; Sarkar 1973.

496 Kali

1908
Lithograph pasted on board, image 30.3 × 24.3 ($12 \times 9\frac{1}{2}$), mount 40.6 × 31.8 ($16 \times 12\frac{1}{2}$)
Inscribed on reverse by B.A. Gupte: *Corner of Dalhousie Square*
Royal Anthropological Institute, London, Photographic Collection

This chromolithograph of Kali trampling her consort, Shiva, was produced by the Calcutta Art Studio as a calendar for Kali Cigarettes of Bowbazar Street, Calcutta. The Studio was founded in 1878 and its photographically-influ-

496

enced mytho-pictures 'seemed to draw a magic wand over its images, transforming gods and goddesses to living persons, bringing to familiar mythological narratives a sensational simulation of life' (Guha Thakurta 1988, p.12).

This particular example was collected, together with several others, for Sir Herbert Risley, Director of Ethnography for India, by his assistant B.A. Gupte, with the intention of monitoring concealed political messages within this very popular art form. Gupte detected a representation of a 'symbolical British Lion couchant' in the top left-hand corner, turned into a decapitated soldier in the bottom right-hand corner, and asserted that this 'leaves no doubt as to the intention of the designer.'

The goddess Kali had become the centre of a politicized Hindu cult after the partition of Bengal in 1905. This followed a pattern established several years earlier in Bombay, where B.G. Tilak had helped turn the Ganpati (no.500) festival from a private domestic rite into a huge public ceremony in which Hindus could come together and hear anti-British speeches (Barnouw 1954). The figure of Kali has always been used by the West to represent a particularly derogatory view of Hinduism, from the Thuggee cult (Thugs were said to be her devotees) to *Indiana Jones and the Temple of Doom*. But her embodiment of an unrestrained, fierce energy demanding blood sacrifice fitted her well to political struggle, with each imperialist killed becoming one of her sacrificial 'white goats'. In the advertisement consumers are urged to buy Kali cigarettes 'to look after the interests of this country's poor and humble workers'. C.P.

LITERATURE: Barnouw 1954, pp.74–88; Guha Thakurta 1988, pp.3–46.

497 Bal Ganghadar Tilak (1856–1920)

Oleograph, 53 × 40.6 (18 × 12¾)
National Portrait Gallery, London

Tilak came from an orthodox Chitpavan Brahmin family from the Ratnagiri district near Bombay. Chitpavans were energetic and influential administrators within the Maratha state, and it was from their caste that the Peshwa family had come (see no.87). Maharashtrian patriotism and a profound uneasiness with the consequences of British rule marked many Chitpavans, even the large numbers who worked in British Government offices. Educated mainly at Poona, Tilak started life as an orthodox constitutional nationalist, founding the Deccan Education Society in 1885. His later sparring partner, G.K. Gokhale (see no.490), was also a founder member of this institution. Tilak soon lost patience with the quiet and deferential political work which characterized the first few years of the Congress. He urged that India should demand change from the British rulers, rather than beg for it, and he promulgated an increasingly radical set of policies through the pages of his newspapers *Kesari* and *Mahratta*.

Tilak was learned in the Hindu holy

497

books, and though he had once been influenced by T.H. Green and the English idealists, he came to reject many features of Western ideology and society. His orthodoxy was evidenced by his opposition to the Age of Consent Bill, a measure pressed by some Indian social reformers, which sought to raise the legal age for marriage in India and so prohibit child marriages. Once he took tea in a Christian missionary school and had to do penance for it. All the same, Tilak was by no means ultra-orthodox, and despite his 'extremism' he sought election to the Bombay Legislative Council and used Western methods of political propaganda with consumate success.

Tilak's criticism of the Government became more bitter following the famine of 1896, which he believed it had mishandled, and the subsequent plague epidemic (nos.491–4) when the authorities were accused of aggression in trying to contain the disease. When Rand, the Plague Commissioner, was assassinated by a young zealot in June 1897, Tilak was accused of sedition and tried. He received an eighteen-month prison sentence. Following his release Tilak and radical leaders from several parts of India tried to take over the central machinery of the Congress, provoking the famous split at Surat in 1907. C.A.B.

LITERATURE: Tahmanhkar 1965; Johnson 1973.

498 Tilak and his family†

Narayan Vinayak Virkar
Photograph
Rajendra Shriram Virkar

Tilak is seen here in the traditional dress of a Chitpavan Brahmin which he wore throughout his life, making no concessions to the Western dress sported by many of his political contemporaries. His devotion to this clothing – the toga-like *uttariya*, red shoes and red turban – anticipated Gandhi's equally firm rejection of Western clothes. F.N.

499 Bal Ganghadar Tilak, Lala Lajpat Rai, and Bepin Chandra Pal, leaders of the 'extremist' movement

Copyprint after photograph (*c.* 1906) in the Nehru Memorial Museum and Library, New Delhi

This famous photograph represented the alliance of the political malcontents of three provinces against the Indian empire. Bepin Chandra Pal was spokesman for a Bengal in turmoil as a result of Curzon's ill-judged partition of 1905. Tilak represented Maharashtra, where much of the intelligentsia and many townspeople had been alienated by British famine and plague measures. In the Punjab government measures to restrict the passage of land from the 'agriculturalist' to professional people and moneylenders had annoyed the urban Hindus, while strict rules for the agricultural colonies along the newly-constructed canals had agitated hitherto acquiescent countrypeople. 'Extremism', with its demand for 'full independence' (*purna swaraj*), also arose from the frustrations of the educated youth and the students who felt that the quiet, constitutional ways of the old leadership of Congress had done little but perpetuate the intransigence of the Government. In 1907, in the western Indian city of Surat, these radical leaders split the Congress for the first time. Though Tilak was later imprisoned again and the 'moderates' generally had their way before the outbreak of the First World War, the experience of aggressive political agitation, 'sedition' and popular enthusiasm for more rapid change was

499

not forgotten by the radicals of the next decade. C.A.B.

LITERATURE: Johnson 1973.

500 Ganpati Festival in Dhar, western India

Copyprint after photograph by Vernon and Co. (1913) in the India Office Library (photo 10/14 [196] Reading; B11765)

Ganpati had always been worshipped in western India, especially by farmers and tradesmen, and he was the family deity of the Peshwas (no.173). His cult became

500

even more popular after 1895 when Tilak and other leaders began to use his annual festival as a celebration of Maharashtrian popular culture and a reaffirmation of regional identity. Sometimes the celebrations took on a menacing, distinctly anti-British tone, so festivals were regularly guarded by armed police. Generally the celebrations seemed to have been motivated by the upper castes. More controversial still was Tilak's lauding of the virtues of Shivaji, hero of Maratha resistance to the Mughal empire (see no.87). While the message was anti-imperial rather than anti-Muslim, more conservative Muslim leaders resented the veneration of Shivaji, who was accused by them of having treacherously murdered the Muslim general Afzal Khan during a peace parley. It was the strident, Hindu attitude of some of the followers of the 'extremist movement' that alienated the Muslims from the radical wing of the Indian National Congress before 1916. C.A.B.

LITERATURE: Cashman 1975.

501 Madame Bhikaji Cama (1861–1936)

Copyprint after photograph (*c.*1910) in the Nehru Memorial Museum and Library, New Delhi

The Home Political files of the Indian Government in the years between 1909 and 1914 are filled with almost hourly details of Bhikaji Cama's meetings and political activities in London and Paris. She was brought up in a wealthy Parsi family in Bombay and was educated conventionally at the Alexandra Girls School. But in middle age she was profoundly influenced by the radical Indian nationalism of Bengal after the partition. Travelling first to Stuttgart, where she spoke of Indian freedom to the Socialist Congress, she met Bepin Chandra Pal (see no.499) in London and then set up house in Paris. Here she presided over a political *salon*, where most of the younger revolutionaries among Indian students and intelligentsia passing through Europe came to visit and to plot. Madame Cama helped to smuggle explosives and revolutionary literature into India. During the First World War the French Government imprisoned her, concerned by her links with European socialist revolutionaries and alerted by pressure from the British Government. C.A.B.

LITERATURE: Government of India Home, fortnightly intelligence reports, 1907–10.

501

502 Annie Besant (1847–1933)

Herbert Rose Barraud, 1891
Bromide print, 36 × 26 ($14\frac{1}{10} \times 10\frac{1}{4}$)
National Portrait Gallery, London (X5543)

Annie Besant was of mainly Irish descent, but she was born in London and grew up in the south of England. In the 1870s she joined the National Secular Society and later became active in the Fabian Society in the circle of the Webbs, George Bernard Shaw and Ramsay MacDonald. In 1889 she read Madame Blavatsky's *The Secret Doctrine* and converted to theosophy. Drawn to India by her new faith, she quickly became involved in movements for social and political reform. In 1898 she established the Central Hindu College in Benares but later moved to Madras, where the village of Adyar became the centre for the Theosophical Society. The height of her political activity came during the middle years of the First World War, when she founded the Home Rule Movement to press for a more rapid drive towards self-government in India. Though the movement attracted wide support in the towns, particularly in the Madras Presidency, it

502

did not make the critical leap into the countryside. Mrs Besant became President of the Calcutta Session of the Indian National Congress in 1917, but by then her influence was beginning to fade in the face of powerful Indian leaders such as Tilak and Gandhi himself. She was intensely disliked by the British bureaucracy who distrusted her socialism, feminism and theosophy as much as they scorned her nationalism. But she was important in imparting new techniques of organization and publicity to Indian political movements. C.A.B.

LITERATURE: Besant 1893.

503 The transition of Motilal Nehru

(i) Motilal Nehru as a young boy in Kashmiri dress
Copyprint after photograph in the Nehru Memorial Museum and Library, New Delhi
(ii) Nehru sitting on a chair in barrister's gown and hood
Copyprint after photograph (*c.*1909) in the Nehru Memorial Museum and Library, New Delhi
(iii) Motilal Nehru, with top hat and umbrella, in London
Copyprint after photograph in the Nehru Memorial Museum and Library, New Delhi
(iv) Motilal Nehru in *khadi* (homespun dress) and Gandhi cap
Copyprint after photograph (after 1920) in the Nehru Memorial Museum and Library, New Delhi
(v) Motilal and Jawaharalal Nehru
Copyprint after photograph (*c.*1929) in the Nehru Memorial Museum and Library, New Delhi

This set of photographs illustrates the changing self-image and different identities of Motilal Nehru, founder of India's greatest political dynasty. His family were Kashmiri Brahmins, a group which had provided Persian-speaking administrators and clerks in the service of the Mughals, and had adopted some Mughal customs and aspects of Mughal costume before the British conquered Delhi and

503(v)

the north-west. No. 503 (i) shows the young Motilal in Mughal-influenced Kashmiri traditional dress. The Nehru family had migrated to Allahabad, which had been selected as the administrative and educational capital of the North-Western Provinces and Awadh after 1858. Motilal Nehru was one of the first members of the community to travel to England where he qualified as a barrister. He returned to India to become one of the most important and wealthy advocates working in the High Court of Allahabad. During this phase of his life Nehru adopted a fashionable European lifestyle and dress. He was also a moderate constitutionalist in politics. More politically radical and socially conservative leaders of the extremist movement in Allahabad denounced him as a 'foreigner from head to foot'. But the experiences of the First World War and the Amritsar massacre were to transform Motilal's attitudes and his appearance. By 1918 he and his son Jawaharalal had adopted a much more radical political stance themselves. Both men began to wear the homespun garments and cap which Gandhi had introduced to the Congress as a uniform, both for the party and the nation. This new garb was uncompromisingly Indian, but unlike more traditional garments including Nehru's boyhood dress, it did not betray the community, religion or caste of the individual who wore it. Such marks of division the Mahatma wished to obliterate. The elder Nehru is said to have disliked wearing homespun, but the abandonment of European dress was symbolically important. C.A.B.

LITERATURE: Nanda 1962; Bayly 1975.

504 John Morley (1838–1923)

Unknown photographer
Bromide print, 45.5 × 34 ($17\frac{7}{8} \times 13\frac{1}{4}$)
India Office Library and Records (F547)

Morley, a radical liberal journalist and onetime editor of the *Morning Star* and *Pall Mall Gazette*, became Secretary of State for India in 1905. He had been Cabinet Secretary for Irish affairs in Gladstone's Government in 1886 and developed sympathy for Irish nationalism. When it came to India, he was no less firm than the Viceroy, Lord Minto, in measures for the suppression of the terrorism which followed the partition of Bengal (no.495). However, his liberal distrust of central government led him to put his weight behind reform of the provincial legislative councils. The Reform Scheme of 1909 (known as the Morley-Minto Reforms) allowed Indians to question civil servants on budgetary and other matters, and extended the principle of indirect election to the non-official members of these

504

councils. However, the Reforms also enshrined the principle of separate representation for Muslims at the request of the newly formed All-India Muslim League (no.509) and the private urging of British officials. Indians have always regarded this as an example of the imperial tactics of 'divide and rule'; in Pakistan it is viewed as a tardy recognition of the Indian Muslims' status as a separate nation. C.A.B.

505 Gilbert John Elliot-Murray-Kynynmond, 4th Earl of Minto (1845–1914)

E. Walker after P.A. de Laszlo
Engraving, 61 × 37.4 (24 × $14\frac{7}{10}$)
India Office Library and Records (P696)

A descendant of the Lord Minto who was Governor-General early in the nineteenth century, Minto joined the Scots Guards in 1867, serving with Lord

505

Roberts in the Second Afghan War (1878–9). He was later with Lord Lansdowne in Canada and became Governor-General of the Dominion in 1898. In 1905 he became Viceroy of India, following Curzon's premature departure from the subcontinent. A Conservative in politics, he had little sympathy with Indian nationalism, but the change of government in Britain left him little alternative to co-operating with the Liberal Secretary of State, Morley, with whom he developed a working relationship. C.A.B.

506 Letter from John Morley to Lord Minto, 17 June 1908

Autograph manuscript, 22.8 × 18.7 (9 × $7\frac{4}{10}$)
The Trustees of the National Library of Scotland, Minto Papers (MSS 12732 ff.256–57)

Here Morley, the literary man and historian, spells out his general philosophy for the government of India which is that the men-on-the-spot should be strictly under the control of the House of Commons and British Government. He denounces the notion of the 'free hand' (which he attributes to Lord Curzon). He quotes Edmund Burke (no.148) on the issue, referring to 'this sage reflection of the greatest of men'. Morley manages to write approvingly of the earlier Lord Minto, implying that he steadied India after the excesses of Wellesley, another man who demanded a free hand. C.A.B.

LITERATURE: Das 1964, pp.52ff.

You say that a crisis will come one of these
days: "if the G. of I. is not given a free
hand to rule the country they understand."
Let me note in passing that this is what
Fuller ~~says~~ argues about E. Bengal: "I was on the
spot; I understood the conditions: I knew
India: what did Ld. Minto and Mr. Morley,
then fresh to power, ~~and~~ know or understand."
It is also what Curzon proclaimed in all sorts
of ways and places, and it is what his own
party Cabinet would never allow, and sooner let him
resign rather than accept. This notion of the
"free hand" is really against both letter and
spirit of law and constitution. It cannot be;
and let me assure you, on my word and honour
as a student of our political history, that nobody
would have been more opposed to it than that

506

507 An Indian butcher's shop and cattle for slaughter, Bengal

Copyprint after S. Bourne (*c.*1863) in the India Office Library (photo 29 [42]; B6923)

While nationalist unrest grew in India after 1880, so apparently did the number of conflicts between religious communities (what scholars of Indian call 'communalism'), and their implications. One fertile ground for conflict was when ebullient Hindu religious festivals clashed with the sombre Muslim Mohurrum. Another was the slaughter by Muslims and Europeans of the cow which was sacred to the Hindus. In the 1880s and '90s, and again in the 1920s and '30s, Hindus raised large scale agitations and developed a powerful grass-roots organization to protest against cow-slaughter and to rescue the animals from butchers, who were usually Muslims. Serious riots sometimes followed such incidents. It was the feeling that some Congress leaders were associated with 'communal' programmes of this sort that made some Muslims suspicious of the organization. C.A.B.

LITERATURE: Robinson 1974; Freitag 1989.

507

508 *Ayodhya Dasa*, Anti Cow-slaughter Paper, 1933

Handbill, 12.5 × 9.5 ($4\frac{4}{5} \times 3\frac{3}{4}$)
India Office Library and Records (PP. Hin. B436)

509 Foundation meeting of the All-India Muslim League, Dacca, 30 December 1906

Unknown photographer, 1906
Photograph, 9.1 × 29.2 ($3\frac{1}{2} \times 11\frac{2}{5}$)
Dr Muhammad Saleem Ahmad, Professor of History, Dean Faculty of Islamic Learning, Islamia University, Bahawalpur

In the late nineteenth century the Muslims of northern India, under the leadership of Sir Sayyid Ahmad Khan and his helpers at Aligarh College, had stood aloof from the political activity of the Indian National Congress. They felt that their interests were best served by a clear stance of loyalty to the British. Their response to the establishment of the Indian National Congress in 1885 had been the foundation of an All-India Muslim Educational Conference in the following year.

By 1906 it was evident that a focus on purely educational matters was not enough. The Congress was protesting vigorously against the partition of Bengal, a measure which benefited Muslims. Moreover, the Secretary of State for India, John (later Viscount) Morley, had announced that he was planning to increase Indian involvement in the Raj's system of legislative councils. In consequence the last day of the Muslim Educational Conference at Dacca in December 1906 was scheduled as a political meeting.

The photograph shows those present at this occasion. The Turkish coats and fezzes worn by many, as well as the Western clothes of the younger men, indicate the dominance of northern India's Urdu-speaking elite. Seated in the front row, nine places from the left, is Nawab Salimullah Khan, who invited the Conference to Dhaka. Two places further to the right is Nawab Mushtaq Husain, who presided over the political meeting. Seated on the ground, fourth and seventh from the left, are the brothers Muhammad and Shaukat Ali, who were to become major figures in subsequent Muslim protest movements.

F.C.R.R.

LITERATURE: Hardy 1972; Robinson 1974; Ahmed 1988.

510 The Santal Insurrection, 1856

From the *Illustrated London News*
Two engravings, each 38 × 27 ($14\frac{4}{5} \times 10\frac{1}{2}$)
India Office Library and Records (P1364)

Historical writing on India usually concentrates on the doings of the literate and educated Indian leaders, or at best on the peasants of the great plains. But there was another India, inhabited by 'tribal peoples' who differed from the people of the settled arable lands in their language and culture, and in their domestic economy. In the second half of the nineteenth century such communities came under pressure from the attempts of the British authorities to control them and tax their lands; Indians from the plains such as timber merchants, settlers and moneylenders also invaded their lands. There were a number of serious outbreaks against both the British and these intruders. One such was the Santal rebellion of 1854–6 in Bengal, which tied up a large number of British troops and brought a tremor to nearby Calcutta.

510

The links between such movements and the peasant rebellions of the plains, or later nationalist agitations, were very weak, however. C.A.B.

511 Birsa Munda (*c*.1875–1901)

Copyprint after photograph in the Nehru Memorial Museum and Library, New Delhi

Historians know rather more now about the peasant rebellions which erupted sporadically throughout colonial India, but little is yet known about the movements of opposition among 'tribal' and forest people, who resented the loss of their lands to outsiders and the creation of 'forest reservations' by the authorities. The Mundas were one such tribal group in central India. This is a rare portrait of a tribal political leader. Following an early conversion to Christianity, and then to orthodox Vaishnavite belief (worship of Lord Vishnu), he appears to have reverted to his original tribal religion, using a revived form of it to infuse his Munda followers with a sense of their ancient rights. In 1899 he proclaimed that the Mundas should fight against the 'Kingdom of the Demon', the British empire. Following a mass uprising he was captured by the police and put on trial, during which he died of cholera.

C.A.B.

511

SECTION IV

THE ROAD TO PARTITION AND INDEPENDENCE

1914–47

The Raj and the Nationalist Movements 1911–1947

FRANCIS ROBINSON

Fig. 47 King George V and Queen Mary on the balcony of the Red Fort, Delhi; photograph by Bourne & Shepherd, 1911 (The Commonwealth Trust; no. 485)

Fig. 48 Mace-bearers with royal insignia; photograph by Bourne & Shepherd, 1911 (The Commonwealth Trust; no. 486)

George V was the only reigning British monarch to visit his Indian empire. The high point of that visit in 1911, the great durbar in Delhi when the newly crowned King-Emperor and his Queen-Empress presented themselves to their Indian subjects, was the most magnificent imperial spectacle mounted by the Raj (Figs. 47 and 48). No previous durbar had been on such a scale. The 233 camps of the King-Emperor and his subjects covered 25 square miles of the Delhi plain. Two vast concentric amphitheatres were built for the durbar itself, the outer one to hold 100,000 spectators, the inner one to hold the Princes and other notables, and in the centre on a dais the thrones of the King-Emperor and Queen-Empress. No previous durbar had been the setting for such a dramatic stroke: the King-Emperor proclaimed the transfer of the capital from the Indian seaboard at Calcutta to the traditional centre of Indian empires at Delhi. Throughout, the British presented themselves in the idiom of Mughal power: the strict order of precedence, the exchange of official presents, the royal umbrella held over the monarchs when they moved in procession, the golden cupola over the thrones glittering in the sun. The King-Emperor's proclamation was the finishing touch. Now the British were proposing to rule from the former seat of Mughal power and to raise up a new capital to surpass the imposing relics of Mughal Shahjahanabad.

If the King-Emperor had consulted the voluminous records of his administration in India, he would have noted many achievements since the Crown had taken over responsibility from the East India Company more than fifty years before. External threats had been dealt with: that from the Russians in the north-west by maintaining Afghanistan as a buffer state, that from the French by annexing Upper Burma. The supposed danger from the Russians in Tibet had been revealed by Younghusband's expedition of 1904 to be imaginary. Within his empire the framework of a modern state had been set up. A system of law had been promulgated which, in its penal and civil aspects at least, was common to all. The administration was coming increasingly to reach down to each individual citizen, although not always with the effects that the British intended. More and more posts in the administration itself were open only to those who had passed school and university examinations. At the same time there had been considerable development of economic infrastructure: the building of the largest railway system in Asia; the construction of new irrigation works and the restoration of old ones; the provision of metalled roads, bridges and harbour works. Higher education was also fairly advanced, although general education remained limited and

Fig. 50 Labourers carrying crops; photograph by Cecil Beaton, 1946 (Imperial War Museum; no. 599 [iv])

Fig. 49 Girls' school; photograph by Cecil Beaton, 1946 (Imperial War Museum; no. 599[vi])

illiteracy widespread (Fig. 49). Among the consequences of these improvements in administration and infrastructure were the expansion of commercial agriculture and the lessening of the incidence of famine. Plantation industries were established in jute, cotton and tea, as were mining industries in coal and iron (Fig. 50). If much was owned by British capital and the overall emphasis was on commodity rather than on industrial production, nevertheless Indian industrial leadership was beginning to emerge. In 1907 the Tata Iron and Steel Company was founded at Jamshedpur in Bihar. It was to become the largest single steelworks in the world.

Had the King-Emperor looked at the place of India in Britain's balance sheet, he could hardly have failed to have been impressed. India bought more British exports than any other country, roughly 10 per cent of the total, of which the main item was cotton piece goods. She ranged from the fifth to the second most favoured destination for British capital investment. Most important of all, her taxes paid for a highly trained army of 250,000 men which promoted the British imperial enterprise from China to Africa. She was indeed a crowning jewel.

Loyalty to the King-Emperor had a special force in Britain's system of political control. It had been especially fostered in the cult of Queen Victoria, while the Indian Princes, who controlled two-fifths of the subcontinent and nearly a quarter of its people, were well aware of the importance of conspicuous support for an Imperial royalty. In those areas which the British controlled directly they formed alliances with rural élites, proprietary farmers for instance in the Deccan and the Punjab, or large landowners in northern India. These élites were kept happy with favourable arrangements of land tax, while extra inducements could always be offered through the Raj's elaborate system of honours. As time had gone on the British had created structures for the formal consultation of these allies. By 1911 there was a widespread framework of elected municipal and district boards, as well as provincial legislative councils in which Indians made up just under half the numbers.

Not all Indians were happy to receive only what the British chose to give them. Notably, the new class of those educated in government colleges, and sometimes in British universities, felt keenly the injustices of their situation in particular and that of India in general. They wanted a larger voice in the provincial councils, greater access to the higher ranks of the Civil Service, the raising of tariff barriers against British cotton goods, an end to the colonial status of India's economy, and respect rather than assertion of racial superiority from the British. For more than a quarter of a century these men had come together each Christmas week to debate these issues in the Indian National Congress. The annual sessions had come to be a celebration of India's growing sense of nationhood. Nevertheless, their stance was one of conspicuous loyalty, their approach to government one of humble petitioning; little happened during the rest of the year. Major figures in the movement were S. N. Banerjee, the 'Lion of Bengal'; Pherozeshah Mehta and Dadabhai Naoroji (India's first Member of Parliament) from Bombay; and the Maharashtrian adversaries B. G. Tilak and G. N. Gokhale, the latter being a member of the Viceroy's Council and widely admired for his statesmanlike qualities.

Muslims, rather more than one-fifth of India's population, were not well represented in the Congress. Under the guidance of their outstanding leader in the nineteenth century, Sayyid Ahmad Khan, the founder of Aligarh College, many, particularly from northern India, had avoided the Congress and overt political activity. By 1906, however, they had come to realize that this would not be enough to protect their interests and had founded their own political organization, the All-India Muslim League. This League, moreover, had been notably successful in winning separate electorates for Muslims in the reforms to the legislative councils which had been pushed through by Viceroy Minto and Secretary of State Morley in 1909. Despite this it was an even more humble petitioner to government than the Congress.

Some Indians no longer accepted these methods. Since 1905 small groups of educated Indians had emerged in Bengal, in western India and in the Punjab who favoured direct action against the Raj. Connected as they were with the cult of Kali, the goddess of destruction, in Bengal and with the Hindu revivalist celebrations of Shivaji and Ganpati in western India, they were much less receptive to the cultural, economic and political offerings of Western civilization. Their most notable actions were the *Swadeshi* movement, calling for the boycott of foreign cloth (Fig. 51); and, particularly in Bengal, the use of the gun and the bomb. Tilak was their leading supporter in the Congress, which in 1907 split into 'extremist' and 'moderate' factions; in 1909

Fig. 51 A march during the *Swadeshi*/Non-cooperative movement in Bombay; photograph by N.V. Virkar, 1921–2 (Mr Rajendra Shriram Virkar; no. 535)

he was gaoled for incitement to murder. Terrorism certainly alarmed the British – the Viceroy himself was injured by a bomb in 1912 – but it had little support in political India as a whole. Representative of the politics of the vast majority was the Congress session of 1910, which proclaimed its loyalty to the King-Emperor and chose an Englishman, Sir William Wedderburn, to be its president.

This situation was transformed by World War One. 'Before 1914 the Government of India on the whole held the initiative,' writes Percival Spear; 'after 1918 it was grasped by the Congress.'[1] One reason was the enormous contribution Indians made to the war effort; almost all were keen to support the Empire, the Princes in the forefront and even Tilak toured the countryside in 1918 to raise more men and material. By these means 1,200,000 men were recruited, over £100 million was given outright to Britain and a further £20 to £30 million raised each year. Indian troops served with distinction on the Western Front and in Mesopotamia, although the latter campaign was managed so badly that the Secretary of State for India had to resign. Among the economic consequences were sharp rises in taxes, a doubling of prices between 1913 and 1920, falling living standards, bottlenecks and disturbances. Indians felt that government should reward them for their loyalty; the conditions favoured mass political action.

The war changed the way the Indians felt about their place in the world. The British were no longer seen, along with Russia, as one of the two superpowers, but to be merely one of several roughly equal powers; their aura of mastery was diminished. The decade before the war had seen revolutions in the despotic regimes of Persia, Turkey and China, while the war itself saw one in Russia; change in the most inflexible political structures now seemed possible. By 1916 the Congress and the League had come together to make a joint demand to establish Indian majorities in the legislative councils, the League exacting as its price Congress support for separate Muslim electorates. This demand, moreover, was strengthened by the return of Tilak to the Congress and the formation of Home Rule leagues by him and by the Irish theosophist Annie Besant. By 1917 these leagues were pulling many new groups into politics.

British intentions as to India's future also began to change, although not always fast enough to match Indian aspirations. Nevertheless, when the British made their political move it was a radical one. On 20 August 1917 the Secretary of State, Edwin Montagu, promised Indians the same kind of government as the white dominions:

> The policy of His Majesty's Government, with which the Government of India are in complete accord, is that of the increasing association of Indians in every branch of the administration and the gradual development of self-governing institutions with a view to the progressive realisation of responsible government in India as an integral part of the British Empire.[2]

This was followed by reforms to the legislative councils in 1919, which bear the names of Montagu and Viscount Chelmsford, the Viceroy, in which Indians were given a substantial majority of the seats. Through the power-sharing mechanism of 'dyarchy' they gained complete control over the development areas of government, and the way was prepared for a federal political system.

The war and its aftermath was also the context in which Mohandas Karamchand Gandhi came to the leadership of the nationalist movement. The Mahatma ('great soul'), as he came to be known after being given the title by Rabindranath Tagore, spent more than twenty years struggling against racial discrimination in South Africa. During this time he developed a religious vision of India's freedom (*Swaraj*), which he saw not just as a political goal but also as a moral one involving a complete transformation of the relationship between Indians and the world in which they moved. It was, moreover, to be pursued by non-violent resistance to injustice (*Satyagraha* or 'truth-force'), which he regarded as the appropriate method because it actually helped forward his goal of moral transformation. After returning to India in 1915 he did not involve himself in politics, but toured the country making several experiments with non-violent resistance. Then, when the British demonstrated in their Rowlatt Bills of 1919 that they were going to maintain in peacetime the emergency measures they had used against 'sedition' in wartime, he found his issue. He led a nationwide protest in the form of a complete cessation of activity for one day. Unfortunately the protest sparked off disturbances in the Punjab, the province most severely affected by wartime demands, which led to a massacre at Amritsar in which troops fired without warning on crowds in the enclosed Jallianwala Bagh, killing 379 and wounding 1,200.

Finally, the war created the circumstances in which several of India's Muslim élites moved from a largely passive acquiescence in British rule to large-scale protest against it. The spur was the final decline of the Ottoman empire and the consequent reduction in the power of the Turkish Caliph (*Khalifa*) as the leader in succession to the Prophet of the Islamic community,

Fig. 52 Muhammad and Shaukat Ali before the First World War; unknown photographer (Nehru Memorial Museum and Library, New Delhi; no. 523 [i])

a process which mirrored in the world at large the growing powerlessness of Muslims in the subcontinent in particular. Before and during the war growing concern about this development brought together young Western-educated Muslims, such as Muhammad and Shaukat Ali (Fig. 52), and traditionally educated Muslim scholars (the *ulama*), like Abul Kalam Azad and Abdul Bari Firangi Mahali, in protests against their British rulers. After the war, as the very Ottoman heartland came to be dismembered, these men came to lead an enormous protest through a Khilafat organization, founded to defend the Turkish Caliphate. This was powerful because it united the skills in modern politics of the Western-educated Muslims with the mass-mobilizing abilities of the *ulama*.

In the summer of 1920 Gandhi and these Muslims came together to protest over their grievances in the Punjab – the Amritsar Massacre – and their concern over the Turkish Khilafat. They led the Khilafat and Congress organizations in a campaign of non-violent non-cooperation with government (*Swadeshi*), which meant among other things not participating in elections to the Montagu-Chelmsford legislative councils, withdrawing from government law courts and schools, and making a point of using goods made in India. Many Congressmen were drawn into this action, some of them because they saw that the Montagu-Chelmsford franchise was so weighted towards the rural areas that they were unlikely to win council seats. Nevertheless, there was mass support for the movement throughout India, and although it was not enough to bring government to a halt, it was enough for numbers of pupils to fall in schools, excise revenue to dry up in some areas and imports of cloth to decline. When Gandhi, worried by rising violence in February 1922, called off the movement, some were calling for complete freedom from the Raj.

By this time the nationalist movement was utterly changed from that which existed before World War One. Now it was truly national, supported by men and women from all regions, all cultures and all social backgrounds. It was no longer just a movement supported by the speeches of an educated élite,

Fig. 53 Gujarati, Maharashtrian and Parsi women united under the Indian National Congress banner in Bombay; photograph by N. V. Virkar (Mr Rajendra Shriram Virkar; no. 533)

but now one carried forward by the strikes of factory workers, the walkouts of tea-garden coolies, and the tax boycotts of peasants. In 1920 Gandhi reorganized the Congress so that it reached down to the Indian masses. In consequence its local branches were no longer based on the administrative divisions of government, but on the linguistic divisions of Indians. It no longer reflected the Raj but Indian society (Fig. 53). The former shaping force of the colonial power was now denied, and the colonial mentality was cast off[3]. The watchwords of nineteenth-century British liberalism came to be discarded by many in favour of indigenous symbols: for Muslims the crescent, which spoke of over a thousand years of successful Islamic history, for the Hindus the spinning wheel (*charkha*) which spoke of self-help against the foreigner. In his autobiographical fragment Muhammad Ali tells of the precise moment when his brother gave up his taste for fancy English shirts in favour of Muslim dress.[4] The Nehrus, too, who were once conspicuous consumers of the finest British goods, now wore homespun clothes (*khaddar*) with pride. However, for all that the nationalist movement came to present itself in self-consciously Indian form, it must not be forgotten that its dialogue with the Raj took place primarily within structures of power created by the British.

In the years between the world wars India came to look a rather less promising item on Britain's balance sheet. With the decline of Britain's cotton industry and the shift in the British economy towards services and the production of consumer goods, India became less attractive as a market for British exports; by the 1930s the balance of trade had turned in India's favour. India also became less attractive as a focus for British investment; indigenous firms such as the Birlas and the Tatas were increasingly beginning to outstrip their British rivals. Most important, however, the Government of India was no longer able to maintain the armaments of its army at modern levels; Indian politicians had far more important things on which to spend the country's resources. By the late 1930s it was clear that, if the army was to be used for Imperial purposes, the British taxpayer would have to bear a substantial amount of its cost. Such a decline in India's value to Britain made the matter of how long Britain's constitutional connection with India should continue one of growing importance.[5]

Over the same period mass support for the nationalist movement, which had first emerged in the Khilafat-non-cooperation period, broadened and deepened; Indians from all regions and from all classes increasingly came to sport the symbols of national identity: homespun clothes, the Gandhi cap and the Congress colours of saffron, white and green. As a whole this movement of peoples enormously diverse in language, in religion and in material interest was held together by the Congress organization, accessible to most, with a hierarchy of committees that mounted from the district through the provincial to the all-India level. Policy making and day-to-day decision making was in the hands of the 'Working Committee', a body often under the influence of Gandhi even though he was usually not a member of it. Alongside the Congress, and finding varying degrees of sympathy with it, ran other parties: the Muslim League, the nationalist movement's main rival for the Muslim vote; the Hindu Mahasabha, which represented conservative Hindus' interests; several socialist groups which flourished in the favourable atmosphere of the 1930s; and the Communist Party of India. There were also

Fig. 54 Caricature of Pandit Madan Mohan Malaviya, Elsa King, 1931; pen, ink and wash (India Office Library and Records; no. 555 [iv])

Fig. 55 Caricature of Mahatma Gandhi, Elsa King, 1931; pen, ink and wash (India Office Library Records; no. 555 [vi])

regional parties, such as the Unionist Party, which resisted Congress and League attempts to establish themselves in the Punjab until the 1940s. Political activity also took place outside the framework of parties: in organizations of writers, factory workers and peasants; movements for social uplift such as that to improve the lot of India's 50 million Untouchables; and movements of terrorist action such as that led by the Hindustan Socialist Republican Army.

Considerable political skills were required to navigate in these waters: arguably, political leadership was the greatest expression of Indian genius at this time. By the 1930s the leaders who were to take the nationalist movement to independence were in place. In addition to Gandhi, there was Jawaharlal Nehru from the United Provinces, who was regarded as the Mahatma's heir as the man best able to hold the nationalist movement together; Vallabhbhai Patel from Gujarat, who had great organizing skills; Abul Kalam Azad from Bengal, a profound theologian whose leading political role gave heart to nationalist Muslims; Rajendra Prasad from Bihar; and Rajagopalachariar from Madras. S. C. Bose was also part of this group, but fell out with Gandhi and in World War Two sought with German and Japanese help a military solution to ending British rule. Outside the Congress Muhammad Ali Jinnah, a gifted lawyer from Bombay, had already come to dominate the Muslim League.

The year 1927 saw the beginning of the next great contest between the nationalist movement and the Raj. Under the Government of India Act of 1919 the working of the Montagu-Chelmsford constitution was to be reviewed after ten years. In 1927, two years early, Parliament appointed a Commission of Inquiry under Sir John Simon. Unfortunately all its members were British. Indians were infuriated that their future was to be decided without participation. Congress responded by boycotting the Commission throughout India and by leading an all-parties conference to produce its own constitutional proposals, in the name of Motilal Nehru, the father of Jawaharlal, of which the most important was the achievement of full Dominion status by December 1929. The Viceroy, Lord Irwin, was prepared to discuss matters, but no satisfactory solution could be found. So Gandhi launched a campaign of civil disobedience in 1930 by marching from Ahmedabad to Dandi on the Gujarat coast to challenge the government monopoly on salt by making salt from the sea. For the next four years Congress and the government were in deadlock. Round Table Conference followed Round Table Conference in London (Figs. 54 and 55). One civil disobedience campaign followed another in India, winning unprecedented support as the impact of the great depression brought a sharp fall in agrarian prices and standards of living. Such agreement as was eventually reached between the two sides was represented in the Government of India Act of 1935, in which the British retreated to the centre of India's federal system, leaving the eleven provinces to be governed by Indians on a franchise which produced 30 million voters.

While Indians pressed forward against British power, they were beginning to make their mark on the world stage in other spheres. 1913 saw Rabindranath Tagore receiving the Nobel Prize for literature; 1919 saw the Maharaja of Jodhpur as India's representative at the Versailles Peace Conference. In science the output of the laboratories of the Nobel Prize-winning physicist

C. V. Raman in Bangalore, and of the biochemist J. C. Bose in Calcutta, were the high points of a scientific achievement which was growing in international reputation. In philosophy Sarvepalli Radhakrishnan was establishing himself as a thinker of world class, while the Punjabi Muslim poet Muhammad Iqbal was the leading Islamic thinker of his time. In history Jadunath Sarkar was making the field of the later Mughals his own. In literature there were the first of what was to become a stream of important novelists in English: Mulk Raj Anand, R. K. Narayan and Ahmed Ali. In sport the performance of India's hockey team was voted the most outstanding exhibition of skill in any event in the 1932 Olympics.

In India itself the interdependence of British and Indian lives remained as always, although in almost every field Indians were pressing forward into positions once held by their masters. This was taking place in the army officer corps, in the Civil Service and in the police; after World War Two only 500 senior civil servants and only 200 senior policemen were British. Similar changes were also under way in the universities, businesses, plantations and clubs. In other areas, most notably the game of cricket, the abilities of players such as Ranjitsinhji, C. K. Naidoo and the Nawab of Pataudi were suggesting that it would not be long before Indians would be the equals, if not the betters, of their rulers. But for all the changes in the balance of the relationship between Briton and Indian, there remained great friendships across the racial divide whose warmth was proof against the competing claims of imperialism and nationalism: such were the friendships of E. M. Forster and Sayyid Ross Masood, of Harcourt Butler and the Maharaja of Mahmudabad, and of Edwina Mountbatten and Jawaharlal Nehru.

In the last twelve years of British rule from 1935 to 1947 most British accepted that they were going to leave India. The main problems were how they were going to do it and when. Certainly the Raj demonstrated in World War Two that it still had considerable power. Two million Indians were recruited to the army, vast quantities of material were raised for the war effort, and a concerted attempt by the Congress in the Quit India movement of 1942 was stopped with ease. Yet it was clear that the British no longer needed to rule to win what benefits India still held for them. Moreover, they had already transferred too much power to Indians to be sure of being able to rule for any length of time. For the Congress, on the other hand , the main problems were how to get rid of the British in the quickest possible time, and how to do so in a way which enabled them to take over the strong centre of the federal system which the British had created. As a step in this direction, although with some reservations about British intentions, the Congress took office after victories in the general elections of 1937 in seven out of eleven provinces.

Two substantial unresolved problems loomed over the plans of the British and the Congress. One was the fate of the Princes. In 1921 these controllers of two-fifths of British India had been given a Chamber of their own to advise government on their interests. The 1935 Government of India Act created a federal framework into which they could be absorbed. But the Princes were incapable of agreeing on any scheme for federation. By 1939 they had lost their chance and these conservative Indian potentates, despite their special relationship with the British Crown, were bundled to one side by events. After independence they had no choice but to accept the few pitiful crumbs on offer in exchange for their territories.

The second problem was that of the Muslims. Throughout the 1920s and 1930s this had not seemed overwhelming. Muslim politicians, most notably in the important Muslim majority provinces of the Punjab and Bengal, had participated in political alliances with non-Muslims. The Muslim League, the organization of Muslim separatism, was virtually moribund from 1931 to 1934; its performance at the 1937 elections was unimpressive, winning only 22 per cent of the seats reserved for Muslims. The Muslims of the majority provinces seemed to feel that they were secure with provincial autonomy. In the late 1930s there seemed no reason to believe that Muslim separatism would lead to the division of India.

World War Two transformed Indian politics as the previous war had done. First, the Congress let slip its normally tight grip on the political scene. Straight after the Viceroy, the Marquess of Linlithgow, had declared war on behalf of Britain without discussing the matter with the nationalist leadership, the Congress instructed its ministries in the provinces to resign. The immediate consequence of its Quit India movement of 1942 was the imprisonment of the nationalist leadership and 60,000 party activists. For the whole of the war Congress hands were off the levers of power; for half of that time it was an enfeebled organization. Second, the British needed all the allies they could find in India to fight the war. On the very day after war was declared, Linlithgow invited Jinnah, the leader of the Muslim League, for talks on an equal footing with Gandhi; the man whom, before the war, government had been able to ignore, was now sought after as the most important representative of the Muslims. Less than three years later, the need for Indian support was so desperate that Sir Stafford Cripps made on behalf of the British Government his offer of independence after the war in exchange for the cooperation of the political parties for its duration. Indians now knew that independence was a real possibility in the near future. Thirdly, Jinnah made full use of the opportunities provided to improve the Muslim League's position. Within seven months of the declaration of war the League had laid down its terms for independence; in what is known as the Lahore or Pakistan Resolution it demanded the grouping of provinces in which Muslims were numerically in a majority into 'Independent States'. Precisely what the relationship was to be between these states and the rest of India was left unclear. These terms were both a bargaining counter to get the best possible results for Muslims at independence and a stick to persuade Muslim leaders in the majority provinces to support the League. By the end of the war Jinnah had been successful in achieving the latter, and he had also built the League into an effective organization for mass political mobilization. The results were seen in the League's overwhelming victory in the general elections of 1945–6, in which it won nearly 90 per cent of the seats reserved for Muslims. The war did much to create the circumstances in which, whatever claims the Princes were able to make, and also towards the end the Sikhs, there were only two players that mattered alongside the British in the endgame, the Congress and the League.

In the first half of 1946 the British were still hoping to hand on their Raj to a single successor state. To this end the home government intervened directly, sending a delegation of Cabinet ministers to India who, in May, proposed an ingenious solution involving three tiers of government. The first was represented by the existing provinces; the second was to be formed out of separate Hindu and Muslim federations of provinces, to which the princely states could accede; and in the third – the central government – representatives of these federations would come together on an equal basis to deal with defence, foreign affairs and communications. For a few weeks both sides accepted the plan; indeed, recent scholarship has made an excellent case for this being the solution that Jinnah sought,[6] but then agreement broke down. There was deadlock. Civil disorders grew. Partition became inevitable.

In February 1947 the home government intervened once more. Viscount Wavell was replaced as Viceroy by Lord Mountbatten, and Prime Minister Clement Attlee announced that the British intended to hand over power in India no later than June 1948. The politicians were to be pressured into agreement. Able and energetic, Mountbatten quickly saw that Britain could only withdraw by transferring power not to one government but to two. He also saw that it would not be possible to leave the large Hindu and Sikh minorities of the Punjab and the Hindu minority of Bengal under Muslim rule. The partition of India also meant the partition of Bengal and the Punjab. Congress accepted partition as the price it would have to pay to take over the strong centre which the British had created. The League was eventually forced to accept a 'truncated' Pakistan. To try to limit the growing problems of disorder, Mountbatten brought forward the date of withdrawal to August 1947. On the 14th, Pakistan inherited its share of the British Raj, and on the 15th so did India.[7]

The last rites of the Raj were performed in the great new capital which some thirty-five years before the King-Emperor George V had proclaimed would be built by the British for their Indian Empire. Here, amid the magnificent symbols of central power, the Viceroy's palace – larger than Versailles and approached down the two-mile-long processional route of King's Way – Nehru announced to the Indian people that they had redeemed the pledge they had made in their tryst with destiny long years ago. Here, too, Nehru was sworn in by Lord Mountbatten as the first prime minister of the new Dominion. The former Viceroy stayed on for a year as Governor-General; some Britons stayed on for very much longer in industry and commerce, the army and the Civil Service. The lack of a sharp break in personnel emphasizes how much of a joint project it had been to build the new India, despite all the conflicts and sorrows there had been. Nor were the long and deep historical linkages between the peoples of Britain and the subcontinent to come to an end. For now they have another joint project: to build a new Britain.

NOTES

1. Spear 1965, vol. 2, p. 181.
2. *Report on Indian Constitutional Reform* 1918, Cd. 9109, para. 6.
3. Brown 1989, pp. 1–136.
4. Ali 1942, p. 49.
5. Tomlinson 1976, pp. 7–31.
6. Jalal 1985.
7. A succinct analysis of the issues involved in Britain's withdrawal from power in India can be found in the articles by Gordon Johnson in Robinson (ed.) 1989, pp. 131–47.

Artistic Responses to Colonialism in India: An Overview

PARTHA MITTER

Of the different aspects of the impact of the West on traditional Asian societies, none is more intriguing and yet less explored than the artists' responses to European naturalism, ultimately derived from Renaissance art. Unlike the obvious impact of technology from the West, the reception of European painting and sculpture has been uneven and problematic, oscillating between enthusiastic acceptance and vehement resistance, reflecting the historical process from an initial period of unquestioning Westernization to the growth of nationalist consciousness.

The history of this phenomenon may be divided into three main phases covering the period from 1850 to 1947; in other words, from the climactic period of the Empire to the transfer of power to the Indians. The first period was one of active Westernization with the wholehearted support of the English-educated in the three maritime provinces, Bengal, Bombay and Madras. In art it corresponded to the introduction of linear perspective, chiaroscuro, oil painting and other technical devices, employed since the Renaissance to create a faithful likeness of the subject. With this technical equipage came Western Romanticism, the concept of artistic individualism, and literary and sentimental themes for painting; in short, the whole ideological underpinning of Victorian high art with history painting as its highest expression. During the second phase, which coincided with the rise of nationalism, artists sought to construct an alternative, anti-colonial world view that drew its inspiration from India's pre-industrial past in a nostalgic evocation of the period.

The ideological clashes between the Westernizers and the new Orientalists continued to the year of Indian independence. The debate owed much to parallel developments in the *Swadeshi* nationalist movement and its demands for the creation of an indigenous art that would be consonant with Indian cultural aspirations. While this was the main discourse for the period, a 'subtext' makes its appearance in the 1920s in the form of Modernism. The occasion was marked by the exhibition of works of Klee, Kandinsky and other Bauhaus artists in Calcutta in 1922.

The historical background

In the late eighteenth century, with the establishment of British rule, the vogue for Western neo-classical architecture, for oil portraits by itinerant European artists and for collecting European art, spread among the Indian nobility. Although traditional artists declined as a class, European technology

Fig. 56 The *dhobi* (washerman), Lockwood Kipling, *c.* 1872; pencil and wash (India Office Library and Records; no. 454 [ii])

Fig. 57 The blacksmith, Lockwood Kipling, *c.* 1872; pencil and wash (India Office Library and Records; no. 454 [iv])

and ideas gave rise to the Company School of Painting, to a 'traditional' variant of oil painting, as well as to the popular art of Kalighat. The introduction of processes of mechanical reproduction led to a massive growth in popular prints. Media capable of wide diffusion, such as woodcuts, chromolithography, oleography and, above all, photography came to dominate the market.

The Raj as a patron of art

Although the East India Company exerted political pressure on Indian rulers to adopt Western art and architecture, this was often indirect and haphazard. It was not until the 1850s that the Raj embarked on an ambitious plan of moulding the taste of the elite, motivated by the Victorian belief that 'good taste' could be inculcated by 'enlightened' measures. The project was conceived in two ways. The first objective was to disseminate a uniform art education policy through the newly founded art schools in Calcutta, Bombay and Madras. The government was stung into action by allegations of its neglect of Indian artisans, made by Owen Jones, Henry Cole, William Morris and other radical critics (Figs. 56 and 57). It decided to help artisans by improving their designs with Western scientific methods.

However, measures advocated for art schools were doomed from the very outset because of the conflicting ideological imperatives informing them. The most serious weakness of the art education policy was the failure to recruit artisans; they could afford neither the time nor the fees. Secondly, students were expected to emulate Indian design but treat Indian sculpture and painting as inferior. Hence, if the schools were meant to improve the artisans' lot, they were a failure. If, on the other hand, they were meant to encourage the taste for European academic art – and there is evidence that this was precisely what a powerful section of the rulers wanted – then they were a success.

Fig. 58 Portrait of a Woman, Ravi Varma; oil on canvas (The Victoria & Albert Museum; no. 463)

While official reports constantly bemoaned the various crises in art schools, they failed to recognize a silent revolution that was taking place in India: the new colonial artist no longer came from the traditional artisan strata but now enjoyed a high gentlemanly status. As the elite had taken to English education with alacrity, so they embraced Victorian history painting with eagerness. The trickle of artisans was swept away in Calcutta and Bombay art schools by the flood of sons of the elite. The culmination of the official patronage of salon art was the gallery of Western art in Calcutta founded by the Viceroy, Lord Northbrook, to inspire the youth of the country.

Indeed, by the end of the nineteenth century, salon art was well ensconced in urban centres as art graduates began to be turned out in numbers by the art schools. It owed its success to the new means of mass communication, with the press forming and informing public opinion, while art societies, typical Victorian cultural institutions founded in India with indirect official encouragement, controlled and disseminated the taste for academic art. The art-school-educated salon painters who were supported by these societies belonged to the elite groups: the Bengali *bhadralok*, the Maharashtria Prabhus and the Parsis, Jews and Catholics of Bombay – all those who had profited from an English education. Portraiture was the most lucrative genre, but landscapes and historical narratives were also important. In Bombay memorial sculpture was successfully practised. There are fascinating stories told about these artists, stories of ambition and privation, professional success and personal tragedy: the talented Abalal died in poverty; Mhatre became an instant celebrity with his student work; Sashi Hesh journeyed to Italy amid hardships, determined to receive training at the fountainhead of western art; the sculptor Fanindra Bose was made an Associate of the Royal Scottish Academy for his decoration of St John's Church in Perth. But if there was one artist who epitomized the Romantic artist as an individualist, it was the charismatic history painter Raja Ravi Varma (1848–1906) (Fig. 58). Unlike the traditional courtly painter, this first gentleman artist's outlook was essentially modern, setting up portraiture as a business enterprise. He was the first Indian artist to successfully break out of the limited confines of traditional aristocratic patronage in search of a wider public, seeking to found a public gallery in order to display his own work. He also responded to emerging nationalism by transforming himself from a leading colonial portraitist to a history painter who engaged in a historicist reconstruction of the Indian past through his large canvases. His final and most striking act was to turn his historical and mythological paintings into inexpensive prints, the wide diffusion of which immediately made him a folk hero.

Swadeshi cultural nationalism and the search for an authentic Indian style

When Varma died in 1906 his position as a national figure seemed unassailable. Yet within a year his works became discredited as hybrid, undignified and incompatible with the spiritual essence of India. The background to this reversal was the gathering momentum of cultural nationalism which inspired him and now was to be his undoing. The Bengal renaissance was the first Indian expression of cultural nationalism, and stemmed from the modernization of the Bengali language and its being printed for the first time. This was the period when modern Hindu identity was being actively constructed in the wake of European Orientalist researches which presented the Hindus as the 'true' and original bearers of the Indian heritage. Indian cultural nationalists belonging to the circle of the poet Rabindranath Tagore forged an alliance with like-minded critics of progress and of Victorian 'materialist' society: the Theosophists, members of the Arts and Crafts movement in Britain, and Pan-Asianists such as Okakura Kakuzo of Japan, all of whom believed in the spiritual unity of Asia.

The *Swadeshi* ideology of art – to which Sister Nivedita, Swami Vivekananda's disciple; E. B. Havell, art teacher (see below); and Ananda Coomaraswamy, a critic and scholar, made the most important contribution – rested on the essential polarity between the 'spiritual' East and the 'materialist' West. Western academic art was rejected as a product of the colonial 'materialist' ethos, leading to a search for an alternative style that did not derive from the Renaissance mimesis. The nationalists found an unexpected ally in the British Raj, which came to cherish the image of an unchanging India that was incompatible with Western notions of progress, especially in the aftermath of 1857. In architecture the neo-classical gave way to the Indo-Saracenic as the Imperial style.

With the rise of the *Swadeshi* ideology the concept of the 'authentic' in art came into focus; it was contrasted with the 'hybrid' that was colonial art, a concept that urged the recovery of 'authentic' indigenous art as a 'historicist' exercise. Yet the early attempts in this direction were frustrated by confusions about what truly constituted the 'authentic'. The turning point came with the rejection of Ravi Varma's particular reconstruction of the past. In 1896, Abanindranath Tagore (1871–1951) joined forces with E. B Havell (1861–1934) to Indianize teaching at the art school in Calcutta, effecting far-reaching changes. One of the areas that drew the attention of the new Bengal School of painting was the human form treated naturalistically by Western academic art; the nationalist art drew its inspiration, not from a study of the nude, but from the 'inner eye' of the artist. The first generation of Abanindranath's students engaged in recovering 'the lost language of Indian art'. The distinct style that evolved was named 'Oriental art', celebrating Pan-Asian ideals that transcended national boundaries.

Havell's abrupt departure from India following a breakdown led to the reassertion of the pro-Western elements in the school and the eventual resignation of Abanindranath. The Raj however, realizing the potential of cultural nationalism in defusing political violence, continued to favour the Orientalists. The Indian Society of Oriental Art came into existence in 1907 with government funding to hold exhibitions of Oriental art. Meanwhile Havell continued his own campaigns in London, helping to found the India Society in 1910 to propagate the merits of Indian art, ancient and modern. Ultimately, Orientalist teaching was most effectively imparted by Abanindranath's pupil, Nandalal Bose, in Tagore's university at Santiniketan. He was one of the few artists to have direct links with the Indian Congress. Seeing himself as a disciple of Mahatma Gandhi, he decorated the 'marquees' at the Haripura Congress session (1937) with patriotic themes. In the West, the first exhibitions of Oriental art took place in Paris in 1914, in Berlin in

Fig. 59 Rabindranath Tagore, A. Bose, *c.* 1920; chalk on paper (India Office Library and Records; no. 459)

1924 and in London in both these years, followed by shows in the United States. Orientalists were soon in control of art teaching in India when Abanindranath's pupils were made heads of art institutions throughout the subcontinent.

The Orientalists succeeded in ousting Westernizers as arbiters of national taste, but not without bitter opposition from academic artists. *Sahitya*, a nationalist journal from Bengal with an extreme academic bias, which had adopted Reynolds as its patron saint, engaged in a deadly feud with the pro-Orientalist papers *Modern Review* and *Prabasi*. It was through these journals that the taste for Western, especially Victorian art was created in Bengal. Though despised and neglected, the Westernizers of Bengal regrouped during the 1920s and again sought to present their case to the public. The circle of academic artists formed by Atul Bose, a fine draughtsman (Fig. 59), and Hemen Majumdar, who earned a *succès de scandale* with his erotic 'wet-sari' figures, brought out glossy magazines and organized rival art magazines where they could show their works. On being accused of violating Indian sensibility with their naturalism they retorted that their subject matter was genuinely Indian and that Oriental artists were not able to draw properly. The most serious challenge to Oriental art came from the Bombay School of Art under Gladstone Solomon in the 1920s. Realizing the economic potentials of large-scale murals, Solomon established a successful course in Bombay based on figure studies. He challenged the Orientalist monopoly of art at the Empire Exhibition at Wembley (1924) by claiming to offer an alternative national style centred in Bombay. Through a series of shrewd manoeuvres Solomon succeeded in winning the commission for the mural decorations of Lutyens's New Delhi buildings for his students. The Raj, wishing to maintain its policy of balancing different interest groups in India, then offered the decoration of the India House in London to the Orientalists of Bengal. This unleashed a shrill press campaign in Bombay against the Bengal School and government officials.

However, in the 1920s, both Westernizers and Orientalists were overtaken by events abroad. By this time Pan-Asian ideas had lost their charm among Asian nationalists. The Bengal School was further weakened by the news of Western avant-garde movements reaching India, the whole coming to a head in 1922 with the exhibition of Klee, Kandinsky and other Bauhaus artists in Calcutta. Benoy Sarkar, a fascinating polymath and peripatetic scholar, championed Modernism with his controversial manifesto *The Futurism of Young Asia*, condemning Oriental art as parochial, and urging Indian artists to embrace the truly cosmopolitan movement; that is, European avant-garde. Two close members of Abanindranath's family, his uncle Rabindranath and his own brother Gaganendranath, had been lukewarm about nationalist art from the beginning. The former constructed a disturbing world reflecting the dark side of his psyche, which he peopled with birds, women and monsters, while the latter borrowed freely from Cubism to create yet another fairytale world. The poet Tagore's dazzling reputation in the West may have contributed to the favourable reception of his paintings there, but the sheer power of his radical imagination could not fail to appeal to Europeans already attuned to the poetic license of Paul Klee and Max Ernst.

The Bengal School encountered increasing hostility in the 1930s, including a scathing attack by Amrita Sher-Gil (1913–41), a remarkable artist and a tragic figure, whose early death left a large gap in the development of contemporary Indian art. Her own work expressed a nostalgic and elegiac view of village India in an idiom that reflected her part-Hungarian roots and training in Paris. Before the *Swadeshi* movement had spent its creative force it managed to leave a lasting imprint on the artistic map of India.

The old debate between Westernizers and Orientalists continued down to 1947, giving rise to another remarkable artist of the pre-independence generation. Trained at the colonial art school in Calcutta, Jamini Roy (1887–1972) went through an academic phase, followed by an Orientalist reaction, as was the case with many sensitive young men of the nationalist period. He then embarked on an experimental period, creating pastiches of European and Far Eastern styles of art, all the while using this knowledge to evolve his own indigenous expression. Failing to find satisfaction in these 'parodies' of different artists, he turned to the simple art of rural Bengal, which was enjoying a revival in this period among the intelligentsia. Roy gave up the use of foreign commercial paints in favour of traditional pigments, for he believed that an authentic indigenous expression demanded its own medium and materials. This was the period when he moved away from artistic individualism towards a 'communal' view of art and refused to sign his works. Roy's mature style perfected a ruthlessly simplified form through a slow process of elimination, concentrating on a few bold lines and colours and attaining a balance between tradition and modernity, and between East and West. For inspiration he turned to traditional village art rather than to national history. His search for cultural identity marks the end of the debate between academic art and Orientalism in colonial India.

'Strangers in the Land': India and the British since the Late Nineteenth Century

RAJNARAYAN CHANDAVARKAR

From the onset of colonial rule until its divided freedom in 1947, India's relationship with the West was filtered exclusively through Britain. No other Western country had a significant or even comparable cultural and commercial contact with India. Since 1947, India's connections with the West have rapidly diversified, and in barely four decades the term has come to signify not so much Britain as the United States of America. In 1990 British travellers expecting to encounter the familiar as a residue of two centuries of colonial rule are liable to be bemused and swamped by difference. Two centuries of colonial rule failed to fashion India in Britain's image. If the traces of British rule disappeared so quickly, it should not be assumed that its effects were light or its consequences for the development of Indian society insignificant.

These consequences were not manifested, as commonly supposed, in the cultural sphere. The dominant theme of India's history is not its gradual, if inexorable, anglicization. In 1807, the Governor of Madras had observed,

> the Europeans know little or nothing about the customs and manners of the Hindus ... We understand very imperfectly their language. They perhaps know more of ours ... We do not, we cannot, associate with the natives ... all our wants and businesses which could create a greater intercourse with the natives is done for us, and we are, in fact, strangers in the land.

And strangers, indeed, they were to remain. When British rule had ended, less than two per cent of the population had even the most rudimentary command of the English language. Fewer still knocked and had the door opened unto them; and many of these had been called, if not necessarily chosen, by the Jesuits and other Catholic missionaries before the British became the paramount power in the land. The colonial impact fell less heavily upon the mind of South Asia than upon its pocket and the conventions of its political practice.

This is not surprising. The British in India were not concerned about saving souls, civilizing natives or educating them to rule themselves. Rather, their purpose was both more limited and more ambitious. Britain ruled India in the interests of her global imperial system. This fact specified the nature of British rule. In its light, it is possible to match the apparently overwhelming power of colonialism with its seemingly irredeemable weaknesses.

By the later nineteenth century, the Indian empire had begun to dovetail neatly into Britain's international commercial and political system: as an important market, an increasingly important supplier of raw materials and a safe and guaranteed field of investment. India's exports to the United States and Europe helped to settle about two-fifths of Britain's balance of payments deficits between 1870 and 1914. From India, as Lord Salisbury famously observed, 'we may draw as many troops as we wish without paying for them' and they were used extensively to protect British interests from the Yellow Seas to the Persian Gulf. 'We could lose all our dominions and still survive,' Curzon had declared with prescience in 1900, 'but if we lost India, our sun would sink to its setting.'

That India was ruled for purposes more limited than the good government of the subcontinent and for interests which extended far beyond its shores widened British options as they fashioned their system of rule. In particular, it enabled colonial rulers to rely upon the collaboration of Indians, so long as this did not impede the deployment of Indian resources to imperial ends. Indeed, such collaboration was indispensable. If the empire was to be run, as it was acquired, on Indian resources raised primarily from the land, the British had to offset the political risks of their extraction by devolving substantial powers to important Indian interests. This also facilitated cheaper government, a requirement imposed by the sacred ark of colonial rule that the Indian empire should cost the British taxpayer nothing.

Fig. 60 Hindu women seeking the blessing of the descendant of a Muslim saint (*pir*); modern photograph by C. A. Bayly

The simple-minded sometimes mistook this collaboration for loyalty and the Guardians were readily flattered by the formal addresses of Indian notables, professing their unshakeable faith in the benefits of British rule. In fact, collaboration was conditional. So long as colonial rule served their particular interests or provided a vehicle for their aspirations, Indian magnates might confess their loyalty in orotund phrases. But when their interests were disturbed, they could move swiftly into opposition. There was nothing static about collaboration. Her Majesty's most loyal subject today could also become her most ardent enemy tomorrow. So for the British it was vital not to be seduced by the loyalty of some of their subjects or become prisoners of their own collaborators. Satisfying the needs of one set of collaborators could narrow their freedom of manoeuvre as they tried to manipulate Indian society in the interests of their empire. To retain their autonomy, therefore, the British had to expand their social base and diversify their sources of collaboration. But the more diverse their allies, the more demanding became the task of managing them. With its aims and purposes – and, therefore, its constraints also – thus defined, British rule played upon, and was in turn moulded by, Indian society.

The strictures which, according to Bentinck, had rendered Englishmen 'strangers in the land' also applied to most Indians. This was, indeed, a subcontinent of strangers. Although goods, capital and labour had long moved easily across the land, most people experienced little beyond their own locality. In the late nineteenth century, successive census returns showed that less than ten per cent of the population lived outside the district of their birth and the vast majority of these were residents of the neighbouring district. Caste described little more than the individual's *jati* or wider kinship group. Religious practice focussed on the local shrine and village goddess while the mosques found their faithful among those who fell within earshot of the muezzin's call (Figs. 60 and 61). Most Indians had little knowledge of,

Fig. 61 Temple chariots in procession at the Mylapore festival, Madras; modern photograph by C. A. Bayly

or access to, information about their neighbouring districts and provinces. Newspapers based in the provincial capitals closely reported affairs in their city, but rarely, and then often erroneously, covered its hinterlands. For most Indians, the customs and manners of the cohabitants of their subcontinent were the subject of curiosity, sometimes even suspicion, but, above all, of stereotypes. Fevered debates about how 'Madrasis' could really be so clever when they did not eat fish, or characterizations of the earthy, rugged, even barbaric Maratha echoed through the warrens of Calcutta's bazaars. What later writers have identified as the Orientalist discourse of colonial rulers might also have been heard as *charpoy* chatter in the *mohallas* and *chowks* of India's towns and villages.

The divisions of Indian society were many and deep. Every form of social organization known to anthropology was to be found in the subcontinent: from hunter-gatherers and forest-dwellers to modern industrial entrepreneurs, from nomads and pastoralists to independent peasants, from bonded labourers to industrial working classes. Its villages and urban back-streets echoed with the babel of every tongue. In the late nineteenth century, no less than 179 languages and 544 dialects had been identified in the subcontinent: thus, Indian spoke unto Indian. Nearly every faith known to man was practised in the subcontinent. Hindus formed the largest religious grouping. Their religion was not enshrined in a single text but defined by practice and in relation to the challenge and stimulus of other doctrines. But the changing definition of Hinduism did not gather its practitioners into a single and happy flock, and caste, believed by some to be its defining characteristic, rent them irretrievably apart. Muslims and Sikhs, expected to share equally in the community of all true believers, nonetheless observed caste. They were differentiated internally by all the factors, regional and doctrinal, linguistic and economic, social and political, which divided all Indians. The Urdu-speaking elite of the United Provinces, whose folk-memory could recall the *mushairas* and discourses of the Mughal court in its pomp, despised the low-caste Islamic converts from Hinduism in East Bengal and scoffed at what the frontiersmen of the Punjab, who shared their faith, might make of the delicacy of their verse and their cuisine. It is one of the many ironies of the subcontinent's history that these diverse elements were to be gathered up into a single nation, on a theocratic and awkwardly territorial principle, in 1947.

In the nineteenth century India was, as it remains today, largely an agrarian society. If anything, it was becoming more rural than it had been in the heyday of the Mughals. The proportion of the population living in towns in the 1880s was marginally smaller than it had been even a hundred years earlier, while more rural dwellers had come to depend upon agriculture for their livelihood. Most commonly, Indian agriculture was characterized by smallholdings, no larger than the area which could be cultivated by the labour of a peasant household. Production conditions and social structures varied enormously in their local and regional detail. But three broad types of agrarian development may be identified. In the richest, and oldest, agricultural tracts, along the banks of the major rivers and in the coastal plains, holdings became increasingly fragmented and sub-divided, and they were more intensively

Fig. 62 Bengal labourer; photograph by Cecil Beaton, 1946 (Imperial War Museum; no. 599 [i])

cultivated as the population grew in the late nineteenth century. These areas suffered decline and the rapidly diminishing returns from smallholding agriculture scarcely attracted investment. Elsewhere, population growth facilitated the extension of cultivation on its margins. But these tracts were always vulnerable to drought, flood and disease, and small surpluses acquired by stealth and diligence could be wiped out at a stroke. However, the expansion or intensification of cultivation in some regions, like the Punjab and south Gujarat, the Doab region and the Narmada valley, paid handsome returns. These were the success stories of Indian agriculture. Favourable soils and climates were sometimes afforced by the provision of irrigation and improvements in transport. In these areas, substantial peasants effectively exploited new and better market opportunities and adapted to the lucrative cash-crops (Fig. 62).

At the first sign of structural change in agrarian relations – a brisker market for land, produce and credit, the steady cheapening and swelling of the labour supply – the British realized that they were not modernizers. Their aim was to conserve and protect. They were not concerned to develop the Indian economy. Their purpose was to take resources out of India, not to invest their own in the subcontinent. Of course, the development of the Indian economy might have facilitated its more effective exploitation by a wider range of British capitalist interests. But it could also set in motion more fundamental processes of social change which might disturb the fragile alliances upon which Britannia's pax somewhat wistfully relied. In a recurrent fit of high-mindedness, the British had preached that moral progress under their tutelage would bring India material rewards. Now material progress posed grave moral problems for the colonial rulers.

Seeking to prevent capitalism from working its magic in rural India for fear of the political consequences which it might unleash, the British found themselves inadvertently shoring up the small-holding structure of Indian agriculture. From the 1850s onwards, but especially in the last quarter of the century, the British began increasingly to define tenants' rights, protect debtors and prevent the alienation of land from sturdy peasants to grasping money-lenders and landlords. Thus, the state acted to blunt the forces of commercialization it had helped to unleash and crucially, by wrestling to conserve the fragile base of the economy, it also firmly etched into the twentieth century the limits of its possible transformation. Its consequences were laid bare between the wars when the favourable circumstances which had underwritten the satisfactory performance of this smallholding agrarian base in the late nineteenth century finally passed. Inflation during the First World War was followed by the boom of the early 1920s; prices collapsed in the depression of the 1930s and soared once again in the 1940s. The agrarian structure was too atrophied to absorb or respond effectively to the shocks of these rapid and violent market fluctuations. The more closely the state intervened to protect the internal economy and its stagnant agrarian base, the less it had to intervene with, the fewer were the aspirations it could satisfy, the greater the hopes it disappointed and the wider the coalition of interests it alienated. These pressures were eventually to squeeze the colonial state to extinction.

Two centuries of colonial rule, which had frozen the dynamism of India's

Fig. 63 Jute factory; photograph by Cecil Beaton, 1946 (Imperial War Museum; no. 599 [vii])

agrarian economy, scarcely provided ideal beginnings for industrialization. In its first phase, industrialization was characterized by the processing of agrarian produce, primarily for the export trade. The first cotton mills, pioneered and developed almost entirely by Indian capital, were built in Bombay in the 1850s. In the late nineteenth and early twentieth century, Indian entrepreneurs sought more fully to exploit the possibilities of import-substitution in the domestic market. These entrepreneurs were assisted by the disruption of international trade during the two world wars and the depression, and by the halting and discriminating introduction of tariffs. Expatriate British entrepreneurs did not venture into the internal economy but relied upon their formidable connections with the bureaucracy and the Presidency banks and India's monopoly of the world's raw jute to dominate the export trade and the industrial economy centred on Calcutta. But this refusal to venture into the internal economy allowed Indian jute traders to drive them to the wall in the difficult days of the 1920s and 1930s (Fig. 63). The best known mercantile family to emerge from this nexus were the Birlas whose generosity and wisdom provided the millions that helped to keep Gandhi in poverty.

Finally, the depression of the 1930s was accompanied by considerable industrial expansion, largely because its shock re-oriented both capital and labour towards the towns. Falling grain prices made rural money-lending and trade less appealing and creditors switched their capital to the towns. As credit dried up, more peasant households sought access to cash and sent their men to the towns in search of wages. Thus, capital fleeing the depression in the countryside gained access to a swelling supply of cheap labour.

Peasants had often in the past left their villages in search of waged employment. Their objective in most cases had been to defend their village holdings. In the 1930s, a new pattern of migration emerged. Now men sought work in the largest towns, where the range of economic activity was greatest and where the contraction of employment in one sector might be compensated by its expansion in another. Some found their urban earnings insufficient or too intermittent to sustain their village base, and as they became entirely dependent upon urban livelihoods, they swelled the ranks of the town-dwelling unemployed. From the 1930s onwards, it was the largest cities which for this reason grew the fastest. Urbanization in a poor, predominantly agrarian society is usually interpreted as a sign of economic development. The growth of the largest cities since 1931 has been more a symptom of rural impoverishment.

If colonialism thus shaped the contours of Indian poverty, it also influenced the conventions of Indian politics in unexpected ways, and sometimes with lasting consequences. It is a superficial, sometimes self-regarding, view which finds this legacy embodied in the adoption of democratic forms. Apologists for British rule have often detected an inherent liberalism in the colonial system. In India, however, the British constructed an Oriental Despotism. Certainly, nineteenth-century liberals in Britain swiftly appreciated the difference and feared that the creeping authoritarianism of colonial rule might return to haunt the free-born Englishman in his castle.

Of course, the British sought to attach Indians to their rule through measures of political devolution. Yet even as greater powers were devolved at higher levels – for instance, when the central legislative assembly was allowed a non-official Indian majority or parliamentary majorities in provincial assemblies were enabled to form their own governments – the British reserved sufficient executive powers so that they could conduct business without recourse to the elected legislators, and provincial governors could, if they deemed it necessary, suspend the governments over which they presided and simply rule by ordinance. Britain's legacy to South Asian democracy is to be more accurately located in those aspects of political practice which have sometimes tended to elevate government and bureaucracy above civil rights, liberal freedoms and the political process itself.

What the British bequeathed to India was sectarian politics rather than liberalism or democratic institutions. Colonialism imparted to the protean languages of Indian politics a fresh vocabulary of sectarianism. It is not intended to suggest that India's history was free from communal tensions before the British reached its shores; nor should it be supposed that sectarian conflicts were simply the outcome of colonial conspiracies to divide and rule. This vocabulary of communal politics, like Britain's Oriental Despotism, arose out of the political structure which it fashioned to rule India in their imperial interests.

If India was to be ruled in their global interests, it would be necessary for the British to centralize and unify their command. If the aims and purposes of their rule required that they ride roughshod over local immunities, it was imperative that they also re-define them and allow Indians larger areas of influence and control within the colonial system. But if Indians were to be associated more fully with British rule, how were they to be chosen? The resolution of this riddle rocked the British back onto their most basic assumptions about Indian society. It was honeycombed, they assumed, with innumerable but definite interests, some of which derived their integrity from the bonds of caste, race or religion, others from occupation or economic status. Necessarily, the British defined these interests with an enviable sweep and magisterial simplicity.

In the process, they created a political language of social and communal interests within which competition of diverse sorts and a wide range of conflicts were likely to be expressed. This competition was stimulated both by the policies of government as well as the response it evoked among its subjects. Prudence suggested that the British secure the broadest possible representation of Indians within their institutions at every level from the *tahsildar's* office to the Viceroy's Executive Council. It was also important not to accord permanence to any particular pattern of distribution of jobs and resources between different castes, religious communities and social classes. To achieve the proper representation of society necessarily required them to shuffle the weight of each group, advancing the backward, cutting back the rampant, and suppressing some altogether.

This official rhetoric of representation, with its claim to provide suitably for each deserving interest, was simply an invitation for people to band together, to define themselves in its terms, assert their significance and negotiate for a larger share of the spoils. If their rulers wished them to gather behind the banner of fictitious communities, Indians saw no reason to refuse. Once special interests were so defined, individuals and social groups, whenever appropriate, began to act inside them. 'Muslims' had an incentive to organize and act as 'Muslims'; so did every possible social group, whether identified by caste, language, region or religion. To profess allegiance to any single identity, however, did not oblige them to refrain from defining it variously. Thus, when Edwin Montagu visited India to prepare a fresh constitutional settlement in 1918 he was inundated with petitions and deputations from each of the categories imagined by the Raj, each claiming to be more truly representative than the next. No fewer than 44 Muslim associations petitioned him with their own distinct vision of the just future. Lord Willingdon, trying to implement the reforms in Madras, complained that he was 'being bombarded by all sorts of sub-castes of non-Brahmins for special representation' amounting to an irreducible minimum of 250 equally representative and deserving constituencies. It could hardly be supposed these communities or special interests formed the natural constituencies of Indian society. On the contrary, the more the British streamlined and rationalized their system of rule, the more their rough-cut taxonomy of Indian society grew abstracted from its realities. Yet no matter how baroque the categories devised by the British, Indian politicians could only ignore them at their peril.

British India witnessed numerous political movements organized along caste, linguistic, religious and regional lines. They focussed primarily upon issues of access to education and government jobs and demanded special representation within the political institutions of British rule. But if these movements, whether of Muslim separatism, non-Brahminism or the Depressed Classes, appeared to be no more than the trade unions of the scribal classes, they did not run a closed shop and their social significance was never as limited as their vision. Education and government employment provided the most ready means of social mobility. The control of local government could place in the hands of local politicians considerable powers of patronage, which could be deployed to discriminate between factions and social groups, castes and religious communities. An individual who came to be lodged within the institutional framework of the state held out the hope of advancement to his friends, kinsmen and caste-fellows. When fresh social categories were defined and became entrenched, opportunity knocked for all those who could identify or associate with them. Similarly, local elites, marginalized within provincial politics, kept the political cartographers busy by demanding the redrawing of district or, more controversially, provincial boundaries: in Bengal, between 1905–11 and once again in the 1940s; in Andhra, intermittently between the 1910s until its achievement in the 1950s; or in Sind, seeking separation first from the Bombay Presidency in the 1930s and then from Pakistan after 1947.

Of course, these were not the only lines of conflict in Indian politics. The Indian countryside was not the peaceful haven of sturdy, if acquiescent, peasants which colonial officials liked to imagine. Dacoity, food riots and jacqueries peppered its vast open spaces. Working class action occurred on a scale rarely rivalled elsewhere. In Bombay city alone, there were eight general strikes between 1918 and 1940, none of which ended in less than a month, while the general strikes of 1928–29 continued more or less without interruption for eighteen months. Bombay was a dramatic case in the history of India's labour movement, but it was by no means unique.

The great Congress agitations of non-cooperation in the early 1920s, civil disobedience in the early 1930s, and the Quit India campaign of 1942 posed what the British feared as the most serious threat to their future. The timing of these agitations, often determined by the enunciation of constitutional policy or the state of negotiations over political reform, suggests that they were not simply spontaneous effusions of popular patriotic sentiment. Moreover, the vigorous and enthusiastic public response found by Gandhi and the Congress rarely offered a steady base. Towns and villages which appeared insurrectionary during non-cooperation might turn somnolent during civil disobedience. Whole districts which launched themselves vigorously into the Quit India campaign had seemed passive and loyalist two decades earlier. No insurance company, it was said, was prepared to insure the life of the District Magistrate of Midnapur in Bengal, but elsewhere in the same province his colleagues wondered what the fuss was all about. Frequently those who were embroiled in long-running local conflicts found that the Congress agitations provided a wider focus for their specific grievances. But if local discontents thus recruited the Congress to their cause, the latter were in turn sometimes willing to attach themselves to the coat-tails of particular struggles which offered them the appearance of a wider and deeper social base. The Congress was less a tightly organized political party than a loose, often shifting coalition of diverse elements. Its diversity made it flexible and adaptable. But it could not easily be moved in a single social or ideological direction and indeed, such movement was always liable to expose its internal contradictions. Just as the British had to humour and empower their collaborators and reconcile their often conflicting interests, so the Congress struggled within the same constraints to negotiate, manoeuvre and manage its own heterogeneous allies.

In the 1920s and 1930s, the British found that they could no longer freely and easily commit Indian resources to their imperial purposes. Indian exports no longer played the same vital role in settling Britain's balance of payments deficits. British industry proved decreasingly competitive in the Indian market, which became increasingly stagnant. The Indian Army could no longer be used at will to protect British interests at the Indian taxpayers' expense and Indian legislators seemed to become particularly noisy and vociferous over issues of defence expenditure, on which they could not vote. Although India served as a British bastion in the Second World War, London had to pay, mainly by borrowing against the Indian revenues. By 1947, Britain's debt to India amounted to about one-fifth of its own Gross National Product.

So there were growing and increasingly severe political constraints on administering India, or extracting its resources, for Britain's imperial system. Some of these emanated from Britain, whose own huddled masses were now yearning to be free; more spent on the empire would mean less for trying once again to build a home for heroes in the mothercountry. In India, the British found themselves, in their ceaseless quest for collaboration and accommodation, and cut-price government, committed to successive rounds of political reform, extending their systems of representation and election to provincial and Viceregal levels, and opening out their administration to increasing Indian control. As the colonial state became more and more Indian, its freedom of manoeuvre in serving the interests of its imperial masters was steadily narrowed. Step by step, the colonial state was forced to develop in ways which contradicted and eventually undermined its essential purposes.

But no one embarrassed the British more than Gandhi. He mercilessly mocked their pretensions; his idiom and language bewildered and perplexed them; he attacked the very core of their most favoured self-perceptions. Against the British claim that their government in India had been constituted by law, Gandhi insisted that it had originated in conquest and was founded on force. He poured scorn upon a civilization supposedly demoralized by its material greed and its spiritual poverty. Colonial rulers attempted to mark the acceptable limits of dissent on the edge of mass protest and social violence; Gandhi showed that it was the British who could not desist from clubbing hunger-strikers and trampling non-violent *satyagrahis* under their horses' hooves. Imperious proconsuls feared that they might be teased into becoming commercial bag-men.

Indian nationalism came of age after its greatest triumphs had been concluded. By the 1970s and 1980s, large numbers of Indians had embarked, not necessarily by choice, on their own discovery of India (Figs. 64 and 65). The Hindi cinema and the diffusion of the radio and television helped to make acquaintances of strangers. The emergence of a strong national political arena created a greater need for the collection and dissemination of infor-

Fig. 64 A marriage procession in a bazaar; modern photograph by C. A. Bayly

mation about the nation. The making of the nation, however, has served to entrench its particularisms. By the end of the 1980s, economic development had created a vast middle class even if it failed to prevent 40 per cent of the population from being pushed beneath the poverty line. Dislocated from its old social moorings, this new bourgeoisie grew increasingly concerned to re-invent its past and recall the happy solidarities of village, caste and religion. As poverty increased for many and prosperity became possible for some, political discourse came to be centred upon a fresh cultural quest for the 'real' India. Not necessarily couched in punctiliously secular terms, and indeed, in deference to a Hindu preponderance, frequently clothed in a spiritual saffron, it has held out the promise of creating a community of sentiment around which the state and its dominant classes could legitimize their rule. But the attempt to create this community and to define the nation in this way has scarcely been untroubled and necessarily it has encountered resistance and provoked dissent.

Fattened on the burgeoning vocabulary of communal politics, sectarian conflicts have often developed along lines which were firmly in place during the colonial period, although they have not conformed entirely to the old pattern. Provincial elites, seeking to extract a larger share of an increasingly strong centre's economic and political resources, have repeatedly deployed the threat of secession, sometimes drawing upon linguistic or religious identities, to drive harder bargains with it. As the weight of the state in the Indian economy has increased, government jobs and access to them through the educational system have become more, rather than less, important as a focus of social competition and political conflict. For various middling groups, government employment has remained the major avenue for social mobility while the rapid growth of the educated unemployed has increased the clamour for quotas of jobs and educational places for particular communities. Already established for the Scheduled Castes or untouchables, as well as the somewhat more elastically defined 'Backward Classes', the migration of larger numbers of Indians to sometimes distant states has also prompted local residents to demand special privileges for 'the sons of the soil.' These conflicts over quotas and reservations have readily joined up with agitations over language and states' rights. The demand for the linguistic reorganization of the states in the 1960s reflected the attempts by regional elites, competing with each other, to gain a firmer grip upon the institutions of provincial government at the expense of their rivals. Although regional separatism in the 1980s has been driven by the demand of provincial elites for a larger share of central resources, it is possible that the increasing strength of the centre has begun to re-direct such regional competition upon itself. For the assertion of states' rights in Kashmir and the Punjab, and at least rhetorically in west Bengal, has reflected a search for the redistribution, not only of the centre's resources but also its political power.

Fig. 65 A traditional scent shop in a bazaar; modern photograph by C. A. Bayly

Just as nationalism reached its apogee several decades after independence, so it was only in the 1960s and 1970s that the cultural characteristics which the British had perceived as their very own began to manifest themselves more widely in India. Universal adult suffrage became a reality and, exercised with vigour, it infused democratic politics with an extraordinary energy and dynamism. Larger numbers now spoke the English language and the phenomenal expansion of universities gave India, which already had one of the highest rates of illiteracy in the world, a substantial technical and scientific manpower. Cricket became a mass sport, no longer confined to the Presidency capitals and their gymkhana clubs but played and followed with zeal and devotion throughout the subcontinent. This was not the result of the evolution of a taste first inculcated in the 1920s by the 'Quadrangular' tournaments between 'Hindus', 'Muslims', 'Parsis' and 'Europeans'. Nobody who has heard the Bombay crowd chant 'bowled' to the time of a fast bowler's paces as he approaches the wicket or attempted to cross the Azad Maidan at the height of the cricket season could imagine that this was an English game. Those who participate in or benefit from these activities sometimes recognize them as part of an international culture but scarcely perceive in them the trappings of empire. Indeed, once the Union Jacks were lowered and the sahibs and their mems had booked their passage back to Blighty, it did not take long for the British to be forgotten. The British Raj quickly faded into a remote antiquity, whose memory could evoke nostalgia as much as it might fuel resentment. It is ironical and seemingly paradoxical – but perhaps reflective of the nature of this particular imperial relationship – that it was in Britain that the Raj came increasingly alive, less a matter for nostalgia than a source of pride. Here it continued to play a crucial, perhaps defining role in the construction of a national identity: a means, though not the only one, for distilling the very essence of Britishness. By contrast, in India, the nationalism which devoured the Raj has, in achieving its pomp, bared its teeth and demonstrated its menace to the integrity of the nation it created.

War and Mass Protest

India and the First World War

The Great War was a turning point for British India. Before 1914 radical nationalism had been on the rise, but it was still mainly an urban phenomenon, and one strongest in Bengal and the Bombay Presidency. The suffering and change inflicted on India by her participation in the World War gave the whole subcontinent common grievances and common aspirations. Indians felt that their contribution to the war of loans and more than 1,200,000 men, who fought in the Middle East and France, ought to be recompensed by the British with constitutional changes and a rapid advance towards free Dominion Status, already enjoyed by Canada and Australia. But the British, insisting on the preeminence of security, clamped down on political expression and imprisoned members of the Home Rule Leagues established by Tilak, and by Mrs Besant. Even more disruptive than the rapid inflation of the war years was the slump that followed. Indian troops returned from the various Fronts, their faith in European leadership already broken, to find both the urban and rural economies in recession. Dashed political expectations and widespread economic grievances provided a powerful fuel for the great political campaigns soon to be initiated by Mahatma Gandhi.

The Indian Muslims were the first to wage mass campaigns of opposition to the British authorities. Before 1914 younger Muslim leaders had already persuaded the Muslim League to adopt the attainment of self-government as one of its objectives. But even conservative landlords and Muslim religious authorities were outraged by the British policy of breaking up the Ottoman empire, and the threat to their spiritual leader, the Ottoman Sultan and Caliph. This sense of outrage was the origin of the Khilafat Movement, a mass Muslim agitation against the Indian Government. In fact Delhi itself urged caution on the home government with regard to the Middle East. C.A.B.

512 Indians on the Western Front, 1914–18

i) Hodson's Horse
Copyprint after photograph in the National Army Museum (5307–25–2)
ii) 2nd Battalion, Burma Rifles
Copyprint after photograph in the National Army Museum (6107–21–2)
iii) Havildar Sheo Narain Singh of the 89th Punjabis with a Lewis gun
Copyprint after photograph in the National Army Museum (6212–13–17)
iv) Naik Shahamad Khan, machine gunner, 89th Punjabis
Copyprint after photograph in the National Army Museum (7902–38)

512(i)

512(ii)

512(iii)

512(iv)

513

514

513 Indians loading a train, France

Adrian Hill
Pen and ink on paper, 29.8 × 47 ($11\frac{3}{5}$ × 18)
The Trustees of the Imperial War Museum (285)

514 Indians dismantling fortifications, France

Adrian Hill
Pen and ink on paper, 25.5 × 45.7 (10 × $17\frac{4}{5}$)
The Trustees of the Imperial War Museum (286)

The Mesopotamian and Palestine Campaigns (1915–18)

Since the early nineteenth century the Indian Army had been sent as an imperial 'fire-brigade' to trouble spots in Asia and Africa. The Middle East, however, was of particular importance to the British: as the two fastest routes from Britain to India, the Mesopotamian plain and the Red Sea-Suez Canal were strategically and economically critical. In 1914 the Ottoman empire, which ruled Mesopotamia and was suzerain of Egypt and the Arabian peninsular, took the German side and went to war with the British empire. Two campaigns were fought to attack this supposed 'soft-underbelly' of the Central Powers: one later commanded by Sir Edmund Allenby from Egypt into Palestine, and the other from Basra towards Baghdad. Indian troops fought in both campaigns but the Mesopotamian campaign was entirely an Indian one, with 100,000 men in action. C.A.B.

LITERATURE: Tomlinson 1975.

515 Deccan Horse guarding Muslimie Junction (Syria)

James McBey, 1918
Watercolour, 52.5 × 36.5 ($20\frac{1}{2}$ × $14\frac{1}{5}$)
Inscribed b.l.: *James McBey, 8 November 1918 Aleppo*
The Trustees of the Imperial War Museum (1584)

515

516

517

516 Sikh Sappers blasting an artillery road over the Ladder of Tyre

James McBey, 1918
Watercolour, 49.5 × 37 ($19\frac{3}{10} \times 14\frac{2}{5}$)
Inscribed b.l.: *James McBey ladder of Tyre, October 1918*
The Trustees of the Imperial War Museum (1863)

517 A Sepoy of the 114th Marathas

J.D. Revel
Watercolour, 50.8 × 35.5 ($19\frac{4}{5} \times 13\frac{4}{5}$)
The Trustees of the Imperial War Museum (2350)

518 Disaster in Mesopotamia, 1916

i) Action in Mesopotamia
Norman Rybot
Pencil on paper, 10.5 × 13.5 ($4\frac{1}{8} \times 5\frac{3}{10}$)
India Office Library and Records (WD1242)
ii) Action in Mesopotamia
Norman Rybot
Pencil on paper, 10.5 × 13.5 ($4\frac{1}{8} \times 5\frac{3}{10}$)
India Office Library and Records (WD1243)
iii) Action in Mesopotamia
Norman Rybot
Manuscript, 20.3 × 16.2 ($8 \times 6\frac{4}{10}$)
India Office Library and Records (WD1244)
iv) Panorama, Mesopotamia
Norman Rybot
Pen and ink on paper, 23 × 56 (9 × 22)
India Office Library and Records (WD1245)
v) Bird's-eye view of Kut-al-Amara, Mesopotamia
Norman Rybot
Pen and ink on paper, 39 × 31 ($15\frac{3}{8} \times 12\frac{2}{8}$)
India Office Library and Records (WD1246)
vi) Caricature
Norman Rybot
Pen, ink and watercolour, 24 × 20.2 ($9\frac{2}{5} \times 8$)
India Office Library and Records (WD1258)

In no. 518(vi) Rybot caricatures the muddle and incompetence of the British and Indian army operations in Mesopotamia using themes drawn from the Bayeux Tapestry. In 1916 an Indian expeditionary force under Major-General Townshend thrust northward up the Tigris-Euphrates valley, reaching the town of Ctesiphon only 16 miles from the Ottoman provincial capital at Baghdad. But Townshend suffered heavy casualties and lost half his British officers. He ordered his exhausted force to dig in at Kut-al-Amara where considerable stores had been collected (no. 518[v]) in anticipation of relief forces from the south. But the relieving force, which itself suffered 23,000 casualties, never reached the embattled garrison. On 29 April 1916, after a five-month siege, Townshend and 10,000 men surrendered. This was the worst defeat of the Indian Army since the first Afghan war. Though Baghdad was taken a year later by Sir Stanley Maude, the disaster ruined the end of Lord Hardinge's viceroyalty and set the Indian Government's finances on the road to collapse. Norman Rybot (1876–1961) served in the Indian Army 1896–1920. C.A.B.

518

The Political Temperature Rises

519 Home Rule Delegation

Copyprint after photograph (1918) in the Nehru Memorial Museum and Library, New Delhi

Despite official hostility to political activity during the war, Annie Besant (no.502) and B.G. Tilak (no.497), who had been released from jail in July 1914, planned new and more vigorous campaigns of agitation based on Irish models. At the end of 1917 Mrs Besant's Home Rule League had 27,000 members, mainly from Madras and many of them from among her old theosophical contacts. By early 1918 Tilak's League had 32,000 members, mainly drawn from the Bombay Presidency. Quickly developing mass propaganda methods, the leagues set the tone for Gandhi's later campaigns. Tilak and G. S. Khaparde (in the large Maratha tur-

519

ban) are seen at the time of the League's abortive visit to London. C.A.B.

LITERATURE: Brown 1985.

520 'Lokmanya' (B.G.) Tilak addresses a crowded meeting in Bombay

Narayan Vinayak Virkar, 1917–19
Photograph, 15.9 × 20.8 ($6\frac{1}{5}$ × 8)
Mr Rajendra Shriram Virkar

The bunting slogans advertise the nationalist newspaper *Young India*, a pamphlet on the Tilak trials, and Tilak's famous slogan 'Swaraj [home rule] is my birthright'. The crowd reflects the regional diversity of Bombay: Hindus, Muslims and Parsis (note the distinctive conical *fenta* headgear) all appear in this photograph.

Narayan Vinayak Virkar (1890–1968) was one of India's most important early political photographers. He was born, like many Marathi-speaking immigrants to Bombay, in the nearby Ratnagiri District. He learnt about photography from the artist and Vedic scholar Pandit Shreepad Damodar Satvalekar in Lahore. Virkar appointed himself unofficial photographer to the Nationalist Movement, and followed Con-

520

gressmen and their meetings all over the country. Apart from standard studio work he also did portraits of musicians, dancers, religious leaders and domestic groups. G.J./J.M./F.N.

521 Cloth traders in Bombay listen to the call to practise *Swadeshi* (home industry) in everyday life

Narayan Vinayak Virkar, 1916–20
Photograph, 15.9 × 21.6 ($6\frac{1}{5}$ × $8\frac{2}{5}$)
Mr Rajendra Shriram Virkar

Since the Partition of Bengal in 1905, the boycott of British products and the call to consume only Indian-made goods had been central to the symbolism and policies of the Nationalist Movement. Gandhi was to insist that true *swadeshi* meant the use of only artisan-manufactured cloth. Such campaigns were only partially successful; more important in reducing the volume of British imports to India were the tariffs which the Indian Government began to raise

521

against foreign imports after 1919. This new fiscal policy was not only a response to the pressure of Indian business, which now leant towards the Congress and the Muslim League; it also reflected the Government's dire need for money after the massive expenditure on the campaigns in the Middle East. Before the Nationalist Movement it would have been unusual to see women present at a gathering of workers and traders. Here they have been allocated a special area. F.N./C.A.B.

LITERATURE: Tomlinson 1975.

522 Khilafat volunteers

Copyprint after photograph by N.V. Virkar (*c*.1919) in the Nehru Memorial Museum and Library, New Delhi

Many Indian Muslims regarded the Ottoman Sultan in his role of Khalifa, or inheritor of the earthly authority of

522

the Prophet, as their spiritual leader. The dismemberment of the Ottoman empire and the harsh peace terms imposed on Turkey at the end of the First World War called forth a massive movement of opposition from Muslim merchants and professional people as well as from the doctors of Islamic law (the *ulama*). Between 1919 and 1923 the Congress and the Khilafat Associations worked together in their agitations against British policies and British rule. C.A.B.

LITERATURE: Minault 1982.

523(i) Muhammad and Shaukat Ali before the First World War

Copyprint after photograph in the Nehru Memorial Museum and Library, New Delhi
(Illustrated Fig. 52)

523(ii) Muhammad and Shaukat Ali during the Congress session, 1924

Copyprint after photograph in the Nehru Memorial Museum and Library, New Delhi

523(ii)

Two of the foremost leaders of Muslim opinion in India, the Ali brothers were typical of the 'Young Party' of more radical politicians who emerged from the Aligarh College after the turn of the present century. They were active in several movements which stressed international Muslim links, especially during the Balkan Wars between the Christian powers and the Ottomans. Later, as leaders of the Khilafat Movement, they participated in Gandhi's first Non-cooperation Movement. But they were later to drift away from the Congress, emphasizing their Muslim identity. Nos. 523 (i) and (ii) show them dressed in more traditional Islamic style. C.A.B.

524 Tilak blesses the flags of the Khilafat Movement volunteers

Narayan Vinayak Virkar, 1919
Photograph, 16.2 × 21.3 ($6\frac{3}{8} \times 8\frac{3}{8}$)
Mr Rajendra Shriram Virkar

This photograph illustrates some of the paradoxes, and also the iconographic complexity, of the Indian national movement. Tilak's revolutionary symbols (eg. Ganpati and Shivaji, nos.500,87) were predominantly Hindu in character and during the 'extremist' agitation of 1905–9 some Muslims had been suspicious of this. But here Tilak blesses a flag which incorporates the Union Jack (which includes, of course, the cross of St George), the Muslim crescent moon and the symbol of the constellation known to Hindus as the Saptarishi, or seven sages (the Great Bear in the West). At this period the Khilafat volunteers did not wish to raise doubts about their allegiance to the Crown, and they positively sought the participation of Hindus. F.N./C.A.B.

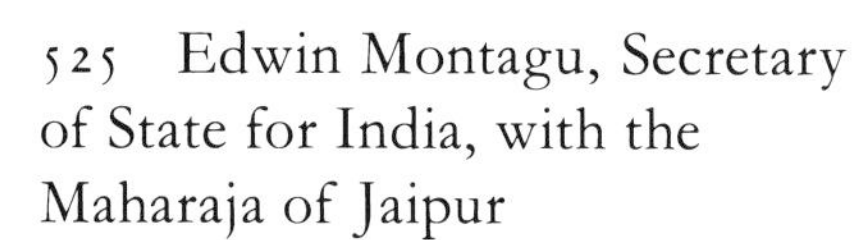

525 Edwin Montagu, Secretary of State for India, with the Maharaja of Jaipur

Copyprint after photograph (1918) in the India Office Library (Mss. Eur. D523/39 [157a])

526 Frederic John Napier Thesiger, Viscount Chelmsford (1868–1933), Viceroy of India 1916–21

Unknown photographer, *c.*1921
Photograph, 27 × 17.2 ($10\frac{6}{10} \times 6\frac{3}{10}$)
National Portrait Gallery (x 6013)

By the end of the First World War the British Government realized that India's contribution to the Allied effort would have to be recognized by constitutional advance. In August 1917 the Secretary of State for India, Edwin Montagu, a Liberal politician and lawyer, announced that the aim of the government was 'to take substantial steps' in the 'progressive realization of responsible government in India as an integral part of the British Empire'. Though it is now clear from Cabinet papers that this variety of 'dominion status' was not expected to be as full as that already enjoyed by Canada, Australia and New Zealand, Indians anticipated great things. Montagu himself paid a visit to India in the winter of 1917–18 to sample Indian political opinion, which set him reeling with its complexity. His aim was to bring about a limited broadening of the franchise and to introduce responsible Cabinet government in some areas of provincial administration. This policy was effected in the Government of India Act, 1919, known as the Montagu-Chelmsford Reforms after the Secretary of State and the Viceroy of the time. The reforms enshrined the principle of 'dyarchy' or 'dual rule' between Indian politicians and British Indian civil servants. Indian leaders who commanded a majority in provincial legislative

524

525

assemblies would henceforth become ministers in departments such as education and local government, while the ICS would control more significant portfolios. Radical Indian leaders were desperately disappointed by the scope of the concessions. Their anger, however, was overshadowed by the public reaction to the the Khilafat Movement and events in the Punjab. C.A.B.

LITERATURE: Robb 1976.

527 Sir Michael O'Dwyer with the Reforms Committee

Copyprint after photograph (1918) in the India Office Library (MSS Eur. D783/9)

The British were particularly concerned about the situation in the Punjab as it was a strategic territory adjoining Russian (now Bolshevik) Central Asia besides being a bread basket for India and the nursery of its army. During the First World War there had been rumours of Russian and German plots among radical Sikhs and Hindus. Besides the general problems of the post-war economic slump, urban Punjabi Hindus were worried that any increase in rural representation under British constitutional schemes might put them permanently at the mercy of the large rural Muslim majority, which was also politically conservative. Sir Michael O'Dwyer here with members of the Reforms Committee, was the Lieutenant-Governor charged with keeping the peace in the Punjab. His response appeared heavy-handed and unimaginative to Indians; they felt that he set in train the events that led to the tragedy of the massacre at Jallianwallabagh in Amritsar. C.A.B.

527

528

528 General Reginald Dyer

Frontispiece from *The Life of General Dyer* by Ian Colvin, Edinburgh and London, 1929
Photograph, 13.8 × 9.9 ($5\frac{1}{2} \times 3\frac{9}{10}$)
India Office Library and Records (V 8014)

529 A citizen of Amritsar points to one of the bullet holes punctuating the anti-Dyer graffiti covering the walls of the Jallianwallabagh, Amritsar

Narayan Vinayak Virkar, 1919
Photograph, 16.5 × 21.6 ($6\frac{2}{5} \times 8\frac{2}{5}$)
Mr Rajendra Shriram Virkar

529

After the end of the First World War discontent spread rapidly in the cities of the Punjab. Deteriorating economic conditions were matched by a sense of frustration that the promised political reforms were 'too little and too late'. Fearing for the stability of this important province which shared a border with a defiant Afghanistan, the Punjab authorities reacted with severe repression, proclamations of martial law and the banning of all political activity. In Amritsar an unarmed crowd led by local political leaders decided to flout the declaration of martial law and gather in the walled area of Jallianwallabagh. General Reginald Dyer, the local military commander, fired on the crowd which was penned into the walled area and unable to make its escape through the crowded gateways (some said they were deliberately blocked by the British). At least 300 were killed and 1,000 wounded, though Congress sources put the casualties much higher. General Dyer, who faced a court of inquiry following the incident, made it quite clear that his actions were not so much an attempt to restore order as a show of force to 'teach the crowd a lesson'. In seeking to defend the power of the Indian Government, however, he dealt it a mortal blow.

The massacre dramatically changed Indian perceptions of British rule. 'Dyerism' became a term of abuse in the Indian press, similar to 'Nazism' in a later decade. Gandhi began to refer to British rule as a 'satanic' regime and coupled the 'Punjab wrongs' with the Khilafat agitation (see nos.522–4) in an attempt to get Hindus and Muslims to join together in anti-British agitation. Gandhi helped set up a Congress inquiry into the Punjab atrocities, claiming that the British authorities had 'white-washed' the actions of officials and soldiers. He said 'I have discovered that the present representatives of the Empire have become dishonest and unscrupulous.' In some ways the response of public opinion and the British establishment at home was more of a jolt to Indian sentiment than the massacre itself. The House of Lords presented an address to Dyer (who had been forced to resign by the Indian Government), a fund was established for his benefit and most newspaper opinion took the view that his actions were justified by the 'revolt' in the Punjab.

Richard Attenborough's film *Gandhi* (1983) gave great prominence to the Amritsar massacre, a mark of the onward march of the post-imperial age in Britain, though one which jarred with more sentimental visions of the Raj.

C.A.B.

530

Gandhi's Return

Mohandas Karamchand Gandhi (1869–1948) will always be remembered as a man of the people who sympathized with and roused the masses. But his origins were privileged. He came from a merchant caste family in Gujarat, western India, but it was one which had reached the pinnacle of influence to which this caste of the old India aspired (see no.231), for his father had become *diwan* (chief minister) of the small state of Purbandhar. Gandhi went to London to pursue his legal studies and became a member of the Inner Temple. Here, as his autobiography recounts, he dressed in Western clothes (no.530) and was temporarily involved in London political and social groups. Practising law in South Africa, Gandhi championed the cause of the Indian indentured labourers who had settled there, aiding them in their campaigns against the harsh local legislation which denied them ordinary freedoms. In 1915 Gandhi returned to India, making contact with G.K.Gokhale (no.490) and the moderate social reformers among the Bombay Congressmen. But he was soon galvanized to action by the poverty and what he saw as the mis-government around him. He took up the Home Rule agitation, the campaign against the repressive Rowlatt Bill which was designed to fight terrorism, and championed various peasant struggles.

From the beginning, however, Gandhi was more than simply a political leader. He preached self-control, a simple lifestyle, and the need to develop inner 'soul-force' (*satyagraha*) before cleansing the nation. One visible symbol of this simplicity and self-control was the practice of spinning which Gandhi and his wife Kasturbai (1869–1944; no. 533) made part of their daily round, but which was also to become a membership requirement of the new Indian National Congress and a badge of nationhood. Gandhi's own dress and deportment marked the emergence of his sense of national destiny and the essence of 'Indianness'. The Inner Temple lawyer adopted the traditional turban of the Gujarati Bania (merchant caste) when he first returned to the country (no. 531). But he soon came to feel that emphasis on caste distinction was as dangerous to national integration as unthinking Westernization. He therefore adopted the cap, later known as the 'Gandhi cap', which was the typical headgear of people throughout Gujarat, regardless of caste (no.532). But as time went on he abandoned even the cap, becoming a virtual political *sanyasi* and dressing as a wandering ascetic. This provoked Churchill's description of Gandhi as a 'seditious fakhir'.

C.A.B.

531

532

LITERATURE: Nanda 1958; Brown 1972.

530 Gandhi in Western dress

Copyprint after photograph by L.G. Peasarty (*c.* 1892) in the Nehru Memorial Museum and Library, New Delhi

531 Gandhi wearing a turban

Narayan Vinayak Virkar, *c.* 1916
Photograph, 21.6 × 15.2 ($8\frac{2}{5} \times 6$)
Mr Rajendra Shriram Virkar

532 Gandhi wearing a cap

Narayan Vinayak Virkar, 1921
Photograph, 21.6 × 16.5 ($8\frac{2}{5} \times 6\frac{2}{5}$)
Mr Rajendra Shriram Virkar

534

533

533 Kasturbai Gandhi spinning yarn on a *charka*

Narayan Vinayak Virkar, 1920s
Photograph, 21.6 × 16.5 ($8\frac{2}{5} \times 6\frac{2}{5}$)
Mr Rajendra Shriram Virkar

534 A Congress member spinning

Copyprint after photograph in the Nehru Memorial Museum and Library, New Delhi

535 A march during the Non-cooperation Movement in Bombay

Narayan Vinayak Virkar, 1921–2
Photograph, 16.5 × 22.2 ($6\frac{2}{5} \times 8\frac{3}{5}$)
Mr Rajendra Shriram Virkar
(Illustrated Fig. 51)

In 1920, with the support of a mass of people enraged by the Amritsar massacre, the Middle East peace terms and the harsh post-war economic conditions, Gandhi laid siege to, and took control of, the Congress. Hereafter he took on the 'satanic' government with a campaign of non-cooperation, causing the Congress to boycott the elections held that year under the terms of the Montagu-Chelmsford Reforms. He asked people to return medals and honours given by the British Government, to give up government jobs and law practices, and finally to court arrest. In 1921 and early 1922 India nearly slipped from the grasp of the British authorities as rural disturbances combined with urban demonstrations. C.A.B.

Leaders and Followers

536 C.R. Das (1870–1925)

Copyprint after photograph in the Nehru Memorial Museum and Library, New Delhi

Not only young men such as Jawaharlal Nehru, who had recently returned to India from Cambridge, but also the old guard of Congress politicians were swept along by the force of Gandhi's movement. Among these were C.R. Das, the great Bengali political leader, and Motilal Nehru, Jawaharlal Nehru's father. Both these politicians had dominated the moderate, constitutional wing of their respective provincial Congress organizations before 1916. They went along with the call for non-cooperation in 1920 and boycotted the elections to the new assemblies under the Reforms scheme. But by 1923, with Gandhi jailed by the British and the Non-cooperation and Khilafat Movements petering out, both men opted for a partial return to constitutionalist politics. They formed the Swarajya ('Home Rule') Party as an organized wing within the Congress to contest the elections of 1923. The initial aim was to 'non-cooperate from within' the legislative councils, but by 1926 several Congressmen had actually become ministers in provincial governments under the dyarchy system. After his release from jail, Gandhi, shocked by the violence that the Non-cooperation Movement had generated, withdrew from active politics for several years, only to become active again in the aftermath of the appointment of the Simon Commission. C.A.B.

537

537 Madan Mohan Malaviya (1861–1946)

Copyprint after photograph by Narayan Vinayak Virkar in the Nehru Memorial Museum and Library, New Delhi

Malaviya never deviated from the dress and lifestyle of an orthodox Hindu, and this photograph gives an indication of his concern for proper dress and deportment. Born in Allahabad to a poor Brahmin family, Malaviya trained in a traditional Hindu school but then went on to English-speaking secondary and further education institutions. He was active in many local charitable associations, but much of his social and political work had a distinctly Hindu tone. He was a leading activist for the Indian National Congress in the Allahabad area and he was elected President of the Congress in 1909 and 1918. His brand of Hindu 'revivalism' and his family's roots in the north Indian countryside encouraged him to seek to make the Congress a more popular organization. In 1919 he founded a Peasants' Association at Allahabad which was to carry out social and political work in a countryside transformed by the effects of the First World War. But he was never a radical leader. His links with north India's landlords were valuable to him in his campaign for the establishment of the Hindu University at Benares, and he differed both from Gandhi and from Congress Socialist leaders in his approach to the British Government. C.A.B.

538 Sardar Vallabhbhai Patel (1875–1950) and peasants at Bardoli

Copyprint after photograph (late 1920s?) in the Nehru Memorial Museum and Library, New Delhi

538

One of the greatest of the nationalist leaders, who later became Minister of Home Affairs in independent India, Patel was always closely associated with his home state, Gujarat, and the thrifty peasant class, the Pattidars, from which he came. Pattidars were at the heart of the rich rice and dairy economy of the Gujarat countryside, but they were also innovative and business-like, taking to education, trade and foreign travel. Members of this community became wealthy in East Africa, and some now live in Britain. Patel himself was not wealthy enough to afford higher education, but he took a course in law and set up a small practice in the Kheda District of Gujarat. Having accumulated sufficient money, he finally went to London to study law at the Middle Temple. On his return to India in 1913 he quickly became involved in Congress activities. By 1918 he was a leading member of the movement initiated by Mahatma Gandhi to secure exemption from land revenue in Kheda District following a crop failure. Hereafter, he was to be a key leader both in Gujarat and the country at large, retaining a strong influence among, and affection for, the peasantry. An organizer of great ability, Patel helped to hold the Congress organization together during the traumas of the 1930s and 1940s. Shortly before his death he achieved his greatest triumph, the generally smooth incorporation of the princely states into the Indian Union.

C.A.B

539 Gandhi and peasants at Bardoli

Copyprint after photograph (late 1920s) in the Nehru Memorial Museum and Library, New Delhi

One critical success for the Congress in the 1920s and 1930s was the nationalists' ability to gain and hold the affection of the peasantry, particularly the more substantial members who were both voters and village elders. By taking up the cause of many peasant agitations, Gandhi and his lieutenants helped to express the grievances of this vast constituency. One of the most famous campaigns was at Bardoli in Gujarat in 1928, when the peasants fought Government attempts to raise the land-tax by withholding payment of rents and revenues. During the struggle, when the assets of many peasants were seized and many arrested, Vallabhbhai Patel played a prominent role in organizing resistance. The Government finally relented but the stage had been set for more general and more bitter conflicts between the peasantry and the Government as the effects of the world depression were felt on farm incomes.

C.A.B.

LITERATURE: Hardiman 1974.

539

540(i) Hakim Ajmal Khan, Nationalist Muslim leader of Delhi (1863–1927)

Copyprint after photograph in the Nehru Memorial Museum and Library, New Delhi

540(ii)

540(ii) Khan Abdul Ghaffar Khan, 'The Frontier Gandhi' (1890–1989)

Narayan Vinayak Virkar
Photograph, 21.3 × 16.4 ($8\frac{3}{10} \times 6\frac{2}{5}$)
Mr Rajendra Shriram Virkar

540(iii) Khan Abdul Ghaffar Khan with Gandhi

Copyprint from photograph in the Nehru Memorial Museum and Library, New Delhi

The Khilafat Movement had been a mass expression of Muslim opposition to the British Government and it had provided much of the force behind Gandhi's first Non-cooperation campaign. After 1924, however, it was a spent force. The Turks themselves under Mustafa Kemal Ataturk abolished the Khilafat, much to the chagrin of India's Muslims. Some more conservative leaders returned to their traditional policy of limited cooperation with the government, and worse, Hindus and Muslims clashed in 'communal' and agrarian riots. The mainstream of Muslim leadership and opinion began to drift away from Congress again, seeking power and protection in the provinces, and it was not until after 1937 that Muhammad Ali Jinnah (no.541) began to revivify Muslim aspirations to all-India organization and influence. However, there were some Muslims, both of traditional and Western education, who felt that Muslims should participate fully in the Indian National Movement. Among these was Hakim Ajmal Khan, the learned Delhi intellectual who hailed from an ancient physician family (hence the appellation 'Hakim' or 'Doctor'). A close associate of Nehru, he became President of the Congress in 1921. Another nationalist Muslim of a different stamp was the fiery Khan Abdul Ghaffar Khan. A Pathan from Peshwar in the North-West Frontier Province, he became politically active during the agitation against the repressive Rowlatt Act of 1919. During the 1930s and '40s he led a series of passive resistance movements against the British authorities and spent nearly fourteen years in prison. He vigorously opposed the Partition of 1947.

C.A.B.

541 Muhammad Ali Jinnah (1875–1948) as a young man

Copyprint after photograph (*c.* 1920) in the Nehru Memorial Museum and Library, New Delhi

Jinnah, the political leader and founder of Pakistan, was born in Karachi, the

541

son of a merchant and member of the Khoja sect of Muslims who followed the leadership of the Aga Khan. He went through English schooling in Karachi and Bombay and then studied law in London. He was called to the Bar from Lincoln's Inn in 1896, and on his return to India threw himself into 'moderate' Congress politics in Bombay, inspired by the ideas of Banerjea, Naoroji and above all, Gokhale (no.490). Jinnah was one of the few important Muslim leaders in the pre-1914 Congress. At this stage in his life, he opposed special representation for Muslims and worked hard to bring about common action between the Congress and the Muslim League.

A critical turning point in his life was the year 1920, when Jinnah opposed Gandhi's Non-cooperation Movement against the British. Why he took this stand is not clear; a distrust of Gandhi's anti-Westernism and Hindu symbolism combined with a sense of being marginalized by a new, radical generation probably lay at the heart of his change of mind. Certainly, Jinnah continued to present the image of an acute, Westernized lawyer, as shown in this photograph. While others donned Indian dress and conducted politics in regional languages, Jinnah was prepared to make no compromises. C.A.B.

LITERATURE: Wolpert 1984.

542 Jawaharlal Nehru 1889–1964

Narayan Vinayak Virkar, 1920s
Photograph, 16.9 × 10.5 ($6\frac{1}{2} \times 4$)
Mr Rajendra Shriram Virkar

Nehru returned home from Harrow and Cambridge in 1914. He was active in the United Provinces branch of the Congress but, along with his father and other members of his family, he became more radical during the First World War and was outraged by the Amritsar massacre.

During this period the Bolshevik Revolution heightened Nehru's interest in socialism which had been awakened in England. More important still for the history of India was Nehru's meeting during 1919 and 1920 with the rebellious peasantry of the District of Partabgarh, near his Allahabad home. He wrote in his book, *Discovery of India*, that personal knowledge of rural hardship had transformed his view of India's politics. C.A.B.

542

543 Gujarati, Maharashtrian and Parsi women united under the Indian National Congress banner in Bombay

Narayan Vinayak Virkar
Photograph, 23.5 × 31 ($9\frac{1}{5} \times 12$)
Mr Rajendra Shriram Virkar
(Illustrated Fig. 53)

In Bombay the Congress movement also acted as a powerful stimulus in the social emancipation of women after 1920. In this photograph, N.V. Virkar, by placing the Congress flag in a central position and distancing the camera, has emphasized the prime importance of the Nationalist Movement as well as the social cohesion of the group drawn from different communities. Yet, characteristic of Virkar's work, the women are also depicted as individuals. F.N./J.M.

544 Women demonstrators confront the police

Copyprint after photograph in the Nehru Memorial Museum and Library, New Delhi

544

545 Sarojini Naidu addresses a Freedom Movement gathering at Chowpatty Beach, Bombay

Narayan Vinayak Virkar
Photograph, 16.5 × 21.9 ($6\frac{1}{2} \times 8\frac{5}{8}$)
Mr Rajendra Shriram Virkar

The Simon Commission, the Depression and Civil Disobedience, 1928–35

546

546 Demonstrators against the Simon Commission, 1928

Copyprint after photograph (1928) in the Nehru Memorial Museum and Library, New Delhi

In the mid-1920s the effect of the Montagu-Chelmsford Reforms and the improved state of the economy had restored some degree of normality to Indian politics. But in 1927 the political temperature rose once again. In that year the British Government appointed a Royal Commission under the lawyer Sir John Simon to report on the workings of dyarchy and the possibilities of further constitutional advance. To the fury of nationalist opinion in India, no Indian was appointed to the Commission; consequently demonstrations and boycotts greeted the Commission throughout the subcontinent. The political impasse was broken by Gandhi, who had spent much of the previous few years working for social reform from the solitude of his *ashram* or retreat in Ahmedebad. Gandhi's re-entry onto the political scene and his call for complete independence once again galvanized the Congress Movement and led to a series of campaigns, culminating in the Civil Disobedience Movements of 1930–2. Popular support was forthcoming at least in part because economic conditions had deteriorated once more with the onset of the world depression and a dramatic fall in the prices of primary agricultural commodities. Peasants who had to pay the old high levels of rent or revenues with dramatically reduced income became militant again.

Gandhi brilliantly symbolized the plight of ordinary people when he staged his salt marches. Salt is essential for life, particularly in the tropics, but in order to preserve their own revenues from the salt monopoly, the British authorities banned the private production and sale of sea salt. Gandhi and his following therefore marched to the sea at Dandi in Gujarat to break the salt laws. His imprisonment and that of more than 60,000 Congress activists further dramatized the national struggle and brought it to the attention of the international media. As the situation worsened the British Government convened a Round Table Conference in London to discuss India's constitutional future (no.555). The meetings foundered on the divisions between the different representatives of Indian opinion, and on the British determination to continue to control decision-making at the imperial centre in New Delhi.

In 1932 and 1933 the British staged a counter-offensive against the Congress in India, imprisoning most of its leaders and many of its rank and file. But the scene was set for a further loosening of British control in the Government of India Act, 1935. Under this measure full responsible government was conceded in the Indian provinces. This meant that Indian ministers, selected from the dominant party in the provincial councils, ruled the regions, subject only to the advice of the British Indian civil service and the ultimate veto of the provincial governor. In the elections of 1937, however, to the considerable surprise of the British who had hoped that landlord parties would do well, the Congress triumphed. The nationalists had taken the important step from being a political party to being an elected government over much of India. It heralded the reopening of the issue of the status of India's minorities, especially that of the Muslims. C.A.B.

547 *Swantantrata ka Sachcha Marg* (The Right Path of Liberty)

Published by N.D. Sahgal and Sons, Lahore, *c.*1931
Poster, 51 × 38 ($20 \times 14\frac{4}{5}$)
India Office Library and Records, (PIB 37/1E)

This is an example of a Congress propaganda poster, banned by the British,

547

which employs mythological themes to dramatize the national struggle. Indians are seen marching to liberty along a road, but their way is blocked by a broken bridge. Those who fall through the gap are plunged into an underground dungeon where Mahatma Gandhi, Kasturbai, Motilal and Jawaharlal Nehru, Vallabhbhai Patel and Hakim Ajmal Khan are languishing. (The Urdu says 'Jawaharlal [Nehru] is in jail in order that you should be free'). Others have fallen into a torrent, reminiscent of the cursed river of Hindu mythology which bars the dead soul's path on its way to rebirth. Mother India addresses the god Krishna, alluding to a promise he made to the hero Arjuna in the *Bhagavad Gita* (one of the central texts of the Hindu scriptures). Krishna answers that with a little more sacrifice the road will be complete. The poster depicts the unity of the nation in its diversity: the figures marching are intended to represent Hindus, Muslims, Parsis and Bohras, all with their distinctive dress, headgear and styles of beard. As in the work of Virkar and other nationalist photographers, this depiction challenges the British image of a land irrevocably fragmented by caste, tribe and religion. C.A.B.

549

549 Jawaharlal Nehru and the young Indira demonstrating at Lucknow

Unknown photographer, 1930s
Photograph, 50.8 × 40.6 (20 × 16)
D.A. Low

550 Gandhi†

Copyprint after photograph in the Nehru Memorial Museum and Library, New Delhi

552

552 Mohandas Karamchand Gandhi (1869–1948)

J.H.M. Amshewitz, 1931
Oil on board, 26.2 × 20 ($10\frac{3}{8}$ × 8)
India Office Library and Records (F839)

This was painted while Gandhi was in London for the Round Table Conference in 1931. During this time he visited the poor of the East End and the mill workers of Lancashire. C.A.B.

LITERATURE: Archer 1986.

548

548 Gandhi's salt march, Ahmedebad

Copyprint after photograph in the Nehru Memorial Museum and Library, New Delhi

551

551 Gandhi and Nehru

Copyprint after photograph in the Nehru Memorial Museum and Library, New Delhi

553 *Bharatuddhar* (Gandhi the protector of India)

Prabhu Dayal, *c.*1930, published by Lakshmibilas Press, Calcutta
Poster, 35 × 25.5 ($13\frac{1}{2}$ × 10)
India Office Library and Records (PP Hin. F. 58)

This nationalist poster, which exhibits great symbolic complexity, is based on a mythological scene, common in popular lithographs, in which Shiva comes to protect Markandiya from the Lord of the Dead. Here Mahatma Gandhi appears as guardian of India in the guise of the many-armed Lord Shiva. The female figure of India is identified by a Congress flag which states 'Long live Mother India!' (*Bharat Mata ki Jai*). Her arms are wrapped around a black lingam, symbol of Lord Shiva and of generative power in the cosmos, which is inscribed 'The Land of the Aryas' (*Aryavarta*, another ancient name for India). Mother India, however, is tied by a rope to the foot of a buffalo on which is seated a figure in British political service uniform, complete with pith helmet. The British officer is identified as Yama Raja, Lord of the Dead in Hindu scriptures. In temple carvings Yama, a doleful divinity of annihilation, is traditionally shown seated on a buffalo, an animal which often represents demonic power. The rope symbolizes dependence or submission (*parantrata*) and the buffalo stands for foreign rule (*bideshi rajya*). The British are therefore being identified with malevolent and destructive forces in the cosmos, recalling Gandhi's statement that he was fighting a 'satanic' government. Gandhi-Shiva is crowned with a band inscribed 'non-violence' (*ahimsa*).

553

His arms hold symbols of *swadeshi* (home industry) including a piece of cloth or *khadi* (the rough country weave in which Congress workers dressed), a spinning wheel and a spindle. The legend on the vessel to the lower right urges people to become companions in tribulation. Gandhi is therefore shown banishing foreign rule through the power of non-violence, weaving and home industry. Like no.483, this poster demonstrates the Indian ability to utilize the Hindu religious tradition in secular or light-hearted contexts. C.A.B.

554 Rev. Charles Freer Andrews (1871–1940)

Howard Coster, 1935
Bromide print, 26.5 × 19.5 ($10\frac{3}{10}$ × $7\frac{3}{5}$)
National Portrait Gallery, London (x 10319)

554

Andrews was one of Gandhi's closest British friends and supporters. It was important for the Congress cause in Britain and the Western world that from the time of Hume and Mrs Besant onwards, it had a body of staunch friends amongst British liberals and socialists. Andrews represented a strand of Christian socialism which was attracted by Gandhian non-violence and concern for the under-privileged. After reading classics and theology at Cambridge, Andrews was ordained as an Anglican minister and went to work among the poor in the East End of London. In 1904 he went to India to teach at St Stephen's College, Delhi. Here he became increasingly hostile to the British Raj. In 1914 he went to South Africa, becoming a close friend and co-worker of Gandhi. Back in India he championed the cause of emigrants to Fiji, of dock-workers, of untouchables and of serf-labourers in Rajasthan. He was particularly active on Gandhi's behalf during the period of the Round Table Conference in 1931. Throughout his life he was active in Christian movements in India, Britain and South Africa, but from 1914 to 1936 he laid aside the formal aspects of his ministry. C.A.B.

LITERATURE: Tinker 1979.

555 Caricatures of Round Table Conference personalities

Elsa King, 1931
Pen, ink and wash, each 29.5 × 19 ($11\frac{1}{2}$ × $7\frac{1}{2}$)
India Office Library and Records (WD 1400–05)

i) SIR TEJ BAHADUR SAPRU (1875–1949)
Sapru was a Kashmiri Brahmin lawyer from Allahabad in the United Provinces. A former law member of the Viceroy's Executive Council (1920–3), he was a leading member of the Indian Liberal Party. At the time of the first Round Table Conference he urged the British Government to make an immediate declaration that India would be offered dominion status within the empire, but generally he distanced himself from Congress campaigns of civil disobedience. He became a Privy Councillor in 1934.

ii) (SIR) SRINIVASA SASTRI (1869–1946)
A leading Indian Liberal Party politician from Madras, Sastri had previously been a President of the Servants of India Society. He became a Privy Councillor in 1925.

iii) SIR PURSHOTAMDAS THAKURDAS (1879–1961)
Thakurdas was one of India's most important industrialists. One-time President of the Federation of Indian Chambers of Commerce and a leading figure in the Bombay cotton trade, he served on the Central Legislative Council as a

555(i)

555(ii)

555(iii)

555(v)

representative of the Indian Merchants' Chamber. He was concerned to raise tariff barriers in order to protect nascent Indian industries. A moderate nationalist, he worried about the potential of civil disobedience to degenerate into social disorder.

iv) PANDIT MADAN MOHAN MALAVIYA
Malaviya had been active in the Congress since its earliest days. He attended the 1931 sessions of the Round Table Conference at the Government's request. He was widely regarded as a spokesman of Hindu interests and strongly opposed the creation of separate electorates for untouchables, one of the big issues at the Conference, on the grounds that this would further divide Indian from Indian. See also no.537. (Illustrated Fig.54)

v) M.R. JAYAKAR (1873–1959)
A lawyer from Bombay, Jayakar was a moderate nationalist who played a major part in encouraging Indian representatives to attend the Round Table Conference and in arranging the Gandhi-Irwin Pact (see no.555 [vi]). He had been a member of the Bombay Legislative Council (1923–6) as a representative of the Swarajya party, which favoured 'non-cooperation from within' the constitutional machinery. Later he became a member of the Nationalist Party in the Central Legislative Assembly.

vi) MAHATMA GANDHI
The cartoonist here relished the contrast between the suave constitutionalist politicians she has portrayed and the humble Mahatma. The Round Table Conferences (1930–2) were held in London in order to try to compromise the political differences between the British Government, the Congress and other sections of nationalist opinion, which had sharpened following the visit of the Simon Commission to the subcontinent. Lord Irwin, the Conservative Viceroy, found some support for the idea of a conference among members of the Labour government, which had come to power after his appointment. At first the Congress, many of whose leaders were in jail, refused to attend the Conference so the field was left to the Liberals, Muslims, princes and representatives of smaller parties. But later, following a pact between Lord Irwin and Gandhi, the Congress leaders were released and Gandhi himself travelled to London. Whereas the first session of the Conference made some headway towards a new Indian constitution based on federal principles, the second session was a complete failure. In India civil disobedience and agrarian agitation resumed almost immediately. (Illustrated Fig.55) C.A.B.

LITERATURE: Brown 1985; Moon 1989.

556 Communist Party of India Manifesto, 1930

Handbill, 21 × 17 ($8\frac{1}{5} \times 6\frac{3}{5}$)
India Office Library and Records (PIB/71/10)

P.I.B. 71/10

THE INDIAN COMMUNIST PARTY.

(हिन्दुस्तानी साम्यवादी दल)

OBJECT.

Establishment of Complete Swarajya & the system of Society based upon the [illegible]non ownership and communal control of the means and instruments of production and [illegible]bution of wealth by and in the interest of the whole community of India.

PROGRAMME.

Organisations of three kinds (a) of workers' resedential areas (b) of country peasants' areas and (c) of the intellectual middle class. And to establish permanent connections between the intellectuals and the workers.

METHODS.

(a) Conducting propoganda in non-literary working masses as chiefly Trade Union Workers, and to affiliate such bodies to the nearest section. (b) Winning the majority of the Working class by active participation in every day struggle of the workers and peasants. (c) Securing the leadership of the struggle of the workers for themselves. (d) Distributing of literature including vernacular papers and pamphlets and establishing socialist reading rooms and liabraries. (e) Establishing contact between employed and unemployed.

PRINCIPLES.

(1) Our party holds it is unnatural and unjust for any nation or country to rule over another nation or country, and therefore, it is the birth right and the foremost duty of Indians to gain Complete Swarajya at the earliest possible time.

(2) Our party holds that Indian Society as at present constituted, is based upon the ownership of the means of living (that is, land, factories, and means of transportation) by the capitalist or the master class and the consequent enslavement of the working class by whose labour alone wealth is produced.

(3) Our party holds that in society, therefore, there is an antagonism of interests manifesting itself as a class struggle between those who possess but do not produce and those who produce but do not possess.

(4) Our party holds that this antagonism can be abolished only by the emancipation of the working class from the domination of the master class by the conversion of the common property of the society, of the means of production and distribution and their control by the whole community.

556

Since 1917 the Indian National Congress had absorbed Marxist influences. Leaders such as Jawaharlal Nehru in Uttar Pradesh and Jayaprakash Narayan in Bihar later helped to found the Congress Socialist party as an organized wing within the wider movement. They argued for a more radical approach to land-reform than the Gandhians and those who represented industrialists or the more substantial peasants. In

Bombay and Calcutta, however, committed Communists had begun to mobilize. A militant Indian Socialist-Labour party, founded in 1922 by S.A. Dange, had gained support amongst industrial workers in the cotton and jute industries after the end of the First World War. A Bengali intellectual living in Moscow, M.N. Roy, had provided the party with a programme more suited to Indian conditions. The Communist Party of India was finally founded in 1925. The British authorities, fearful of the prolonged strikes which hit the Bombay mills in 1928, tried to suppress the movement. The Communists went underground but many of their leaders were implicated in the Meerut conspiracy case (1929–30), and were tried and imprisoned. Congress ministries in Bombay (1937–9) were equally hostile to the CPI. This statement of aims is signed by S. Satya Bhakta (Secretary). C.A.B.

557 Volunteers in Bombay at drill shortly after the formation of the Hindu Mahasabha (Greater Hindu Association)

Narayan Vinayak Virkar, 1920s
Photograph, 16.5 × 21.6 ($6\frac{2}{5} \times 8\frac{1}{2}$)
Mr Rajendra Shriram Virkar

During the 1920s and '30s a variety of organizations claiming to represent the 'Hindu interest' entered the all-India political arena. One such movement was the Hindu Mahasabha which drew support from Maharashtra and the Punjab, and other areas where old established Hindu elites felt themselves threatened in the new era of mass politics. Some of the Mahasabha's members operated within the Congress to the dismay of the latter's socialist and secularist members. Here, against a background typical of Bombay's medium-density housing, officials of the Mahasabha are seen reviewing the drill from a shallow dais. The bearded leader of the movement, Guru Golwalkar, is on the far right. Though the volunteers, who

557

include children, are dressed in Indian costume, they are imitating imperial drill formations like those of many other political organizations. The sash worn by the man on Golwalkar's right is derived from the British practice of identifying the employer or professional standing of a person with an inscribed sash. C.A.B./J.M./F.N.

558 Bhagat Singh (1907–31)

Oleograph, 54 × 35.5 ($21\frac{1}{4} \times 14$)
Private Collection

Not all Indian nationalist activity was peaceful and non-violent. From the 1900s revolutionary terrorist cells had flourished in Bengal and western India, and a number of British officers and civilians had been assassinated. The events

558

of 1919, and particularly the Amritsar massacre, gave this tendency a fillip.

Bhagat Singh and Chandra Shekhar, with whom he is often linked, turned to violence after a revered and elderly Congress leader, Lala Lajpat Rai, had been severely beaten in a police charge against a demonstration during the visit of the Simon Commission (1928). They shot a police head constable in revenge. Later, Bhagat Singh and another militant, B.K. Datta, threw a bomb during a session of the Central Legislative Assembly in Delhi. They were arrested, tried and hanged in Lahore Central Jail on 23 March 1931. The oleograph shows Bhagat Singh as a heroic warrior contemplating deeds of national liberation. Luxuriant moustaches had been a mark of warrior status from early times and they were emphasized in depictions from large popular paintings on cloth to delicate miniatures. The warrior-hero theme was, and remains, one of the most celebrated and evocative topics of historical 'bazaar' art. While liberal opinion in Britain and India has emphasized the non-violent aspects of India's freedom struggle and the leadership of Gandhi, there is no doubt that popular sentiment revered the 'men of violence', even if it was from a distance. C.A.B.

The Latter Days of the Raj: Life, Work and Leisure

Landscapes of Urban India

The percentage of the Indian population living in cities of over 100,000 still remained quite small – in 1947 it was about 14 per cent. But slow industrialization and the rise of nationalism had given the towns greater political clout. The Depression decade of the 1930s marked a significant growth in industrial investment as rural land values declined dramatically. It also saw the resounding victory of the Congress over its landlord competitors. The face of the towns also changed noticeably in the latter days of the Raj. Victorian gothic architecture gave way to the neo-classical; there were even a few modernist structures in the large commercial cities. The greatest architectural feat of the age was undoubtedly the completion of New Delhi, designed by Sir Herbert Baker and Sir Edwin Lutyens. C.A.B.

559(i) South front of the Viceroy's House, New Delhi

William Walcot, 1913
Watercolour, 45 × 108 ($17\frac{3}{4} \times 42\frac{1}{2}$)
Lord Romsey

559(ii) North front of the Viceroy's House

William Walcot, 1913
Watercolour, 59 × 71 ($23\frac{1}{4} \times 28$)
Lord Romsey

The Viceroy's House (now Rashtrapati Bhawan, seat of the President of India) was Lutyens' masterpiece and the dominating building of New Delhi. It was conceived by Lutyens in 1912 and 1913 as an embodiment of the British ideal of Indian empire: 'the hues and shadows of Mughal facades were married to the sculptural massing and subtle proportions of European architecture' (Irving 1981, p.170). The Viceroy's House was 630 feet from north to south and 530 feet from east to west; when completed in 1930 it comprised more than 200,000 square feet, including its internal courts, and was larger than the Palace of Versailles. 'To the visitor, Lutyens' creation seems to be at once a giant Indian bungalow, embattled Rajput palace, and Mughal tomb' (ibid., p.174), yet in basic structure, Lutyens never moved far from the canons of European classical architecture.

William Walcot specialized in working up watercolours from architects' sketches. Lutyens was a great admirer of his brilliant perspectives, and was one of the first architects to employ him after his arrival in London in 1907. Having previously painted the Union Buildings at Pretoria for Sir Herbert Baker, Walcot was commissioned to produce watercolours of New Delhi which afford a vital impression of the rhythmic and monumental quality of Lutyens' design. Several of Walcot's perspectives of New Delhi were exhibited at the Royal Academy in 1914. Eleven of them remain in the corridors of the Viceroy's House.

These watercolours formed a part of the presentation to the Viceroy and Council of the architectural designs for New Delhi; but, unfortunately, the perspectives revealed inaccuracies in design that further marred the already tense relationship between Lutyens and Baker, who was responsible for the Secretariat Buildings. The towers in this picture were never executed. C.A.B./J.H.

LITERATURE: Irving 1981.

EXHIBITIONS: London, Royal Academy, 1914; London, Hayward Art Gallery, *Lutyens*, 1981–2.

560 Lord Irwin, Viceroy of India, being presented with models of the New Delhi buildings by Sir Edwin Lutyens and Sir Herbert Baker

Marjorie Shoosmith, 1931
Watercolour, 41.3 × 33 ($16\frac{1}{4} \times 13$)
Halifax Collection

This lighthearted caricature on a Mughal miniature shows Baker and Lutyens presenting models of the Viceroy's House and Secretariat Buildings respectively to Lord Irwin. Sir Alexander Rouse, Chief Engineer, holds a plan and Lady Irwin is in *purdah* in the top left-hand corner. The artist's husband, Arthur Gordon Shoosmith, was Lutyens' resident representative at New Delhi (1920–31). C.A.B.

LITERATURE: Irving 1981, ill. pl.1, p. ii.

561

561 Caricature bust of Sir Edwin Lutyens (1869–1944)

Wood, height 76 ($29\frac{3}{5}$)
British Architectural Library Drawings Collection, RIBA

Lutyens' head is formed out of the Indian cupola (*chattri*) with which he embellished the Viceroy's House and his other monuments. One of fourteen children of an army captain turned artist and his Irish wife, Lutyens was virtually self-educated. Showing an early aptitude for art and design he spent two years at what is now the Royal College of Art in South Kensington. In his early work he sought to find a modern idiom for the English country house. But Lutyens later decided that the future lay in the classical form in keeping with Britain's new imperial stance. He set out for Delhi in 1912, was knighted in 1918, married the daughter of a Viceroy (Lord Lytton) and became Vice-President of the Royal Institute of British Architects. C.A.B.

LITERATURE: Irving 1981; Tillotson 1989.

562

564

568

562 British cantonment bungalow, Poona

Foy Nissen
Photograph, 16.2 × 23.8 ($6\frac{1}{5} \times 9\frac{3}{10}$)
Foy Nissen

563 The Town Hall, Bombay

Foy Nissen
Photograph, 16.2 × 23.9 ($6\frac{1}{5} \times 9\frac{3}{10}$)
Foy Nissen

This classical structure, built in 1833, now houses the Asiatic Society of Bombay and its library. C.A.B.

564 Entrance lobby of the Town Hall, Bombay

Foy Nissen
Photograph, 16.5 × 24 ($6\frac{2}{5} \times 9\frac{2}{5}$)
Foy Nissen

Shown here in the entrance lobby of Bombay's Town Hall is a marble bust of Jagganath Shankarseth, a Bombay merchant prince, sculpted by Matthew Noble in 1865. F.N.

565 The Mechanics Institute, Bombay, 1870–3

Foy Nissen
Photograph, 24 × 16.2 ($9\frac{2}{5} \times 6\frac{1}{5}$)
Foy Nissen

This neo-gothic building now houses the David Sassoon Library. The Sassoons, Baghdadi Jews by origin, were one of the most important Bombay commercial families in the later nineteenth century. C.A.B.

565

566

566 East-facing first floor of the David Sassoon Library, Bombay

Foy Nissen
Photograph, 24 × 16.2 ($9\frac{2}{5} \times 6\frac{1}{5}$)
Foy Nissen

567 Rajabai clocktower, Bombay University Library

Foy Nissen
Photograph, 16.2 × 23.8 ($6\frac{1}{5} \times 9\frac{3}{10}$)
Foy Nissen

A fine example of Indian gothic architecture, the library building was designed by G. Gilbert Scott. C.A.B.

568 A domestic villa in Bombay

Foy Nissen
Photograph, 16.2 × 23.8 ($6\frac{1}{5} \times 9\frac{3}{10}$)
Foy Nissen

This building, unfortunately demolished in 1974, was typical of the palatial residences built by members of Bombay's mercantile élite in the later nineteenth and early twentieth centuries. Like many similar structures it displays an exuberant mixture of European baroque and oriental influences F.N.

569 Timber-framed domestic building in Bombay

Foy Nissen
Photograph, 23.5 × 16.2 ($9\frac{3}{10} \times 6\frac{1}{5}$)
Foy Nissen

This building, demolished in the mid-1970s, is one form of the Indian domestic bungalow, but its eaves, high verandahs and slatted-wood design are reminiscent of indigenous house styles in the old ports bordering the Arabian Sea and in Ahmadebad. C.A.B.

570 View of M.A. Jinnah's house, Bombay

Foy Nissen
Photograph, 16.2 × 23.8 ($6\frac{1}{5} \times 9\frac{3}{10}$)
Foy Nissen

Jinnah's house was situated in the exclusive Malabar Hill area of Bombay, residence of civil servants and the richest

570

Indian lawyers and businessmen. It was designed as a modernist transformation of the colonial bungalow, but the arches show a hint of Islamic architectural influence. Although the future founder of Pakistan had begun to argue forcibly for the interests of Indian Muslims on his return from a period in England in 1934, his lifestyle remained quite Westernized. C.A.B.

571 New premises in Clive Street, Calcutta, designed by H.S. Goodhart-Rendel

C. Gascoyne, 1933
Pencil and watercolour, 70.5 × 55.5 ($27\frac{1}{2} \times 21\frac{3}{5}$)
British Architectural Library Drawings Collection/RIBA (RAN 11/A/4)

An example of 1930s modernism, this was to be a new commercial building in the heart of Calcutta. C.A.B.

571

572

574

572 Interior of The Old Mess House, Chetput, Madras, 1930s

Copyprint after photograph in the Centre of South Asian Studies, Cambridge, Stokes Collection (14, p.8)

573 Lady Stokes taking tea on the verandah of The Grange, Madras

Copyprint after photograph (1928–36) in the Centre of South Asian Studies, Cambridge, Stokes Collection (14, p.11)

Sport in India

574 K.S. Ranjitsinhji (1872–1933)

G. Beldam
Photograph, 55.5 × 31.5 ($21\frac{8}{10} \times 12\frac{4}{10}$)
Marylebone Cricket Club, Lord's (363)

'Ranji' – Colonel His Highness Shri Sir Ranjitsinhji Vibhaji, Maharajah Jam Saheb of Nawanagar, KCSI – was one of India's most outstanding cricketers before Independence. A life-long Sussex player, he first played for England in 1896, making a century in his first test match. In 1899 and 1900 he scored over 3,000 runs, but it was the grace of his strokes which remained in the memory of his supporters. In 1907 he ascended the *gadi* (throne) of the state of Nawanagar in the Kathiawar District of Gujarat. In 1914 the Jam Saheb (his official title as ruler) led a contingent of state troops to the Western Front to fight on behalf of the empire. Towards the end of his life he struggled hard to maintain the independence of the princes, viewing the projected absorption of Indian states into an Indian Federation with foreboding. Though Ranjitsinhji did not play an active role in the development of Indian cricket, his example, like that of his nephew Duleepsinhji, inspired the country's rise to international status in the game. Neville Cardus later wrote, in orientalizing mood, 'Who will ever forget the cricket ground at Hove in those days, salt tang in the air, and the deck chairs full, and a stand in progress between Ranji and Fry? East and West twain for hours, the occult and the rational' (cited Ross 1983, frontispiece). C.A.B.

LITERATURE: Ross 1983.

575 Polo

Copyprint after photograph in the *Illustrated London News* (16 November 1935)

576

576 Polo in the street in Kashmir

Copyprint after photograph in the *Illustrated London News* (27 December 1924)

577

578

579

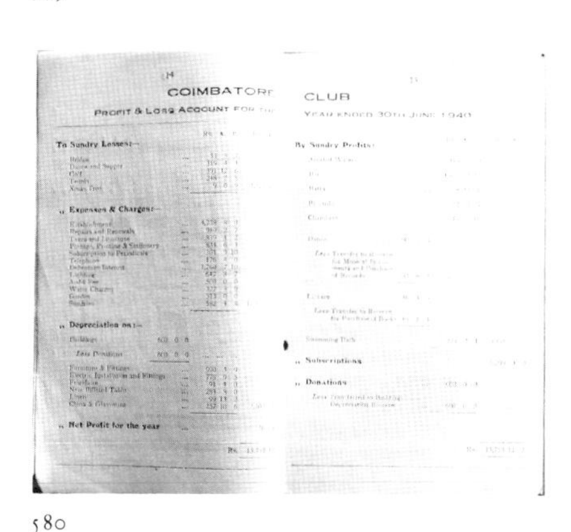

COIMBATORE CLUB

PROFIT & LOSS ACCOUNT

To Sundry Losses

Expenses & Charges

Depreciation on

Net Profit for the year

By Sundry Profits

Subscriptions

Donations

580

581

577 After a Gond shoot

Copyprint after photograph in the *Illustrated London News* (25 August 1923)

Gonds were a tribal people of southern central India; large parts of India's forest areas were reserved by the Forest Department or used as hunting grounds. C.A.B

578 A record bag in India

Copyprint after photograph in the *Illustrated London News* (4 February 1922)

579 India as a winter-sports ground

Article from the *Illustrated London News* (2 February 1935)
36 × 25 ($14\frac{2}{10} \times 9\frac{8}{10}$)
National Portrait Gallery

580 The Club, focus of social life for Anglo-Indians

i) Coimbatore Club Committee's *Report on the Workings of the Coimbatore Club, 1 July 1938–30 July, 1940*, Coimbatore, Madras 1940
Printed pamphlet, 7.6 × 10 (3 × 4)
Centre of South Asian Studies, Cambridge (Milne Box no.38)
ii) *Rules and Bye-laws of the Tuticorin Club, revised 1931*, Tuticorin, 1931
Printed pamphlet, 7.6 × 10 (3 × 4)
Centre of South Asian Studies, Cambridge (Milne Box no. 2)

The rules contain sub-sections on the Billiard Room, Tennis Court, Card Room and Library. There are also strict rules for the payment of members' bar bills. C.A.B.

581 Not-at-home box

Wood, 12.7 × 9 × 14 ($5 \times 3\frac{1}{2} \times 5\frac{1}{2}$)
Mr John Wall

Anglo-Indian life remained quite formal. Visitors to a station were expected to leave their cards in boxes such as these. C.A.B.

The Raj at Work

582 Day uniform of the Indian Political Service

c. 1940
K.V.F. Morton Esq.

The Indian Civil Service itself was not a uniformed service, taking some pride in its civilian status. In the early Victorian era its members are shown dressed in black frock-coats and stove pipe hats. Members of the Civil Service, however, might have found themselves wearing a

582

uniform such as this if appointed to the Political Department, the branch of government which dealt with matters outside British India itself, such as relations with the princely states and certain border areas. The Foreign and Political Service of the Indian Government was staffed in about equal proportions by officers selected from the Civil Service and the Indian Army. Through its network of Residents and Agents responsible to the Governor-General, the Foreign and Political Departments managed relations with the larger states. But in some cases relations with smaller states were conducted by officers in the Home and Political Departments of provincial governments. Mr Morton writes that he was supplied with this uniform when appointed Under-Secretary to the Government of the Punjab in the Home and Political Departments. Decorative uniforms had long been considered appropriate for attendance at the durbars of rajas and nawabs; it may have been felt that otherwise the diplomatic efforts of civilian members of the political services would suffer by comparison with those of their more dashingly attired military colleagues. C.A.B.

583 Insignia of a Knight Commander of the Order of the Indian Empire awarded to M.G.H.Cursetjee, *c.* 1930

Lent by The Director of the National Army Museum, London SW3 4HT (6501–22–13)

583

584 The visit of Sir Lancelot Graham, the Governor of Sind, to Nawabshah and Sakrand, 1938

Unknown photographer
Photograph from album, 30.5 × 40.6 (12 × 16)
Centre of South Asian Studies, Cambridge, Salmon Collection (vol. ii, pl.14–15)

After the Government of India Act 1935 and the provincial elections of 1937, the role of the governor became less administrative and more constitutional in nature, though he still retained substantial 'reserve powers' in case of a breakdown in party government. Here the Sind governor meets local notables in a small town, addressing the Municipal Board and the local Anjuman-i-Islamia (Islamic Society), and visiting an agricultural research station. In practice local government in Sind still depended on a close relationship between British officials and local landlords. C.A.B.

584

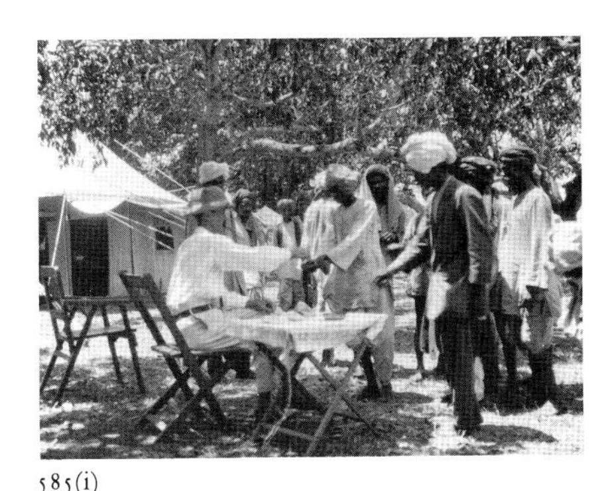

585(i)

587(i)

585 An official on tour

i) Reginald Maxwell paying beaters
ii) Reginald Maxwell in camp with car, Bardoli District, Gujarat
Unknown photographer
Photographs
Centre of South Asian Studies, Cambridge, Maxwell Collection (9)

(Sir) Reginald Maxwell KCSI, CIE was collector and magistrate, Bombay Presidency 1924–8. He became Home Member of the Viceroy's executive council in 1938. C.A.B

586 Silver Commemoration padlock with key, 1926

Indian silver (no hallmark), *c.*800 g
Inscribed on one side of key: *Delhi Cloth and General Mills Co. Ltd, Mill no. 2*, and on reverse: *Opened by the Hon. Mr E.R.Abbott, C.I.E., I.C.S., Chief Commissioner, Delhi, 24 January 1926*
Stuart E. Abbott Esq.

After the Indian Tariff Agreement of 1919, Indian cloth manufacturers received increased protection from British and Japanese imports in the form of higher duties. Not only old centres of manufacturing such as Bombay and Ahmedebad, but up-country towns such as Delhi, Kanpur and Coimbatore saw a rapid growth of industrial investment, though this was from a very narrow base. Provincial governments became more active in promoting industrial growth, as Victorian laissez-faire ideas gave way to state intervention prompted by the effects of war and economic depression. C.A.B.

587(ii)

587(iii)

587 Constructing the Mettur Dam, April 1933

? Lady Stokes
Photographs
i) Arrival by trolley at the Power House
ii) Inaugurating the hydro-electric scheme: Sir George Stanley and Lady Stanley, Sir M. Kumaraswami Chetty, A.H. Stokes and G. Stokes
iii) The Mettur Dam under construction
iv) Lady Stokes on a picnic with Indian ladies
Centre of South Asian Studies, Cambridge, Stokes Collection (13)

Though provincial and imperial budgets were closely controlled, civil engineering works continued to be inaugurated during the 1930s matching the growth in some sectors of the economy. Whereas steel production declined as a result of the Depression, the development of sugar refining quickened as did other intermediate agricultural industries such as oilseed and rice pressing. C.A.B.

588

588 George William Adamson 1882–1922

Unknown photographer
Photograph, 17.5 × 24.6 ($6\frac{4}{5} \times 9\frac{3}{5}$)
George Adamson

589

589 G.W.Adamson and the Indian workforce of the Bombay tramways

Unknown photographer
Photograph, 12.7 x 20.3 (5 × 8)
George Adamson

590 W.O. Milne with his staff and their families on the tea estate, High Range, Travancore

Copyprint after photograph in the Centre of South Asian Studies, Cambridge (Milne Collection)

British business in India became increasingly cautious during the early part of

590

the century. The Agency Houses and other large firms developed well established trades rather than following Indian business into new products and investments. The growing role of Indians in provincial government and the economic uncertainties of the post-war era helped entrench this conservatism. However, one area in which expatriate endeavour flourished was that of the tea and coffee estates. British-owned tea gardens were found in Assam and other parts of north India, while coffee planting was more important in Mysore and the south. This tea estate, however, was located in the princely state of Travancore on the south-west tip of the subcontinent. In both north and south estate workers were often drawn not from among the populations of the plains but from tribal hill people.

C.A.B.

591(i)

591(iii)

591 Missionaries in Mysore, 1890s and 1900s

i) The Mission House, Shimoga
Copyprint after photograph (2 July 1892) in the Centre for South Asian Studies, Cambridge (J. Alfred Vanes Collection 1/50)
ii) Missionary Conference at Karur, January 1894
Copyprint after photograph (January 1894) in the Centre for South Asian Studies, Cambridge (J. Alfred Vanes Collection 1/82)
iii) Missionaries distributing food to seated children
Unknown photographer
Photograph
Centre of South Asian Studies, Cambridge (J. Alfred Vanes Collection 2/8)

After the debacle of 1857 links between the British government and Christian missionary activity atrophied again. A slow rate of conversion was maintained by the Roman Catholic churches of the Madras Presidency which had strong indigenous roots, but Protestant activity was mainly limited to elite educational ventures or to work among tribal groups, the very low castes and lepers. In Mysore for instance, where these pictures were taken, there were only about 20,000 Protestant Indian Christians during the 1920s, compared with 60,000 Roman Catholics. This ?Wesleyan mission appears to have had about 7,000 adherents of whom a substantial number were tribal Adikarnataka people. C.A.B.

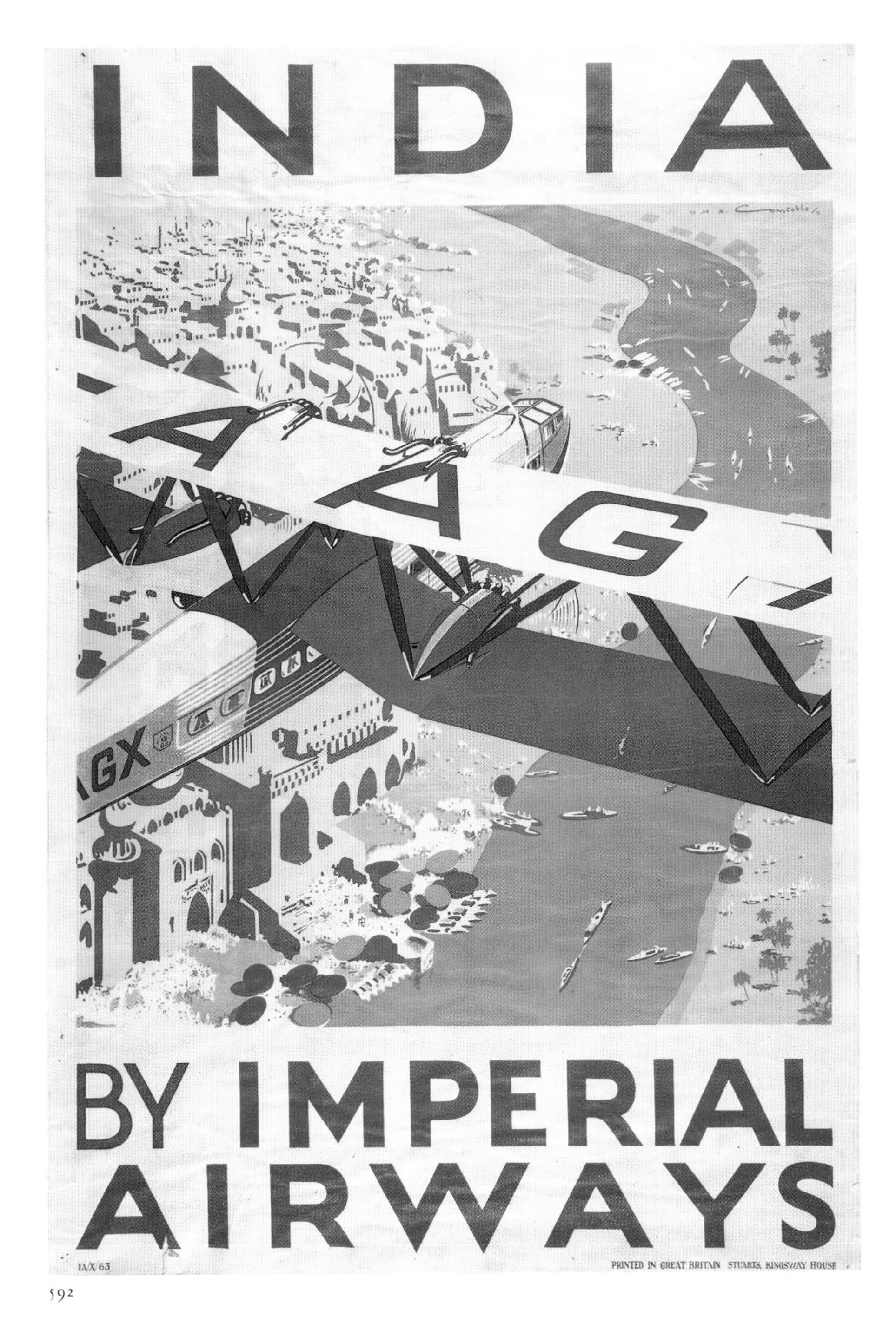

592

592 *India by Imperial Airways*

W.H.A. Constable, *c.* 1935
Poster, 75 × 50 (29¼ x 19½)
British Airways Archives and Museum Collection

Communications greatly improved in India in the course of the 1930s. Following the completion of the railway network and direct telegraph links with Britain at the turn of the century, the introduction of the lorry and the bus began to create an integrated transport system in the country after the First World War. Imperial Airways' flights linking Britain and India and the major cities within the country were established by 1939. This poster shows a Handley Page HP42 G-AAGX Hannibal flying over an Indian river town. This type of aircraft covered the sector from Egypt to Karachi in the 1930s.

C.A.B.

Images of India's People

With the development of fluid camerawork by European and Indian photographers, the people of the subcontinent began to be portrayed as individuals as well as representatives of caste or religious types. The tradition of Din Dayal and political photographers such as N.V.Virkar blossomed. But as the pace of historic change quickened a new generation of European and American photographers came to India. Margaret Bourke-White for *Time*, Henri Cartier-Bresson, and Cecil Beaton for Her Majesty's Government caught the face of the last days of the Raj. C.A.B.

593

593 A European family group, Bombay

Narayan Vinayak Virkar
Photograph, 21.9 × 16.5 (8½ × 6½)
Mr Rajendra Shriram Virkar

594

595

597

594 Portrait of three men and a girl with a background of film posters

Narayan Vinayak Virkar
Photograph, 30.5 × 25.4 (12 × 10)
Mr Rajendra Shriram Virkar

595 A Marathi musical of the early 1920s

Narayan Vinayak Virkar
Photograph, 21.9 × 16.5 ($8\frac{1}{2} \times 6\frac{2}{5}$)
Mr Rajendra Shriram Virkar

596 Scene from a Marathi drama

Narayan Vinayak Virkar
Photograph, 15 × 18.9 ($5\frac{4}{5} \times 7\frac{2}{5}$)
Mr Rajendra Shriram Virkar

As in no. 595, the female role is taken by a male, in this case Bal Gandharva (centre), the most famous Marathi stage actor of the time. C.A.B.

597 The 35th Conference of the Akhil Bharatiya Sahitya Sammelan

Narayan Vinayak Virkar
Photograph, 16.5 × 21.6 ($6\frac{2}{5} \times 8\frac{2}{5}$)
Mr Rajendra Shriram Virkar

The Sammelan met annually for discussions on the current state of creative writing in Hindi and other Indian languages. There were close links between cultural movements such as this and Indian politicians, witness the presence here of K.M.Munshi, Govind Ballabh Pant and Purshottam Das Tandon, all important Congress leaders from north India. 'Chicago Radio' advertised here was neither a radio nor from Chicago but rather the trade name of Bombay's pioneering commercial company specializing in the provision of public address systems and services. J.M./F.N.

598 The Maharani of Jaipur, Gayatri Devi

Vivienne, *c.* 1945
Photograph, 20.3 × 25.4 (8 × 10)
Camera Press

Gayatri Devi was born in London in 1919, granddaughter of the Gaekwad of Baroda. One of the best known members of the Indian nobility in the West and one of the world's most beautiful women, the Maharani went to a London school and later studied at the London College of Secretaries. She married the Maharaja of Jaipur in 1940. After Independence she was active on the political scene. C.A.B.

LITERATURE: Vadgama 1984, p.223.

599 Photographs of everyday life, 1945

i) Bengal Labourer
Cecil Beaton
Photograph, 30.5 × 40.6 (12 × 16)
The Trustees of the Imperial War Museum (IB 1810) (Illustrated Fig. 62)

ii) Coolie Boy, Bengal
Cecil Beaton
Photograph, 30.5 × 40.6 (12 × 16)
The Trustees of the Imperial War Museum (IB 1735)

iii) Boy Spinning
Cecil Beaton
Photograph, 30.5 × 40.6 (12 × 16)
The Trustees of the Imperial War Museum (IB 1795)

iv) Labourers Carrying Crops
Cecil Beaton
Photograph, 30.5 × 40.6 (12 × 16)
The Trustees of the Imperial War Museum (IB 1892) (Illustrated Fig. 50)

v) A Rag Merchant in Old Delhi
Cecil Beaton
Photograph, 30.5 × 40.6 (12 × 16)
The Trustees of the Imperial War Museum (IB 113)

vi) Girls School
Cecil Beaton
Photograph, 30.5 × 40.6 (12 × 16)
The Trustees of the Imperial War Museum (IB 1511) (Illustrated Fig. 49)

vii) Jute factory
Cecil Beaton
Photograph, 30.5 × 40.6 (12 × 16)
The Trustees of the Imperial War Museum (IB 340) (Illustrated Fig. 63)

599(ii)

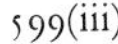

599(iii)

599(v)

599(viii)

viii) Fishnet weaver
Cecil Beaton
Photograph, 30.5 × 40.6 (12 × 16)
The Trustees of the Imperial War Museum
(IB 1733)

These images of ordinary people taken in the mid-1940s are almost lyrical in tone, evoking the peace and contentment of the traditional Bengal countryside. They prefigure some of the happier scenes in the films of Satyajit Ray. It must be remembered, however, that Beaton was at this time working for the Ministry of Information and he was studiedly non-political. Another photographer working at the same time, Margaret Bourke-White, was by contrast a representative of the international media, seeking to project and dramatize the triumph, and the horror, of the last stages of India's fight for Independence. Her images are in consequence both starker and more disquieting. C.A.B.

LITERATURE: Beaton 1945.

Partition and Independence

On 12 August 1946 Lord Wavell, the Viceroy, wrote in his diary that he had told leaders of loyalist landholders that '... it is better to be honest and say that we are going to hand over power; that it is right to do so and leave Indians to govern themselves; that while the Congress is not a body one would have chosen as representatives of the great mass of the Indian people, it is the body the Indian people have chosen themselves and we have to deal with the men of their choice' (Moon 1973, p. 333, cited Brown 1983, p. 319). Thus had the British position changed out of all recognition over the ten years since the Government of India Act of 1935, when they had hoped to create a federal India in which the princes would bulk large and the Crown would continue to hold power at the centre in Delhi.

The main reason for this dramatic change was the impact of the Second World War which impoverished Great Britain and transformed the political landscape in the subcontinent. Indians would now accept no less than total independence. But which Indians, and how? Though Wavell spoke of 'the Congress', a revitalized Muslim League led by Muhammad Ali Jinnah, and inspired by Muhammad Iqbal's idea of Pakistan, was now a key player on the scene. Many Muslims believed they would be at a disadvantage in a Congress-ruled India. The League's successes in the general elections of 1946, the Congress's desire for a strong unitary state and the British Labour Government's desire to relinquish power as soon as possible pointed inexorably towards the partition of the subcontinent and the accompanying slaughter. C.A.B.

LITERATURE: Hodson 1969; Moon 1989; Brown 1985.

India and the Second World War

The Indian Army increased in size from 205,058 men in October 1939 to 2,251,050 in July 1945. Defence expenditure soared and between 1941 and 1946 India provided 286.5 million rupees of materials for the war, mainly textiles, clothing and ordnance. Indian soldiers fought valiantly in the Western Desert, in Italy and in France, but the main theatre of operations was in Burma where the Army held the Japanese thrust against Imphal and Kohima, and later thrust back through Arakan. From 1942 price inflation in essential commodities took off sharply and the disruption of transport contributed to the appalling and avoidable tragedy of the Bengal famine of 1943. But the greatest effect of the war was on people's thinking. In 1942 the British appeared weak and Japanese prowess was lauded in every bazaar. Refugees from Burma flooded into eastern India and military movements disrupted everyday life. In the Quit India movement of 1942 hundreds of police stations and miles of railway tracks were damaged; thousands of Congressmen were jailed once again, and many were killed during police firings on crowds. The British were able to put down what had been the most serious rising since 1857 because they had troops on the ground and the Army and the police stayed firm. But in one sense the suppression of the 1942 movement was a 'bee's sting', and the pillars of the Raj were beginning to crumble by 1945. A small but significant number of Indian troops joined Subhas Chandra Bose's Indian National Army which fought with the Japanese against Britain; by 1946 the Indian police were also restive as high prices and nationalist propaganda undermined their morale. The combination of disaffection and the severe pressures of war threatened a complete breakdown of administration by 1946, as Wavell privately acknowledged. Orderly withdrawal and a negotiated settlement with the leaders of Congress and the League seemed the only feasible option. C.A.B.

600 Ramzak Field Force: Gurkha Machine Gun

Copyprint of photograph (1937) from album compiled by Lieutenant Col. H. G. Eccles in the National Army Museum (5310-63-50)

Until the onset of the war the Indian Army was mainly deployed in a policing role on the Northwest Frontier. In 1937, however, there was a significant development: the British Government agreed to a general re-equipment of the Indian Army and the fact that a large part of the cost of this was to fall on British rather than Indian taxpayers was significant. Indian revenues were not now as easily accessible to the British, with the result that by the end of the war the British Government was debtor to India rather than *vice versa*, as had been the case after the First World War.

C.A.B.

600

601 Indian Troops in Action, Burma

Leslie Cole
Oil on canvas, 65.5 × 91.5 ($25\frac{3}{4}$ × 36)
Signed b.r.: *Leslie Cole*
The Trustees of the Imperial War Museum (LD 5687)
PROVENANCE: War Artists' Advisory Committee Commission.

602

601

602 The Battle of Arakan, Group of 7th Brigade

Anthony I. A. Gross
Watercolour, 38 × 55.8 (15 × 22)
The Trustees of the Imperial War Museum (LD 3179)

603

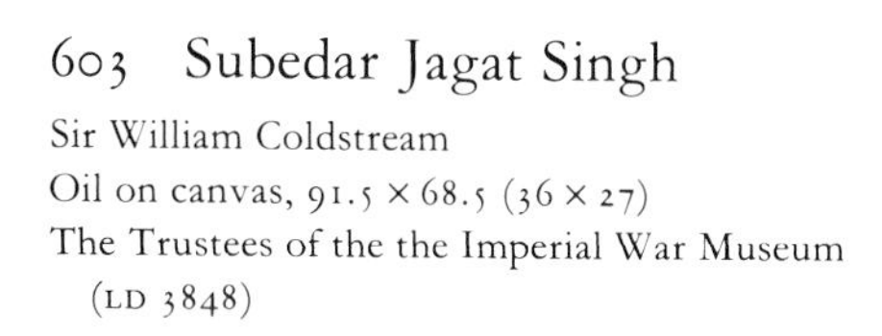

603 Subedar Jagat Singh

Sir William Coldstream
Oil on canvas, 91.5 × 68.5 (36 × 27)
The Trustees of the the Imperial War Museum (LD 3848)

604

605

606

607

604 Carrying the Wounded from the Arakan Jungle

Cecil Beaton, 1945
Photograph, 30.5 × 40.6 (12 × 16)
The Trustees of the Imperial War Museum (IB 285)

605 Stokers' Mess Deck, Royal Indian Navy

Cecil Beaton, 1945
Photograph, 30.5 × 40.6 (12 × 16)
The Trustees of the Imperial War Museum (IB 1557)

606 Punjabi Mussulman Petty Officer, Royal Indian Navy

Cecil Beaton, 1945
Photograph, 30.5 × 40.6 (12 × 16)
The Trustees of the Imperial War Museum (IB 1534)

The Royal Indian Navy was essential to

the protection of shipping lanes in the Arab Sea and the Indian Ocean during the war. However, a mutiny of some of its ships in 1946 was another piece of evidence that the British could no longer count on the loyalty of India's fighting forces. C.A.B.

607 Ordnance factories in India

Cecil Beaton, 1945
2 photographs, 30.5 x 40.6 (12 × 16) each
The Trustees of the Imperial War Museum (IB 1616, 1624)

608 ARP Nurse and Doctor

Cecil Beaton, 1945
Photograph, 30.5 × 40.6 (12 × 16)
The Trustees of the Imperial War Museum (IB 1751)

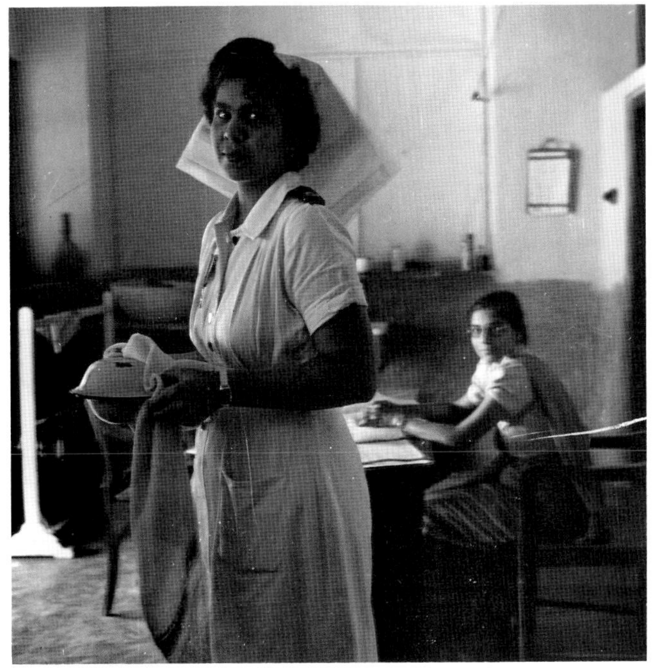

608

609 Subhas Chandra Bose (1897–1945) as 'Netaji'

Oleograph, 46.3 × 32.9 ($18\frac{1}{4}$ × 13)
Private Collection

Subhas Chandra Bose is India's favourite popular hero of the Independence movement by virtue of his armed resistance to the British Raj. Having abandoned a career in the Indian Civil Service as a result of the events of 1919, Bose became a radical member of the Congress in Bengal. Along with Jawaharlal Nehru he was among the young activists who demanded complete independence rather than dominion status within the British empire at the Calcutta Congress session of 1928. He made contacts among leaders of the future Axis powers during a journey to Europe in the mid-1930s and fiercely opposed the Viceroy's declaration of war on behalf of India in 1939. In early 1941, Bose evaded CID surveillance and fled to Berlin 'to supplement from outside the struggle going on at home'. On 2 July 1943 he arrived at Singapore where he established an Indian Government in exile and organized an Indian Independence Army, drawn mainly from prisoners of war in

609

Japanese hands, to fight against the British in Burma. Bose reportedly died in an air crash in Taiwan on 18 August 1945, but many of his supporters refused to believe the news of his death. No. 609 shows Bose riding a white horse. The slogan 'Chalo Delhi!', 'Onward to Delhi!', was one of the war-cries of the Indian National Army, but it had also been heard one hundred years before, on the lips of the mutinous sepoys of 1857. C.A.B.

610 Victor Alexander John Hope, 2nd Marquess of Linlithgow (1887–1952), Viceroy of India 1936–43†

Copyprint after photograph in the National Portrait Gallery

An Etonian who had served as Civil Lord of the Admiralty, Linlithgow served on various commissions on Indian affairs in the course of the early 1930s. He was, therefore, an obvious choice when Baldwin sought someone to go to India as Viceroy and oversee the introduction of the 1935 Reforms Scheme. Ultimately, Linlithgow's main role was to galvanize the Indian empire for service in the Second World War despite the hostility of the Congress.

C.A.B.

LITERATURE: Glendevon 1971.

611

611 Sir Richard Stafford Cripps (1889–1952)

Isaac Michael Cohen, 1931
Oil on canvas, 76.2 × 63.5 (30 × 25)
National Portrait Gallery, London (4672)

A brilliant socialist lawyer educated at Haileybury and University College, Oxford, Cripps had been Solicitor General in the 1929 Labour Government. Between 1940 and 1942 he was ambassador to the Soviet Union, but in 1942, as Lord Privy Seal, he was sent to India by Churchill to resolve the constitutional impasse which threatened to damage the war effort on the Japanese front. Cripps was apparently empowered to offer the Indians full dominion status after the war, or even independence, provided they cooperated fully with the government in the short run. The mission failed and Congress went on to stage the Quit India revolt against the Raj. It seems doubtful whether the Congress could have held their more radical elements in check, or pre-empted the popular disaffection building up in eastern India. But, quite apart from that, the hostility of many in the Cabinet, including Churchill, to any clear commitment to independence, and the lukewarm attitude of the Viceroy Linlithgow (no. 610), doomed Cripps's efforts to failure. C.A.B.

LITERATURE: Moore 1979.

612 Linlithgow to Gandhi, 27 September 1943†

Autograph manuscript, 16.5 × 10 (6½ × 4)
India Office Library and Records
(R/311/99.ff.43–4)

In 1939 the Congress gave up office in the provincial governments as a protest against the Viceroy's declaration of war on behalf of India. Gandhi initially opposed the war, but did not seek to embarrass the Government in its hour of crisis by calling for Nonco-operation. However, relations between Congress and the Government deteriorated in the course of 1941, Gandhi was arrested and the full force of the Quit India Movement was released in 1942. Gandhi spent the rest of the war in prison, during which time his wife Kasturbai died. Here he writes to the Viceroy regarding Linlithgow's departure from India.

C.A.B.

613 Allama Muhammad Iqbal (1877–1938) offering prayer in Masjid-e-Qartaba

Ahmad Kamal
Oil on canvas, 101 × 76.2 (39¾ × 30)
Department of Archaeology and Museums, Government of Pakistan

Muhammad Iqbal was one of the subcontinent's greatest literary men and philosophers of religion, but it is as the leader who first formally enunciated the concept of an Indian Muslim state of 'Pakistan' that he is chiefly remembered. He was born in Sialkot in the Punjab but later moved to Lahore. Here he developed great expertise in Indian, Persian and Arabic literature, becoming Assistant Professor of Philosophy at Government College, Lahore. He was in England from 1905 to 1908, where he studied idealist philosophy and read for the Bar. He also received a PhD from Munich University. As India's preeminent Islamic thinker and a poet in both Urdu and Persian, he took little part in agitational politics. However, in the late 1920s Iqbal became increasingly concerned about the fate of Muslims in any future constitutional arrangement, particularly since the Congress's Nehru Report of 1929 was thought by them to have rejected any special safeguards for the minority. At the end of 1930, Iqbal presided over the annual session of the All-India Muslim League at Allahabad.

613

Here he argued that 'Self government within the British Empire, or without the British Empire, the formation of a consolidated Muslim state appears to me to be the final destiny of the Muslims at least of North-West India'. This speech was the harbinger of the Pakistan Resolution which in 1940 tied the Muslim League to the creation of a separate state for India's Muslims. C.A.B.

614 Muhammad Ali Jinnah, 'Qaid-i-Azam' or Founder of the Nation

J. Harley, 1948
Oil on canvas, 92 × 122.5 (36¼ × 48¼)
Department of Archaeology and Museums, Government of Pakistan

When Jinnah returned to England from India in 1934, he was already concerned that an expansion of the franchise might put Muslims at a disadvantage within India. His political path diverged more and more from his former colleagues in

614

the Congress and he began to try to rebuild the fragmented All-India Muslim League as an expression of the common purpose of India's Muslims. In the event the League did not perform very well in the elections of 1937, but thereafter as Congress ministries took over in many parts of the country, his support began to build up, especially in those areas where the Muslims were in a clear minority, such as in the United Provinces and Bihar. Here Muslim leaders became alarmed by some of the initiatives of Congress leaders and harboured the feeling that provincial governments were covertly biased towards the Hindu population. However, Jinnah's real breakthrough came during the war. The British needed a prominent Muslim to negotiate with, and Jinnah proved more cooperative from their point of view than Congress, which was rapidly moving back to Non-cooperation. After 1942, moreover, Congress members were imprisoned and by dint of tireless campaigning Jinnah managed to consolidate the League's position in Bengal and to begin to make headway in the Punjab, both provinces where the Muslims formed a large part of the population. There has been some debate about whether Jinnah envisaged a completely separate Pakistan and the partitioning of the Indian provinces at any time before 1947. Suffice it to say that the British desire to retreat from India, Jinnah's zeal for India's Muslims, and the Congress's concern to inherit a unified state make any other outcome extremely difficult to envisage. C.A.B.

615 Jinnah, the Aga Khan, and other officials of the Muslim League

Copyprint after photograph (*c.*1946) in the Nehru Memorial Museum and Library, New Delhi

Lord Wavell (1883–1950) succeeded Lord Linlithgow as Viceroy in 1943. A professional soldier, he had held command in the Middle East and South-east Asia. After a year in office concentrating on the war effort, the Viceroy began to try to break the political deadlock. Gandhi had been released from jail, following a serious attack of malaria. Jinnah and the Congress leaders were brought together at the hill-station of Simla in July 1945, but the talks foundered on the League's demand that all Muslim members of a new Central Legislative Council should be nominated by them. The end of the Second World War brought economic discontent and a heightening of tension between Hindus and Muslims. The sweeping Labour victory in the British general election and the unconditional surrender of Japan (14 August 1945) made possible a new initiative, a mission to India by members of the British Cabinet, including Pethick-Lawrence, the Secretary of State, and Sir Stafford Cripps. The choice was between a truncated Pakistan and a loose federation of Hindu-majority and Muslim-majority provinces (no.614) with a three tier constitution (see 'The Raj and the Nationalist Movements 1911–47', p.360). Both the League and the Congress initially accepted these proposals, although with different degrees of enthusiasm. But after the Mission's return to Britain it became clear that no agreement was possible; at heart Congress leaders, especially Patel (no. 538), realized that India had to have a strong central executive and that a loose federal system was doomed. Although Jinnah probably favoured such a federation himself, he had little faith in its practicality and was to opt for a 'moth-eaten' Pakistan, as he put it, with full independence. C.A.B.

615

616 The Bengal famine

Photograph by Margaret Bourke-White published in *Time* magazine (20 September 1943, p. 11)
12 × 16 $(4\frac{7}{10} \times 6\frac{3}{10})$
European Photo Service (FPG)

The famine that occurred in Bengal in the second half of 1943 was one of the most dreadful events to afflict the end of the Raj. Since the late nineteenth century, the introduction of a Provincial Famine Code to deal with such disasters along with better communications, had reduced the incidence of mass starvation. During 1943, however, prices in Bengal rose dramatically as a result of a shortage of transport brought about by wartime requisitioning. Ordinary people in town and country simply could not afford to buy food, even though large stocks were available at various points of the country. The ineffective response of the authorities in Bengal and Delhi compounded the problem of food availability. Perhaps three million people perished in the course of five months. C.A.B.

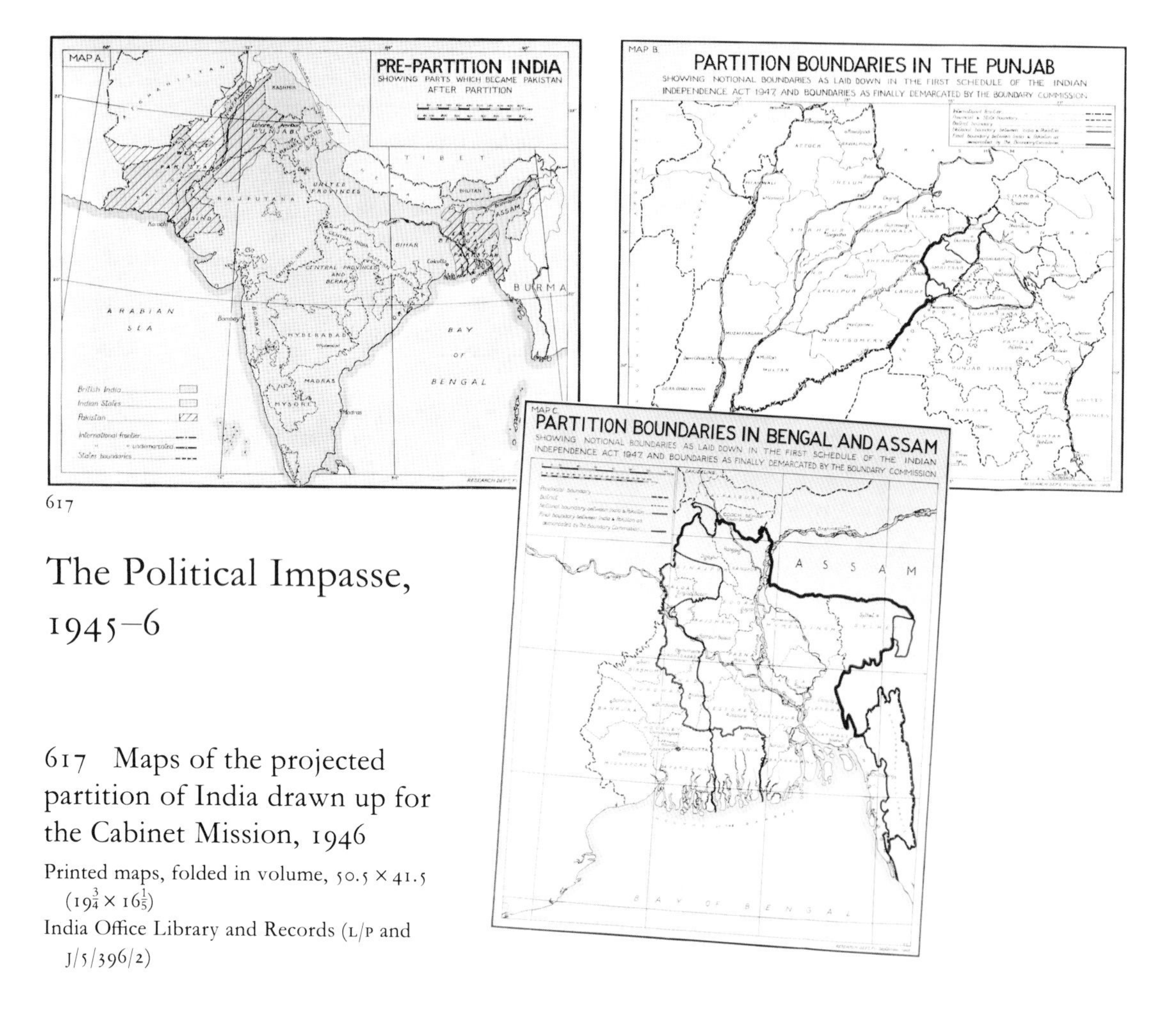

617

The Political Impasse, 1945–6

617 Maps of the projected partition of India drawn up for the Cabinet Mission, 1946

Printed maps, folded in volume, 50.5 × 41.5 ($19\frac{3}{4} \times 16\frac{1}{5}$)
India Office Library and Records (L/P and J/5/396/2)

618 Jawaharlal Nehru

Copyprint after photograph in the Nehru Memorial Museum and Library, New Delhi

619 Jawaharlal Nehru, Lord Wavell, Sardar Vallabhbhai Patel and Rajendra Prasad

Copyprint after photograph (*c.* 1946) in the Nehru Memorial Museum and Library, New Delhi

619

620

620 Gandhi trying to stop rioting

Copyprint after photograph (*c.*1946) in the Nehru Memorial Museum and Library, New Delhi

When the Cabinet Mission proposals broke down, Jinnah, who had previously stood aloof from mass campaigns of civil action, opted for a show of Muslim strength, the so-called programme of Direct Action, which began with a demonstration in Calcutta. There is still intense controversy regarding the responsibility for what followed, but the demonstration soon degenerated into an orgy of mass-murder and destruction in which about 5,000 people were killed, 15,000 injured and over 100,000 rendered homeless. Riots also spread to other major cities. The civil and military authorities seemed powerless to deal with them, and they further poisoned the increasingly embittered relations between the Congress and the Muslim League. Outbreaks of rioting and murder between Hindus and Muslims continued over the next year or more, reaching a peak with the arrival of Independence when over a million people were killed and tens of millions driven from their homes as new national boundaries were fixed. Modern research suggests that criminal elements and recently demobilized soldiers were often active in these ferocious attacks, but boundaries hardened quickly and links between Hindu, Muslim and Sikh families, which had persisted over generations, were savagely ruptured. The scars left by these events have never healed.

C.A.B.

621 Clement Attlee (1883–1967)

George Harcourt, 1946
Oil on canvas, 76.4 × 62.9 ($31\frac{1}{4} \times 24\frac{3}{4}$)
National Portrait Gallery, London (4593)

Educated at Haileybury (the former Indian civil service college) and University College, Oxford, Attlee was an able socialist barrister and a lecturer at the London School of Economics. He served at Gallipoli and in the Mesopotamian campaign, rising to the rank of Major. He was later Labour M.P. for Limehouse. In 1927–9 he served on the Simon Commission (no.546) and gained first-hand knowledge of Indian affairs and of the strong popular support for the Congress. He developed good relations with Congress leaders, whom he considered quite capable of governing an independent India. He was Deputy Prime Minister under Churchill in 1942 and Prime Minister from 1945 to 1951. The decision of Attlee and his Cabinet to grant independence to India was not the product of sentiment, although there was a high regard for Nehru and the Congress. The Labour Cabinet had no intention of dismantling the empire in

621

Africa or Malaysia. With regard to Palestine and India, however, the Cabinet dreaded the prospect of having to hold down restive populations riven by internal conflict. Its first concern was to get the troops home and invest in the reconstruction of British society. Hindu-Muslim rioting and increasing numbers of attacks on British personnel strengthened this intent. In principle, Attlee wished to bequeath power to a unified Indian state, but he was only prepared to wait a short time to achieve this end. Lord Mountbatten was therefore ordered to set a date for British withdrawal.

C.A.B.

622

622 Lord Louis Mountbatten, 1st Earl Mountbatten of Burma (1900–79)

Clara Quien
Plaster, height 43 (16⅞)
Rhea Quien Monro

Earl Mountbatten was the son of Prince Louis of Battenberg and closely related on both his mother's and father's side to the British Royal Family. Following naval training he was attached to the Mediterranean fleet and during the early years of the Second World War he saw almost continuous action in this theatre, commanding the destroyer *Kelly* with great distinction. He developed expertise in the field of combined operations between the services, took over and galvanized the Southeast Asia Command, and saw the surrender of the Japanese forces in Singapore in 1945. On 18 December 1946 he was offered the post of the last Viceroy and Governor-General of India, for the Cabinet was looking for a new man who would bring the fruitless three-party negotiations between the British, the Congress and the Muslim League to a quick and decisive conclusion. Mountbatten was only prepared to take up office when the Cabinet had agreed on a precise month for the termination of British rule in India, which was fixed at June 1948 and announced by Attlee in the House of Commons on 20 February 1947. Mountbatten's sincerity and energy captivated most Indian leaders, including Gandhi and Nehru, and it was thus that he was able to move rapidly towards securing the Partition of the subcontinent. He now announced that the transfer of power would take place 'no later than' 15 August 1947, sensing that the impetus for his plan might become bogged down in haggling over the precise details of the new frontiers. The Bengal and Punjab legislative assemblies voted for the partition of these two provinces where the Hindu and Muslim populations were evenly divided. The Indian Independence Bill received Royal Assent on 18 July and the division of the spoils went ahead. C.A.B.

623 Model of a Guardsman of the Jaipur State, 1947

1947
Silver
Lord Romsey
PROVENANCE: Presented to Lord Mountbatten.

624 Viceroy's banner and trumpet

Lord Romsey

625

625 Jawaharlal Nehru

Clara Quien
Bronze, height 53.5 (21)
Rhea Quien Monro

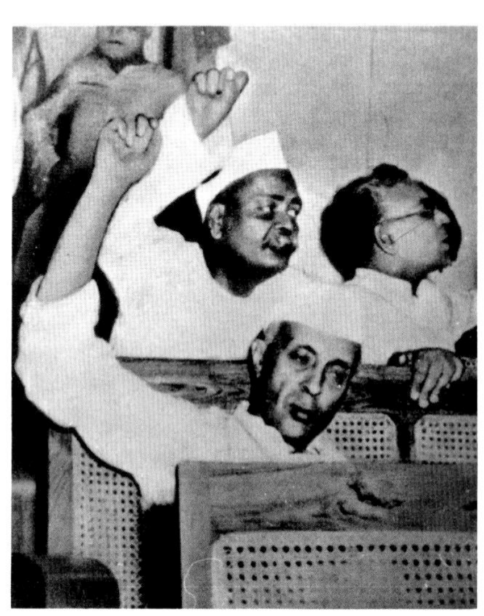

626

626 Nehru votes for Partition, June 1947

Copyprint after photograph (1947) in the Nehru Memorial Museum and Library, New Delhi

Nehru contemplated the division of India with the greatest sorrow and foreboding. He had always believed that the economic and social interests of Indian peasants and labourers united them more than religion divided them. But events since 1942 had made it clear that a united and independent India would have inherited enormous problems of inter-communal conflict, quite apart from its need for rapid economic reconstruction. C.A.B.

627 *The Times* reports the Independence of India, 15 and 16 August 1947

Newspapers
The Times

The Viceroy travelled to Karachi on 14 August 1947 to give good wishes to Jinnah, who now became Governor-General of an Independent Pakistan within the Commonwealth. It was later that night that Nehru addressed the Indian Constituent Assembly announcing that India was about to awake 'to life and freedom. A moment comes, which comes rarely in history, when we step out from the old to the new, when an age ends, and when the soul of a nation, long suppressed, finds utterance.' The next day, as the Indian tricolour flew over buildings from the Himalayas to Cape Comorin, the British Raj, if not its historical consequences, came to an end.

C.A.B.

628 Lady Edwina Mountbatten and Pandit Nehru

Kohli Brothers
Photograph
Lord Romsey

Edwina Cynthia Mountbatten, née Ashley (1901–60), was daughter of Colonel W.W. Ashley, M.P. and granddaughter of Sir Ernest Cassel. She married Lord Louis Mountbatten in 1922. Throughout the war she was active in charitable schemes and in projects to help Allied prisoners. She carried on her relief work as Vicereine and wife of the Governor-General of India before and after Independence. It was her interest in welfare, along with the close relationship which both Mountbattens established with Jawaharlal Nehru, that endeared them to the Indian people and eased political tensions.

C.A.B.

629 *The Times* reports the assassination of Gandhi, 31 January 1948

Newspaper
The Times

After Partition the scale of rioting and inter-communal clashes grew, especially in the Punjab and Bengal, two provinces which had been dissected. Estimates of those killed range from 200,000 to half a million and at least ten million refugees fled from their homes. India and Pakistan fought three debilitating wars, and conflicts which derive from the consequences of Partition still persist in several parts of the subcontinent. Mahatma Gandhi himself fell victim to the passions created by Partition when he was assassinated by a Hindu extremist in January 1948. Nehru spoke of a light going out of their lives as tens of thousands of people flocked to Delhi to watch Gandhi's body being conveyed down the great triumphal avenue of Rajpath to the cremation ground at the riverside.

C.A.B.

630 Mahatma Gandhi's funeral

3 copyprints after photographs (1948) in the Broadlands Archives

631 Shawl woven by Gandhi for Her Majesty the Queen, Elizabeth II on the occasion of her marriage, 1947

Her Majesty The Queen

Reviewing the Past

The visual image of the British Raj did not end with 1947. Hollywood occasionally returned to the theme in films such as *Bhowani Junction*, while 'Thuggee' and 'Suttee' made their appearance in productions such as *The Far Pavilions*. In the 1970s Britain developed a fitful and nostalgic interest in the Raj, the most distinguished visual product of which was the television drama *The Jewel in the Crown*. In these later works the Indian demand for independence was portrayed more dispassionately, but the ancient stereotypes of Indian caste and religion, princes and poverty persisted. Ironically, the south Asian tourist industry and the growth of religious fundamentalism in the region even helped to reinvigorate them. Meanwhile in India, martyrs to the British, and latterly Mrs Indira Gandhi, have joined the Hindu gods and goddesses and ancient heroes, such as Shivaji, on the gaudy oleographs.

C.A.B.

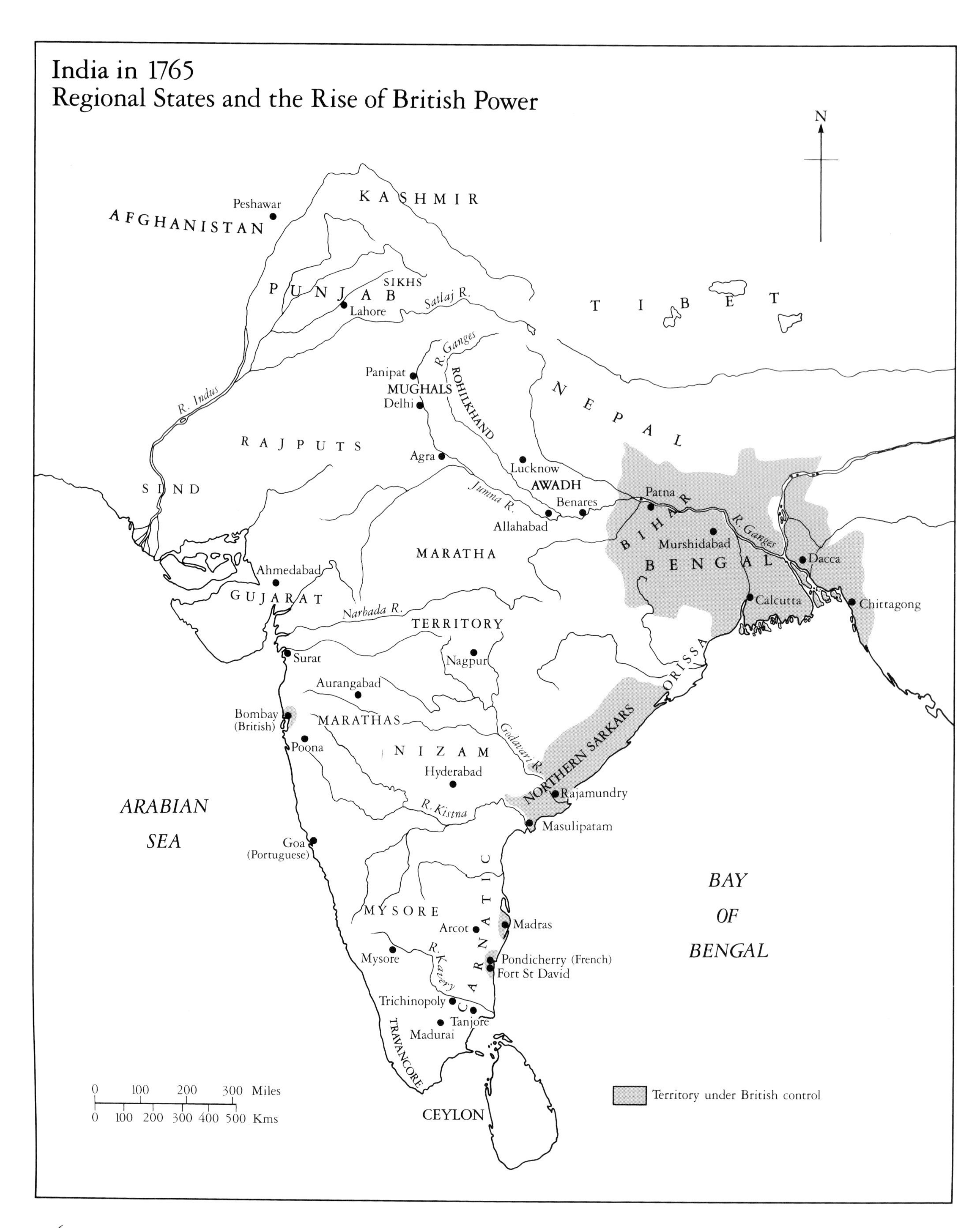
India in 1765
Regional States and the Rise of British Power
N
KASHMIR
Peshawar
AFGHANISTAN
SIKHS
PUNJAB
Lahore
Satlaj R.
TIBET
R. Ganges
Panipat
MUGHALS
ROHILKHAND
Delhi
NEPAL
R. Indus
RAJPUTS
Agra
Lucknow
AWADH
SIND
Jumna R.
Patna
Benares
BIHAR
Allahabad
R. Ganges
Murshidabad
MARATHA
BENGAL
Dacca
Ahmedabad
GUJARAT
Calcutta
Chittagong
Narbada R.
TERRITORY
Surat
Nagpur
ORISSA
Aurangabad
Bombay
(British)
MARATHAS
NORTHERN SARKARS
Godavari R.
Poona
NIZAM
Hyderabad
Rajamundry
ARABIAN
SEA
R. Kistna
Masulipatam
Goa
(Portuguese)
BAY
OF
BENGAL
MYSORE
CARNATIC
Madras
Arcot
Mysore
R. Kavery
Pondicherry (French)
Fort St David
Trichinopoly
Tanjore
Madurai
TRAVANCORE
0 100 200 300 Miles
0 100 200 300 400 500 Kms
CEYLON
Territory under British control

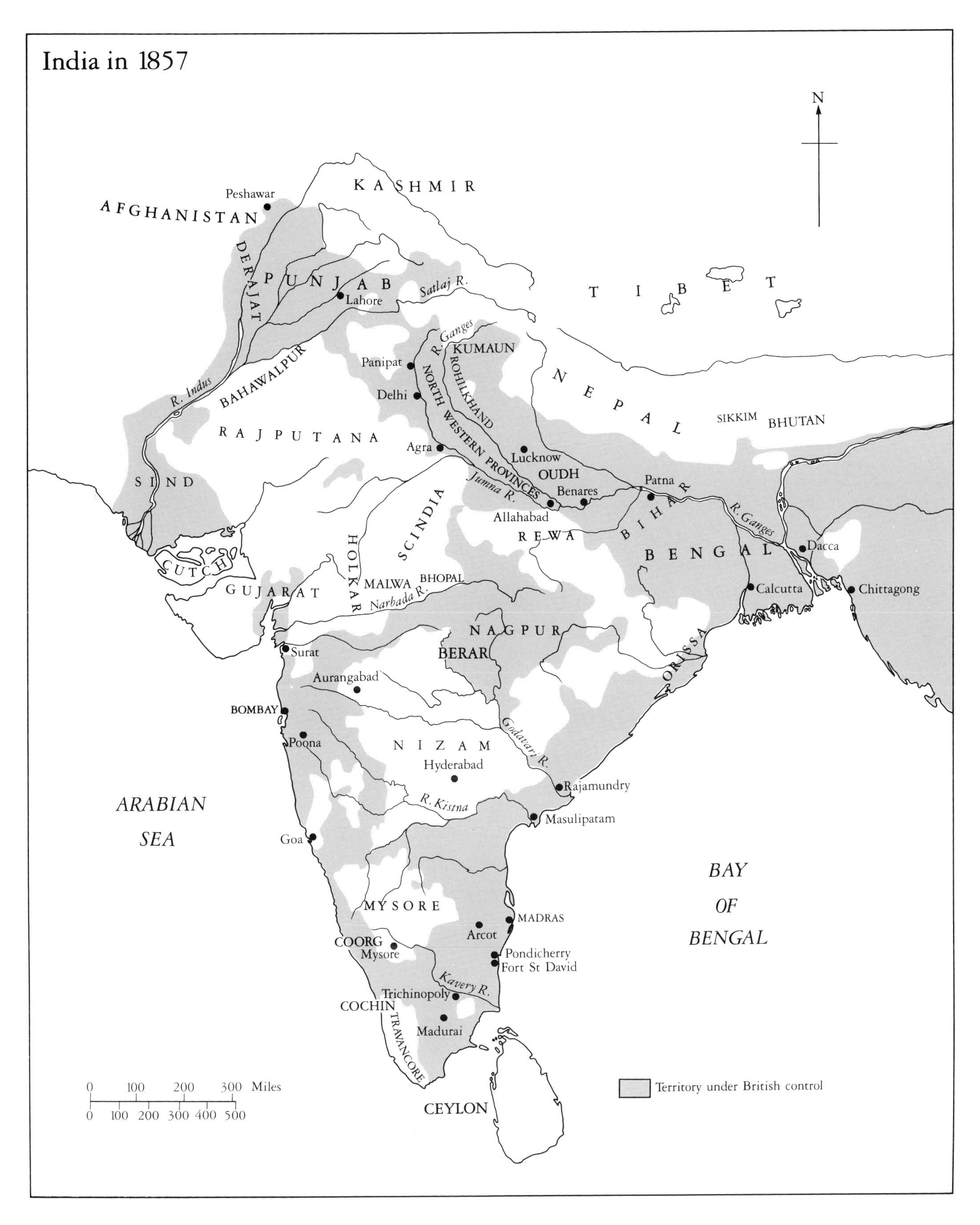
India in 1857
N
AFGHANISTAN
Peshawar
KASHMIR
DERAJAT
PUNJAB
Lahore
Satlaj R.
TIBET
R. Ganges
KUMAUN
ROHILKHAND
Panipat
Delhi
NORTH WESTERN PROVINCES
NEPAL
R. Indus
BAHAWALPUR
RAJPUTANA
SIKKIM
BHUTAN
Agra
Lucknow
OUDH
SIND
Jumna R.
Benares
Patna
Allahabad
BIHAR
SCINDIA
R. Ganges
REWA
HOLKAR
BENGAL
Dacca
CUTCH
MALWA
BHOPAL
GUJARAT
Narbada R.
Calcutta
Chittagong
NAGPUR
BERAR
Surat
ORISSA
Aurangabad
BOMBAY
Poona
NIZAM
Godavari R.
Hyderabad
Rajamundry
ARABIAN SEA
R. Kistna
Masulipatam
Goa
BAY OF BENGAL
MYSORE
MADRAS
Arcot
COORG
Mysore
Pondicherry
Fort St David
Kavery R.
Trichinopoly
COCHIN
TRAVANCORE
Madurai
0 100 200 300 Miles
0 100 200 300 400 500
Territory under British control
CEYLON

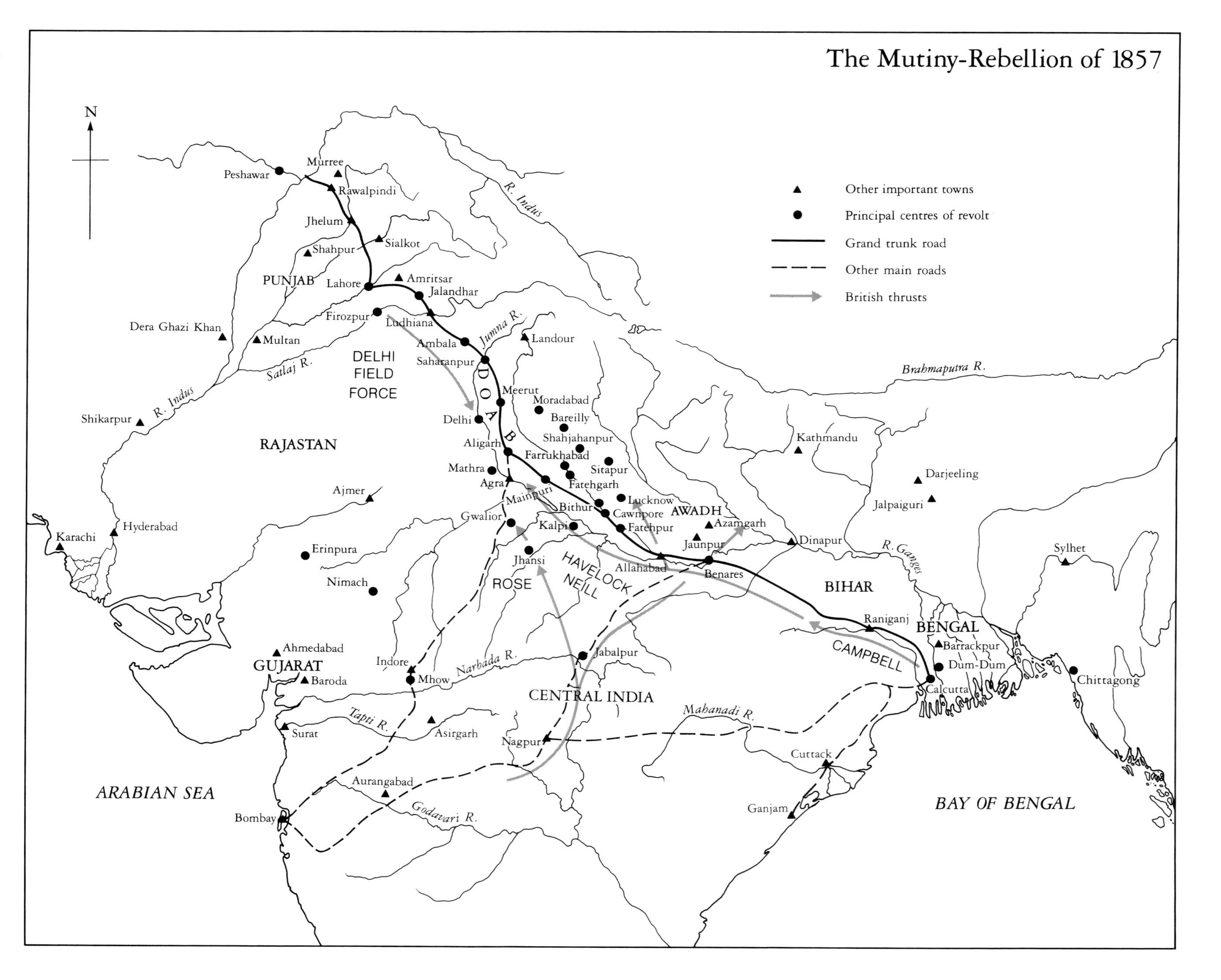
The Mutiny-Rebellion of 1857
Other important towns
Principal centres of revolt
Grand trunk road
Other main roads
British thrusts
N
PUNJAB
RAJASTAN
GUJARAT
DOAB
AWADH
BIHAR
BENGAL
CENTRAL INDIA
DELHI FIELD FORCE
HAVELOCK
NEILL
ROSE
CAMPBELL
BAY OF BENGAL
ARABIAN SEA
R. Indus
Satlaj R.
Jumna R.
R. Ganges
Brahmaputra R.
Mahanadi R.
Narbada R.
Tapti R.
Godavari R.
Peshawar
Murree
Rawalpindi
Jhelum
Shahpur
Sialkot
Lahore
Amritsar
Jalandhar
Firozpur
Ludhiana
Ambala
Saharanpur
Landour
Meerut
Delhi
Moradabad
Bareilly
Shahjahanpur
Aligarh
Farrukhabad
Sitapur
Mathra
Fatehgarh
Agra
Mainpuri
Lucknow
Bithur
Cawnpore
Gwalior
Kalpi
Fatehpur
Azamgarh
Jaunpur
Jhansi
Allahabad
Benares
Dinapur
Kathmandu
Darjeeling
Jalpaiguri
Sylhet
Raniganj
Barrackpur
Dum-Dum
Calcutta
Chittagong
Jabalpur
Nagpur
Cuttack
Ganjam
Indore
Mhow
Asirgarh
Aurangabad
Nimach
Ajmer
Erinpura
Ahmedabad
Baroda
Surat
Bombay
Dera Ghazi Khan
Multan
Shikarpur
Hyderabad
Karachi

List of Lenders

Her Majesty The Queen 208, 473, 484, 631
Stuart E. Abbott Esq. 586
George Adamson 588, 589
Dr Muhammad Saleem Ahmad, Professor of History, Dean Faculty of Islamic Learning, Islamia University, Bahawalpur 509
The Warden and Fellows of All Souls College, Oxford 275
The Visitors of the Ashmolean Museum, Oxford 21, 204, 400, 408
Baptist Missionary Society 273
Birla Museum, Rajasthan 424
Birmingham City Museums and Art Gallery 238
Bodleian Library, Oxford 64, 130, 131
The Trustees of the Bowood Collection 409
British Airways Archives and Museum Collection 592
British Architectural Library Drawings Collection/RIBA 198, 467, 468, 561, 571
The British Library Board 2, 3, 6, 39, 56, 57, 58, 99, 110, 134, 135, 185, 268, 295, 298, 299, 300, 301, 319, 320, 348, 361, 379, 390, 461, 489
The Trustees of the British Museum 85, 86, 87, 145, 281(i–ii), 292, 294(i–ii), 341, 344, 347, 354, 356, 357, 359, 360, 363, 367, 392, 442
The Trustees of the British Museum, Department of Coins and Medals 28(i–ix), 63, 230(i–v)
The Trustees of the British Museum, Department of Oriental Antiquities 11, 29, 31, 32, 50, 84, 229(i–ii), 285
The Trustees of the British Museum, Department of Prints and Drawings 4, 103, 146
The Trustees of the Broadlands Archives 630
The Syndics of Cambridge University Library 20, 119(iii–vii), 155, 177, 192, 219, 271, 291, 342
Cambridge University Museum of Archaeology and Anthropology 282, 364, 365, 366, 373(i–ii), 382, 383, 386(i–iv), 387(i–vi), 393(i–v), 443
Cambridge University Press 462
Camera Press 598
Centre for South Asian Studies, University of Cambridge 394(i–ii), 572, 573, 580(i–ii), 584, 585, 587, 590, 591(i–iii)
Cheltenham Art Gallery and Museums 68, 69, 70
The Trustees of the Chester Beatty Library, Dublin 5, 19, 25
Clive Museum, Powis Castle (HM Treasury and the National Trust) 100, 101
Clive Museum, Powis Castle (The National Trust) 159, 165
Clive Museum, Powis Castle (Powis Estate Trustees) 89, 158
Lord Cobbold 416
R. H. N. Dashwood Esq. 123
Marquis of Dufferin and Ava 223
Elton Hall Collection 328
Mr Vivian V. Esch 469
European Photo Service 616
Giles Eyre Esq. & Charles Greig Esq. 262, 278
The Syndics of the Fitzwilliam Museum, Cambridge 24, 71, 72, 75(i–ii), 142, 256
Charles Greig Esq. 248, 264
Halifax Collection 560
Heim Gallery Ltd, London 173
Honourable Society of Lincoln's Inn 129
Hosain Books 211
Howard Hodgkin, London 26
The Trustees of the Imperial War Museum 513, 514, 515, 516, 517, 599(i–viii), 601, 602, 603, 604, 605, 606, 607, 608
India Office Library and Records 8, 9, 10, 27, 38, 40, 42, 43, 44, 45, 46, 47, 48, 49, 53, 54, 55, 60, 61, 62, 65, 66, 73, 74, 76, 78, 79, 90, 92, 94, 96, 98, 102, 104, 109, 111, 117, 118, 119(i), 120, 122(i–iii), 127, 128, 136, 140, 143, 147, 151, 154, 156, 176, 182, 183, 184, 191, 200, 201, 202, 212, 213, 214, 215, 216, 217, 218, 222, 226, 231, 233, 235, 236, 240, 241, 242, 243, 244, 245, 246, 247, 250, 251, 254, 255, 258, 259, 260, 261, 266, 267, 269, 272, 277, 279, 284, 286, 287, 288, 296, 297, 306, 307, 308, 309, 310, 311, 312, 321, 334(ii), 346(i–v), 370, 371, 375, 396, 398(i), 401(i–ii), 405, 406, 407, 412, 413, 414, 415, 418, 422, 423, 425, 426, 427, 428, 429, 430, 431, 432, 433(i–ii), 434, 435, 440, 441, 444, 454(i–iv), 459, 466, 474, 476, 477, 479, 481(i–ii), 488(i–ii), 491, 492, 493, 494, 495, 500, 504, 505, 507, 508, 510, 518(i–vi), 525, 527, 528, 547, 552, 553, 555(i–vi), 556, 612, 617
James Ivory 205
Dr Gordon Johnson 483
Keir Collection, Ham 23, 30, 36
Kobal Collection 293
Professor Ira M. Lapidus 399
D. A. Low 549
Marylebone Cricket Club, Lord's 574
Melanesia International Trust Company Limited 93
Rhea Quien Monro 622, 625
K. V. F. Morton Esq. 582
National Army Museum, London 113, 114, 116, 157, 170, 175, 178, 179, 180, 181(i–ii), 187, 190, 313, 322, 324, 326, 327, 329, 330, 337, 338, 339, 343, 448, 472, 512(i–iv), 583, 600
National Gallery of Ireland 126
The Trustees of the National Gallery, London 67
The Trustees of the National Library of Scotland 506
National Maritime Museum 51, 52, 224, 420
The Trustees of the National Museums of Scotland 166, 167, 168, 169, 171
National Portrait Gallery, London 1, 95, 106, 107, 108, 132, 141, 148, 149, 150, 152, 153, 160, 174, 195, 199, 209, 210, 265, 276, 302, 303, 304, 305(i–x), 331, 332, 334(i), 336, 410, 411, 437, 438, 439, 445, 456, 465, 470, 471, 475, 497, 502, 526, 554, 575, 576, 577, 578, 579, 610, 611, 621

National Trust for Places of Historic Interest or Natural Beauty 457, 458

Nehru Memorial Museum, New Delhi 333, 397, 402, 460, 490, 499, 501, 503(i–v), 511, 519, 522, 523(i–ii), 530, 534, 536, 537, 538, 539, 540(i), 540(iii), 541, 544, 546, 548, 550, 551, 615, 618, 619, 620, 626

Foy Nissen 455, 562, 563, 564, 565, 566, 567, 568, 569, 570

Dr R. O'Hanlon 403

Department of Archaeology and Museums, Government of Pakistan 206, 207, 613, 614

P & O Art and Memorabilia Collection 80, 81, 82, 119(ii)

Pitt Rivers Museum, University of Oxford 352

Earl of Plymouth 112

Powis Castle (The National Trust) 144

Private Collection 7, 22, 59, 88, 139, 196, 197, 205, 232, 239, 280, 283, 289, 290, 325, 335(i–iii), 340, 376, 377(i–iv), 398(ii), 404, 449, 451, 452, 453, 464, 558, 609

Private Collection of Yasmin and Shahid Hosain 189

Rijksmuseum, Amsterdam 41

Lord Romsey 559(i–ii), 623, 624, 628

Royal Anthropological Institute, London 350, 351, 353(i–ii), 355, 358(i), 358(ii), 368, 372(i–iv), 380, 381(i–iii), 391, 419, 450, 496

Royal Armouries, HM Tower of London 12(i–ii), 13, 14, 15, 16, 105(i–iv), 162(i–ii), 163, 188, 203, 314, 315, 316, 317, 318

Royal Artillery Historical Trust 115

Royal Asiatic Society, London 172, 186, 227, 228, 234

Royal Commonwealth Society Library 323, 345, 417(i–ii), 447, 478, 485, 486

Lent by his widow in remembrance of Sir Anthony Rumbold, Bt. 193

Viscount Scarsdale and the Trustees of the Kedleston Estate Trusts 480, 482

School of Oriental and African Studies, University of London 349, 362, 369, 374, 378(i–iii), 384, 385, 388, 389

Scottish National Portrait Gallery 274

Dr Maurice Shellim 252, 253, 263

The Trustees of Sir John Soane's Museum 161(i–ii)

Spink & Son Ltd 221, 237, 270

The Trustees of the Tate Gallery, London 249

The Times 487, 627, 629

The Master, Fellows and Scholars of Trinity Hall, Cambridge 395, 436

The Trustees of the Victoria and Albert Museum 17, 18, 33, 34, 35, 37, 83, 121, 164, 220, 421, 463

Victoria Memorial Hall, Calcutta 97, 133, 138

Mr Rajendra Shriram Virkar 498, 520, 521, 524, 529, 531, 532, 533, 535, 540(ii), 542, 543, 545, 557, 593, 594, 595, 596, 597

Mr John Wall 581

Yale Center for British Art, Paul Mellon Collection 77, 91, 137, 194, 257

York City Art Gallery 124, 125

Select glossary of Indian terms

bagh gardens

bania member of Indian trading classes

banian Indian intermediary working with European merchants of officials (northern India)

bhadralog ranks of literate gentry (Bengal)

bhakti Hindu devotionalism

bhumihar landholder

Brahmin member of the Indian priestly class

darbar Indian royal assembly; referred to in anglicized form as durbar

diwan chief financial officer of Mughal province or Indian state

dubashes trade agents in southern India

farman charter or royal document conveying royal grant

gadi throne

Gujar member of pastoralist caste

jagir an assignment of land revenue to support a military contingent

kazi Mughal judicial official

Khattri member of mercantile caste (northern India)

Khalifat movement movement in defence of the Ottoman Sultan in his role as spiritual leader of the world's Muslims (hence Caliph)

Nawab Muslim ruler; originally 'deputy' to the Mughal Emperor; later a virtually independent prince

pir Sufi teacher or mystic

poligar southern Indian petty chieftain

raja Hindu king (hence Raj = rule)

sanyasi Indian ascetic who has withdrawn from the world

sati (suttee) ritual self-immolation of widows on their husband's funeral pyres

sepoy (*sepahi*) Indian soldier of the Company's army

Sikh Major religious group within Indian subcontinent predominating in part of the Punjab

Subahdar Mughal provincial governor

sufi a follower of the mystical tradition within Islam, usually organized into orders

Swadeshi 'home industry' movement to promote indigenous artisan products and Indian self-reliance

Swaraj self-rule, independence

Thuggee ritual strangling and murder of wayfarers

ulama learned and religious classes within Islam

zamindar landholder

Bibliography

ABU'L-FAZL, *The Akbar Nama II*, H. Beveridge (trans.) Calcutta, 1902.

AIJAZUDDIN, F.S., *Sikh Portraits by European Artists*, London, 1979.

ALAM, M., *The Crisis of Empire in Mughal North India: Awadh and the Punjab, 1707–48*, New Delhi, 1986.

ALAVI, S., *The transition of military culture in north India 1770–1830*, unpublished MSS, 1990.

ALEXANDER, M., and ANAND, S., *Queen Victoria's Maharajah: Duleep Singh 1838–93*, London, 1980.

ALKAZI, E., (ed.), *Between Battles: The Album of Colonel James Skinner*, introduction and notes by M. Archer, London, 1982.

ALLEN, B., *Francis Hayman*, New Haven and London, 1987.

ALLEN, C., *Plain Tales from the Raj*, London, 1975.

ALLEN, C., and DWIVEDI, S., *Lives of the Indian Princes*, London, 1984.

ANDERSON, J.D., *The Peoples of India*, Cambridge, 1913.

ANNESLEY, G., (Viscount Valentia), *Voyages and Travels to India, Ceylon, the Red Sea, Abyssinia and Egypt 1802–1806*, 3 vols, 1809.

APPADURAI, A., 'Kings, Sects and Temples in South India 1300–1700 A.D.', *Indian Social and Economic History Review*, XIV, 1, 1977.

APPASAMY, J., *Tanjavur Painting of the Maratha Period*, New Delhi, 1980.

ARASARATNAM, S., 'Indian Commercial Groups and European Traders 1600–1800: Changing Relationships in South-Eastern India', *South Asia*, 1978.

ARCHER, M., 'The Daniells in India', *Country Life*, 23 January 1958.

ARCHER, M., 'A Georgian Palace in India', *Country Life*, 9 April 1959.

ARCHER, M., 'The Two Worlds of Colonel Skinner', *History Today*, September 1960.

ARCHER, M., 'The Daniells in India and their Influence on British Architecture', *Journal of the Royal Institute of British Architects*, September 1960.

ARCHER, M., 'The Two Worlds of Colonel Skinner', *History Today*, September 1960, pp. 608–15.

ARCHER, M., *The Daniells in India, 1786–1793*, Washington, 1962.

ARCHER, M., 'India Revealed: Sketches by the Daniells', *Apollo*, 76, no.9, November 1962.

ARCHER, M., '"Company" architects and their influence in India', *The Journal of the Royal Institute of British Architects*, vol.70, no.8, 1963.

ARCHER, M., 'The East India Company and British Art', *Apollo*, no.92, 1965.

ARCHER, M., 'British Painters of the Indian Scene', *Journal of the Royal Society of Arts*, vol.115, no.5135, October 1967.

ARCHER, M., *Indian architecture and the British, 1780–1830*, Feltham, 1968.

ARCHER, M., 'Baltazard Solvyns and the Indian Picturesque', *The Connoisseur*, vol. 170, January 1969.

ARCHER, M., 'Benares and the British', *History Today*, vol. 19, no.6, June 1969.

ARCHER, M., *British Drawings in the India Office Library*, 2 vols, London, 1969.

ARCHER, M., '"The Talented Baronet": Sir Charles D'Oyly and his Drawings of India', *The Connoisseur*, vol. 175, no.705, November 1970.

ARCHER, M., *Company Drawings in the India Office Library*, 2 vols., London, 1972.

ARCHER, M., 'An artist engineer – Colonel Robert Smith in India (1805–1830)', *The Connoisseur*, vol. 179, February 1972.

ARCHER, M., 'Hills and Forts of South India', *Country Life*, vol. 154, no.3984, 1 November 1973.

ARCHER, M., 'Architecture of Oriental Genius', *Country Life*, vol. 154, no.3985, 8 November 1973.

ARCHER, M., *India and British Portraiture, 1770–1825*, London, 1979.

ARCHER, M., 'Works by William Alexander and James Wales: Pictures of Note by British Artists in the Collection of the Royal Asiatic Society', in *The Royal Asiatic Society: Its History and Treasures*, Simmonds, S., and Digby, S., (eds.), 1979.

ARCHER, M., *Early Views of India: The Picturesque Journeys of Thomas and William Daniell 1786–1794*, London, 1980.

ARCHER, M., Introduction and Notes to *Between Battles: The Album of Colonel James Skinner*, London, 1982.

ARCHER, M., *The India Office Collection of Paintings and Sculpture*, London, 1986.

ARCHER, M., *Visions of India: The Sketchbooks of William Simpson, 1859–1862*, Oxford, 1986.

ARCHER, M., and ARCHER, W.G., *Indian Painting for the British, 1770–1880*, Oxford, 1955.

ARCHER, M., and FALK, T., *Thomas and William Prinsep in India*, London, 1982.

ARCHER, M., and LIGHTBOWN, R., *India Observed: India as Viewed by British Artists 1760–1860*, London, 1982.

ARCHER, M., ROWELL, C., and SKELTON, R., *Treasures from India: The Clive Collection at Powis Castle*, London, 1987.

ARCHER, M., ROWELL, C., and SKELTON, R., 'British Art Lessons in India', *Country Life*, 10 November 1988.

ARCHER, W.G., *Kangra Painting*, London, 1952.

ARCHER, W.G., *Indian painting from Rajasthan*, London, 1957.

ARCHER, W.G., *Indian Painting*, London, 1959.

ARCHER, W.G., *India and Modern Art*, 1959.

ARCHER, W.G., *Romance and Painting in Indian Painting*, London, 1965.

ARCHER, W. G., *The Painting of the Sikhs*, London, 1966.

ARCHER, W.G., *Kalighat Paintings*, London, 1971.

ARCHER, W.G., 'Benares through the Eyes of British Artists', *Apollo*, vol. 92, no.102, August 1970.

ARIS, M. (ed.), *Views of Medieval Bhutan: The Diary and Drawings of Samuel Davis, 1783*, London, 1982.

ARMSTRONG, SIR W., *Lawrence*, London, 1913.

ARNOLD, D., *Police Power and Colonial Rule: Madras 1859–1947*, Delhi, 1986.

ARNOLD, SIR T.W. and WILKINSON, J.V.S., *The Library of A. Chester Beatty: A Catalogue of the Indian Miniatures*, 3 vols, London, 1936.

ASHER, C.B., *Mughal Architecture: New Cambridge History of India*, Cambridge, forthcoming 1991.

ASHTON, L., *The Art of India and Pakistan*, London, 1950.

Asiatic Journal and Monthly Register, 1828.

ATKINSON, G.F., *Curry and Rice on Forty Plates*, London, 1859.

ATKINSON, J., *Sketches in Afghanistan*, 1842.

BALA-RATNAM, L.K., *Anthropology on the March: Recent Studies of Indian Beliefs, Attitudes and Social Institutions*, Madras, 1963.

BALL, C., *The History of the Indian Mutiny*, 2 vols, London, 1858–9.

BALL, V., 'Nicobarese Hieroglyphics or Picture Writing', *Indian Antiquary*, 1875.

BARNETT, R.B., *North India Between Empires: Awadh, the Mughals and the British 1720–1801*, Berkeley, 1980.

BARNOUW, V., 'The Changing Character of a Hindu Festival', *American Anthropologist*, 56, 1954.

BARRETT, D., Introduction and Notes to *Faber Gallery of Oriental Art: Painting of the Deccan XVI-XVII Century*, London, 1952.

BARRIER, N.G., *Banned: Controversial Literature and Political Control in British India, 1904–47*, Columbia, 1974.

BARVE, V.N., *A Brief Guide to Dr Bhau Daji Lad Museum*, Bombay, 1985.

BAYLY, C.A., *The Local Roots of Indian Politics: Allahabad 1880–1920*, Oxford, 1975.

BAYLY, C.A., *Rulers, Townsmen and Bazaars, North Indian Society in the Age of British Expansion 1770–1870*, Cambridge, 1983.

BAYLY, S.B., *Saints, Goddesses and Kings*, Cambridge, 1989.

BEATON, C., *Far East*, London, 1945.

BERREMAN, G.D., 'The Brahaminical View of Caste', *Contributions to Indian Sociology*, 5, 1971.

BECK H., (ed.), *Victorian Engravings*, London, 1975.

BENCE-JONES, M., 'Clive of India as Builder and Collector II: A Nabob's Choice of Art', *Country Life*, 1971.
BENCE-JONES, M., *The Viceroys*, London, 1982.
Bengal Past and Present, XVII, 1918.
BERRY-HILL, H. and S., *George Chinnery 1774–1852: Artist of the China Coast*, Leigh-on-Sea, 1963.
BERRY-HILL H. and S., *Chinnery and China Coast Paintings*, Leigh-on-Sea, 1970.
BESANT, A., *An Autobiography*, London, 1893.
BETEILLE, A., *Caste, Class and Power: Changing Patterns of Stratification in a Tanjore Village*, Berkeley, 1965.
BHATIA, B.M., *Famines in India*, London, 1963.
BICKNELL, P., *Beauty, Horror and Immensity: Picturesque Landscape in Britain 1750–1850*, Cambridge, 1981.
BINGLEY, A.H., *Handbook of Castes and Tribes*, 1924.
BIRDWOOD, G.C.M., *Report on the Government Central Museum and on the Agricultural and Horticultural Society of Western Indian from 1863 (Selections from the Records of the Bombay Government*, New Series, LXXXIII), 1864.
BIRDWOOD, G.C.M., *Handbook to the British Indian Section, Paris Universal Exhibition, 1878*, 1878.
BIRDWOOD, G.C.M., *The Industrial Arts of India*, London, 1880.
BIRDWOOD, G.C.M., 'Illustrations from the Records and Relics of the Late Honourable East India Company', *The Journal of Indian Art*, III, 1890.
BIRDWOOD, G.C.M. and FOSTER, W., (eds), *The Register of letters &c., of the Governor and Company of Merchants of London leading into the East Indies 1600–1619*, 1893.
BIRDWOOD, G.C.M. and FOSTER, W., *Relics of the Honourable East India Company*, London, 1909.
BIRLA, G.D., *In the Shadow of the Mahatma*, Bombay, 1958.
Birmingham City Museum and Art Gallery, *Catalogue of Paintings*, 1960.
BLAGDON, F.W., *The European in India from a collection of drawings by C. Doyley, Esq.; with a Brief History of Ancient and Modern India*, London, 1813.
BLOCHET, E., *Musulman Painting*, London, 1929.
Blochmann, H., (trans, ed.), *Ain-i-Akbari*, Calcutta, 3 vols., 1873–96.
BODEN CLOSS, C., *In the Andamans and Nicobars*, 1903.
Borg, A., 'A Crusader in Borrowed Armour', *Country Life*, 18 July 1974.
BOSE, S.C., *The Indian Struggle*, 1942, reprinted 1962.
BOXER, C.R., *The Portuguese Seaborne Empire, 1415–1825*, London, 1969.
BRECKENRIDGE, C.,'The Aesthetics and Politics of Colonial Collecting: India at World Fairs', *Comparative Studies in Society and History*, 1989.
BREEKS, J.W., *An Account of the Primitive Tribes and Monuments of the Nilagiris*, 1873.
BREEZE, G., *Thomas Hickey 1741–1824*, unpublished M.A. thesis, University of Birmingham (Barber Institute of Fine Arts), 177, 1973.
BRIGGS, H., *The Nizam: His History and Relations with the British Government*, London, 1861.
British Library Reference Division, India Office Library and Records: Oriental Manuscripts and Printed Books, *Newsletter* 31, April 1984.
BRITTEN, F.J., *Old Clocks and Watches and their Makers*, 1911.
BROUGHTON, T., *The Costume, Character, Manners, Domestic Habits, and Religious Ceremonies of the Marathas*, London, 1813.
BROWN, J.M., *Gandhi's Rise to Power*, Cambridge, 1972.
BROWN, J.M., *Modern India: The Origins of an Asian Democracy*, Delhi, 1985.
BRUCE, J., (ed.), *Calender of State papers, Domestic Series, of the Reign of Charles I 1633–4*, 1863.
BUDDLE, A., 'The Mark of Tipu Sultan', *Sultan Annual Journal* vol. 2, (Tipu Sultan Research Institute and Museum, Srirangpatna) 1984–5.
BULLOCK, W., *A Companion to Mr Bullock's London Museum and Pantherion*, 12th edn, London, 1812.
BURKE, E., *A Philosophical Enquiry into the Origin of Our Ideas of the Sublime and the Beautiful*, London, 1757.
BUTLER, I., *The Eldest Brother: The Marquess Wellesley*, London, 1973.
CARMAN, W.Y., *Indian Army Uniforms: Artillery, Engineers and Infantry*, London, 1969.
CASHMAN, R.I., *The Myth of the 'Lokamanya'*, Berkeley, 1975.
CAUNTER, REVD H. and DANIELL, W., *The Oriental Annual*, 5 vols, London, 1834–8.
A Catalogue of the Pictures at Elton Hall, 1924.
CHAITANYA, K., *Ravi Varma*, Delhi, 1984.
CHAKRABARTY, D., *Re-thinking Working-Class History: Bengal 1890–1940*, Princeton, 1989.
CHANDAVARKAR, R., *Labour and Politics in Bombay*, Cambridge, 1991 (forthcoming).
CHANDER, S., 'From a Pre-Colonial Order to a Princely State: Hyderabad in Transition, c.1748–1865', unpublished Cambridge Ph.D dissertation, 1987.
CHANDRA, B., *The Rise and Growth of Economic Nationalism in India*, New Delhi, 1966.
CHANDRA, S., *Parties and Politics at the Mughal Court 1707–40*, Aligarh, 1958.
CHANTRY, SIR F., 'Sir Francis Chantrey's Ledgers of Accounts' (2 MSS volumes in the Royal Academy Library and British Library).
CHAUDHAURI, B.B., *The Growth of Commercial Agriculture in Bengal*, Calcutta, 1964.
CHAUDHURI, K.N., *The English East India Company: The Study of an Early Joint-stock Company 1600–40*, London, 1965.
CHAUDHURI, K.N., *The Trading World of Asia and the English East India Company, 1660–1760*, Cambridge, 1978.
CHESNEAU, E., *The English School of Painting*, London, 1885.
CHEVERS, N., *A Manual of Medical Jurisprudence for India Including the Outline of a History of Crime Against the Person in India*, Calcutta, 1870.
CHICHELEY PLOWDEN, W.F.C., *Records of the Chicheley Plowdens, A.D. 1590–1913*, 1914.
City Museum and Art Gallery, *Catalogue of Paintings*, 1960.
CLIFFORD, J., 'On Ethnographic Authority', *Representations*, 1, 2, 1983.
CLIVE, J., *Thomas Babington Macaulay: The Shaping of The Historian*, London, 1973.
COHN, B., 'The Past in the Present: India as a Museum of Mankind. Classifying the Peoples of India: 1500–1800', paper delivered at Smithsonian symposium, 'The Poetics and Politics of Representation', 1988.
COHN, B., 'The Changing Status of a Depressed Caste', in M. Marriott (ed.), *Village India: Studies in the Little Tradition*, Chicago, 1955.
COHN, B., 'Notes on the History of the Study of Indian Society and Culture', in *Structure and Change in Indian Society*, Chicago, 1968.
COHN, B., 'Representing Authority in British India', in *The Invention of Tradition*, E. Hobsbawm and T. Ranger (eds), Cambridge, 1983.
COHN, B., 'The Census, Social Structure and Objectification in South Asia', *An Anthropologist Among the Historians and Other Essays*, Delhi, 1987.
COLE, J.R.I., *The Iranian and Iraqi Roots of North Indian Shiism*, Berkeley, 1986.
COLEBROOKE, T.E., *The Life of H. T. Colebrooke*, London, 1873.
COMFORT A., (trans.), *The Koka Shastra*, London, 1964.
CONNER, P., *Oriental Architecture in the West*, London, 1979.
CONNER, P., *The Overland Route of William Prinsep (1794–1874), Martyn Gregory Catalogue 37*, London, 1984.
CONNER, P., *The China Trade 1600–1860*, Brighton, 1986.
CORMACK, M., *A Concise Catalogue of Paintings in the Yale Center for British Art*, New Haven, 1985.
CONLON, F., 'Caste, Community and Colonialism: The Elements of Population Recruitment and Urban Rule in British Bombay, 1665–1830', *Journal of Urban History*, XI, 2, 1985.
COTTON, SIR E. *Letters to National Portrait Gallery, 13 December 1927 and 23 January 1928*, National Portait Gallery Archive, 1927–8.
COTTON, SIR E., 'Robert Home in India', *Bengal Past and Present*, XXXV, 1928.
COTTON, H.E.A., *Calcutta, Old and New*, Calcutta, 1907.
COTTON, W., *Sir Joshua Reynolds and his Wales*, 1857.
COURTNEY, N., *The Tiger: Symbol of Freedom*, London, 1980.
COWELL, E.B., *The Jataka, or Stories of the Buddha's former births*, 7 vols, Cambridge, 1895–1913.
CROFT-MURRAY, E., *Decorative Painting in England 1537–1837*, 2 vols, 1962, 1970.
CROOKE, W. *The Tribes and Castes of the North-Western Provinces and Oudh*, 4 vols, Calcutta, 1896.
CROOKE, W., *Rural and Agricultural Glossary*, S. Amin (ed.), Delhi, 1989.
CURZON, G.N., *Tales of Travel*, London, 1923.
CUST, L., *Anthony Van Dyck: An Historical Study of his Life and Works*, 1900.
DANIELL, T. and DANIELL, W., *Oriental Scenery: Twenty-four views in Hindoostan drawn by Thomas Daniell and engraved by himself and William Daniell*, London, 1797.
DANIELL, T. and DANIELL, W.T., *A Picturesque Voyage to India by the Way of China*, London, 1810.
DANIELL, W., *Views in Bootan*, London, 1813.
DAS, M.N., *India Under Morley and Minto*, London, 1964.
DAS GUPTA, A., *Indian Merchants and the decline of Surat* c. *1700–1750*, Wiesbaden, 1979.
DAVIES, P., *Splendours of the Raj: British Architecture in India, 1660–1947*, London, 1985.
DAVID, M.D., *History of Bombay, 1661–1708*, Bombay, 1973.
DAVIDSON, H., *History and Services of 78th Highlanders*, Edinburgh, 1901.
DEGRANDO, J.M., *The Observation of Savage Peoples*, 1969.
DERBYSHIRE, I., 'Opening up the Interior: Railways and the U. P. Economy, 1850–1920', unpublished Cambridge PhD dissertation, 1987.
Descriptive Catalogue of a Very Costly and Superb Collection of Military Antiquities, n.d., *c.* 1820.
Desmond, R., *Victorian India in Focus*, London, 1980.
DESMOND, R., *History of the India Museum*, 1982.
DESMOND, R., 'Photography in Victorian India', *Journal of the Royal Society of Arts*, 134, 1985.
DIFFIE, B.W., and WINIUS, G.D., *Foundations of the Portuguese Empire, 1415–1580*, Minneapolis, 1977.
DIGBY, S., *'A Corpus of Mughal Glass', Bulletin of SOAS*, vol. 36, 1973.
DIGBY, S., and HARLE, J.C., *Toy soldiers and Ceremonial in post-Mughal India*, Oxford, 1982.

DILKS, D., *Curzon in India*, 2 vols, London, 1969–70.
DILLENBERGER, J., *Benjamin West: The Context of His Life's Work*, San Antonio, 1977.
DILLON, VISCOUNT, *The Armouries, Towers of London*, London, 1910.
DIRKS, N.B., *The Hollow Crown: Ethnohistory of an Indian Kingdom*, Cambridge, 1987.
DOBSON, G.E., 'On the Andamans and the Andamanese', *Journal of the Anthropological Institute*, vol. 22, 1875.
DODWELL, H.H., *British India, 1497–1858*, The Cambridge History of India, vol. V, Cambridge 1929.
DOYLE, A., *The Doyle Family through Five Generations*, London, 1911.
D'OYLY, SIR C., *Tom Raw, the Griffin: A Burlesque Poem in Twelve Cantos*, London, 1828.
DU BOIS, ABBÉ J. A., *Hindu Manners, Customs and Ceremonies*, London, 1906.
DUFF, J.G., *A History of the Mahrattas*, 3 vols, London, 1826.
DURAND, M., *Nadir Shah*, 1908.
EBIN, V., and SWALLOW, D.A., *The Proper Study of Mankind: Great Anthropological Collections in Cambridge*, Cambridge, 1984.
EDEN, E., *Up the Country*, 2 vols, London, 1866.
EDEN, E., *Portraits of the Princes and People of India*, London, 1844.
EDWARDS, E., 'Images of the Andamans: The Photography of E. H. Man', *Journal of Museum Ethnography*, 1, 1980.
EGERTON OF TATTON, LORD, *An Illustrated Handbook of Indian Arms*, London, 1880.
EINBERG, E., *George Lambert (1700–1765)*, Kenwood, 1970.
The European Magazine, October 1788, 1793.
EVENSON, N., *The Indian Metropolis: A View Toward the West*, London and New Haven, 1989.
The Faber Gallery of Oriental Art, London, 1952.
FABIAN, J., *Time and the Other: How Anthropology Makes its Object*, New York, 1983.
FALCONER, J., 'Ethnological Photography in India, 1850–1900', *The Photographic Collector*, 5, 1984.
FALK, T., and ARCHER, M., *Indian Miniatures in the India Office Library*, London, 1981.
FALK, T., and ARCHER, M., *India Revealed: The Art and Adventures of James and William Fraser 1801–35*, London, 1989.
FARINGTON, J., *The Diary of Joseph Farington*, K. Garlick and A. Macintyre *et al.* (eds), 16 vols, London, 1978–84.
FARRER, REVD E., *Portraits in Suffolk Houses (West)*, 1908.
FEAVER, G., *From Status to Contract: A Biography of Sir Henry Maine 1822–88*, London, 1969.
FEILING, K., *Warren Hastings*, 1954.
FERGUSSON, J., *History of Indian and Eastern Architecture*, 1910.
FINBERG, H.F., 'Samuel Scott', *Burlington Magazine*, August 1942.
FISHER, M.H., *A Clash of Cultures: Awadh, the British and the Mughals*, New Delhi, 1987.
FITCHETT, W.H., *The Tale of the Great Mutiny*, London, 1901.
FORBES-WATSON, J., *The Textile Fabrics of India*, London, 1868, 2nd series.
FORREST, D., *Tiger of Mysore*, London, 1970.
FORSTER, G., *A Journey from Bengal to England, through the Northern Part of India, Kashmire, Afghanistan and Persia,and into Russia*, 2 vols, London, 1798.
FORTESCUE, J., *Narrative of the Visit to India of their Majesties King George V and Queen Mary and of the Coronation Durbar held at Delhi 12th December 1911*, London, 1912.
FOSTER, W., *A Descriptive Catalogue of the Paintings, statues, etc, in the India Office*, 1906.
FOSTER, W., *A Guide to the India Office Records, 1600–1858*, London, 1919.
FOSTER, W., *Early Travels in India 1583–1619*, Oxford, 1921.
FOSTER, W., *A Descriptive Catalogue of the Paintings, Statues, etc. in the India Office*, London, 1924.
FOSTER, W., *The East India House: Its History and Associations*, London, 1924.
FOSTER, W., 'William Hodges, R.A., in India', *Bengal Past and Present*, 30, 1925.
FOSTER, W., *The Embassy of Sir Thomas Roe to India, 1615–19, as narrated in his journals and correspondence*, Oxford, 1926.
FOSTER, W., 'British Artists in India, 1760–1820', *The Walpole Society*, 19, 1930–31.
FOUCAULT, M., *Discipline and Punish: The Birth of the Prison*, Harmondsworth, 1979.
FOX, R.G., *Lions of the Punjab: Culture in the Making*, Berkeley, 1985.
FRASER, J.B., *Journal of a Tour through part of the Snowy Range of the Himala Mountains*, London, 1820.
FURBANK, P.N., *E. M. Forster: A Life*, 2 vols, London, 1977–78.
FREITAG, S., 'Collective Crime and Authority in North India', in A. Young, (ed.), *Crime and Criminality in British India*, University of Arizona, 1985.
FREITAG, S., *Culture and Power in Benares*, Berkeley, 1989.
FURBER, H., *Rival Empires of Trade in the Orient, 1600–1800*, Minneapolis, 1976.
GADGIL, D.R., foreword to Ghurye, 1943.
GALT, J., *'A Catalogue of the Works of Mr West', The Life, Studies, and Works of Benjamin West, Esq., President of the Royal Academy of London*, 1820.
GAMBHIRANANDA, SWAMI, *The History of Ramakrishna: Math and Mission*, Calcutta, 1957.
GARLICK, K., 'A Catalogue of the Paintings, Drawings and Pastels of Sir Thomas Lawrence', *Walpole Society*, 39, 1964.
GARLICK, K., 'A Catalogue of the Pictures at Althorp', *Walpole Society*, 45, 1974–6.
GARLICK, K., *Sir Thomas Lawrence: A complete catalogue of the oil paintings*, 1989.
Gazette des Beaux-Arts, 1 September 1867.
GEORGE, M.D., *Catalogue of Political and Personal Satires preserved in the Department of Prints and Drawings in the British Museum, V, 1771–1783*, London, 1935.
GHOSE, H., *Bulletin of the Victoria Memorial*, vol.X, 1976; vol. XII, 1979, Calcutta.
GERSON DA CUNHA, J., 'Professor Lombrose and Criminal Anthropology with reference to the Population of Bombay', *Journal of the Anthropological Society of Bombay*, vol. 2, 1890.
GHURYE, G.S., *The Aborigines – 'So-called' – And Their Future*, Poona, 1943.
GILPIN, W., *Observations . . . Relative Chiefly to Picturesque Beauty*, 8 vols., London, 1782–1809.
GILPIN, W., *Three Essays: On Picturesque Beauty: on Picturesque Travel: and on Sketching Landscape*, London, 1792.
GILPIN, W., 'Instructions for Examining Landscape, Illustrated by a few drawings', MS Fitzwilliam Museum no.3674 (*c.*1794).
GLYNN, C., 'Early Painting in Mandi', *Artibus Asiae*, 1983.
GLYNN, J., 'Crimean Simpson: A Biography of a Victorian Travel Artist', MS, 1989.
GODREJ, P., and ROHATGI, P., *Scenic Splendours: India through the Printed Image*, London, 1989.
GOETZ, H., *The Art and Architecture of Bikaner State*, Oxford, 1950.
GOKHALE, B.G., *Poona in the Eighteenth Century: An Urban History*, Delhi, 1988.
GOLD, C., *Oriental Drawings*, London, 1806.
GOODREAU, D., 'Nathaniel Dance R.A.', unpublished Ph.D. dissertation, University of California, Los Angeles, 1973.
GOPAL, S., *British Politics in India 1858–1905*, Cambridge, 1965.
GORE, R.S., *Powis Castle, Montgomeryshire*, 1972.
Gothic Hall, Pall Mall, *Catalogue of the Splendid Collection of Antient Armour*, London, 1818.
Government of India Home Poll. B, fortnightly intelligence reports, 1907–10, National Archive of India, New Delhi.
GOWER, LORD R., *Sir Thomas Lawrence*, 1900.
GRANT, M.H., *A Chronological History of the Old English Landscape Painters*, 3 vols, 1926–47, 1926.
GRANT, M.H., 'A Catalogue of British Medals since 1760', Part I, *The British Numismatic Journal*, 22, 1936–7.
GRAVES A., and CRONIN, W.V., *A History of the Works of Sir Joshua Reynolds*, 4 vols, 1899–1901.
GREENBERG, M., *British Trade and the Opening of China, 1800–42*, Cambridge, 1951.
GREENHALGH, P., 'Education, Entertainment and Politics: Lessons from the Great International Exhibitions', in P. Vergo (ed.) *The New Museology*, London, 1989.
GREWAL, J.S., *The Sikhs in the Punjab*, New Cambridge History of India, Cambridge, 1990 (forthcoming).
GRIERSON, G.A., *Bihar Peasant Life: Being A Discursive Catalogue of the Surrounding of the People of that Province*, Patna, 1926.
GRIFFITHS, P., *To Guard My People: The History of the Indian Police*, London, 1971.
GUHA THAKURTA, T., 'Artists, Artisans and Mass Picture Production in the Late Nineteenth- and Early Twentieth-century Calcutta: The Changing Iconography of Popular Prints', *South Asia Research*, 8, 1988.
GUPTA, B.K., *Sirajuddaulah and the East India Company*, Leiden, 1966.
GUPTA, N., *Delhi Between Two Empires, 1803–81*, New Delhi, 1981.
GURNEY, J.D., 'Fresh Light on the Character of the Nawab of Arcot', in A. Whiteman, J.S. Bromley and P.G.M. Dickson (eds), *Statesmen, Scholars and Merchants*, Oxford, 1973.
GUTMAN, J.M., *Through Indian Eyes*, New York, 1982.
HABIB, I., *The Agrarian System of Mughal India*, Bombay, 1963.
HADDON, A.C., *History of Anthropology*, 1910.
HALL, H., 'The India Costume Piece of the Early Moghul Period',in *Facets of Indian Art*, R. Skelton (ed.), 1986.
HAMBLY, G., *Cities of Mughal India*, 1968.
Handbook of Castes and Tribes employed on the Tea Estates in North East India, Calcutta, 1924.
HARCOURT, G.J., *The Regimental Records of the First Battalion the Royal Dublin Fusiliers*, 1910.
HARDEN, D., PAINTER, K., PINDER-WILSON, R., and TAIT,H., *Masterpieces of Glass*, London, 1968.
HARDIE, M., and CLAYTON, M., 'Thomas Daniell, R.A.; William Daniell, R.A.', *Walker's Quarterly*, nos. 35–36, 1932.
HARDIMAN, D., *Peasant Nationalists of Gujarat: Kheda District, 1917–1934*, Delhi, 1981.
HARDY, J., *India Office Furniture*, London, 1982.
HARDY, P., *The Muslims of British India*, Cambridge, 1972.
HARLE, J.C., and TOPSFIELD, A., *Indian Art in the Ashmolean Museum*, Oxford, 1987.
HARRIS, F.R., *Jamsetji Nusserwanji Tata: A Chronicle of His Life*, Bombay, 1925.
HARROLD, P., 'The India Office Library's Prints of Calcutta', *India Office Library and Records Report*, 1 April 1972–31 December 1973.

HASAN, M., *History of Tipu Sultan*, 2nd edn, Calcutta, 1971.
HASLAM, R., 'Oakly Park Shropshire', *Country Life*, 22 March 1990.
HASWELL A.E., and DAWNAY, N.P., *Military Drawings and Paintings in the Collection of Her Majesty The Queen*, 2 vols, London, 1966.
HEAD, R., 'An endless source of amusement: Amateur artists in India', *The Connoisseur*, vol.203, February 1980.
HEAD, R., 'From Obsession to Obscurity: Colonel Robert Smith, Artist, Architect and Engineer – I', *Country Life*, vol.169, May 1981.
HEAD, R., 'Indian Fantasy in Devon: Colonel Robert Smith, Artist, Architect and Engineer – II', *Country Life*, vol.169, May 1981.
HEAD, R., *The Indian Style*, London, 1986.
HEAD, R., *Paintings, Drawings, Engravings and Busts in the Collection of the Royal Asiatic Society*, unpublished MS in possession of the Royal Asiatic Society.
HEBER, A., *The Life of Reginald Heber, D.D.*, London, 1980.
HENNING, B.D. (ed.), *The History of Parliament: The House of Commons 1660–90*, London, 1983.
HENRY, E.R., 'Finger Prints and the Detection of Crime in India, Describing the System of Classifying Finger Prints and how all the Great Departments of India have brought Finger Prints into use', *British Association for the Advancement of Science Reports*, Dover, 1899.
HERMANN, A., and SCHLAGINTWEIT, E.D., *Results of a Scientific Mission to India and High Asia Undertaken Between the Years MDCCCLIV and MDCCCLVIII (1854 and 1858) by order of the Court of Directors of the Honourable East India Company*, 1858.
HERSCHEL, W.J.,*The Origin of Fingerprinting*, Oxford, 1916.
HERSHKOWITZ, R., *The British Photographer Abroad: The First Thirty Years*, London, 1980.
HEWITT, J., *The Tower, Its History, Armouries and Antiquities*, London, 1841, 1845, 1854.
HEWITT, J., *Official Guide to the Tower Armouries*, London, 1859.
HEWITT, J., *Official Catalogue of the Tower Armouries*, London, 1865.
HICHBERGER, J.W.M., *Images of the Army: The Military in British Art 1815–1914*, Manchester, 1988.
HILL, D., *Mr Gillray*, London, 1965.
HIND, A.M., *Engraving in England in the Sixteenth and Seventeenth Centuries*, 3 vols, Cambridge, 1955.
HOBBES, J.O., *Imperial India: Letters from the East*, London, 1903.
HODGES, W., *Select Views in India drawn on the spot in the years 1780, 1781, 1782, and 1783*, London, 1785–8.
HODGES, W., 'An Account of Richard Wilson Esq., Landscape Painter, FRA', *The European Magazine and London Review*, vol.17, June 1790.
HODGES, W., *Travels in India during the years 1780, '81, '82 and '83*, London, 1794.
HODSON T.C.,, *India: Census Ethnography 1901–1931*, Delhi, 1937.
HOLLAND, L.G., 'Notebooks', National Portrait Gallery Archives, III.
HOLMAN, D., *Sikander Sahib*, London, 1961.
HOSSEIN, H., 'Alienation of weavers 1750–1800', *Indian Economic and Social History Review*, XVI, 1979.
HOWLETT, D.J., 'An End to Expansion: Influences on British Policy in India *c.* 1830–1860', unpublished PhD dissertation, Cambridge, 1981.
HUGHES, D., *Bishop Sahib: A Life of Reginald Heber*, Worthing, 1986.
HUSSEY, C., *The Picturesque: Studies in a Point of View*, London, 1927.
HUTCHEON, R., *Chinnery, the Man and the Legend*, Hong Kong, 1975.
HUTCHINSON, H.N., GREGORY, J.W., and LYDEKKER, R., *The Living Races of Mankind: a popular illustrated account of the customs, habits, pursuits, feasts and ceremonies of the races of mankind throughout the world*, London, n.d.
HYMAN S., (ed.), *Edward Lear in the Levant: Travels in Albania, Greece and Turkey in Europe 1848–1849*, London, 1988.
IBBETSON, D., *Memorandum on Ethnological Inquiry in the Punjab*, 1882.
IBBETSON, D., 'The Study of Anthropology in India, *Journal of the Anthropological Society of Bombay*, II, 1890.
IBBETSON, D., *Panjab Castes: being a reprint of the chapter in 'The Races, Castes, and Tribes of the People' in the Report on the Census of the Panjab published in 1883*, Lahore, 1916.
Illustrated London News, 15 May 1858, 19 February 1876.
Imperial Gazeteer of India, 28 vols, Oxford, 1908.
INDEN, R., 'Orientalist Constructions of India', *Modern Asian Studies*, 20, 3, 1986.
IRVINE, W., *The Army of the Indian Moghuls: Its Organization and Administration*, London, 1903.
IRVING, R.G., *Indian Summer: Lutyens, Baker and Imperial Delhi*, New Haven and London, 1981.
IRWIN, J., *The Kashmir Shawl*, London, 1973.
IRWIN, J., and BRETT, K.B., *Origins of Chintz*, 1970.
IYER, L.K.A., *Cochin Tribes and Castes*, 3 vols, Madras, 1909–12.
JAIN, L.C., *Indigenous Banking in India*, London, 1929.
JESSEN, J., *George Frederick Watts*, 1901.
JOHNSON, G., *Provincial Politics and Indian Nationalism*, Cambridge, 1973.
JONES, K., *Arya Dharm*, Berkeley, 1976.
JORDENS, J.T., *Dayananda Saraswati: His Life and Ideas*, Delhi 1978.
JOURDAIN, M., 'Furniture at the India Office', *Country Life*, 65, 1929.
Journal of the Anthropological Institute, 1892.
Journal of Indian Art, III, 1890; XII, no.107, July 1909.
Journal of Indian Art and Industry, XV, no.120, pp.77–8, October 1912.
Journal of the Royal Society of Arts, 79, 1931.
JOSHI, S.N., *Half-Tone Reprints of the Renowned Pictues of the Late Raja Ravi Varma*, Poona, 1911.
KARAKA, D.F., *History of the Parsis*, London, 1884.
KALUS, L., 'Inscriptions Arabes et Persanes sur les Armes Musulmanes de la Tour de Londres', *Gladius*, 15, 1980.
KAYE, J.W., *History of the Sepoy War in India*, 3 vols, London, 1867.
KAYE, J.W., *Life and Correspondence of Charles Lord Metcalfe*, London, 1984.
KAYES, M.M., *The Golden Calm*, London 198?.
KEANE, A.H., Review of *Tribes, Castes of the North-Western Provinces ... Journal of the Anthropological Institute*, 1898.
KERSLAKE, J., *National Portrait Gallery Early Georgian Portraits*, 2 vols, London, 1977.
KHAN, Y.H., *Nizamu'l Mulk Asaf Jah I*, Mangalore, 1936.
KIERNAN, V.G., *The Lords of Humankind*, Harmondsworth, 1972.
KING, P., *A Viceroy's Journal*, preface by E. Longford, London, 1984.
KINGZETT, R., 'A Catalogue of the works of Samuel Scott', *Walpole Society*, XLVIII, 1982.
KLASS, M., *Caste: The Emergence of the South Asian Social System*, Philadelphia, 1980.
KLING, B.B., *The Blue Mutiny*, Philadelphia, 1966.
KLING, B.B., *Partner in Empire, Dwarkanath Tagore and the age of enterprise in Eastern India*, Berkeley, 1976.
KNIGHT, R.P., *The Landscape: A Didactic poem in three books*, London, 1794.
KNIGHT, R.P., *An Analytical Inquiry into the Principles of Taste*, London, 1808.
KOLFF, D.H.A., *Naukar, Rajput and Sepoy: The Ethnohistory of the Military Labour Market in Hindustan, 1450–1850*, Cambridge, 1990.
KOPF, D., *The Brahmo Samaj and the Mind of Modern India*, Berkeley, 1984.
KRAUSS, R., *L'Amour Fou: Photography and Surrealism*, New York, 1985.
KUMAR, N., *The Artisans of Banaras: Popular Culture and Identity, 1880–1986*, Princeton, 1988.
KUPER, A., *Anthropologists and Anthropology: The British School 1922–72*, London, 1983.
La Belle Assemblée, 'A Correct List of the Works of Benjamin West, Esq.', *La Belle Assemblée or Bell's Court and Fashionable Magazine*, IV, 1808, supplement, p.15.
LAIRD, M.A., *Missionaries and Education in Bengal, 1793–1837*, Oxford, 1972.
LAMBRICK, H.T., *Sir Charles Napier and Sind*, Oxford, 1952.
LAMPREY, J.H., 'On a Method of Measuring the Human Form, for the Use of Students in Ethnography', *Journal of the Ethnological Society of London*, 1, 1868–9.
LANE POOLE, R., *Catalogue of Portraits in the Possession of the University, Colleges, City and County of Oxford*, 3 vols, 1925.
LANGHAM, I., *The Building of British Social Anthropology*, Dordrecht, 1981.
LARSEN, E.,*L'Opera completa di van Dyck*, Milan, 1980.
LARSEN, E., *The Paintings of Anthony Van Dyck*, 1988.
LEACH, E.R., 'Notes on the Mythology of Cambridge Anthropology', *Cambridge Anthropology*, 9, 1984.
LEAR, E., *Indian Journal: Watercolours and Extracts from the Diary of Edward Lear, 1873–5*, R. Murphy (ed.), London, 1953.
LELYVELD, D., *Aligarh's First Generation*, Princeton, 1978.
LITTLE D.M., and KAHRL G.M., (eds), *Letters of David Garrick*, 3 vols, London, 1963.
LITTLE, J.H., 'The Black Hole: The Question of Holwell's Veracity', *Bengal Past and Present*, 11, 1915.
LLEWELLYN, B., *The Orient Observed: Images of the Middle East from the Searight Collection*, London, 1989.
LLEWELLYN-JONES, R. *A Fatal Friendship: the Nawabs, the British and the city of Lucknow*, Delhi, 1985.
LOCKHART, L., *Nadir Shah: A Critical Study, based mainly on contemporary sources*, London, 1938.
LOGIN, E., *Court life and camp life (1820–1904)*, 1904.
The London Magazine, January 1760.
LONG, J, *Statement by the Rev. J. Long of his Connection with the Nil Durpan*, Calcutta, 1861.
LONG, J., *The History of the Nil Durpan with the State Trial of the Rev. J. Long of the Church Mission*, Calcutta, 1898.
LONGFORD, E., *Wellington: the Years of the Sword*, London, 1969.
LOVE, W.D., *Vestiges of Old Madras, 1640–1740*, 3 vols and index, London, 1913.
LUARD, C.E., *A Bibliography of the Literature Dealing with the Central India Agency to which is added a series of Chronological Tables*, 1908.
LUCAS, E.V., *Roving East and Roving West*, London, 1921.

LUDDEN, D., *Peasant History in South India*, Princeton, 1985.
McALPIN, M.B., *Subject to Famine*, Princeton, 1983.
MACAULAY, T.B., Macaulay's 'Journal', unpublished MS, in Trinity College, Cambridge.
McCULLY, B.T., *English Education and the Origins of Indian Nationalism*, New York, 1983.
McKENZIE, R., '"The Laboratory of Mankind": John McCosh and the Beginnings of Photography in British India', *History of Photography*, 2, 1987.
McLANE, J.R., *Indian Nationalism and the Early Congress*, Princeton, 1977.
MACMILLAN, H., *Life-Work of George Frederick Watts, R.A.*, 1903.
MALCOLM, J., *The Political History of India, from 1784 to 1823*, London, 1826.
MALET, A., *Notices of an English Branch of the Malet Family*, London, 1885.
MAN, E.H., 'On the Andamanese and Nicobarese Objects Presented to Maj. Gen. Pitt Rivers', *Journal of the Anthropological Institute*, vol. 11, 1882.
MAN, E.H., *The Nicobar Islands and their People*, n.d.
MANI, V., *Puranic Encyclopaedia*, Delhi, 1964.
MANNERS, LADY V. and WILLIAMSON, G.C., *John Zoffany, R.A.*, 1920.
MARKHAM, C.R., (ed.), *Voyages to the East Indies, with abstracts of journals [of Sir James Lancaster]*, London, 1877.
MARSHALL, P.J., *East Indian Fortunes*, Oxford, 1976.
MARSHALL, P.J., *The British Discovery of Hinduism in the Eighteenth Century*, Cambridge, 1970.
MARSHALL, P.J., 'A Free Though Conquering People: Britain and Asia in the 18th Century', Inaugural lecture, King's College, London, 1981.
MARSHALL, P.J., *Bengal: The British Bridgehead: Eastern India, 1740–1828*, (*The New Cambridge History of India*), Cambridge, 1988.
MARSHALL, W.E., *A Phrenologist Amongst the Todas*, 1873.
MARTIN, G., *The Flemish School* c.*1600*–c.*1900*, 1970.
MASON, P., *A Matter of Honour: An Account of the Indian Army, its Officers and Men*, London, 1974.
MAYER, A.C., *Caste and Kinship in Central India*, London, 1960.
MEADOWS TAYLOR, P., *The Story of My Life*, 1882.
MESITER, M.W., (ed.), *Encyclopaedia of India Temple Architecture*, Delhi, 1983.
METCALF, B.D., *Islamic Revival in British India*, Princeton, 1982.
METCALF, T.R., *The Aftermath of Revolt, 1857–70*, Princeton, 1965.
METCALF, T.R., *Land, Landlords and the British Raj*, Berkeley, 1979.
METCALF, T.R., *An Imperial Vision: Indian Architecture and Britain's Raj*, London, 1989.
METROPOLITAN MUSEUM OF ART, *The Emperors' Album: Images of Mughal India*, New York: 1987.
MILES, E., 'Thomas Hudson (1701–1779): Portrait Artist to the British Establishment', unpublished Ph.D dissertation, Yale University, 2 vols, 1976.
MILES, W., (trans., ed.), *Kirmani's History of Hyder Ali and Tipoo Sultaun*, London, 1834.
MILLAR, O., *Later Georgian Pictures in the Collection of Her Majesty the Queen*, 2 vols, 1969.
MILLAR, O., *Van Dyck in England*, London, 1982.
MILLAR, O., *Victorian Pictures in the Collection of Her Majesty the Queen*, forthcoming.
MINAULT, G., *The Khilafat Movement: Religious Symbolism and Political Mobilization in India*, New York, 1982.
'Minutes of The Court Book of East India Company', 1–2 November 1732; MS in India Office Library.
MITCHELL, C., *Hogarth's Peregrination*, 1952.
MITCHELL, L.K., *The Art of Photography with Special Reference to its Practice in India*, Bombay, 1908.
MITCHELL, T., *Colonising Egypt*, Cambridge, 1988.
MITTER, P., *Much Maligned Monsters: History of European Reactions to Indian Art*, Oxford, 1977.
MITTER, P., *Photography in India*, 1982.
MOLLO, B., *The Indian Army*, Poole, 1981.
MOON, P., *The British Conquest and Dominion of India*, London, 1989.
MOORE, H.B., *The Chronicles of the East India Company trading to China 1635–1834*, vol. III, London, 1926.
MOORHOUSE, G., *India Britannica*, London, 1983.
MOOSVI, S., *The Economy of the Mughal Empire: c.1595: A Statistical Study*, Delhi, 1987.
Morning Chronicle, 6 May 1795.
MORRIS, J., *Stones of Empire: The Buildings of the Raj*, Oxford, 1986.
MUKHERJEE, R., *Awadh in Revolt, 1857–1858*, Delhi, 1984.
MUKHERJEE S.N., and LEACH E., (eds), *Elites in South Asia*, Cambridge, 1970.
MULLER, M., *India: What Can it Teach Us?*, London, 1919.
NAINAR, S.M.H. *Sources of the History of the Nawabs of the Carnatic, II, Ghulam Abdul Qadir Nazir's Bahar-i Azamjahi*, Madras, 1950.
NANDA, B.R., *Mahatma Gandhi*, Boston, 1958.
NANDA, B.R., *The Nehrus: Motilal and Jawaharlal*, London, 1962.
NANDA, B.R., *Gokhale: the Indian Moderates and the British Raj*, Delhi, 1977.
NATARAJAN, S., *A History of the Press in India*, London, 1962.
National Army Museum, *Annual Report*, 1968–9.
National Art-Collections Fund *Annual Report*, 1950, 1979.
National Art-Collections Fund *Newsletter*, 1979.
National Gallery of Ireland, *Illustrated Summary Catalogue of Paintings*, Dublin, 1981.
National Portrait Gallery, *Illustrated Report and List of Acquisitions 1985–6*.
The National Trust, *Powis Castle, Powys*, London, 1978.
A New and Improved History and Description of the Tower of London, London, 1834.
NESBIT, A., *A Catalogue of the Glass Collection Formed by Felix Slade Esq.*, London, 1871.
NILSSON, S., *European Architecture in India 1750–1850*, London, 1968.
NORRIS, J.A., *The First Afghan War, 1838–1842*, Cambridge, 1967.
O'HANLON, R., *Caste, Conflict and Ideology: Mahatma Jotirao Phule and Low Caste Protest in Nineteenth Century Western India*, Cambridge, 1985.
O'HANLON, R., 'Cultures of Rule, Communities of Resistance: Gender, Discourse and Tradition in Recent South Asian Historiographies', *Social Analysis* (special issue, 'Identity, Consciousness and the Past'), 25, 1989.
OPLOTHECA, *Catalogue of a Most Splendid and Instructive Collection of Antient Armour, exhibiting at the Oplotheca, No 20 Lower Brook Street*, London, 1816.
OPPE, A.P., *Alexander and John Robert Cozens*, London, 1952.
ORANGE, J., *Pictures by George Chinnery in the J.O. Collection*, London, 1923.
ORANGE, J., *The Chater Collection: Pictures Relating to China, Hongkong, Macao, 1655–1860*, London, 1924.
Oriental Annual, 1834, 1835, 1838.
Oriental Art, XX, 4, 1974.
Oriental Scenery, 1797.
ORME, R., *A History of the Military Transactions of the British Nation in Indostan from 1745*, London, 1763.
ORME, R., *Historical Fragments*, 4th edn, 1805.
ORMOND, R., 'George Chinnery's Image of Himself', 2 parts, *The Connoisseur*, vol. 167, February and March 1968.
ORMOND, R., *Early Victorian Portraits in the National Portrait Gallery*, 2 vols, 1973.
ORMOND R., and BLACKETT-ORD, C., *Franz Xaver Winterhalter and the Courts of Europe 1830–70*, London, 1987.
OWEN, S.J., (ed.), *A selection from the dispatches relating to India of the Duke of Wellington*, London, 1880.
PAL, P., and DEHEJIA, V., *From Merchants to Emperors: British Artists and India 1757–1930*, Ithaca, 1986.
PARGITER, F.E. *Revenue History of the Sunderbans from 1765 to 1870*, Calcutta, 1885.
PARKS, F., *Wanderings of a Pilgrim in Search of the Picturesque*, (1850) E. Chawner (ed.), 2 vols, London, 1975.
PARRY, J.P., *Caste and Kinship in Kangra*, London, 1979.
PAVIERE, S.H., *The Devis Family of Painters*, 1950.
PEARSON, M.N., *The Portuguese in India*, The New Cambridge History of India, Cambridge, 1987.
PEERS, S., *Mr William Simpson of the Illustrated London News*, London, 1987.
PENNY, N., (ed.), *Reynolds*, London, 1986.
PETRUCCIOLI, A., *Fathpur Sikri, Cittadele delle Acque*, Rome, 1988.
PINDER-WILSON, R.H., 'A Glass Huqqa Bowl', *British Museum Quarterly*, 25, 1962.
PHILLIMORE, R.H., *Historical Records of the Survey of India, 1800 to 1815*, 3 vols, Dehra Dun, 1945–54.
PINNEY, C., 'Representations of India: Normalisation and the Other', *Pacific Viewpoint*, 29, 1988.
PINNEY, C. 'Classification and Fantasy in the Photographic Construction of Caste and Tribe', *Visual Anthropology*, 1990.
RAHEJA, G.G., 'India: Caste, Kingship and Dominance Reconsidered', *Annual Review of Anthropology*, 17, 1988.
'Picturesque India with the Daniells', *The Connoisseur*, March 1963.
POIGNANT, R., *Observers of Man*, London, 1980.
PORTMAN, M.V., *A History of Our Relations With the Andamanese*, 2 vols, Calcutta, 1899.
POTTS, E.D., *British Baptist Missionaries in India 1793–1837*, Cambridge 1967.
PRAINE, D., *Memoir*, in E. H. Man, *The Nicobar Islands and their People*, 1932.
PRAKASH, O., *The Dutch East India Company and the Economy of Bengal, 1630–1720*, Princeton, 1985.
PRICE, U., *An Essay on the Picturesque*, London, 1794.
PYTHIAN, J.E., *George Frederick Watts*, 1906.
QUINN, D.B. (ED.), *The Hakluyt Handbook*, 2 vols., Cambridge 1974.
RAESIDE I., (trans.), *The Decade of Panipat: 1751–61 Marathi Historical Papers and Chronicles*, Bombay, 1984.
RAHEJA, G.G., *The Poison in the Gift*, Chicago, 1988.
RALEIGH T., (ed.), *Lord Curzon in India*, 1906.
RAMASWAMI, N.S., *Political History of the Carnatic under the Nawabs*, New Delhi, 1984.
RAMASWAMI, N.S., and MUTHIAH, S., *Parrys 200: A Saga of Resilience*, Madras, 1988.
RAY, N.B., (ed.), *The Allies' War with Tipu Sultan 1790–1793, English Records of Maratha History: Poona Residency Correspondence*, vol. 3, Bombay, 1937.

REYNOLDS, G., 'British Artists in India', *The Art of India and Pakistan: a commemorative catalogue of the exhibition held at the Royal Academy of Arts London, 1947–8*, Sir Leigh Ashton (ed.), pp.183–91, London, 1950.
REYNOLDS, G., *Painters of the Victorian Scene*, 1953.
REYNOLDS, G., *Victorian Painting*, 1966.
REYNOLDS, SIR J., *Discourses on Art*, Robert Wark (ed.), New Haven and London, 1981.
RICHARDS, J.F., (ed.), *Precious Metals in the later Medieval and Early Modern Worlds*, Durham, N.C., 1983.
RICHARDS, J.F., (ed.), *Document Forms for Official Orders of Appointment in the Mughal Empire*, E. J. W. Gibb Memorial, Cambridge, 1986.
RICHARDSON, T., '*The Tong Crusader*', *Country Life*, 2 April 1987.
RIEU, C., *Catalogue of the Persian Manuscripts in the British Museum*, 3 vols, London, 1883.
RISLEY, H.H., 'The Study of Ethnology in India', *Journal of the Royal Anthropological Institute*, 20, 1891.
RISLEY, H.H., *The Tribes and Castes of Bengal*, 4 vols., Calcutta, 1891.
RISLEY, H.H., *Manual of Ethnography for India*, Calcutta, 1907.
RISLEY, H.H., 'Ethnology and Caste', *The Imperial Gazetteer of India*, Oxford, 1909.
RISLEY, H.H., 'The Methods of Ethnography', *Journal of the Anthropological Institute* 41, 1911.
RISLEY, H.H., *The People of India*, Calcutta, 1915.
RIVERS, W.H., '*A Genealogical Method of Collecting Social and Vital Statistics*', Journal of the Anthropological Institute 30, 1900.
RIVERS, W.H.R., *The Todas*, 1906.
RIZVI, S.A.A., *Shah Wali-Allah and His Times: A Study of Eighteenth Century Islam, Politics and Society in India*, Canberra, 1980.
RIZVI, S.A.A., *Religious and Intellectual History of the Muslims in Akbar's Reign, 1556–1605*, New Delhi, 1975.
RIZVI, S.A.A., and BHARGAVA, M.L., (eds), *Freedom Struggle in Uttar Pradesh*, Lucknow, 1957–61.
ROBERTS, E., *Scenes and Characteristics of Hindostan, with sketches of Anglo-Indian society*, 3 vols, London, 1835.
ROBERTS, F.S., *Forty-one Years in India*, London, 1897.
ROBINSON, F.C.R., *Separatism amongst Indian Muslims*, Cambridge, 1974.
ROBINSON, H.R., *Oriental Armour*, London, 1967.
ROBB, P.G., *The Government of India Act 1919*, London 1976.
ROHATGI, P., *Portraits in the India Office Library and Records*, London, 1982.
RONALDSHAY, LORD, (ed.), *Life of Lord Curzon*, 3 vols, 1928.
ROOKSBY, R.L., 'W. H. Rivers and the Todas', *South Asia*, 1, 1971.
ROSS, A., *Ranji: Prince of Cricketers*, London, 1983.
ROSSELLI, J., *Lord William Bentinck*, London, 1974.
ROTHERMUND, D., 'Emancipation and Re-integration: The Politics of Gopal Krishna Gokhale and Herbert Hope Risley', in D. A. Low (ed.), *Soundings in Modern South Asian History*, 1968.
ROY, S.C., *The Mundas and their Country*, Calcutta, 1912.
ROY, S.C., *The Oraons of Chota Nagpur*, Ranchi, 1915.
Royal Armoury, Haymarket, *Descriptive catalogue of a Very Costly and Superb Collection of Military Antiquities*, London, 1820.
RUSSELL, R.V., and H. LAL, *Tribes and Castes of the Central Provinces of India*, 4 vols., London, 1916.
RUTHERFORD, A., *Kipling's Mind and Art*, London, 1964.
SAHNI, K., 'An Indian Journey through Russian Eyes', *The Indian Magazine*, 8, July 1988.
SAID, E., *Orientalism*, London, 1978.
SALT, H.,*Twenty-four Views taken in St Helena, the Cape, India, Ceylon, Abyssinia and Egypt*, London, 1809.
SARDA, H.B., *A Life of Dayananda Saraswati: World Teacher*, Ajmer, 1946.
SARDESAI, G.S., (ed.), *Poona Affairs 1786–1797*, (*Malet's Embassy*), English Records of Maratha History: Poona Residency Correspondence, vol. 2, Bombay, 1936.
SARKAR, S., *The Swadeshi Movement*, 1973.
SAVARKAR, V.D., *The Indian War of Independence of 1857*, London, 1909.
SCAMMELL, G.,V., *The World Encompassed: The First European Maritime Empires c.800–1650*, London, 1981.
SCHARF, G., 'Sketchbooks', NPG Archives.
SCHULBERG, L., *Historic India*, New York, 1968.
SCHLAGINTWEIT, E.D., 'Notes in Reference to the Question of the Aboriginal Tribes of India', *Proceedings of the Asiatic Society of Bengal*, 1867.
SCHWAB, R., *The Oriental Renaissance: Europe's Rediscovery of India and the East 1680–1880*, New York, 1984.
SEAL, A., *The Emergence of Indian Nationalism*, Cambridge, 1968.
SEARLE-CHATTERJEE, M., *Reversible Sex Roles: The Special Case of Benares Sweepers*, Oxford, 1981.
Select Views in India, 1787.
SEN, G., *Paintings from the Akbar Nama: A Visual Chronicle of Mughal India*, Varanasi, 1984.
SEN, S.N., *The Military System of the Marathas*, Calcutta, 1958.
SEN, S.P., *The French in India, 1763–1816*, Calcutta, 1958.
SHAKEB, M.Z.A., *A Descriptive Catalogue of Miscellaneous Persian Mughal Documents from Akbar to Bahadur Shah II*, London, 1982.
SHAW, R., *Visits to High Tartary, Yarkand and Kashgar*, (1871) repr. Oxford, 1984.
SHELLIM, M., *The Daniells in India and the Waterfall at Papanasum*, Calcutta, 1971.
SHELLIM, M., *India and the Daniells*, London, 1979.
SHELLIM, M.,*India and the Daniells: Additional Oil Paintings*, London, 1988.
SHELLIM, M., *Oil Paintings by Sir Charles D'Oyly, 7th Baronet*, London, 1989.
SHERRIFFS, W.R., 'Hindu Caste Marks', *Madras Christian College Magazine*, 1916.
REV. M. A. SHERRING, *Hindu Tribes and Castes as Represented at Benares*, 3 vols, Calcutta, 1872.
SHORTLAND, M., 'Skin Deep: Barthes, Lavater and the Legible Body', *Economy and Society*, 14, 1985.
SIMMONDS S., and DIGBY, S., (eds.), *The Royal Asiatic Society: Its History and Treasures*, Leiden, 1979.
SIMPSON, W., *India, Ancient and Modern*, 1867.
SINGH, K., *A History of the Sikhs*, 2 vols, Princeton, 1963–66.
SINGH, K.S., *Tribal Society in India: An Anthropo-historical Perspective*, New Delhi, 1985.
SINHA, N.K., *The Economic History of Bengal from Plassey to the Permanent Settlement*, 2 vols, Calcutta, 1956–62.
SINHA, S., 'Is There an Indian Tradition in Social/Cultural Anthropology? Retrospect and Prospect', paper presented during Wenner-Gren conference on *The Nature and Function of Anthropological Traditions*, 1968.
SINHA, S., *In Andamans: The Indian Bastille*, New Delhi, 1988.
SKELTON, R., 'Murshidabad Painting', *Marg*, 10, 1956.
SKELTON, R., 'Indian Painting of the Mughal Period', in *Islamic Painting and the Arts of the Book*, B.W. Robinson (ed.), London, 1976.
SLEEMAN, J.L., *Thug, or a Million Murders*, London, 1936.
SLEEMAN, W.H., *Rambles and Recollections of an Indian Official*, 2 vols, London, 1844.
SLOBODIN, R., *W. H. Rivers*, New York, 1978.
SMITH, B., *European Vision and the South Pacific*, London, 2nd edn, 1985.
SMITH, J., *A Catalogue Raisonné of the Works of the Most Eminent Dutch, Flemish and French Painters*, 3 vols, 1831.
SMITH, J.C., *British Mezzotinto Portraits*, 4 vols, 1878–83.
SMITH, R., 'Pictorial Journal of Travels in Hindustan from 1828 to 1833', 2 vols., MS, Victoria & Albert Museum (IM 15–1915).
SOLVYNS, B., *Les Hindous*, 4 vols, Paris, 1808–12.
Sotheby's Catalogue, 26 April 1990.
SPEAR, T.G.P., *The Twilight of the Mughuls: studies in late Mughul Delhi*, Cambridge, 1951.
SPEAR, T.G.P., *Master of Bengal: Clive and his India*, London, 1975.
SPENCER, A., (ed.), *Memoirs of William Hickey (1749–1775)*, 4 vols, London, 1913–25.
SPUHLER, E.,*Islamic Carpets and Textiles in the Keir Collection*, London, 1978.
STAMP, G., 'British Architecture in India 1857–1947', *Journal of the Royal Society of Arts*, 129, May 1981.
STEEGMAN, J., *A Survey of Portraits in Welsh Houses*, 2 vols, Cardiff, 1957–62.
STEIN, B., *Vijayanagara*, The New Cambridge History of India, Cambridge, 1989.
STEIN, B. *Sir Thomas Munro*, New Delhi, 1990.
STEVENS M.A., (ed.), *The Orientalists: Delacroix to Matisse*, London, 1984.
STEWART, S., *On Longing: Narratives of the Miniature, The Gigantic, The Souvenir, The Collection*, Baltimore, 1984.
STOCKING, G. W., '*What's in a Name? The Origins of the Royal Anthropological Institute (1837–71)*', 1971.
STOCKING, G.W., *Observers Observed: Essays on Ethnographic Fieldwork*, History of Anthropology, Madison, 1983.
STOKES, E., 'The Voice of the Hooligan',in McKendrick (ed.), *Historical Perspectives: Studies in English Thought snd Society in Honour of J.H. Plumb*, London, 1974.
STOKES, E.T., *The Peasant Armed: The Indian Rebellion of 1857*, Oxford, 1986.
STONE, I., *Canal Irrigation in British India*, Cambridge, 1984.
STRACHAN, M., *Sir Thomas Roe, 1581–1644*, Salisbury, 1989.
STRONG, S., 'Metalwork: Bidri Ware', in A. Mitchell (ed.), *Islamic Heritage of the Deccan*, Bombay, 1986.
STROUD, D., 'A Capability Brown Discovery: Designs for Claremont for Lord Clive', *Country Life*, 108, 1950.
STUEBE, I., 'William Hodges and Warren Hastings: A Study in 18th-Century Patronage', *The Burlington Magazine*, October 1973.
STUEBE, I.A., *The Life and Works of William Hodges*, New York, 1979.
SULLIVAN, M., 'Chinnery the Portrait Painter', *Orientations*, 11, April 1980.
SUTHERLAND, L.S., *The English East India Company in Eighteenth-Century British Politics*, Oxford, 1952.
SUTTON, D., 'Sahib and Guru', *Apollo*, XCII, August 1970.
SUTTON, T., *The Daniells: Artists and Travellers*, London, 1954.
SWEETMAN, J., *The Oriental Obsession: Islamic Inspiration in British and American Art and Architecture 1500–1920*, Cambridge, 1988.

SYKES, P.M., *History of Persia*, 1915.
SYMONDS, R.W., 'Furniture in the Soane Museum', *Country Life*, 27 January 1950.
TAHMANKHAR, D.V., *Lokamanya Tilak*, London, 1956.
TANDAN, B., 'The Architecture of the Nawabs of Awadh between 1722 and 1856 A.D.', Cambridge Ph.D dissertation, 1979.
Tea District Labour Association, *Handbook of Castes and Tribes Employed on the Tea Estates in North East India*, Calcutta, 1924.
TEMPLE, R.C., 'William Crooke 1848–1923', *Proceedings of the British Academy*, 1926.
TEMPLE, R.C., 'Report on the Census of the Andaman and Nicobar Islands', *Census of India 1901*, vol. 3, n.d.
THEYE, T., *Wir und die Wilden*, Hamburg, 1985.
THOMAS, G., 'The "Peccavi" Photographs', *History of Photography*, 1, 1980.
THOMAS, N., *Out of Time: History and Evolution in Anthropological Discourse*, Cambridge, 1989.
TOMLINSON, B.R., *The Political Economy of the Raj*, London, 1975.
THOMPSON, E., *Suttee*, London, 1928.
THURSTON, E., *Castes and Tribes of Southern India*, 7 vols, Madras, 1909.
TILLOTSON, G.H.R., *Fan Kwae Pictures: Paintings and Drawings by George Chinnery and Other Artists in the Collection of the Hongkong and Shanghai Banking Corporation*, London, 1987.
TILLOTSON, G.H.R., *The Tradition of Indian Architecture: Continuity, Controversy and Change*, London and New Haven, 1989.
TINKER, H., *The Ordeal of Love: C. F. Andrews and India*, Delhi, 1979.
TITLEY, N.M., *Miniatures from Persian manuscripts; A Catalogue and Subject Index of Paintings from Persia, India and Turkey in the British Library and the British Museum*, London, 1977.
TOD, J., *The Annals and Antiquities of Rajasthan*, 3 vols, reprint, Oxford, 1920.
TOPSFIELD, A., 'Ketelaar's Embassy and the Farangi Theme in the Art of Udaipur', *Oriental Art*, Winter 1984.
TURNER, CAPT S.,*An Account of an Embassy to the Court of the Teshoo Lama in Tibet*, London, 1800.
TREVELYAN, R., 'Thomas Woolner: Pre-Raphaelite Sculptor', *Apollo*, 107, 1978.
VADGAMA, K., *India in Britain*, London, 1984.
VALENTIA, G.A., *Voyages and Travels to India, Ceylon, the Red Sea, Abyssinia and Egypt in 1802–1806*, 3 vols, London, 1809.
VERTUE, G., 'George Vertue's Notebooks III', *Walpole Society*, 22, 1933–4.
Victoria and Albert Museum, *The Indian Heritage: Court Life and Arts under Mughal Rule*, London, 1982.
VIDYARTHI, L.P., 'The Rise of Social Anthropology in India (1774–1972): A Historical Appraisal', K. David (ed.), *The New Wind: Changing Identities in South Asia*, The Hague, 1977.
VITSAXIS, V.G.,*Hindu Epics, Myths and Legends in Popular Illustrations*, Delhi, 1977.
VON ERFFA, H., and STANLEY, A., *The Paintings of Benjamin West*, 1986.
WADELL, L.A., *Among the Himalayas*, 1899.
WADIA, R.A., *The Bombay Dockyard and the Wadia Master Shipbuilders*, 2nd edn, Bombay, 1955.
WALKER, R.J.B., *Regency Portraits*, 2 vols, London, 1985.
WALPOLE, H., *Anecdotes of Painting in England*, 4 vols, 1765–71.
WASHBROOK, D., 'Ethnicity and Racialism in Colonial Indian Society', R. Ross (ed.), *Racism and Colonialism*, The Hague, 1982.
WATERHOUSE, E.K., 'Preliminary Check List of Portraits by Thomas Gainsborough', *Walpole Society*, 33, 1953.
WATERHOUSE, E.K., *Reynolds*, 1941.
WATERHOUSE, E.K., *Painting in Britain 1530–1790*, 1953.
WATERHOUSE, E.K., *Gainsborough*, 1958.
WATKIN, D., *The English Vision: The Picturesque in Architecture, Landscape and Garden Design*, London, 1982.
WATT, G., *The Commercial Products of India*, London, 1908.
WATTS, M.F., 'Catalogue of Works by G. F. Watts', complied by Mrs M. F. Watts.
WEBSTER, M., '*The Mystery of the Lucknow Cock-Fight: Zoffany in India I*', *Country Life*, 153, 8 March 1973.
WEBSTER, M., *Johann Zoffany, 1733–1810*, London, 1976.
WEDDERBURN, W., *Allan Octavian Hume*, 1913.
WELCH, S.C., *The Art of Mughal India*, New York, 1963.
WELCH, S.C., *Indian drawings and painted sketches: 16th through 19th centuries*, New York, 1976.
WELCH, S.C., *Imperial Mughal Painting*, London, 1978.
WELCH, S.C., *Room for Wonder: Indian Painting during the British Period, 1760–1880*, New York, 1978.
WELCH, S.C., *India: Art and Culture 1300–1900*, New York, 1985.
WELLESLEY, LORD G. and STEEGMAN, J.E.H., *The Iconography of the First Duke of Wellington*, London, 1935.
WHITCOMBE, E., *Agrarian Conditions in Northern India*, Berkeley, 1972.
Whitechapel Art Gallery, *Arts of Bengal: the heritage of Bangladesh and Eastern India*, London, 1979.
WHITLEY, W.T., *Thomas Gainsborough*, 1915.
WHITLEY, W.T., *Artists and their Friends in England 1700–1799*, 2 vols, 1928.
WILKINSON, T., *Two Monsoons*, London, 1976.
WILLIAMS, M., *Modern India and the Indians*, London, 1879.
WILSON, W.J., *History of the Madras Army*, 3 vols, Madras, 1882.
WITTLER, L., 'Samuel Scott, the Canaletto of London', *International Studio*, July 1928.
WISER W.H., and WISER, C., *Behind Mud Walls in India*, London, 1932.
WOLPERT, S., *Jinnah of Pakistan*, New York and Oxford, 1984.
WOOD, C., *Victorian Panorama*, London, 1976.
WOOLNER, A., *Thomas Woolner, RA Sculptor and Poet: His Life and Letters*, 1917.
WORSWICK, C., *Princely India*, London, 1980.
YANG, A.A., *The Limited Raj: Agrarian Relations in Colonial India, Saran District, 1793–1920*, Berkeley, 1989.
York Art Gallery, *Preview*, 10 April 1950.
YUNG, K.K., *National Portrait Gallery Complete Illustated Catalogue 1856–1979*, 1981.
ZEBROWSKI, M., 'Decorative Arts of the Mughal Period', in B. Gray (ed.), *The Arts of India*, Oxford, 1981.
ZEBROWSKI, M., *Deccani Painting*, London, 1983.

Index of Exhibits

PHOTOGRAPHIC ACKNOWLEDGEMENTS

The exhibition organizers would like to thank the following for making copyright photographs available in the following figures and catalogue entries. All other photographs are copyright and were provided by owners of exhibits or the sources given in the catalogue:
By Gracious Permission of Her Majesty The Queen no. 208 and cover; Windsor Castle Royal Library © Her Majesty The Queen Fig. 17; nos 473, 484; Asiatic Society of Bombay Fig. 29; C. A. Bayly Figs 2, 4, 5, 15, 16, 60, 61, 64, 65; Birla Museum, Rajasthan no. 424; British Architectural Library Drawings Collection/Royal Institute of British Architects nos 198, 467, 468, 561, 571; by courtesy of Cambridge University Press and Amrit Rai no. 462; Commonwealth Relations Office Fig. 6; *Country Life Library* no. 112 (detail); Dr Bhau Daji Lad Museum, Bombay Figs 27, 30, 31, 32, 33; by courtesy of Vivian V. Esch no. 469; by courtesy of Hazlitt, Gooden & Fox, London Figs 21, 22; Howard Hodgkin, London no. 26; Jain Picture Publishers, Bombay nos 88, 160, 280, 334 (i), 404, 497, 528, 609; Professor Ira M. Lapidus no 399; courtesy of the Director, National Army Museum London Fig. 12; nos 113, 114, 116, 157, 170, 175, 179, 180, 181 (i–ii), 187, 190, 313, 322, 324, 326, 327, 329, 337, 338, 339, 448, 472, 512 (i–iv), 583, 600; Nehru Memorial Museum, New Delhi Fig. 52; nos 333, 397, 460, 490, 499, 501, 503 (i–v), 511, 519, 522, 523 (ii), 530, 534, 537, 538, 539, 540 (i), 541, 544, 548, 551, 615, 619, 620, 626; Foy Nissen nos 455, 562, 564, 565, 566, 568, 570; Private Collection, photograph by Martyn Gregory Fig. 25; © William Proby no. 328; reproduced by permission of *Punch* nos 305 (i), 305 (iii–v), Rijksmuseum, Amsterdam 41; Royal Anthropological Institute, Photographic Collection Figs 36, 37; nos 350, 351, 353 (i–iii), 355, 358 (i), 358 (ii), 368, 372 (i–iv), 381 (i), 391, 419, 450, 496; Royal Commonwealth Society Figs 39, 47, 48; nos 323, 345, 447, 478; Spink & Son Ltd nos 221, 237, 270; by courtesy of G. H. R. Tillotson Figs 18, 19; Mr Rajendra Shriram Virkar Figs 51, 53; nos 520, 521, 524, 529, 531, 532, 540 (ii), 542, 557, 593, 594, 595, 597; Yale Center for British Art, Paul Mellon Collection Figs 9, 20, 24; nos 77, 91, 137, 194, 257.
The following photographs by Cecil Beaton in the collection of the Imperial War Museum are Crown copyright ©: Figs 49, 50, 62, 63; nos 599 (i–iv), 604, 605, 607, 608.